DATE DUE	DATE RETURN
OCT 22 1998	

LIBRARY

HIGH ENERGY PHYSICS

Volume II

PURE AND APPLIED PHYSICS

A SERIES OF MONOGRAPHS AND TEXTBOOKS

CONSULTING EDITORS

H. S. W. MASSEY

University College, London, England

KEITH A. BRUECKNER

*University of California, San Diego
La Jolla, California*

HIGH ENERGY PHYSICS

Edited by

E. H. S. BURHOP

PHYSICS DEPARTMENT
UNIVERSITY COLLEGE
LONDON, ENGLAND

Volume II

ACADEMIC PRESS New York · London · 1967

ACADEMIC PRESS INC.
111 Fifth Avenue, New York, New York 10003

United Kingdom Edition published by
ACADEMIC PRESS INC. (LONDON) LTD.
Berkeley Square House, London W.1

LIBRARY OF CONGRESS CATALOG CARD NUMBER: 66–26271

PRINTED IN THE UNITED STATES OF AMERICA

LIST OF CONTRIBUTORS

Numbers in parentheses refer to the pages on which the authors' contributions begin.

L. Bertocchi, CERN, Geneva, Switzerland (72)

D. H. Davis, Physics Department, University College London, London, England (365)

S. D. Drell, Stanford Linear Accelerator Center, Stanford University, Stanford, California (219)

E. Ferrari, Istituto di Fisica dell'Universita, Rome, Italy (72)

R. Gatto, Institute of Theoretical Physics, University of Florence, Florence, Italy (1)

A. C. Hearn, Institute of Theoretical Physics, Department of Physics, Stanford University, Stanford, California (219)

J. M. Kidd, H. H. Wills Physics Laboratory, The University of Bristol, Bristol, England (265)

Leon M. Lederman, Department of Physics, Nevis Laboratories, Columbia University, Irvington-on-Hudson, New York (304)

J. Sacton, Université Libre de Bruxelles, Brussels, Belgium (365)

PREFACE

The conception behind this three-volume compilation on high energy physics has been described in the preface to Vol II in the following terms:

"While primarily a reference book the individual chapters are intended to provide not merely progress reports of a number of different topics, but also to give sufficient basic material to be of value for graduate students entering the field as well as for experienced research workers."

The chapters of the present volume deal largely with high energy collision processes but also contain important accounts of the validity of quantum electrodynamics at high energy, and of neutrino and hypernuclear physics. Once again the selection of articles for this volume has been determined mainly by the order in which they came to hand. It is hoped that when all three volumes have appeared they will provide a comprehensive account of the whole subject.

E. H. S. BURHOP

May 1967

CONTENTS

Analysis of Present Evidence on the Validity of Quantum Electrodynamics

R. Gatto

High Energy Strong Interactions of Elementary Particles

L. Bertocchi and E. Ferrari

Peripheral Processes

A. C. Hearn and S. D. Drell

Interactions at Very High Energies

J. M. Kidd

Neutrino Physics

Leon M. Lederman

Hypernuclear Physics

D. H. Davis and J. Sacton

CONTENTS OF OTHER VOLUMES

ANALYSIS OF PRESENT EVIDENCE ON THE VALIDITY OF QUANTUM ELECTRODYNAMICS

R. Gatto

La filosofia medesima non può se non ricevere benefizio delle nostre dispute, perchè se i nostri pensieri saranno veri, nuovi acquisti si saranno fatti, se falsi, col ributtargli, maggiormente verranno confermate le prime dottrine.—Galileo Galilei, *I due massimi sistemi del mondo*, Edizione Nazionale, Vol. VII, page 62, La Barbera; Florence, 1897.

I. Introduction

A large amount of work, both theoretical and experimental, is being carried out at this moment on quantum electrodynamics. New experimental facilities are soon expected to increase our possibilities of experimenting with electrons and photons at high energies and large intensities. Prospects of deeper and more decisive experimentation appear extremely exciting.

We present here a discussion on the experimental and theoretical work done in the last years relevant to the problem of the validity of quantum electrodynamics.

We shall be concerned essentially with the question of a possible breakdown of the theory at small distances. Experiments to probe quantum electrodynamics at small distances must be sensitive to modifications of the theory at large momentum transfers. On the other hand the required presence of a large momentum transfer leads, as a general feature, to low cross sections. High energy tests of quantum electrodynamics are thus generally very difficult experimentally. Tests in the field of atomic physics require very high precision to be sensitive to modifications at subnuclear distances.

Colliding electron-electron and electron-positron beam experiments undoubtedly offer the neatest possibilities for verifying the high energy predictions of pure quantum electrodynamics by systematic exploration. The necessity of reaching high center of mass energies in collision with targets at rest requires the use of massive targets, protons or heavier nuclei. The strong interaction effects must however be eliminated, in the required limits of a high accuracy, by extracting them from other experiments and by precise proof of their smallness. This task is theoretically simple in some cases but may not necessarily lead to reliable results in other cases, so that a precise selection of the experiments to be done and of the most convenient detailed experimental conditions is necessary to test the breakdown at small distances of the theory by studying high energy reactions on nuclear targets.

Following a long-standing habit breakdown limits are interpreted in terms of cutoffs. Interpretations are also possible in terms of upper limits on possible new couplings and lower limits on masses of conjectured new fields. Both interpretations will be discussed. The interpretation in terms of conjectured new fields and couplings is however theoretically more sound and it will be useful if future experimental results are interpreted, whenever possible, in such a frame rather than in terms of cutoffs.

II. The Lamb Shift Measurements and Their Implications

A. Measurements of the Lamb Shift

The experiments by Lamb and his collaborators in H, D, and He$^+$ (Lamb and Retherford, 1947, 1950, 1951, 1952; Lamb, 1952; Dayhoff et al., 1953a,b) made use of the possibility of inducing electric dipole transitions from a state $nS_{1/2}$ to a $P_{1/2}$ or $P_{3/2}$ state of same n. The transition can be induced by a magnetic field of frequency corresponding to the energy separation of the two levels. The very long lifetime of the $2S$ state, relative to the lifetimes of the other excited states, in a hydrogenlike atom, makes it possible to separate the $2S$ excitation from the other excitations. The induced transition from $2S_{1/2}$ takes place at the appropriate frequency of the field. It gives rise to a depopulation of the level observable by suitable detectors. The frequency of the applied field, and correspondingly the energy difference between the two levels, is measured with an error much smaller than the natural width of the P lines: the linewidth is about one thousand times larger than the error in the measured energy difference. The fine structure of the $n = 2$ level of atomic hydrogen is shown in the Zeeman diagram of Fig. 1. The levels are conventionally indicated by letters $a, \ldots f$, α, β.

B. Review of the Theoretical Work on the Lamb Shift

In the Dirac theory of a bound electron in a Coulomb field from a point charge, the two levels $nS_{1/2}$ and $nP_{1/2}$, whose difference is referred to as the Lamb shift, are degenerate. The theory of the shift has been worked out by many authors.

The effect results from many contributions which have been analyzed at various stages. In the calculation one takes advantage of the smallness of the independent dimensionless parameters of the theory.

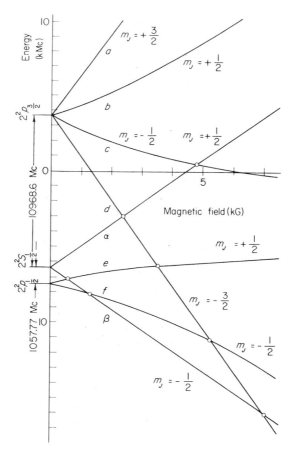

Fig. 1. Zeeman diagram of the $n = 2$ level of atomic hydrogen.

The smallness of the interaction strength with the quantized electromagnetic field makes it convenient to use the perturbation expansion as is usual in electrodynamics. The one-photon contribution, with one virtual photon emitted and reabsorbed by the electron, occurs at second order in the quantized field. Inclusion of the two-photon terms, with two virtual photons emitted and reabsorbed by the bound electron, occurs at fourth order.

For light nuclei the parameter $(Z\alpha)$, measuring the strength of the nuclear field, is also small and, correspondingly, one makes use of a suitable expansion in this parameter. This expansion is not however a simple power series expansion but also contains logarithmic terms.

The smallness of the ratio m/M, of the electron mass to the nucleon mass, is advantageously used to obtain a simple estimate of the recoil effects, correcting the fixed Coulomb field approximation. Finally, one takes advantage of the smallness of the nuclear radius as compared to the atomic radius, to correct for the finite nuclear size.

The bulk of the effect is due to the so-called radiative shift at lowest order. At second order in the quantized electromagnetic field and at first order in the external potential, one separates the radiative shift, the magnetic moment contribution, and the vacuum polarization contribution.

This last contribution arises from the virtual creation of an electron-positron pair by the potential. At this order the vacuum polarization contributes about -27 Mc/sec to the total shift $2S_{1/2}-2P_{1/2}$ in H, which was measured to be (1057.77 ± 0.10) Mc/sec by Dayhoff et $al.$ (1953a,b).

Calculations and speculations on the vacuum polarization effect go back to work by Heisenberg (1934), Uehling (1953), and Weisskopf (1936). The additional binding energy in the $2S_{1/2}$ state as compared to the $2P_{1/2}$ state simply reflects the closer distance of the electron from the nucleus in the S state. The photon propagator for spacelike variable is in fact increased by the vacuum polarization effect, resulting in a stronger attraction (Källen, 1952).

The radiative shift and the magnetic moment term at lowest radiative order were calculated by a number of authors (Bethe, 1947; Kroll and Lamb, 1949; French and Weisskopf, 1949; Schwinger, 1949; Feynman, 1949; Fukuda et $al.$, 1949). The result is expressed in terms of average excitation energies for the states $2S$ and $2P$ (Bethe et $al.$, 1950; Harriman, 1956; Schwartz and Tiemann, 1959). The magnetic moment contribution is identified as arising from the anomalous magnetic moment of the electron and it amounts to more than 6% of the total $2S_{1/2}-2P_{1/2}$ shift in H and D.

At the same radiative order, second order in the quantized field, corrections for multiple scattering in the external potential must be included. The inclusion of two potential scatterings was considered by Baranger et $al.$ (1953) and Karplus et $al.$ (1952). This contribution is of the order of 7%. Layzer (1960), Fried and Yennie (1960), and Erickson and Yennie (1966) have also discussed the next term in the potential, corresponding to three scatterings in the external field.

The smaller effects at fourth order in the quantized electromagnetic field, two-photon contributions, have also been computed. Again one separates a radiative shift, a magnetic moment term, and the vacuum polarization contribution.

The radiative shift, which involves the invariant squared four-momentum from the external field, was calculated by Bersohn et $al.$ (1953). Some of the terms were not however computed exactly, due to the complications of the expressions, but only limited in terms of inequalities.

The fourth-order magnetic moment term was computed by Sommerfield (1957) and Petermann (1957), correcting older estimates, which gave a much larger value for this term.

The fourth-order vacuum polarization was calculated by Baranger *et al.* (1952) and Källen and Sabry (1955).

The finite nuclear mass gives rise, besides the reduced mass effect, to specific corrections that can be discussed starting from a Bethe-Salpeter equation and which are different for $2S_{1/2}$ and for $2P_{1/2}$. These effects were calculated by Salpeter (1952) and Fulton and Martin (1954). They are referred to as finite mass effects, but, as we have said, they are not the only corrections due to the finite nuclear mass, which is principally accounted for by the reduced mass corrections.

The finite nuclear size gives rise to the so-called finite size effects, arising from the deviation of the nuclear potential from that of a point charge. These effects are proportional, in first approximation, to the mean square radius of the nuclear charge density, as obtained from the high energy electron scattering experiments. Numerical evaluations of the finite size effects have been made for H by Aron and Zucchelli (1957) and Ivanenko (1957), for D by Salpeter (1953), and for He^+ by Novick *et al.* (1956).

The alteration of the external potential, because of the finite nuclear size, shifts in first approximation the $2S$ level but leaves the $2P$ level unchanged. The calculated shift in H is of about 0.12 Mc/sec, corresponding to a value of about 0.8×10^{-13} cm for the proton radius.

C. Comparison of Theory with Experiment; Implications with Respect to Possible Breakdowns of Quantum Electrodynamics

Erickson and Yennie (1966) have developed a formal operator technique to calculate radiative level shifts. Their result for the $2S_{1/2}$–$2P_{1/2}$ Lamb shift in H is (1057.643 ± 0.21) Mc/sec against the experimental value of (1057.77 ± 0.10) Mc/sec by Dayhoff *et al.* (1953a,b). The difference between the theoretical and the experimental figures is less than half the combined error limits.

The agreement between theory and experiment is certainly satisfactory. The difference between the two figures is of the same order of magnitude as the calculated finite size effect that we have just discussed. Roughly speaking, we can thus say that the Lamb shift measurement gives an upper limit of about 0.8×10^{-13} cm for the distance at which quantum electrodynamics may possibly break down.

Beside such a possible high energy breakdown of quantum electrodynamics, one may consider the possibility of a breakdown of the theory affecting the low energy region. For such a kind of breakdown the Lamb shift measurement poses a very restrictive upper limit.

For instance, an alteration of the Coulomb law $1/r$, by a small modification of the exponent, to $(1/r)^{1+\varepsilon}$ for values of r around 10^{-8} cm would be excluded, unless ε is smaller than 10^{-10} (Feynman, 1962). The accuracy of the Lamb shift measurement must here be referred to the total binding energy of the electron in the $2S$ or $2P$ state. Such energies are of about 8×10^8 Mc/sec. The over-all precision is thus close to one part in 10^{10}.

The accuracy of the Lamb shift measurements can also be used to put a lower limit to the mass of a hypothetical lepton, with properties similar to the electron and the same interaction with the electromagnetic field. The presence of such a lepton would modify the vacuum polarization contribution. Clearly such a hypothetical lepton must be rather heavy, otherwise it would contribute appreciably to the vacuum polarization correction. One easily finds that the existence of such a particle would still be compatible with the present experimental accuracy provided it is at least ten times heavier than the electron.

D. LAMB SHIFTS IN D AND He$^+$

Erickson and Yennie (1966) have also recalculated the $2S_{1/2}$–$2P_{1/2}$ Lamb shifts in D and He$^+$. The theoretical figure in D is (1058.906 ± 0.27) Mc/sec to be compared with the measured value of (1059.00 ± 0.10) Mc/sec by Day-hoff et al. (1953a,b). In He$^+$ the theoretical figure is $(14{,}040.49 \pm 6.0)$ Mc/sec to be compared to the experimental value given by Lipworth and Novick (1957) of $(14{,}040.2 \pm 4.5)$ Mc/sec. The differences between the experimental and the theoretical figures for D and He$^+$ are less than one-quarter of the combined error limits.

The theoretical figures for H, D, and He$^+$ are all based on the values recommended by NAS-NRC reported in the February, 1964 issue of *Physics Today* (p. 48) for the constants α, R_∞, and c (speed of light): $\alpha^{-1} = 137.0388 + \varepsilon_\alpha \times 10^{-4}$, $R_\infty = (109{,}737.31 + \varepsilon_R \times 10^{-2})$ cm^{-1}, $c = (2.997925 + \varepsilon_c \times 10^{-6}) \times 10^{10}$ cm/sec. Numerical changes in these constants can be corrected by multiplying the theoretical figures by the factor

$$[1 + (-2.0\varepsilon_\alpha + 0.1\varepsilon_R + 0.3\varepsilon_c) \times 10^{-6}].$$

E. RECENT DEVELOPMENTS AND FURTHER PROSPECTS

The satisfactory agreement between the Lamb shift measurements that we have mentioned and the theoretical calculations should not distract from the necessity of further measurements with improved precision and of still more accurate evaluations. Recently, in Chicago, Robiscoe (1965) has used a new method to measure the fine structure of the $n = 2$ levels of hydrogen. The crossing point between the two levels $(2^2S_{1/2}, m_j = -\frac{1}{2})$ and $(2^2P_{1/2}, m_j = +\frac{1}{2})$ was measured and the corresponding value of the Lamb shift calculated. In this experiment the transition $2S \to 2P$ is induced by a static electric field. The value obtained for the Lamb shift is (1058.07 ± 0.10) Mc/sec, differing by about 0.3 Mc/sec from the experimental value of the preceding comparison and by about 0.43 Mc/sec from the theoretical prediction of Erickson and Yennie.

On the theoretical side, more complicated proton structure corrections, such as those arising from the polarizability of the proton, could perhaps be approximately estimated, though it seems improbable that the large discrepancy could arise from such corrections only.

In an independent experiment, Robiscoe and Cosens (1966) have confirmed the determination by Robiscoe (1965) of the Lamb shift in the first excited state of hydrogen.

This new experiment uses the level-crossing technique and measures the crossing point A between the levels $\beta\,(m_F = 0)$ and $e\,(m_F = +1)$ in the original Lamb notation. The crossing occurs in atomic hydrogen near 538 gauss (G).

The previous experiment (Robiscoe 1965) consisted of measuring the crossing between the levels $\beta\,(m_F = -1)$ and $e\,(m_F = 0)$, occurring near 605 G. Combining the two results, Robiscoe and Cosens give a value of 1058.05 ± 0.10 Mc/sec for the Lamb shift in H $(n = 2)$.

The experiment confirms the disagreement with the value of 1057.77 ± 0.10 Mc/sec given by Dayhoff et al. (1953a).

Soto (1966) has recently presented a calculation of the fourth-order radiative corrections for the energy levels of H, D, and He$^+$. In this work previous estimates based on the calculation by Weneser et al. (1953) are substituted by exact computations. The theoretical values of Erickson and Yennie (1966) for the Lamb shifts in H, D, and He$^+$, reported in the preceding sections, are slightly improved. The theoretical values for the Lamb shifts given by Soto are: H = 1057.499 ± 0.11, D = 1058.763 ± 0.17, and He$^+$ = 14038.17 ± 4.4 Mc/sec.

The discrepancy between the experimental value of Robiscoe and Cosens and the above theoretical value is 0.57 ± 0.14 Mc/sec.

A recent theoretical attempt by Artru et al. (1966) appears of great interest. Following the original Feynman suggestion (Feynman, 1962) these authors apply dispersion relation techniques to the Lamb shift problem. The new approach, independent from the usual perturbation theory calculation, may at least provide a check on the conventional results.

A preliminary nonrelativistic calculation, essentially based on an approximate evaluation of the inelastic right-hand cuts in the electron-proton amplitude, agrees very well with the perturbation theory result.

Accepting the present theory of the Lamb shift, and specifically the above latest value for H of 1057.50 ± 0.11 Mc/sec, one may ask whether a slight modification in α might account for the discrepancy between such a theoretical value and the experimental value of 1058.05 ± 0.10 Mc/sec by Robiscoe and Cosens.

The answer is negative: the value of α should have to increase by as much as about one part in ten thousand, making it improbable that this alone may be the origin of the discrepancy.

A new method for Lamb shift measurements has been recently proposed by Series (1964). It is based on the possibility of temporal redistribution of resonant fluorescence. Atoms are excited at a modulated rate, and the changes in the amplitude of modulation of the fluorescent light are examined.

III. The Hyperfine Structure of Atomic Hydrogen

A. The Hyperfine Structure in the Ground State of Atomic Hydrogen

The hyperfine structure is caused by the interaction of the electron with the nuclear magnetic moment. The frequency separations of components of the hyperfine structure are much smaller than for fine structure, corresponding to the smallness of the nuclear magneton relative to the electron magneton.

A fine structure level is split by the hyperfine effect into a number of hyperfine components. If the total angular momentum j of the atomic level is smaller than the nuclear spin I the multiplicity is $(2j + 1)$; otherwise it is $(2I + 1)$.

The energy difference between the highest level and the lowest level of the hyperfine multiplet is usually referred to as the hyperfine splitting. Hyperfine splitting in the ground states of H, D, and T has been investigated by a number of experimentalists using different techniques.

The first measurement of high precision was made by Nafe and Nelson (1948) using the techniques of atomic beam resonance. A technique using paramagnetic resonance was applied by Wittke and Dicke (1956) in a measurement of the splitting in hydrogen. Their results were in agreement with measurements by Kusch (1955). Anderson et al. (1960) measured the hyperfine structure in the three-hydrogen isotopes from the optical transmission of optically oriented rubidium in spin-exchange equilibrium with hydrogen, deuterium, and tritium.

More recently, Crampton et al. (1963) have succeeded in determining the hyperfine splitting in the ground state of atomic hydrogen with a precision of two parts in 10^{11}, by employing a hydrogen maser. The experimental value obtained by these experimenters for the hyperfine structure interval $\Delta\nu_H$ of hydrogen in the ground state is

$$\Delta\nu_H = 1420405751.800 \pm 0.028 \text{ cps.}$$

The frequency interval $\Delta\nu_H$ is one of the most accurately known quantities in physics.

B. Present Status of the Theory

The great experimental precision has not however been matched by the accuracy of the theoretical calculations and it may take a long time before this happens. At such a high degree of accuracy strong interaction effects become strongly mixed up with the purely electrodynamical problem, leaving one suspicious about any definite conclusion. The calculations of the proton structure effects give estimates for these terms of about one part in 10^5 of $\Delta\nu_H$. An explanation of the experimental result, up to its full accuracy, would involve calculating strong interaction effects with a precision far above our present capabilities in this field.

Moreover, the latest calculations by Layzer (1964), Zwanziger (1964), and Brown (1966) indicate the existence of a discrepancy of 25 to 65 ppm (corresponding to 0.03 to 0.10 of a megacycle) between the measured and the calculated value for the hyperfine separation in the ground state of atomic hydrogen.

It is usually accepted that the discrepancy cannot be attributed to an incorrect value of the fine structure constant. In fact an independent determination of α from the hyperfine structure interval of muonium (Cleland et al., 1964) has led to a value in agreement with that determined from the fine structure of deuterium (Dayhoff et al., 1953a,b). Further confirmations would however be welcomed. The question will be further discussed in Section IV.

1. *Corrections to the Fermi Formula*

The original nonrelativistic theory of Fermi (1930) has been corrected for a number of smaller effects in order to compare with the improved experimental accuracies. The use of the Dirac equation in place of the Schrödinger equation in the Fermi derivation leads to the Breit correction (Breit, 1930) of the order α^2. Of the same order α^2 are the radiative corrections (Karplus and Klein, 1952a; Kroll and Pollock, 1952). The correctness of the calculated radiative term can be inferred *a posteriori* from the agreement of the theoretical value for the hyperfine splitting in muonium with the recent very accurate measurement of this quantity by Cleland et al. (1964).

The remaining corrections arise from recoil and proton structure effects. Finite size effects for a proton with infinite mass and with a finite structure were calculated by Zemach (1956). Calculations of the recoil and structure effects by Arnowitt (1953) and Newcomb and Salpeter (1955) showed the strong dependence of the result on the electromagnetic structure of the proton. Iddings and Platzmann (1959a) make the explicit assumption that the exchange of two virtual photons with the proton can be obtained in terms of the form factors for one-photon exchange.

2. *The Two-Photon Contribution*

All these calculations are evidently incomplete. The two-photon exchange contribution certainly deserves more attention.

The quantity needed here is the forward Compton scattering amplitude for virtual photons. The estimates of the effect by inclusion of the proton and N* intermediate states does not lead to agreement with experiment.

We know however that a similar approach in the analogous situation of the neutron-proton mass difference is incapable of reproducing the right value of the mass difference. In particular inclusion of the one-proton intermediate state alone does not even reproduce the correct sign, and the contribution from the intermediate N* gives too small a contribution to the mass difference (Cini *et al.*, 1959). Only recently have new methods of calculation of the neutron-proton mass difference been reported, based on more advanced techniques (Dashen and Frautschi, 1964). A more complete attempt to understand the hyperfine shift discrepancy, by more modern calculational techniques of strong interaction theory, should be carried on before reaching a definite conclusion as to the origin of the discrepancy.

The exchanged meson in the diagram of Fig. 2 can have $J^P = 0^-$, 1^+, or 2^+. However, in the Fermi approximation for the resulting coupling, only exchange of 1^+ contributes, giving rise to an effective Gamow–Teller interaction.

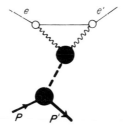

Fig. 2. Contribution of meson exchange to the hyperfine structure of hydrogen.

Fenster *et al.* (1965) were able to develop a model leading to a determination of the coupling strength of the axial vector meson in terms of the π^0-decay rate. The model is based on the assumption of partially conserved axial current. The result of the calculation shows that a considerable reduction of the disagreement between theory and experiment can be imputed to axial meson exchange. The presumed existence of a whole nonet of axial vector mesons (Borchi and Gatto, 1965) will further improve the agreement.

The theoretical prediction for the nucleon structure effect becomes, according to the estimates of Fenster *et al.*, (-10) ppm or $(+14)$ ppm, depending on the undetermined sign of the axial exchange effect. The prediction must be compared with the experimental figure of (-9 ± 18) ppm.

By use of the analyticity properties, Iddings (1965) has expressed the proton structure correction in terms of physical cross sections, obtainable from electron scattering experiments, and of a subtraction term. The tentative estimates made, in the absence of data, do not account for the discrepancy. A possible way out would be an appropriate contribution from a possible exchange of a 1^+ meson between the proton and the two photons. The coupling of such 1^+ meson (with positive charge conjugation) to the two photons is forbidden for physical particles, but not for virtual particles. Among the higher boson resonances, candidates for a $J^{PC} = 1^+$ assignment have been suggested: one of them is A_1 (1080).

3. *Possible Contributions from Weak Interactions to the Hyperfine Splitting*

The coupling required for such contributions would involve a neutral lepton current and there is certainly no evidence at the moment for such a coupling. Furthermore, by assigning to such a hypothetical coupling a typical weak coupling strength, the shift in the hydrogen ground state from this contribution would only amount to something of the order of 1 % of the present discrepancy.

4. *The Hyperfine Splitting and the Subnuclear Structure of the Proton*

The hyperfine structure of hydrogen can be regarded as a sensitive test of the proton structure because of its dependence on the wave function of the electron inside the proton and of the polarization of the proton by the electron. As is well known, the exploration of the proton structure by a single photon measures the ordinary charge and magnetic form factors (see chapter by T. A. Griffy and L. I. Schiff, in Volume I of this treatise). More generally, the structure of the proton will be exhibited by the set of correlations between acts of measurement at different points in space-time, as ordinarily described in terms of correlation functions. The ordinary charge and magnetic form factors exhibit the response of the system to a single act of measurement. In a Compton scattering process, however, one is measuring a typical double correlation, corresponding to the repeated interaction of the system with the electromagnetic field. The proton structure corrections to the hyperfine formula similarly depend on the internal correlation of the structure, insofar as it cannot be entirely expressed in terms of the ordinary charge and magnetic form factors of the proton. The two-photon exchange contribution (depending not only on transverse photons but also on the longitudinal photons not included in the wave function description) is a critical term in the calculation of the structure effects, as we have already emphasized. Such two-photon exchange terms, revealing the internal correlation of the structure, are indeed sensitive to aspects of the subnuclear description of the proton not exhibited by the charge and magnetic form factors.

The success of the SU(3) symmetry scheme has posed the question of a description of baryons in terms of quarks (Gell-Mann, 1964; see also P. T. Matthews, Volume I of this treatise). The proton may then be conceived, according to some intuitively based viewpoints, as a system of heavy, slowly moving quarks, strongly bound to unknown forces, perhaps not describable in terms of the conventional dynamical laws of quantum fields.

Fenster and Nambu (1965) have pointed out that an analogy may exist between the problem of the proton structure terms of the hyperfine formula and the explanation proposed by Bohr of the deuterium hyperfine structure (Bohr, 1948; Low, 1950; Greenberg and Foley, 1960). The electron approaching the bound proton-neutron system follows adiabatically the proton center of mass rather than the center of mass of the deuteron. In the calculation by Fenster and Nambu (1965) the constituent particles are the quarks, approximated with pointlike charge and magnetic moment distributions. The current estimate (Iddings, 1965) of 27 ± 3 ppm for the proton structure effect is reduced to 20 ppm for quarks of fractional charge and to 10 ppm for quarks of integral charge. The correction is in the direction of the experimental data, which require an effect of -9 ± 18 ppm, but it seems insufficient to account for the correct magnitude.

A recent discussion of the proton structure corrections to the hydrogen hyperfine structure is due to Drell and Sullivan (1966). The conclusion of these authors is that the existing discrepancy between theory and experiment may well be attributed to the polarizability corrections. We recall that the "genuine electrodynamic" contributions to the hyperfine splitting formula (see Brodsky and Erickson, 1966), are calculated up to a precision of 1 ppm. The calculation of the additional term however, depending on finite proton mass and proton structure (apart from the reduced mass correction) rests on the theory of strong interactions. The ratio between the theoretical prediction and the very accurate (as we have said, the precision is two parts in 10^{11}) experimental value for the hyperfine splitting in the hydrogen ground state (Crampton *et al.*, 1963) can be written as $r = 1 - (9 \pm 20) \times 10^{-6} - x$, where the uncertainty of ± 20 corresponds to two standard deviations on α as given by Cohen and Dumond (1965) and x is the additional proton mass and structure correction. Not all of x is unknown; one can separate the real polarizability correction x_p, depending on nucleon excitation, from the proton ground state contributions which can be expressed in terms of the proton electromagnetic form factors. According to Iddings (1965), $x = 34 \times 10^{-6} + x_p$, so that the above ratio r now appears as $r = 1 - (43 \pm 20) \times 10^{-6} - x_p$. In such terms the problem is that of deciding whether it is plausible that x_p be so large as to remove the discrepancy. As we have said, the polarizability correction can be expressed as an integral over the forward spin-flip Compton scattering for virtual photon. The lack of knowledge on these amplitudes makes any estimate along this line uncertain. The usual approach of separating a few dominant intermediate contributions, typical of applications of dispersion theory, appears in fact not applicable to this case, where a large number of intermediate contributions are expected to be present, as evidenced by the slow convergence of the weighting functions in the dispersion integrals. As an alternate to dispersion theory Drell and Sullivan (1966) have developed a relativistic Schrödinger model which shows that large polarizability corrections may well be present, and at the same time they are not expected to come only, for instance, from excitation of N* (1238). The resolution of the disagreement concerning the hyperfine structure problem seems to be bound strongly to a precise calculation of the strong-interaction polarizability effects.

Independent of the above speculations, a change in the value of α may modify the comparison between theory and experiment. The 9 ppm uncertainty in the value $\alpha^{-1} = 137.0388$ given by Dayhoff et al. (1953a) corresponds to two standard deviations. This determination of α is obtained from the comparison with theory of the experimental fine structure splitting $2P_{3/2}-2P_{1/2}$ as obtained by adding the intervals $2P_{3/2}-2S_{1/2}$ and $2S_{1/2}-2P_{1/2}$ in deuterium. As speculated by Drell (1966), if one simply adds to the measured $2P_{3/2}-2S_{1/2}$ interval the new Lamb shift value of Robiscoe and Cosens (1966), which is 0.3 MH larger, the value of α would be 13 ppm larger. The increase in the hyperfine splitting would be 26 ppm and no relevant disagreement between theory and experiment would remain.

5. *The Ratio of the Hyperfine Splitting in the Hydrogen and Deuterium Ground States*

This quantity is also of theoretical interest (Low and Salpeter, 1951). Its dependence on the deuteron structure however makes the calculation uncertain.

There is complete agreement (Zwanziger, 1961a; Sternheim, 1963) between the calculated ratio of the hyperfine splittings in the $2S$ and $1S$ states of hydrogen and the experimental value. The hyperfine splitting in the metastable $2S$ state was measured by Herberle et al. (1956). The experimental uncertainty is approximately 0.3 ppm. However, as remarked by Feynman (1962), the Breit contribution to the hyperfine formula already accounts for most of the corrections to the value of $\frac{1}{8}$ predicted by the Fermi formula, leaving only (1.3 ± 0.3) ppm to be explained by the remaining corrections.

IV. Hyperfine Splitting in Muonium. Determinations of the Fine Structure Constant

A. DETERMINATIONS OF α FROM THE HYPERFINE STRUCTURE INTERVAL IN MUONIUM GROUND STATE

Measurement of the hyperfine structure interval in the ground $1^2S_{1/2}$ state of muonium, the system formed by a positive muon and an electron (see E. H. S. Burhop, Volume III of this treatise), allows for an accurate verification of the electromagnetic interaction of muons and electrons. The sensitivity of the measurement to short distance breakdowns of quantum electrodynamics is rather low as compared to the sensitivity of the $g - 2$ experiment or of high energy tests.

The comparison of the experimental value of the hyperfine structure interval with the theoretical prediction leads however to a precise determination of α (Cleland *et al.*, 1964), in agreement with the determination of this quantity from the deuterium fine structure (Dayhoff *et al.*, 1953a,b).

Quantum electrodynamics leads to an unambiguous prediction for the muonium hyperfine structure (Karplus and Klein, 1952a; Kroll and Pollock, 1952; Newcomb and Salpeter, 1955; Arnowitt, 1953; Layzer, 1961; Zwanziger, 1961b). The problem involves only electromagnetic interactions of muons, electrons, and photons.

The theoretical expression for the ground state hyperfine structure interval v_M can be computed in terms of the Rydberg constant R_∞; the speed of light c; the magnetic moment ratios $\mu(e)/\mu(p)$ and $\mu(\mu)/\mu(p)$, where μ is for the magnetic moment of the free particle; the mass ratio m_μ/m_e; and α. The constant R_∞ is inserted in the theoretical expression with an uncertainty of ± 0.1 ppm, c with ± 1.3 ppm, $\mu(e)/\mu(p)$ with ± 1 ppm, $\mu(\mu)/\mu(p)$ with ± 13 ppm, and m_μ/m_e with ± 13 ppm.

The comparison of the theoretical expression to the experimental value of Δv_M obtained at Yale provides a determination of α to ± 9 ppm:

$$\alpha^{-1} = 137.0388 \, (\pm 9 \text{ ppm}).$$

Exactly the same value of α^{-1} had been obtained (Dayhoff *et al.*, 1953a,b) from the $2^2P_{3/2} - 2^2P_{1/2}$ fine structure interval of deuterium. Combination of the two results reduces the error in α^{-1} to ± 6 ppm.

In the Yale experiment polarized muonium was formed by stopping a beam of longitudinally polarized μ^+ in argon gas at high pressure. The transitions $(m_j, \, m_\mu) = (\frac{1}{2}, \, \frac{1}{2}) \to (\frac{1}{2}, \, -\frac{1}{2})$ were induced by microwave technique. The transition was observed through the asymmetry in the angular distribution of the decay positrons. The positrons were observed near $0°$ and $180°$. The number of positrons for a given number of stopped muons showed a maximum when the magnetic field was varied at fixed microwave frequency. The result was

$$\Delta v_M = (4463.15 \pm 0.06) \text{ Mc/sec} \, (\pm 13 \text{ ppm}).[1]$$

B. COMPARISON WITH THE HYPERFINE STRUCTURE INTERVAL OF HYDROGEN

The possibility of attributing to an incorrect value of the fine structure constant the disagreement between the observed and the theoretical value of

---

[1] A fuller description of the experimental technique is given by E. H. S. Burhop in Volume III of this treatise.

$\Delta v_{\rm H}$, the hyperfine structure interval of hydrogen in the ground state, is apparently excluded by the result of this experiment.

One can also instructively compare the experimental ratio $(\Delta v_{\rm M}/\Delta v_{\rm H})$ with its theoretical prediction. In the theoretical ratio some radiative corrections disappear and the chances of theoretical errors are reduced.

The theoretical expression for $\Delta v_{\rm H}$ contains the correction term $(1 - \delta_P)$ which accounts for the effects of proton recoil and proton structure. From comparison between the experimental and theoretical values of $(\Delta v_{\rm M}/\Delta v_{\rm H})$ one obtains $\delta_P = (-9 \pm 18) \times 10^{-6}$. For comparison, the theoretical prediction is $\delta_P = (35 \pm 3) \times 10^{-6}$ (Iddings and Platzman, 1959a,b; Iddings, 1965).

C. Latest Developments

A calculation by Ruderman (1966) on the behavior of μ^+ in aqueous solutions is relevant to the problem of the value for the fine structure constant. The calculation suggests that the current value of the μ^+ magnetic moment should be reduced by almost 20 ppm. The magnetic moment of μ^+ is obtained from the measurement of the frequency of precession in a magnetic field of μ^+ stopped in water or aqueous HCl (Hutchinson et al., 1963) directly from the ratio of the precession frequencies of μ^+ and proton. The determination assumes, however, identical chemical environment for a μ^+ in water and a proton.

This assumption is critically examined by Ruderman. The μ^+ can form a stronger bond between molecules of water than the hydrogen bond, because of its lighter mass and higher zero-point energy. The bonding is not broken during the precession measurement. The chemical shift for the muon in this state is about 15–20 ppm less than for the proton, resulting in a corresponding reduction for the value of the μ^+ moment.

The previous value of the magnetic moment ratio—before introducing such a chemical correction—$\mu_\mu/\mu_p = 3.18338 \pm 0.00004$, together with the value of the muonium hyperfine splitting (Cleland et al., 1964), led to a value $\alpha^{-1} = 137.0388 \pm 0.0013$. This value is to be compared with the two alternative values suggested by the Lamb shift measurements: $\alpha^{-1} = 137.0388 \pm 0.0006$ from the measurements of Dayhoff et al. (1953) and $\alpha^{-1} = 137.0370 \pm 0.0006$ from the measurements of Robiscoe together with fine structure measurements in deuterium (Robiscoe, 1965). In addition, from the hyperfine splitting in hydrogen (Crampton et al., 1963; Cohen and Dumond, 1965) one obtains $\alpha^{-1} = 137.0352$, excluding the unknown polarizability corrections in the theoretical expression.

The Ruderman correction decreases the value of α^{-1} determined from the previous ratio μ_μ/μ_p and the muonium hyperfine splitting. The decrease makes the discrepancy between theory and experiment for the hyperfine structure in hydrogen smaller by almost a factor of two.

The modification of the value of α^{-1} implied by the Ruderman correction is in the same direction as that implied by the Robiscoe measurement. Also, this circumstance makes the experimental problem of solving the discrepancies between the Lamb shift measurements very urgent.

D. OTHER POSSIBLE METHODS OF DETERMINING α

Apart from the problem of the hyperfine structure in the ground state of atomic hydrogen, a more accurate value of α will be useful in the comparison of the predictions of the theory with the experimental results for the hydrogen and deuterium Lamb shifts. The comparison can be carried out at least to terms of order $(Z\alpha)^2 \ln(Z\alpha)$. Also, the ratio of the $2S$ to $1S$ hyperfine shifts in hydrogen and in deuterium is sensitive to terms of order α^3 and α^2 (m/)M.

More accurate determinations of α might be obtained through more accurate experimental and theoretical studies of the fine structure of the ^3P level of two electron atoms. Experimental accuracies have been increased (Brochard et al., 1952; Lamb, 1957; Wieder and Lamb, 1957; Colegrove et al., 1958; Lifschitz and Sands, 1961; Pichanick et al., 1964) and also the theoretical calculations have been improved in the last few years (Araki et al., 1959; Traub and Foley, 1959; Pekeris et al., 1962).

In the latest calculations by Schiff et al. (1965) nonrelativistic eigenvalues for the $2\,^3P$ and $3\,^3P$ states of helium are calculated to one part in 10^9 to 10^{10}. The fine structure splittings of the two levels are obtained with a precision of one part in 10^5 to 10^6.

Similar results have also been obtained by Schwartz (1964) for $2\,^3P$ state. The energy levels of the $1s2p\,^3P$ state of helium are illustrated in Fig. 3.

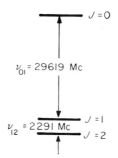

Fig. 3. Energy levels of the $1s2p\,^3P$ state of helium.

Discrepancies with experiment presumably indicate the necessity of including additional quantum electrodynamical corrections of the order α^4.

The hyperfine structure of positronium in the ground state may also allow for a more accurate determination of the fine structure constant. We refer to

Weinstein *et al.* (1954), Hughes *et al.* (1957), and Hughes *et al.* (1966) for the experimental work and to Karplus and Klein (1952b) and Fulton and Martin (1954) for the theory of the positronium hyperfine structure.

V. The Anomalous Magnetic Moment of the Electron

A. Measurements of the Electron g Factor

A series of experiments, carried out at Michigan, has finally led to a very accurate determination of the electron magnetic moment (Wilkinson and Crane, 1963). The electron g factor is measured by double Mott scattering with an intermediate magnetic field. In the first Michigan experiment, by Louisell *et al.* (1954), the g factor was obtained by measuring the rotation in the magnetic field of the plane of polarization. The result was still inaccurate and only gave a 1 % determination of the g factor. A much greater accuracy was reached in the second Michigan experiment by Schupp *et al.* (1961), essentially by making very large the number of revolutions of the plane of polarization, with a magnetic trapping system, and by measuring, instead of the spin precession frequency directly, the difference between such a frequency and the cyclotron frequency. The electron g factor was measured in this experiment with an accuracy of 2 ppm. In the last experiment of the series, by Wilkinson and Crane (1963) the following value for the g factor was obtained:

$$g = 2(1 + 0.001159622 \pm 0.000000027).$$

In the experiment a bunch of electrons moves parallel to a magnetic field and is scattered by a gold foil. The part scattered at 90° is trapped and kept for a measured time interval in the trap, and then scattered again by a gold foil. A fraction of the bunch, depending on the final polarization, strikes a Geiger counter. The difference between the frequency of spin precession and the orbital frequency is obtained from the intensity oscillations in terms of the trapping time. The measurement of the frequency difference gives the difference $g - 2$ in terms of the magnetic induction, of the speed of light, and of the electron mass and charge.

B. Comparison between Theory and Experiment

The anomalous magnetic moment results from the interaction of the electron with the quantized electromagnetic field. The lowest order term in the anomalous moment, second order in the electric charge, was calculated by Schwinger (1948) and Luttinger (1957). The next term in the perturbation expansion, fourth order in the electric charge, was first calculated by Karplus and Kroll (1950) and later corrected by Sommerfield (1957) and Petermann (1957).

The lowest order term arises from absorption and emission of one virtual photon. It contributes an anomalous moment of

$$\tfrac{1}{2}(\alpha/\pi)$$

times the Bohr magneton. The fourth-order term contributes an anomalous moment of

$$-0.328(\alpha^2/\pi^2)$$

times the Bohr magneton.

To compare with the theoretical expression, Wilkinson and Crane (1963) write their result in the form

$$\tfrac{1}{2}(g-2) = (\alpha/2\pi) - (0.327 \pm 0.05)\alpha^2/\pi^2$$

showing a complete agreement with theory. The uncertainty in α^{-1}, assumed to be of ± 0.0006, produces only an uncertainty of 5 ppm in the theoretical expression for $\tfrac{1}{2}(g-2)$, about five times smaller than the experimental uncertainty. Actually, such an uncertainty in the value of the fine structure constant is of the order of (α^3/π^3). The agreement between theory and experiment is within 1% for the coefficients of the α^2 terms in the two expressions.

The next improvement would be the calculation and comparison with experiment of the sixth-order term in the perturbative expansion. An estimate by Drell and Pagels (1966), based on dispersion theory, gives a value of

$$+0.15(\alpha^3/\pi^3)$$

for the sixth-order term of the electron magnetic anomaly, $\tfrac{1}{2}(g-2)$.

The measurement of the coefficient of (α^3/π^3) is however precluded, at the present time, also because of the present error in the fine structure constant, which alone gives rise at least to an uncertainty about three times larger than the calculated α^3 term.

An additional uncertainty in the experimental determination by Wilkinson and Crane comes from the experimental error in the particular combination of physical constants $(mc\gamma_p/e)$ (where γ_p is the gyromagnetic ratio for protons in water), measured by Franken and Liebes (1956), whose value is required for the computation of the gyromagnetic ratio from the data measured in the experiment. This uncertainty is larger than that arising from the fine structure constant.

The measurement of the coefficients of α^3/π^3 in the quantity $\tfrac{1}{2}(g-2)$ for the electron seems thus infeasible at this time. More precise determination of α will presumably be available when the accuracies in the measurements of the hyperfine structure in the muonium ground state, or in the deuterium or helium fine structure will be increased.

The calculation by Drell and Pagels (1966), besides providing a first estimate of the α^3 correction to the electron magnetic moment, is also of interest from a methodological viewpoint.

The calculation is based on an approximation scheme, quite different from perturbation theory, which uses the analyticity properties of the Feynman graphs and the exact limit of low energy photon-electron Compton scattering. A dispersion relation in the squared momentum of the incoming electron is written down and it is assumed to hold without subtractions. In the absorptive amplitude only states with one electron and one photon are included. The "cut" graphs are illustrated in Fig. 4.

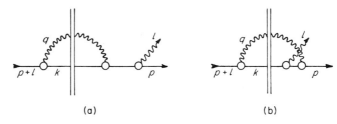

(a)   (b)

Fig. 4. Absorptive contributions to the anomalous magnetic moment of the electron in the calculation by Drell and Pagels.

It can easily be seen, in a nonrelativistic calculation, that a large fraction of the Schwinger term, $\alpha/2\pi$, in the expansion of $\frac{1}{2}(g-2)$, is obtained from the exact classical Thompson amplitude. An extension of this result then follows easily by using the low energy theorem of Gell-Mann, Goldberger, and Low (Low, 1954; Gell-Mann and Goldberger, 1954), who showed that the linear terms in the photon energy of the Compton amplitude can be exactly expressed in terms of the magnetic moment. Inclusion of these terms in a fully relativistic treatment leads to the exact Schwinger correction, $(\alpha/2\pi)$, to a good approximation for the fourth-order term, $-0.328\ (\alpha^2/\pi^2)$, and to the prediction of $0.15(\alpha^3/\pi^3)$ for the sixth-order correction.

The electron anomalous moment is not very sensitive to a breakdown of the theory at small distances.

Introduction of a cutoff in the theory, at an energy Λ—either by modifying the photon propagator for momentum transfers larger than Λ, or by cutting down the dispersion integral for energies larger than Λ—gives a correction to the Schwinger term of the order of $(m_e/\Lambda)^2$.

The present accuracy only assures that Λ cannot be smaller than about 100 MeV.

C. Upper Limit to the Electric Dipole Moment of the Electron

The Wilkinson–Crane (1963) determination of the g factor of free electrons can also be used to put an upper limit to a possible electric dipole moment of the electron.

The existence of an electric dipole moment is incompatible with parity conservation or with invariance under time reversal. The experiment provides an upper limit of e (0.4×10^{-15} cm) for a possible electric dipole moment of the electron. In units of $eh/m_e c$ the upper limit is 1×10^{-5}.

The Lamb shift experiments only provide an upper limit of 0.3×10^{-2} in the same units, as shown by Feinberg (1958). From the absence of parity-violating atomic transitions, Salpeter (1958) derived upper limits of the order of $(2 \div 5) \times 10^{-2}$. More stringent upper limits for the electron dipole moment were obtained by Burleson and Kendall (1960) ($\sim 0.2 \times 10^{-3} eh/m_e c$), and by Goldemberg and Torizuka (1963) ($\sim 0.3 \times 10^{-4} eh/m_e c$), from measurements of differential cross sections of high energy electrons.

In the experiment by Goldemberg and Torizuka the upper limit on the electric dipole moment of the electron is obtained from measurement of the cross section of elastically scattered 41.5 MeV electrons on He^4 at $180°$, corresponding to a momentum transfer of 0.44×10^{13} cm^{-1}. The experiment leads to an upper limit for the sum of the squares of the form factors of the anomalous magnetic dipole moment and of the possible electric dipole moment of the electron. However, the form factor for the anomalous magnetic moment is expected to become negligible at large momentum transfers. In fact its origin is ascribed to the interaction of the electron with the quantized electromagnetic field and the associate typical length is the electron reduced Compton wavelength.

Also, the electric dipole moment may possibly be associated with a distribution in momentum space. This distribution would then be limited at zero momentum from the upper limit ($\sim 1 \times 10^{-3} eh/m_e c$) deduced from the Wilkinson–Crane experiment, and at a momentum of 0.44×10^{13} cm^{-1} from the Goldemberg–Torizuka limit of $0.3 \times 10^{-4} eh/m_e c$.

D. The g Factor of the Positron

A direct measurement of the g factor of the free positron has recently been completed by Rich and Crane (1966). The g factor of the free positron must be equal to that of the electron directly from TCP invariance. The experiment by Rich and Crane does not show evidence for a discrepancy, but the experimental error is still too large for a real test of the coefficient in front of the α^2/π^2 term. Their result for the g factor anomaly a can be written in the form $a = \alpha/2\pi + (1.2 \pm 2)(\alpha^2/\pi^2)$. For comparison, the experimental value for the electron (Wilkinson and Crane, 1963) is $a = \alpha/2\pi - (0.327 \pm 0.05)(\alpha^2/\pi^2)$.

The technique used by Rich and Crane is similar to that of the Wilkinson and Crane experiment, except for the method of polarization and for its analysis. In a more accurate experiment in preparation the authors hope to be able to observe possible differences between the two anomalies down to 0.01%.

VI. The Muon Magnetic Moment

A. Measurement of the Anomalous Muon Gyromagnetic Ratio [the $(g - 2)$ Experiment]

The muon gyromagnetic ratio has been measured at CERN to an accuracy of 4 ppm (Charpak *et al.*, 1961, 1962, 1963). The experiment is based on a direct determination of the anomalous gyromagnetic ratio, $\frac{1}{2}(g - 2)$, from the total change of the polarization angle of initially longitudinally polarized muons, stored for a given time in a static magnetic field of known shape.

The muons are obtained from pions decaying in flight in the forward direction and are longitudinally polarized. They describe a large number of almost circular orbits in a suitably designed magnetic field. The anomalous gyromagnetic ratio causes a difference between the spin precession frequency and the frequency of rotation of the momentum vector. The change in polarization angle is measured as a function of the storage time. The anomalous ratio $\frac{1}{2}(g - 2)$ can then be directly obtained in terms of the magnetic induction B and of the cyclotron frequency, $\omega_0 = e/(m_\mu c)$, in unit magnetic field, for low energy muons.

The nonrelativistic expression for the angle θ between spin and momentum is clearly

$$\tfrac{1}{2}g\omega_0 Bt - \omega_0 Bt = \tfrac{1}{2}(g - 2)\omega_0 Bt.$$

This expression also holds relativistically, as shown by Bargmann *et al.* (1959). It is assumed that the muon does not have any appreciable electric dipole moment, whose existence violates invariance under time reversal and parity conservation.

Indirect evidence for the anomalous g factor of muons was obtained from measurement of the frequency of spin precession in a magnetic field with muons at rest (Hutchinson *et al.*, 1963). The experiment was essentially a measurement of the ratio

$$\frac{eg}{2mc} = \frac{\omega}{B}$$

where ω is the precession frequency and B is the magnetic induction. The ratio was measured with the accuracy of 17 ppm. However, the large uncertainty in the muon mass, of the order of 100 ppm, did not allow a determination of the anomalous g factor with a precision comparable to that of the direct $(g - 2)$ measurements.

B. COMPARISON WITH THEORY

The theoretical prediction of quantum electrodynamics for the muons $(g - 2)$ has been calculated up to fourth order in e (Petermann, 1957; Sommerfield, 1957) and gives

$$\frac{g - 2}{2} = \frac{\alpha}{2\pi} + 0.76\frac{\alpha^2}{\pi^2} = 1165 \times 10^{-6}. \tag{VI-I}$$

The CERN result for this quantity,

$$(1162 \pm 5) \times 10^{-6}$$

is consistent with the theoretical prediction and confirms the correctness of Schwinger's term in Eq. (VI-1), $\alpha/2\pi$.

1. *Confirmation of the Vacuum Polarization*

The experimental uncertainty of 5×10^{-6} is of the order the α^2 term in Eq. (VI-1), which contributes $\sim 4 \times 10^{-6}$. However, the $(g - 2)$ result indirectly contributes (Charpak *et al.*, 1965) to a verification, within 4%, of the electron vacuum polarization effects in muon electrodynamics (Petermann, 1957; Sommerfield, 1957). Indeed from the $(g - 2)$ result and from the measurements of the ratio of muon and proton precession at rest in a magnetic field (Hutchison *et al.*, 1963) and the analogous measurement for the electron (Dumond, 1959), one obtains the result

$$m_\mu/m_e = 206.765 \pm 0.003.$$

Such a mass value can be inserted in the expression for the x-ray energy in the $3D$-$2P$ transition of μ-mesic phosphorus, which depends upon the electron vacuum polarization (Petermann and Yamaguchi, 1959; see also E. H. S. Burhop in Volume III of this treatise). The x-ray energy was measured very accurately (Lathrop *et al.*, 1960a,b; Devons *et al.*, 1960); the experiment had in fact been designed for a determination of the muon mass.

The 4% accuracy of this verification of the electron vacuum polarization effects in muon electrodynamics is to be compared with the slightly better accuracy reached in the verification of the same vacuum polarization effect in electron physics: $\sim 1\%$ from the Lamb shift, and $\sim 2\%$ from the electron $(g - 2)$ measurement.

2. *Validity of the Theoretical Expression*

The theoretical expression (VI-1) is calculated without inclusion of vacuum polarization effects due to strongly interacting particles. These contributions already occur at the order of α^2. A precise estimate of the vacuum polarization effects from strongly interacting particles will be possible when electron-positron colliding beam cross sections are measured (Cabibbo and Gatto, 1960). However, they are expected to be negligibly small here, where they appear as integrated averages, on the basis of the general feature of vacuum polarization diagrams, which contribute proportionately to the inverse square mass of the polarizing particles.

For instance, the perturbation theory diagram with virtual pion pairs, only contributes about two parts in a thousand to the α^2 correction.

A larger contribution is expected from the ρ-meson contribution. A calculation, by Durand (1962), of the ρ-meson contribution to $\frac{1}{2}(g - 2)$ gives about 0.06×10^{-6}, to be compared with the expected magnitude of the α^2 term $\sim 4 \times 10^{-6}$ and with the present experimental uncertainty of 5×10^{-6}. It is evident that a quantitative verification of such an effect must await increased experimental accuracy.

The α^3-quantum electrodynamical corrections, at sixth order in e, are presumably still smaller.

In the absence of a calculation of the α^3 coefficient we merely note that $(\alpha/\pi)^3$ is of the order of 10^{-8}. The approach by Drell and Pagels (1966), that we have already described in connection with the anomalous electron magnetic moment, cannot be extended, in a simple way at least, to estimate the α^3 term in the muon $\frac{1}{2}(g - 2)$.

The calculation was in fact based on a dispersion relation for the vertex, in the squared mass of the incoming fermion, and on the assumption of dominance of the Compton amplitude. This last assumption will however fail for the muon vertex, since states such as $e^+ + e^- + \mu^+$, whose threshold is only 1% higher than the threshold for muon Compton scattering, cannot be neglected.

C. The $(g - 2)$ Measurement as a Test of Quantum Electrodynamics

The anomalous part of the muon gyromagnetic ratio depends, in its evaluation, very strongly on the behavior of the quantum electrodynamical amplitudes for momenta of the order of the muon mass. It therefore provides a very suitable test of quantum electrodynamics at small distances.

This fact has been known for a long time, and was remarked, for instance, by Berestetskij *et al.* (1958).

The strict definition of the minimum length explored by the experiment, corresponding to the experimental accuracy obtained, is mainly a matter of definition. The most frequent procedure consists in arbitrarily introducing a cutoff in some of the relevant electrodynamical quantities, and then determining the limit on the cutoff that is still compatible with the experimental result (Drell, 1958).

In the lowest order diagram for the anomalous magnetic moment one can think of modifying, independently or simultaneously, the photon propagator, the muon-photon vertex, or the muon propagator. We shall briefly report on the different cutoff limits that one derives by such modifications, although one should stress that the main significance of these speculations is perhaps to be found in the practical role that they are playing in stimulating experiments and providing for conventional criteria of comparison.

1. *Interpretations in Terms of a Cutoff*

The introduction of a cutoff in the photon propagator is usually made by multiplying such a propagator by a factor $-\Lambda^2/(k^2 - \Lambda^2)$, where k is the virtual momentum and Λ is the energy cutoff introduced.

Similarly, the modification of the fermion propagator is made by multiplication by a factor $-\Lambda^2/(p^2 - m^2 - \Lambda^2)$, where p is the virtual momentum, m is the fermion mass, and Λ the cutoff energy.

The vertex γ_μ can be modified conventionally by multiplying it by $\Lambda^2/(k^2 - \Lambda^2)$, where k is the photon momentum.

These modifications are connected with theoretical difficulties. Notably, the modification of the charged fermion propagator must be related to modifications of the vertex function, such as to satisfy the Ward identity. Otherwise one may be violating, among other things, the local conservation of the electromagnetic current.

We shall consider this point in more detail later, and just report here on the elementary considerations following from the modifications of the vertex and of the propagators mentioned above.

The modification of the photon propagator, considered above, gives rise to a multiplicative factor,

$$(1 - \tfrac{2}{3}(m_\mu/\Lambda)^2)$$

in the expression for $\tfrac{1}{2}(g - 2)$ (Berestetskij *et al.*, 1958).

The vertex modification evidently introduces a correction factor

$$(1 - \tfrac{4}{3}(m_\mu/\Lambda)^2).$$

The muon propagator modification gives rise to a similar multiplicative correction, of the form (de Tollis, 1960)

$$1 - \tfrac{2}{3}(m_\mu/\Lambda)^2(2 \ln(\Lambda/m_\mu) + \tfrac{1}{3})$$

The CERN experiment puts a lower limit of 0.8 GeV for Λ in the case of modification of the photon propagator; of 1.1 GeV for modification of the electromagnetic muon vertex; and of 2.0 GeV if the muon propagator is modified in the way mentioned. These values are obtained within 95% confidence limit (Charpak *et al.*, 1961, 1962, 1965).

2. *Interpretation in Terms of a New Coupling*

The CERN group has also analyzed the experiment in terms of a new hypothetical coupling of the muon to a massive boson field. The experiment allows the derivation of upper limits for the coupling strength of the boson field to the muon in terms of the assumed mass of the field.

The additional contribution to the magnetic moment comes from graphs such as that in Fig. 5.

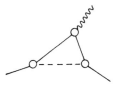

Fig. 5. Contribution to the muon magnetic moment from a hypothetical interaction with a new boson field.

For instance, suppose the new field is a vector field U_μ, coupled to the muon with an interaction term

$$(4\pi)^{1/2} f \bar{\mu} \gamma_\nu \mu U_\nu.$$

The anomalous magnetic moment contributed would be

$$\sim (f^2/3\pi)(m_\mu/m_u)^2.$$

where m_u is the mass of the U field, supposed to be much larger than m_μ.

To be definite, let us take m_u to be of the order of the nucleon mass. One finds, then, with 95% confidence, that f^2 must be smaller than 5×10^{-3}.

D. LATEST DEVELOPMENTS

As a preliminary result of a new $g - 2$ experiment for the muon recently started at CERN, a value of $(1165 \pm 3) \times 10^{-6}$ has been reported for $\frac{1}{2}(g - 2)$ of the μ^- (Farley *et al.*, 1966). This value is to be compared with the corresponding $\frac{1}{2}(g - 2) = (1162 \pm 5) \times 10^{-6}$ for the μ^+ (Charpak *et al.*, 1965). The result confirms, at the very high accuracy of 6 ppm, the validity of TCP in this case. Assuming TCP, it already constitutes an improvement in the determination of the muon magnetic anomaly.

As discussed in the preceding sections, vacuum polarization corrections from intermediate vector mesons are expected to contribute terms $\sim 10(\alpha/\pi)^3$.

Such contributions are presumably higher than the sixth-order electromagnetic contributions. Drell and Trefil (1966) have computed some enhanced terms, proportional to $(\alpha/\pi)^3 \times \ln^2 (m_\mu/m_e)$ and $(\alpha/\pi)^3 \ln (m_\mu/m_e)$, which arise from the insertion, into known second- and fourth-order contributions, of electron-positron vacuum polarization pairs. Their contribution is expected to be $< (\alpha/\pi)^3$.

A small uncertainty also less than $(\alpha/\pi)^3$ is contributed by the uncertainty in α.

The contributions of intermediate vector bosons has been recently calculated by Brodsky and Sullivan (1966) who employ the ξ-limiting formalism of Lee and Yang (1962) to regularize the divergences in a gauge invariant way. The result depends on the value of $\ln \xi$ and on the anomalous moment κ_w of the intermediate meson. For $\kappa_w = 0$ and the choice of ξ suggested by Lee (1962), Brodsky and Sullivan find a contribution of $-0.8(\alpha/\pi)^3$ to the muon $(g - 2)/2$.

E. Upper Limit to the Muon Electric Dipole Moment

The expression for the polarization angle θ would be modified by the presence of a possible electric dipole moment of the muon.

The situation can be visualized in a reference system with fixed origin in the laboratory, but rotating with the muon momentum. To the precession around the direction of the magnetic induction there will now be added, because of the electric dipole moment, a precession around the electric field in the radial direction. The angular velocity for this last precession is

$$2vf\omega_0 B/c$$

where v is the muon velocity and f is the electric dipole moment in units of $eh/m_\mu c$. The spin precession will result from the combination of the two precessions, and the resultant angular velocity will form with respect to B an angle

$$\sim \frac{4vf}{c(g - 2)}.$$

The effect can be measured by observing the produced oscillating component of the muon polarization along B.

By this method Charpak et al. (1961a) obtained an upper limit of

$$e \times (0.6 \pm 1.1) \times 10^{-17} \text{ cm}$$

for a possible muon electric dipole moment or, in units of $eh/m_\mu c$,

$$f < (3 \pm 6) \times 10^{-5}.$$

Previous measurements were due to Garwin and Lederman (1959) and to Berley and Gidal (1960).

VII. Electron and Muon Scattering by Electrons and Nucleons

A. ELECTRON-ELECTRON AND POSITRON-ELECTRON SCATTERING

Electron (or positron) scattering on electrons at rest does not unfortunately allow for a searching test of the theory at the energies now available. The reason is purely kinematical. The transferred four-momentum is

$$-q^2 = \frac{4E_L{}^2 \sin^2(\theta_L/2)}{1 + (2E_L/m)\sin^2(\theta_L/2)}$$

where E_L and θ_L are the incident electron (or positron) energy and scattering angle in the laboratory system. At incident energies ~ 10 GeV, the values of the momentum transfer involved are still less than about 100 MeV. Of course the availability of electron-electron or electron-positron colliding beams will completely change the situation.

B. ELECTRON AND MUON SCATTERING BY NUCLEONS

1. *Limit on Quantum Electrodynamics from Electron-Proton Scattering*

It was remarked by Drell (1958) that electron-proton scattering already gives an upper limit for the distance at which any breakdown of quantum electrodynamics occurs.

From the absence of deviations up to 0.8×10^{-13} cm, one can conclude that $\Lambda^{-1} < 0.33 \times 10^{-13}$ cm, with the usual modification of the photon propagator by the multiplicative factor $(-\Lambda^2)/(q^2 - \Lambda^2)$. More generally the limitation should be extended to the combination of electron vertex and photon propagator.

The deviations at distances less than 0.8×10^{-13} cm are, however, currently attributed to the proton finite size, and 0.8×10^{-13} cm is in fact taken as the proton rms radius. The muon scattering experiments, together with the results of the $(g - 2)$ experiment, indirectly reinforce the current interpretation in terms of the rms radius of the proton.

2. *Comparison of High Energy Muon and Electron Scattering*

Comparison of high energy muon and electron scattering, both elastic and inelastic, on any light nucleus, gives a direct way of testing the equality of the muon and electron vertices. To first order, muon and electron scattering will be equal as soon as the mass difference becomes negligible. The equality is expected to hold also at higher orders, although the absence of terms with singular mass dependence at the higher radiative orders has not yet been rigorously proved. This problem deserves more investigation.

Muon scattering experiments have been carried out at different laboratories. Experiments in carbon and in lead were carried out by Masek *et al.* (1961) with an almost pure muon beam of 2 Gev/c momentum.

Scattering in lead is dominated by multiple Coulomb processes. In carbon, good agreement with theory was found up to momentum transfers ~ 400 MeV/c. Muon scattering on C, with higher accuracy, was measured at CERN by Citron et al. (1962), again finding agreement with comparable electron scattering data. Muon-proton scattering has been measured by the Washington group (Masek et al., 1963), allowing for a further extension of the agreement to a higher energy cutoff.

Recently, muon-proton scattering at high momentum transfer has been measured in a Brookhaven-Columbia-Rochester Collaboration (Cool et al., 1965) at momentum transfers between 700 and 1100 MeV/c. No difference between μ-p and e-p scattering has been found.

The selection criteria employed were such as to practically exclude any contamination from events with pion production.

The result was analyzed so as to derive a lower limit for the quantity D^2, defined from

$$D^{-2} = \Lambda_\mu^{-2} - \Lambda_e^{-2}$$

where Λ_μ and Λ_e are the hypothetical cutoff energies of the muon and electron vertex, respectively (both vertices are taken with form factors $(1 - q^2/\Lambda^2)^{-1}$). The lower limit obtained from the absolute rates is

$$D^2 \geqslant (1.9 \text{ GeV})^2$$

corresponding to a distance of ~ 0.10 fermi, with 95% confidence.

The expected independence of the systematic errors in the experiment (such as flux normalization, scanning losses, etc.) from the momentum transfer suggests a comparison based on the q^2 dependence of the cross sections. From this comparison, again with 95% confidence, one finds $D^2 > (2.9 \text{ GeV})^2$, corresponding to a distance ~ 0.07 fermi.

From the experiment one can derive an upper limit of 3×10^{-14} cm to the electron charge radius, defined as $r_e = \sqrt{6}\Lambda_e^{-1}$, if one makes use of the limits on the muon vertex derived from the $(g - 2)$ muon experiment (Charpak et al., 1961b, 1962, 1965) and from the large-angle muon pair production (de Pagter et al., 1964).

However, as pointed out by Drell and McClure (1965) the three experiments, namely, muon $(g - 2)$, μ-pair production, and μ-p scattering, are rather to be viewed as independent tests of the theory when one allows for modifications along a more satisfactory model maintaining current conservation.

Comparison of the muon and electron electromagnetic vertices can also be obtained from the ratios of vector meson decays into an electron or a muon pair, such as $\varphi^0 \to \mu^+ + \mu^-$ and $\varphi^0 \to e^+ + e^-$, and the analogous decays of ω^0 and ρ^0. The reactions $p + \bar{p} \to e^+ + e^-$ and $p + \bar{p} \to \mu^+ + \mu^-$ have also been proposed for a sensitive comparison of the electron and muon vertices. A systematical exploration of the electron and muon vertices, at timelike momentum transfers, will be possible with electron-positron clashing beams.

VIII. Wide-Angle Electron Pair Production and Bremsstrahlung

In a process such as wide-angle pair production, or large-angle bremsstrahlung in hydrogen, the virtual particle is the lepton, and one can study the behavior of the quantum electrodynamical amplitudes for large virtual lepton mass.

Hopefully, under certain conditions, the dependence upon the proton structure can be eliminated by comparison with electron-proton scattering. This can be done by expressing the expectedly dominant pair production or bremsstrahlung matrix elements in terms of the electromagnetic form factors of the proton.

A. Wide-Angle Production of Electron-Positron Pairs

A detailed analysis of wide-angle pair production in hydrogen was carried out by Bjorken et al. (1958) and Bjorken and Drell (1959) who discussed two different types of experiment.

In a first type of experiment only one of the emerging electrons is observed; in the second type both electrons are observed in coincidence.

The Feynman diagrams for the pair production process are shown in Fig. 6. The Bethe-Heitler diagrams can be expressed in terms of the proton's form factors of elastic electron-proton scattering. The Compton diagram contains however the virtual photon-nucleon amplitude and its estimation in terms of a point nucleon or of a nucleon with form factors may be quite misleading.

In addition to the diagrams of Fig. 6, one must consider the radiative corrections from virtual photons and from undetected bremsstrahlung photons.

1. The Asymmetric Arrangement

Referring again to the two types of experiment proposed, we note that in an experiment of the first type one will observe, for instance, the final positron, with high energy and at large angle with respect to the incident photon. In the first of the two Bethe-Heitler diagrams, Fig. 6a, the incident photon directly produces the positron at a large angle and the virtual electron is very far from the mass-shell. The squared virtual momentum is

$$(k - p_+)^2 \cong -2(kp_+) = -2|K|E_+$$

for positron emission at 90°. In the other Bethe-Heitler diagram, Fig. 6b, the

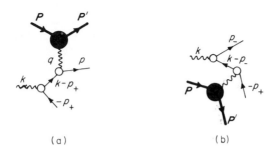

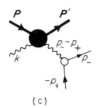

Fig. 6. Feynman diagrams for the pair production process: (a), (b) Bethe-Heitler diagrams, (c) Compton diagram.

positron is scattered by the proton at the large angle. The intermediate positron is close to the mass-shell, its squared four-momentum being

$$(k - p_-)^2 \cong -2(kp_-) = -2|K|E_-(1 - \beta_- \cos \theta_-)$$

where β_- and θ_- are the electron's velocity and angle of emission.

Figure 6a is very sensitive to a modification of the theory at higher virtual momenta.

On the other hand, Fig. 6b, is quite insensitive to such modifications. The retardation factor $(1 - \beta_- \cos \theta_-)$, however, makes its contribution to the cross section, for the conditions considered here, much larger than the contribution from Fig. 6a.

In the typical conditions considered by Bjorken et al. (1958) and Bjorken and Drell (1959) of positron emission at 90° and incident bremsstrahlung photons of 140 MeV peak energy, the intermediate lepton in Fig. 6a is about 140 MeV off its mass-shell, if the positron is emitted with about 100 MeV. However, the contribution of the diagram corresponds only to about 20% of the total expected cross section.

For the simple propagator modification by a multiplicative factor $\Lambda^2/(p^2 - m^2 - \Lambda^2)$, a test up to $\Lambda^{-1} = 0.7 \times 10^{-13}$ cm requires then an accuracy of the order of 5%.

Incidentally, we note that the remarks made herein about each single diagram are not gage-invariant. Although they depend on the particular choice of the gage, they are nevertheless of great usefulness for examining the general features of a reaction, in given kinematical conditions, as a possible probe of the theory.

The experiment performed by Richter (1958) leads to the result $\sigma_{exp}/\sigma_{theor}$ = 0.96 ± 0.14, where σ_{theor} is the calculated cross section (Bjorken et al., 1958; Bjorken and Drell, 1959). In terms of the electron propagator cutoff Λ_e the limit for a possible breakdown is roughly $\Lambda_e^{-1} < 0.9$ fermi.

The calculation of σ_{theor} was performed by including approximate proton recoil corrections in the Bethe-Heitler terms, the experimental proton form factors, the leading terms of radiative corrections, and by estimating the contribution from the Compton diagram.

This last contribution was calculated for a point proton model with anomalous magnetic moment, and it was found that both its squared value and its interference with the Bethe-Heitler amplitude were each less than 1% of the squared Bethe-Heitler term.

The applicability of the point proton model is presumably justified at this energy, the virtual Compton amplitude being still close to its low energy limit.

The smallness of the Compton contributions—both the squared term and its interference—is due partly to the slowness of the proton motion and partly to the different angular behaviors of the electron in the dominant Bethe-Heitler term, Fig. 6a, giving preferential forward emission, and in the Compton diagram, Fig. 6c, which instead gives preference to emission at 90°, along the positron direction.

Radiative corrections were estimated for a fixed proton and by ignoring terms of order less than $\alpha \ln (E/m)$ relative to the Bethe-Heitler cross section. Real photon emission was included with very low resolution, for the conditions of Richter's experiment, and the total radiative corrections were found to be less than 1% with possible errors again of 1%.

2. *The Symmetric Arrangement. Theoretical Analysis*

In the second type of wide-angle pair production experiments proposed by Bjorken et al. (1958) and Bjorken and Drell (1959), the final electron and positron are both detected at large angle. In this case the intermediate lepton lies far from the mass-shell for both Bethe-Heitler diagrams.

Particularly appealing is a symmetric arrangement with the electron and positron, equally energetic, emitted symmetrically with respect to and coplanar with the incident photon.

For such a situation there is no interference between the Bethe-Heitler graphs and the Compton graph as long as charge conjugation is valid. The absence of interference for the symmetric conditions follows in an elementary way from the observation that the Compton term has a behavior, under charge conjugation, as a single photon, whereas the Bethe-Heitler terms behave like two photons.

In the arrangement considered, the proton recoil can be made very small by suitable choice of the kinematical parameters, so that the squared Compton term itself gives a minor contribution and the proton structure effects are reduced.

In the symmetric arrangement the squared virtual lepton momenta, $(k - p_+)^2$ and $(k - p_-)^2$, in the two Bethe-Heitler graphs, Figs. 6a and 6b, have the same value

$$-2|K|E(1 - \cos \theta)$$

where E and θ are the symmetric values of the lepton energy and angle in the laboratory system. For sufficiently large θ both diagrams are thus very sensitive to modification for large virtual lepton momenta.

The sensitivity becomes larger for larger E and larger θ. On the other hand, by increasing E and θ, the Bethe-Heitler cross section gets reduced, making the observation more difficult. Also, a quantum electrodynamical estimate of the ratio of the squared Compton graph, Fig. 6c, to the Bethe-Heitler graphs, Figs. 6a and 6b, gives, neglecting proton's recoil,

$$(E/M)^2 \tan^4 (\theta/2) \tag{VIII-1}$$

where M is the proton mass, indicating a fast increase with E and θ of the Compton contribution.

Bjorken, Drell, and Frautschi considered in particular a situation with both electron and positron produced at 30° and 250 MeV, from a bremsstrahlung beam of 550 MeV maximum energy. A 10% experiment under such conditions would detect a cutoff of $\Lambda_e^{-1} = 0.3 \times 10^{-13}$ cm in the electron propagator.

The Compton term is negligible under these conditions, amounting to a correction smaller than at most $\frac{1}{2}$%. The radiative corrections, again calculated by neglecting terms of order less that $\alpha \ln (E/m)$ and without proton recoil, reduce the cross section by a calculable amount (within a possible error limit of 2% of the cross section), depending on the energy resolution for the undetected photons.

3. Pair Production in the Symmetric Arrangement

Production of wide-angle electron-positron pairs in the region between 1 and 6 GeV, under symmetric conditions, has been measured on carbon by Blumenthal et al. (1965) at the Cambridge electron accelerator. The results of this experiment do not agree with the theoretical predictions of quantum electrodynamics.

Measurements were made at angles $\theta = 4.75°$, $6.26°$, and $7.50°$ with respect to the incident beam and at different energies of the electron-positron pair. The expected theoretical yields were computed from the expressions of Bjorken, Drell, and Frautschi using an analytic fit to the carbon form factor data from elastic electron scattering.

The ratio R between the experimental and the theoretical yields was found to differ from unity and to increase with the mass of the virtual lepton. The radiative corrections were computed and an estimate was made of the nuclear inelastic contributions, without however affecting the main conclusion of an apparent deviation.

As a function of the virtual fermion mass, the ratio R was found to increase from about 0.6 for a virtual mass of 60 MeV to values around 1.5 for a virtual mass of 400 MeV. The authors suggested possible errors (from the theory, the synchrotron energy, the calibration of the quantameters, and the efficiency of the Cherenkov counters) to explain the persistence of the discrepancy even for low momenta, but no simple reason can apparently be given for the dependence of the effect on the momentum of the electrons.

In a later analysis by the authors, recently reported (Pipkin, 1966), the normalization at low momenta has been corrected and agrees with the Bethe-Heitler formula.

4. The Compton Diagram

The possible role of the Compton term, Fig. 6c, has been recently critically reviewed by Drell (1965) in connection with the deviations observed at the Cambridge accelerator by Blumenthal et al. (1965).

The forward dispersion relation for Compton scattering gives the Compton amplitude as an integral over the total cross section for photon absorption. This cross section is known, from measurements at Cambridge, to be almost constant and less than 100 μb in the energy range between 1 and 5 GeV. We can write

$$A(\omega, 0°) = -\frac{\alpha}{M} + \frac{i\omega}{4\pi} \sigma_{tot}(\omega) + \frac{\omega^2}{2\pi^2} P \int_0^\infty \frac{d\omega'}{\omega'^2 - \omega^2} \sigma_{tot}(\omega')$$

for the forward Compton amplitude at the energy ω of the photon. For the symmetric arrangement of the experiment, the interference between the Compton term and the Bethe-Heitler terms vanishes if charge conjugation invariance holds. The squared Compton term can hopefully be estimated from the amplitude $A(\omega, 0°)$ for forward scattering of real photons, although the relevant amplitude involved refers rather to virtual Compton scattering than to physical scattering. The estimate leads to the following correction factor

(Drell, 1965) to the Bethe-Heitler formula for the symmetric arrangement

$$R = \left[1 + \left(\frac{\omega^2 \sigma_{\text{tot}}}{8\pi\alpha} \right)^2 \tan^4 \frac{\theta}{2} \right]. \qquad \text{(VIII-2)}$$

In Eq. (VIII-2), ω is the photon energy and is equal to the total energy of the emitted pair, σ_{tot} refers to the photoabsorption cross section, and θ is the angle of each of the final fermions with respect to the incident photon momentum.

Equation (VIII-2) is to be compared with Eq. (VIII-1) which was obtained from the evaluation of the simplest electrodynamical graphs.

For the experimental conditions of the Cambridge measurements the correction, as calculated from Eq. (VIII-2), turns out to be less than 0.2%. The evaluation is done by correctly integrating, over the experimental resolution, around the sharp dip of the Bethe-Heitler cross section at the symmetry point.

A larger, but still secondary correction (for the Cambridge experiment) to the Bethe-Heitler amplitudes, Figs 6a and 6b, comes from virtual ρ^0 photoproduction, as shown in Fig. 7.

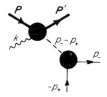

Fig. 7. ρ^0-photoproduction diagram contributing to wide-angle pair production.

Figure 7 is effectively a particular contribution to the general Compton diagram, Fig. 6c, as the ρ^0 decay into $e^+ + e^-$ is expected to proceed through a single virtual photon.

Its contribution can be evaluated in terms of the forward ρ^0-photoproduction cross section and of the rate of $\rho^0 \to e^+ + e^-$.

For the ρ^0-branching ratio into an electron-positron pair one can use the upper limit of 10^{-4} from the experiment of Zdanis et al. (1965). These authors have measured the distribution of opening angles of lepton pairs from a pion beam incident on liquid hydrogen. The analysis of the distribution in terms of background processes and ρ, ω, and φ decays into leptons (for $\omega - \varphi$ mixing angle of 38°) leads to a branching ratio for $\rho^0 \to e^+ + e^-$ of $(0.5^{+0.6}_{-0.3}) \times 10^{-4}$ and a branching ratio of $(1.0^{+1.2}_{-0.8}) \times 10^{-4}$ for $\omega^0 \to e^+ + e^-$.

The ρ^0-photoproduction cross section can be taken from recent Cambridge data (Russel, 1965). In the conditions of the Cambridge wide-angle pair production experiment, such a virtual ρ^0 term gives only a 1% correction, if one correctly integrates over the cross-section dip at the symmetry point according to the experimental resolution.

Along similar lines one expects a contribution also from virtual ω^0. The branching ratio for $\omega^0 \to e^+ + e^-$ is known to lie, with 95% confidence, between 5×10^{-5} and 6×10^{-4} (Binnie $et\,al.$, 1965). Also, the forward ω^0-photoproduction cross section seems to be notably smaller than the ρ^0 cross section. There is therefore no reason to expect any substantial modification of the conclusion by including the virtual ω^0 contribution.

A similar analysis can be done for the virtual φ^0 photoproduction. Taking 2×10^{-4} for the $\omega^0 \to e^+ + e^-$ branching ratio (Binnie $et\,al.$, 1965), and making use of theoretical arguments based on the SU(3) symmetry, the predicted $\varphi^0 \to e^+ + e^-$ branching ratio is $\sim 1 \times 10^{-3}$ for an $\omega - \varphi$ mixing angle of 38°.

5. *Latest Developments in Wide-Angle Pair Production*

A new experiment on wide-angle electron-positron pair production has been performed at the DESY 6.2 GeV electron syncrotron by a Desy-Columbia group (Asbury $et\,al.$, 1966).

The experiment is made on carbon, again under symmetrical conditions, using magnetic spectrometer gas threshold counters and shower counters to separate the electron. The results agree with theory, contradicting the CEA results (Blumenthal $et\,al.$, 1965).

In the kinematical conditions of the experiment the momentum transfer to the virtual electron t is $\leqslant 400$ MeV/c. On the other hand, the momentum transfer to the nucleus is always less than about 50 MeV/c.

The expected Z^2 dependence was verified by comparing the yields in C, O, Al, Cu, and Pb at a 30 MeV/c momentum transfer to the nucleus, all measured with 3% accuracy.

In a comparison with the theoretical formula, contributions from the Compton term were neglected in accordance with the vanishing of its interference term with the Bethe-Heitler amplitude. Contributions from inelastic form factors were also neglected.

Radiative corrections, including the hard-photon contributions calculated by Brodsky (Brodsky, 1966), are said by the authors to be almost constant for all settings of the spectrometers, and they decrease the theoretical yield by $3.0\,(\pm 1.0)\%$.

After a detailed study of the experimental points the authors conclude that no significant systematic errors are present.

The ratio R of experiment to theory is given, as a result of the experiment, as a function of the invariant mass of the electron pair, $M = \sqrt{2t}$. The authors derive a linear best fit $R = 0.95 \pm 0.04 - (0.4 \pm 1.1) \times 10^{-4}$ M (with M in

MeV/c^2). The normalization uncertainty, of the order of 5%, is not included in the above expression. The agreement with zero slope is excellent.

A quadratic best fit, $R = 0.94 \pm 0.02 - (5.8 \pm 15.7) \times 10^{-8} M^2$ again shows no deviation from constancy. The above quadratic fit is suitable for comparison with the CEA result, which is $R = 0.67 \times [(1 \pm 0.04) + (513 \pm 38) \times 10^{-8} M^2]$ and indicates a strong quadratic increase.

An experiment has also been performed at Cornell (Eisenhandler *et al.*, 1966) again under symmetric conditions. The particles are identified with the help of spark chambers. The Cornell experiment concerns lower values of the invariant masses.

In a theoretical paper by Lomon (Lomon, 1966) the separability of the Bethe-Heitler amplitude from the radiative contribution in the current expression for the radiative correction to the Bethe-Heitler cross section is questioned. When the electron-positron pair emits an undetected pair, a shift in the reaction energy is practically induced by the fact that the energy of the pair actually identifies the reaction energy. The effect is investigated by Lomon who finds that it is not negligible. A preliminary discussion of the radiative corrections has also been given by Ferrari and Thurnauer (1966).

In connection with the problem of interpreting the deviations from quantum electrodynamics we mention an investigation by Kroll (1966) concerning the implications of local conservation of charge on a modified quantum electro-dynamical theory. It is known that the Ward-Takahashi identity relates vertex and charged propagator modifications. In general, however, a modi-fication of the propagator also requires additional many-photon vertices. When these vertices are constructed on the basis of a natural extension of the so-called minimality principle one finds that the theory gives the same results as conventional quantum electrodynamics as long as no closed loops are involved. More effective modifications also require the specification of "in-trinsic" many-photon vertices. A simplest example of intrinsic vertex modifi-cation discussed by Kroll corresponds to a kind of off-mass-shell magnetic moment. Large angle-pair production is found in this model to be modified by terms proportional to the fourth power of the momentum transfer rather than to the square of momentum transfer as expected for the usual cutoff modifications.

B. WIDE-ANGLE ELECTRON BREMSSTRAHLUNG

Measurements of the bremsstrahlung reaction

$$e + p \rightarrow e + p + \gamma$$

under kinematical conditions corresponding to high momenta of the virtual electron in the diagrams of Fig. 8 can be used to test quantum electrodynamics at small distances.

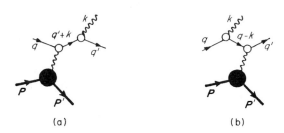

Fig. 8. Lowest order bremsstrahlung diagrams: (a) and (b).

The graphs in Fig. 8 have the same structure as the Bethe-Heitler graphs for pair production and the corresponding amplitudes are sensitive to the behavior of the electron propagator.

The virtual electron momentum is timelike in Fig. 8a, and spacelike in Fig. 8b, As shown in Fig. 8, the virtual electron momentum is $q' + k$ in Fig. 8a and $q - k$ in Fig. 8b. Small distance deviations will be exhibited in the behavior of the cross section for large values of $(q' + k)^2$ or of $(q - k)^2$, or of both invariants.

The calculation of the cross section, including the proton form factors at the virtual photon vertex, has been performed by Isaev and Zlatev (1959).

Fig. 9. Virtual Compton diagram for bremsstrahlung.

The presence of the " virtual Compton " diagram of Fig. 9 requires however careful treatment and does not, unfortunately, allow simple and straight-forward calculations.

Berg and Lindner (1961) and Isaev and Zlatev (1960) have presented esti-mates of the virtual Compton contribution using dispersion relations. Berg and Lindner analyze the virtual Compton effect in its general form involving twelve functions and two nucleon form factors. The intermediate single nucleon state, the one-meson one-nucleon state, and neutral pion exchange are calculated in detail, on the assumption that they contribute the dominant effects.

Accurate estimate of the virtual Compton effect would require, as in similar cases, a deep knowledge of strong interactions.

However, these estimates show that the interference between the Bethe-Heitler diagrams of Fig. 8 and the Compton diagram of Fig. 9 is generally of the order of a few per cent of the Bethe-Heitler contribution.

An experiment on electron-proton bremsstrahlung is at present in preparation at Frascati (Bernardini *et al.*, 1965). The comparison of the results of this experiment to the results of the pair production experiments will be extremely instructive, especially considering the structural identity of the Bethe-Heitler terms for the two processes.

IX. Photoproduction of Muon Pairs

1. *Muon Pair Photoproduction Experiments*

Wide-angle photoproduction of muon pairs has been measured at Frascati (Alberigi-Quaranta *et al.*, 1962) and at the Cambridge electron accelerator (de Pagter *et al.*, 1964).

The first evidence of the process was reported earlier by Masek and Panofsky (1956). Masek *et al.* (1956) confirmed, within $\pm 40\%$ accuracy, the applicability of the Bethe-Heitler formula to this case.

In the Frascati experiment, muon pairs, produced in a carbon target from bremsstrahlung γ rays up to 1 GeV, were detected symmetrically at $10°$ with respect to the incident photon. The small contaminations from electron pairs and from pion pairs decaying into muons were subtracted. The comparison was made with the Bethe-Heitler cross section including a form factor correction for the carbon nucleus, and an additional term accounting for inelastic processes, giving a correction proportional to $Z(1 - F^2)$, was used for the inelastic terms. The calculated inelastic corrections were 3 %. Minor corrections like radiative corrections, nucleon recoil, and Coulomb correction were not included.

The average of the ratios of the absolute experimental cross sections to the theoretical cross sections was found to be 1.00 ± 0.05. From the error one calculates an upper limit of 0.2 ± 10^{-13} cm, with 95% confidence, for the muon propagator cutoff. We recall that the upper limit obtained from the $(g - 2)$ experiment is $\sim 0.1 \times 10^{-13}$ cm, in a model where only the muon propagator is modified. The virtual muon four-momentum in the experiment varies in fact from 135 to 185 MeV/c.

In the experiment carried out at the Cambridge accelerator μ pairs were produced in carbon from a 5-GeV bremsstrahlung beam. The angular distribution between $4.5°$ and $11.5°$ was measured by dividing this interval into nine equal parts. The energies of the muons produced were measured in the range between 1.8 and 2.4 GeV divided into five intervals.

The comparison was carried out in terms of an accurate expression, derived by Bjorken, which also includes terms depending on the muon mass. The carbon form factor was taken from the electron scattering data, through an analytical fit to the experimental points. Errors from the form factor uncertainties increase with increasing momentum transfer to the nucleon, but were found to be smaller than the statistical errors. Accurate corrections were made for inelastic processes including, among them, pion production. The correction was found to be at most 8% for the highest values of the virtual muon four-momentum in the experiment. The uncertainties in the form factors and in the inelastic processes were both included in the systematic errors. Radiative corrections were neglected.

2. *Theoretical Analysis for Muon Pair Photoproduction*

For the symmetric arrangement considered, the interference between the Bethe-Heitler and the Compton terms vanishes as long as charge conjugation invariance holds.

The other advantage of the symmetric arrangement, as we have already discussed, is the related smallness of the momentum transfer to the nucleus, considerably reducing all uncertainties arising from the nuclear structure. In a symmetric arrangement for production at angle θ and energy E from photons of energy ω, the virtual muon four-momentum has the same value

$$\cong (-\omega E \theta^2 + m_\mu^2)$$

in both Bethe-Heitler diagrams.

The Compton term has a background contribution from the photoproduction cross section, as already discussed in connection with the wide-angle electron-pair experiments. Such a contribution is small also in the conditions of the Cambridge experiment.

More significant is the contribution from the virtual ρ^0 photoproduction, particularly when the invariant mass of the pair approaches the ρ^0 pole.

An analysis of the virtual Compton corrections has been performed by Krass (1965), who considers, in particular, terms arising from peripheral production of vector mesons via one-pion exchange. The correction from these terms is found by Krauss to possibly exceed 10% for 10 GeV photon energy and a production angle of 18° in the laboratory.

The diffraction mechanism is however expected to give the dominant contribution to the high energy forward photoproduction of nonstrange vector mesons, which have the same quantum numbers as the photon. The consequences of this assumption have been recently discussed by Drell (1965) and compared with the experimental data.

Needless to say, it is very advantageous to have an angular distribution of produced pairs in order to discriminate empirically, from the angular dependence, against large corrections from virtual Compton terms.

The squared virtual muon four-momentum in the Cambridge experiment extends from 1.3 to 8 F^{-2}. For the selected data, the squared four-momentum transfer to the nucleon was, in 95% of the cases, less than 0.4 F^{-2}.

The ratio of σ_{exptl} to σ_{theor} was fitted in a form

$$R = (1.18 \pm 0.15) \times [1 - (0.011 \pm 0.021)q^2]$$

where q^2 is the squared momentum of the virtual muon.

In terms of a modified muon propagator, the result amounted to an upper limit of $(0.16 \text{ F})^2$ for Λ^{-2}, with 95% confidence. This upper limit is lower than that deduced from the Frascati experiment, but still comparable with that obtained from the $(g - 2)$ experiment interpreted in terms solely of a breakdown of the muon propagator. It is evident however that one should be conscious of the arbitrariness of these conclusions about the limit up to which the theory is being tested, especially when different experiments are compared, such as for the $(g - 2)$ experiments and wide-angle muon pair production.

3. *Latest Developments*

A new investigation on photoproduction of muon pairs on carbon has recently been published (de Pagter *et al.*, 1966). The muons produced by the 5.2 BeV brehmsstrahlung beam are detected in coincidence on both sides of the beam with energies between 1.8 and 2.4 BeV and angles between 4.2° and 10.9°.

The ratio R_{exp} of the experimental yield to the Bethe-Heitler yield can be compared with a suitable R_{theory} constructed on the basis of a simple model including a breakdown linear in q^2, where q_μ is the four-momentum transferred to the virtual muon. Such a form of R_{theory} can be constructed by adding to the Bethe-Heitler yield, Y_{BH}, a term accounting for ρ^0 production, of the form BY_ρ where B is proportional to $\rho^0 \to \mu^+\mu^-$ and Y_ρ is proportional to the ρ^0 yield, and by further adding a breakdown contribution in the form $\beta q^2 Y_{\text{BH}}$. In addition, an adjustable normalization constant A must be introduced, giving a final expression $R_{\text{theory}} = A [1 + (B Y_\rho)/Y_{\text{BH}} + \beta q^2]$.

A best fit of experiment to theory determines the parameters A, B, and β. Restricting the comparison to the upper energy data, with both muons restricted to individual energies higher than 2040 MeV, to reduce the effect of backgrounds from π pairs and their decay products, typical values obtained for A, B, and β are $A = 1.34 \pm 0.14$, $B = (0.33 \pm 0.15) \times 10^{-4}$, $\beta = -0.051 \pm 0.018$, where the errors reported are the (dominating) systematic errors.

The nonzero value of β should mainly be attributed to deviations from quantum electrodynamics. In terms of the cutoff parameter Λ_μ, the result can be expressed as implying $\Lambda_\mu^{-1} = (0.16 \pm 0.08)^2 \ F^2$ for two standard deviations. For comparison, again for two standard deviations, the Frascati experiment (Alberigi-Quaranta *et al.*, 1962) gives $\Lambda_\mu^{-2} < (0.23)^2 \ F^2$, and the

$g - 2$ experiment (Charpak *et al.*, 1962), again for two standard deviations, gives $\Lambda_\mu^{-2} < (0.1)^2 \, F^2$ in a model of breakdown where the whole deviation is supposed to arise from the muon propagator. The previous experiment by the same group (de Pagter *et al.*, 1964) gave $\Lambda_\mu^{-2} < (0.16)^2 \, F^2$ for two standard deviations. It was, however, based on the theoretical assumption that the $\rho^0 \rightarrow 2\mu$ contribution could be neglected, an assumption disproved later (Boyarski *et al.*, 1965).

4. *Prospects for Experiments at Higher Energy*

The high intensity beams from electron linear accelerators are unfortunately in very short pulses. Coincidence experiments, such as muon pair production in the symmetric arrangement are, in these conditions, extremely difficult.

Future progress, at the higher energies of the Stanford linear accelerator (SLAC), may come from measurements in asymmetric arrangements with detection of a single muon in special conditions. An experiment of this kind has been proposed recently by Drell (1964).

In the proposed experiment one selects those events with one muon very energetic while the other is of nonrelativistic energy. More specifically an energetic μ^- is observed in the forward direction, with an energy close to the kinematical maximum energy.

The experiment will be very sensitive to breakdown, with available four-momentum squared of

$$\sim (-2m_\mu \omega + m_\mu^2)$$

for the virtual muon. The virtuality of the internal muon line

$$\sim -2\omega m_\mu$$

is $\sim -(450 \text{ MeV})^2$ for $\omega = 1$ GeV and $-(1.4 \text{ GeV})^2$ for $\omega = 10$ GeV. The measurement will require an accurate experimental resolution.

The Compton diagram interferes here with the Bethe-Heitler diagrams. The contribution from virtual photoproduction of vector mesons, decaying into a muon pair, might be nonnegligible.

The radiative corrections for the particular experimental setup should be properly included; corrections must be estimated for the proton recoil and the slow motion of the emitted positive muon in the Coulomb field.

5. *Tests of Muons Electrodynamics*

We have already mentioned, at different points, the arbitrariness of the usual procedure for modifying the theory by ad hoc regularization of the propagators and vertices. Such modifications must only be intended as a practical way of conveniently defining some sort of sensitivity of the particular experiment to breakdowns of quantum electrodynamics. Neither uniqueness, nor even general consistency of the procedure with the accepted principles of physics, can be claimed.

In particular, it is well known that a regularization of the propagator of the charged fermion should be made, simultaneously with corresponding regularizations of the vertex function, to keep the differential conservation law of the current unaltered. The relation to be satisfied is the Ward-Takahashi identity

$$S'_F(p')q_\mu\Gamma_\mu(p', p, q)S'_F(p) = S'_F(p) - S'_F(p') \qquad \text{(IX-1)}$$

between the propagator S'_F and the vertex function Γ_μ, for fermion momenta p and p' and boson momentum q.

Even the imposition of the identity leaves a great deal of arbitrariness in the choice of a suitable modification. Recently, Drell and McClure (1965) have performed an analysis of the tests of muon electrodynamics, notably $(g - 2)$ (Charpak et al., 1962) and wide-angle muon pair production (de Pagter et al., 1964), with a simple model of propagator modification accompanied by a vertex modification as required by the Ward-Takahashi identity. The recent general results by Kroll (1966) should be taken into account for a more systematic approach.

One expects on this basis that the $(g - 2)$ measurement and the wide-angle photoproduction experiment are actually independent and complementary tests of quantum electrodynamics.

Another independent test of the theory is, of course, the comparison of muon and electron scattering from hydrogen (Davies, 1963; Lederman and Tinlot, 1964). All these experiments should be carried out with maximum possible accuracy, as they actually test different aspects of the theory and together contribute to a more complete check of its correctness.

X. Possible Tests from Trident Processes

A. ELECTRON TRIDENTS

1. The Trident Process

Events where a high energy electron incident on a nucleus produces an electron-positron pair are conventionally called tridents. The process occurs at fourth order in quantum electrodynamics. The fourth-order diagrams are shown in Fig. 10.

The initial and final four-momenta of the nucleus (or nucleon) are called P and P', respectively; p is the incident electron four-momentum, p_1 and p_2 are the four-momenta of the final electrons, and p_+ is the four-momentum of the final positron.

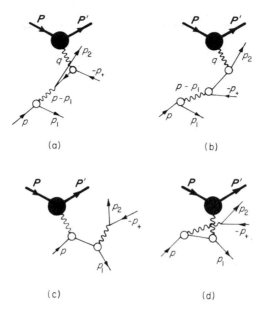

Fig. 10. Fourth-order diagrams for trident production: (a) (b) (c) (d).

To each diagram of Fig. 10 one must add a similar diagram with the two final electrons interchanged.

The occurrence of a virtual photon line in the diagrams of Fig. 10, joining electron vertices, allows for a study of the behavior of the photon propagator at small distances, provided suitable experimental conditions are assumed. In particular one can study the ratio of trident production to electron-positron pair photoproduction, to probe the photon propagator and the electron vertex.

2. *Observation of the Two Electrons in Coincidence*

Different experimental arrangements have been proposed for trident production on protons. Bjorken and Drell (1959) have suggested the observation of the two final electrons in a symmetric arrangement, with the initial electron and the two final electrons moving in the same plane, and with symmetric emission of the final electrons, at an angle to the left and to the right of the incident electron.

For such a choice of the kinematical conditions, the momentum transfer to the proton is made comparatively small and the related nuclear effects are consequently reduced. The final electrons are observed at an angle much larger than (m_e/E), where E is the incident electron energy, but still substantially smaller than $90°$.

Figures 10a and 10b give the biggest contribution to the production cross

section in such kinematical conditions. The cross section is notably comparable to the pair photoproduction cross section in spite of its higher electromagnetic order. The reason is to be found in the appearance of additional retardation factors and in the large contribution, for the arrangement considered,
from the virtual longitudinal photons, as compared to the Bethe-Heitler
amplitude of physical photons.

The latter circumstance follows simply from helicity rules that are valid
in quantum electrodynamics at high energy, which require that the helicities
of the electron and the positron in a pair must be opposite. Consequently the
pair must be in singlet state in the forward direction and will couple with
longitudinal photons rather than with transverse photons.

Figures 10a and 10b also depend very sensitively on the small distance
behavior of the exchanged virtual photon between the two electron lines. To
account for deviations from quantum electrodynamics for large virtual
photon momenta we multiply the cross section by a form factor $(1 + d^2k^2)^2$,
where k is the virtual photon four-momentum.

The squared virtual photon four-momentum

$$|k^2| = |(p - p_1)^2| = 2EE_1(1 - \cos \theta)$$

takes on large values in the proposed conditions, and, for instance, a 10%
deviation in the cross section at $\theta = 20°$ would correspond to a breakdown at
$d = 0.5$ fermi for $E = 500$ McV, and at $d = 0.2$ fermi for $E = 1$ GeV.

For the arrangement considered, Figs. 10a and 10b are "good diagrams"
for testing the small distance behavior of the exchanged virtual photon.
Figures 10c and 10d can be seen instead to be "bad diagrams."

In addition to Fig. 10 there are diagrams corresponding to dynamical
corrections from the proton current, such as in Fig. 11.

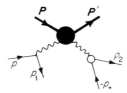

Fig. 11. Proton current contribution to trident production.

The diagrams of Fig. 11 must also be corrected for proton form factor
effects. Radiative corrections are expected to be large in view of the relatively
sharp effective energy resolution defined by the energy of the emitted positron.

3. *Observation of Electron-Positron Coincidences*

An alternative experimental arrangement, with an electron and the positron
detected in coincidence, is analyzed by Chen (1962). The electron and the

positron are detected in a symmetric arrangement: coplanar with the incident electron, at equal energies and at same angle, to the right and to the left, of the incident direction.

Let us choose, for instance, to observe the electron with momentum p_1 and the positron with momentum p_+, again referring to Fig. 10.

A diagram such as Fig. 10b is a "good diagram" for probing the virtual photon behavior at high momenta.

In fact the squared four-momentum transfer of the virtual photon, $k^2 = (p - p_1)^2$, is fixed in the chosen experimental arrangement, and the cross section will be simply modified by a factor $(1 + d^2k^2)^2$, when the over-all form factor $(1 + d^2k^2)$ is introduced in the amplitude to account for possible modifications of the photon propagator and electron vertex at momentum k^2.

On the other hand, the diagram obtained from Fig. 10b by interchanging the two final electrons (this diagram is not included in Fig. 10) is a "bad diagram."

In fact the squared momentum $(p - p_2)^2$ of the virtual photon depends on the momentum of the unobserved electron, and the contribution of the diagram is especially large when such momentum transfer is small.

The "good diagrams" are fortunately found to be more important than the "bad diagrams." A numerical integration of the cross section, performed by Chen (1962), shows that deviations of the order of 10–15% in the cross-section values would correspond to breakdowns at $d \sim 0.5$ fermi.

The calculation is made for a proton of infinite mass, approximated as a Coulomb center. Corrections must be made for finite proton mass, form factor effects, Compton terms, and higher order radiative corrections. These last corrections in particular are expected to be rather large.

B. MUON TRIDENTS

Production of muon pairs by electrons has also been considered (Bjorken et al., 1958; Bjorken and Drell, 1959).

The theory is quite similar to that for electron tridents, except for the absence of exchange terms. The cross section for symmetric detection at 9° of $\mu^+ - e^-$ or $\mu^- - e^-$ of energy 450 MeV, produced from incident electrons of energy 1 GeV, is about the same as for electron trident production, with symmetric detection of $e^- - e^-$ at the same energy but at an angle of 15°.

The distances probed are in both cases of the order of 0.2 to 0.3 fermi with 10% experiments.

Measurements of muon tridents from incident muons like

$$\mu^+ + p \to p + \mu^\pm + \mu^+ + \mu^-$$

would also furnish interesting tests of quantum electrodynamics.

This process would also furnish a test of the Fermi-Dirac statistics obeyed by muons (Feinberg and Lederman, 1962). That muons are Fermi-Dirac particles is suggested by theoretical considerations. However, no direct experimental test of the assertion has been produced so far.

XI. Tests of Quantum Electrodynamics with Electron-Electron and Electron-Positron Colliding Beams

A. ELECTRON-ELECTRON COLLIDING BEAMS

The large number of electron-electron and electron-positron storage rings, working or under construction in different laboratories, makes us hope that important information on the validity of quantum electrodynamics will be obtained from colliding beam experiments (Gatto, 1965). The Stanford-Princeton group has recently reported the results of a first electron-electron colliding beam experiment having quantitative implications on the validity of electrodynamics (Barber *et al.*, 1965).

Electron-electron scattering has been measured at Stanford at a total center of mass energy of 600 MeV and for angles between 40° and 90°. The accumulation of 416 scattering events has required 360 hours of operation of the Mark III linear accelerator at Stanford and a total of 30,000 pictures with the beams interacting. Comparison has been made with the Møller cross section (1932), modified by inclusion of a form factor, depending on the virtual photon momentum, and by the radiative corrections.

The graphs for lowest order $e^- + e^- \to e^- + e^-$ are shown in Fig. 12. The momentum transfers are both spacelike and are given by

$$q^2 = 4E^2 \sin^2(\theta/2) \qquad \text{and} \qquad q'^2 = 4E^2 \cos^2(\theta/2). \qquad \text{(XI-1)}$$

In Eq. (XI-1), E is the energy of each colliding particle in the center of mass system ($2E$ is the total energy) and θ is the scattering angle.

The Møller formula, modified by the introduction of a form factor F, is, with neglect of the electron mass,

$$\frac{d\sigma}{d(\cos\theta)} = \frac{\pi\alpha^2}{4E^2} \left\{ \frac{4 + (1 + \cos\theta)^2}{(1 - \cos\theta)^2} |F(q^2)|^2 + \frac{8}{\sin^2\theta} \mathrm{Re}[F^*(q^2)F(q'^2)] \right.$$

$$\left. + \frac{4 + (1 - \cos\theta)^2}{(1 + \cos\theta)^2} |F(q'^2)|^2 \right\}. \qquad \text{(XI-2)}$$

One can think of the form factor F as a product of a vertex form factor squared and a form factor for the photon propagator. Of course, more complicated forms of modifications of the theory can be imagined but, at a first stage, it will be sufficient to compare with the modified Møller formula, Eq. (XI-2), inserting a typical form for $F(q^2)$. The simplest assumption is

$$F(q^2) = \frac{1}{1 + (q^2/\Lambda^2)}. \qquad \text{(XI-3)}$$

A deviation from $F = 1$ (corresponding to $\Lambda = \infty$) will correspond to a breakdown of the theory, and the parameter Λ (which can be positive or negative) can be taken as a measurement of the deviation. The maximum relative deviation will occur at 90° according to the modified Møller expression.

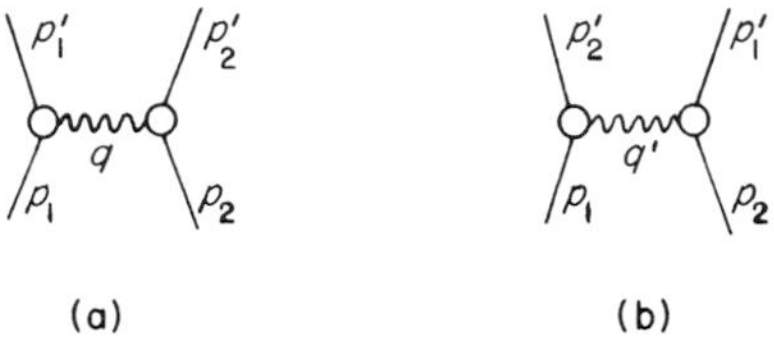

(a)   (b)

Fig. 12. Feynman diagrams for $e^- + e^- \rightarrow e^- + e^-$: (a) (b).

In comparing with experiment one has to include radiative corrections to the modified Møller formula. Calculations of the radiative corrections have been done by Tsai (1960, 1965) and by Bayer and Kheifets (1963). These calculations were made by properly taking into account the experimental conditions for the particular colliding beam experiment, and in this respect they differ from other calculations made with different (and sometimes unrealizable) conditions in view.

The corrected cross section is obtained as

$$d\sigma = d\sigma_{\text{el}} + d\sigma_{\text{soft}} + d\sigma_{\text{hard}}$$

where $d\sigma_{\text{el}}$ is the elastic cross section, which includes radiative corrections from virtual photons: $d\sigma_{\text{soft}}$ refers to the emission of a bremsstrahlung photon with energy up to an isotropic maximum energy ΔE in center of mass; and $d\sigma_{\text{hard}}$ accounts for the remaining bremsstrahlung emission.

Only the addition of $d\sigma_{\text{soft}}$ to $d\sigma_{\text{el}}$ removes, as is well known, the dependence upon the fictitious photon mass. The maximum energy ΔE is chosen, relative to a given experiment, according to criteria of computational convenience.

The more difficult part is the calculation of the hard photon correction $d\sigma_{\text{hard}}$. The definition of the range of integration in the kinematical variables is dictated by the experimental arrangement.

The calculations by Tsai (1960, 1965) for the experimental conditions of the Stanford-Princeton experiment, namely, a maximum angle of 10° between the two collinear tracks and 30 MeV minimum energy of one of the final electrons,

(a)   (b)

Fig. 13. Vacuum polarization graphs: (a) (b).

give at $40°$ a total radiative correction of 3.4% and at $90°$ a correction of 5.6%.

It is interesting to have an idea of the relative magnitude of the various contributions from virtual electrons, muons, pion and proton pairs in the vacuum polarization diagrams that contribute to the elastic radiative corrections (see Fig. 13). Using the known expressions, by Feynman (1949) and by Euwema and Wheeler (1965), valid for particles without structure, one sees that in $e^- + e^- \rightarrow e^- + e^-$, at $E = 500$ MeV and $\theta = 90°$ (where the contribution is expected to be larger), the vacuum polarization contribution is 2% for electrons, 0.35% for muons, 0.09% for pions, and 0.02% for protons in the closed loops of Fig. 13.

For strongly interacting particles the approximation is certainly not valid, and modifications are expected from the effects of strong interactions. This point will be discussed in more detail in relation to the electron-positron colliding beam experiments.

The interpretation of the Stanford-Princeton experiment (Barber *et al.*, 1965) in terms of the parameter Λ^2 in Eq. (XI-3) gives

$$1/\Lambda^2 = 0.83 \pm 0.83 \text{ (GeV/}c)^2 \qquad \text{(with 68\% confidence level)}$$

$$-1.04 \leqslant 1/\Lambda^2 \leqslant 3.26 \text{ (GeV/}c)^2 \qquad \text{(with 99\% confidence level).}$$

The result of the Stanford-Princeton group is extremely important, especially in view of its clean theoretical interpretation. It is to be hoped that independent checks will soon be reported.

The authors have also considered the effect of polarization of the beams. The maximum change in the cross section for a completely polarized beam is however only of the order of 6%, as shown by Tsai (see Barber *et al.*, 1965). Furthermore, the expected average polarization of the beams is only 2%, assuming no depolarizing mechanisms and using the value of the mean rate of polarization given by Sokolov and Ternov (1963). This effect, if existing, should probably be negligible in the experiment.

B. Electron-Positron Colliding Beams

Electron-positron colliding beams offer, in addition to the possibility of testing quantum electrodynamics at high energies, a wide range of experimental possibilities related to the investigation of electromagnetic processes initiated by a virtual timelike photon. We shall not discuss here the large number of experimental possibilities connected with production of strongly interacting particles (Cabibbo and Gatto, 1960, 1961; Gatto, 1965), but shall limit our discussion to possible tests of the validity of quantum electrodynamics (Gatto, 1961). For a rough consideration of the breakdown limits we shall conventionally refer, in the following discussion, to a simple cutoff procedure, although, as we have repeatedly emphasized it can only have at most a heuristic valve.

1. *The Two-Quantum Annihilation Process*

The pair annihilation process

$$e^+ + e^- \rightarrow 2\gamma \qquad\qquad (XI-4)$$

occurs in lowest order through the graphs in Fig. 14. The momentum transfers are both spacelike. In the center-of-mass (c.m.) system one has:

$$q_1{}^2 = 4E^2 \sin^2(\theta/2) \qquad \text{and} \qquad q_2{}^2 = 4E^2 \cos^2(\theta/2)$$

where E is the c.m. energy of e^- (or e^+) and θ is the annihilation angle. To account for a possible breakdown of the theory we introduce a form factor $F(q^2)$, depending on the momentum of the internal photon line, and which

Fig. 14. Lowest order graphs for $e^+ + e^- \rightarrow 2\gamma$.

can be thought of as a product of a squared electron vertex form factor and a form factor modifying the electron propagator. In the relativistic limit and for $\theta \gg m_e/E$, one has in the center-of-mass system

$$\frac{d\sigma}{d(\cos\theta)} = \pi r_0{}^2 \left(\frac{m_e}{E}\right)^2 \frac{|F(q_1{}^2)|^2 \cos^4(\theta/2) + |F(q_2{}^2)|^2 \sin^4(\theta/2)}{\sin^2\theta} \qquad (XI-5)$$

where r_0 is the electron radius, E is the common beam energy, and θ is the scattering angle. With the usual choice, $F(q^2) = (1 + q^2/\Lambda^2)^{-1}$ one finds that, for $\Lambda = 7$ GeV, the cross section at $E = 250$ MeV (i.e., 500 MeV total energy in c.m.) is changed by -12% at $90°$ from its value for ordinary quantum electrodynamics. At smaller angles the deviation is smaller and, for instance, at $60°$, at the same energy and with the same value of Λ, the relative deviation is -7%. We can say, very roughly, that if one can distinguish a 7% effect at

60° one should in principle be able to test quantum electrodynamics to distances of the order of 0.2 fermi. A similar experiment at $E = 500$ MeV would test the theory down to 0.1 fermi.

The use of reaction (XI-4) as a monitoring process for beam collisions is unfortunately not convenient. The monitoring process must be such that in the particular geometry it involves only very small momentum transfers, even at the highest energies. It will then be very reliably predicted by the theory, and from the calculated cross section, one can check the beam dimensions by a uniform and instantaneous procedure. The 2γ annihilation at forward angles would be a possible monitor, except that its cross section is too low in that region in comparison to other processes that show a stronger singularity in the forward direction. In particular the process

$$e^+ + e^- \rightarrow e^+ + e^- + 2\gamma$$

with the photons going in opposite directions is expected to contaminate the measurement of 2γ annihilation (Bayer and Galitsky, 1964). The radiative corrections to $e^+ + e^- \rightarrow 2\gamma$ have been recently calculated by Tsai (1960, 1965) and Tsai *et al.* (1965). Tsai is interested in the possible use of $e^+ + e^- \rightarrow 2\gamma$ to produce high energy γ rays. He therefore calculates the spreading of the photon peak at a fixed angle in positron-hydrogen-atom collisions, which arises from radiative corrections. The radiative corrections obtained by Tsai do not contain dangerous terms of the kind $(\alpha/\pi) \ln^2(4E^2/m_e^2)$, which cancel out after addition of the elastic and the inelastic contributions. Such $\ln^2$ terms had been found in previous calculations but their appearance was due to the unnatural choice of phase-space for the additional bremsstrahlung photon, which had been supposed to include energies ω_3 up to a maximum value $\ll m_e$ and isotropic in the laboratory system. Terms of the kind $(\alpha/\pi) \ln^2(4E^2/m_e^2)$ would become of the order of a few GeV, thus making the whole perturbation approach invalid, for instance, when interpreting a high energy $e^+ - e^-$ colliding beam experiment. The phase-space for the bremsstrahlung photon is dictated by the particular experimental setup. The approximate expression given by Tsai for the radiative corrections contains a cutoff which must be fixed from the energy and angular resolution of the detectors in the particular arrangement. The result resembles quite closely Schwinger's (1949) radiative corrections to potential scattering. A calculation of the radiative corrections to the total $e^+ + e^- \rightarrow 2\gamma$ cross section has also been performed by Andreassi *et al.* (1962, 1964). Andreassi *et al.* calculate the total cross section for $e^+ - e^-$ annihilation into photons to order e^6. The expression for the radiative correction contains a squared logarithmic of the energy. In this connection one is reminded of a theorem by Erikson and Petermann (1960; Erikson, 1961) which says that the radiative corrections (as calculated from soft photons) to a differential cross section, for large values of the squared momentum transfer $q^2 (\gg m^2)$ in the c.m. system, are expandable in a power series of $(\alpha/\pi) \ln (q^2/m^2)$. Specifically, for $q^2 \gg m^2$ in the c.m. system, to order e^6, according to this theorem one expects

$$\delta = \frac{\alpha}{\pi} \left[C_1 \ln \frac{E}{\Delta E} \ln \frac{q^2}{m^2} + C_2 \ln \frac{q^2}{m^2} + C_3 \right] \qquad \text{(XI-6)}$$

where C_1, C_2, and C_3 are angle dependent. Addition of hard photons may add terms $\ln^2(E/\Delta E)$ but not modify the main conclusion. According to Andreassi et al. (1962) the squared logarithmic term comes from the region of small q^2 (where the theorem does not necessarily hold) and precisely from soft photons.

2. Electron-Positron Scattering

The reaction

$$e^+ + e^- \to e^+ + e^- \qquad \text{(XI-7)}$$

electron-positron scattering, is obtained in lowest order from the graphs in Fig. 15. In the c.m. system, $q_1^2 = 4E^2 \sin^2(\theta/2)$ and $k^2 = -4E^2$ (q_1 is space-

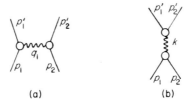

(a)   (b)

Fig. 15. Lowest order graphs for $e^+ + e^- \to e^+ + e^-$: (a) (b).

like, K is timelike). For angles $\neq 0$ and in the relativistic limit

$$\frac{d\sigma}{d(\cos \theta)} = (\pi r_0^2) \left(\frac{m_e}{E} \right)^2 \left\{ \frac{1}{4} \frac{1 + \cos^4(\theta/2)}{\sin^4(\theta/2)} |F(q_1)|^2 \right.$$

$$\left. - \frac{1}{2} \frac{\cos^4(\theta/2)}{\sin^2(\theta/2)} \operatorname{Re}[F(q_1^2)F^*(K^2)] + \tfrac{1}{8}(1 + \cos^2\theta)|F(K^2)|^2 \right\}. \qquad \text{(XI-8)}$$

We have introduced a form factor F which can be thought of as a product of the electron vertex squared and of the photon propagator. This time the vertex form factor refers to a situation where the electron lines are on the mass-shell and the photon is off-mass-shell. On the other hand in the 2γ annihilation of Fig. 14 the incident electron and the photon are on mass-shell and the final electron is off-mass-shell. The two form factors could then strictly be different. At small angles the cross section is due to the transfer of very small momentum. In fact the annihilation graph in Fig. 15 is not singular in the forward direction. The scattering graph dominates in that region and the transferred momentum $q_1^2 \to 0$. Unfortunately, the use of $e^+ - e^-$ scattering as a monitoring process is made difficult just by the singularity of the cross section at $\theta = 0°$. The dependence on the geometry of the apparatus would be too critical because of the rapid variation of the cross section. At larger angles, $e^+ - e^-$ scattering can be measured and used for testing the theory. A rough idea of possible deviations from the quantum electrodynamical cross section can be obtained with the usual choice $F(q^2) = (1 + q^2/\Lambda^2)^{-1}$. One finds that a 10% experiment at an energy $E \geqslant 150$ MeV can test electrodynamics to a distance $\Lambda^{-1} \sim 0.3$ fermi. A similar 10% experiment at $E \geqslant 350$ MeV can test the theory to $\Lambda^{-1} \sim 0.1$ fermi. The maximum deviation is expected at 90°, on the basis of the simple model of breakdown considered here.

3. *Radiative Positron-Electron Scattering*

The reaction

$$e^+ + e^- \to e^+ + e^- + \gamma$$

is the best candidate as a monitoring reaction. A difficulty with such a choice has been considered to be the fact that the beam can produce γ rays also by interaction with the residual gas and it would be difficult to separate the two sources on the basis of the shapes of the γ spectra. However, the Ada group (Bernardini *et al.*, 1964) has examined the problem and concluded that the separation is indeed possible and poses no relevant problem with machines larger than Ada. The theoretical study of single bremsstrahlung production in $e^+ + e^-$ collisions is also of relevance for computing the radiative corrections to $e^+ + e^- \to e^+ + e^-$. An evaluation of the radiative corrections of $e^+ + e^- \to e^+ + e^-$ implies the integration of the hard photon emission cross section for those photons which escape detection in the particular experimental situation. There are eight Feynman diagrams for single bremsstrahlung which are reported in Figs. 16 and 17. We call the graphs in Fig. 16 scattering graphs and those in Fig. 17 annihilation graphs. Particularly powerful approximations can be made in the region of high energies and small angles of the emitted

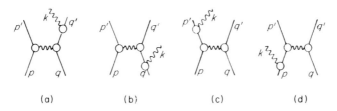

(a) (b) (c) (d)

Fig. 16. Graphs of $e^+ + e^- \to e^+ + e^- + \gamma$: scattering graphs: (a) (b) (c) (d).

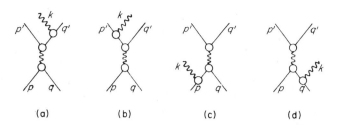

Fig. 17. Graphs of $e^+ + e^- \rightarrow e^+ + e^- + \gamma$: annihilation graphs: (a) (b) (c) (d).

photon with respect to the colliding beam direction. This region is of particular interest for the possible use of this reaction as a monitor. The annihilation graphs can be neglected in comparison with the scattering graphs on the basis that the denominator of the photon propagator is much smaller for a scattering graph than for an annihilation graph. One can also neglect the interferences between the graphs of Fig. 16a,b and those of Fig. 16c,d (scattering graphs). In fact the radiation emitted from the electron is contained in a half-cone around the electron line, with a narrow opening angle decreasing with energy. The radiation emitted from the positron is similarly in a narrow cone around the positron. There is practically no overlap between the two cones in the most frequent situation of scattering at small angles. In such conditions one obtains typical bremsstrahlung distribution as shown by Garybian (1952) and by Altarelli and Buccella (1964). A similar calculation has been done by Tsai *et al.* (1965) who give an approximate analytical expression for the brehmsstrahlung cross section, obtained by directly summing the squared contributions of the first two diagrams, (Figs. 16a and 16b) and the last two diagrams (Figs. 16c and 16d), after some simplifying approximations. A complete numerical calculation by Swanson (reported by Tsai *et al.*, 1965) shows that such an approximate analytical expression has a rather wide range of validity.

4. *Muon Pair Production*

The reaction

$$e^+ + e^- \rightarrow \mu^+ + \mu^- \tag{XI-9}$$

can be useful also to test muon structure. At lowest order the reaction proceeds through the graph in Fig. 18. The transferred four-momentum is timelike, $K^2 = -4E^2$. If the electron mass is neglected

$$\frac{d\sigma}{d(\cos\theta)} = \frac{\pi}{4}\,\alpha^2\lambda^2\beta_\mu\left[\frac{1}{2}\,(1 + \cos^2\theta) + \frac{1}{2}\left(\frac{m_\mu}{E}\right)^2 \sin^2\theta\right]F(K^2) \tag{XI-10}$$

where $\alpha = 1/137$, λ is the reduced wavelength of the incoming e^+ (or e^-), β_μ

Fig. 18. Lowest order graph for $e^+ + e^- \to \mu^+ + \mu^-$.

and m_μ are the velocity and mass of the final μ, and we have introduced a form factor F, which can be thought of as a product of a muon vertex form factor, an electron vertex form factor, and the photon propagator form factor. Note that the angular dependence is not altered by the presence of the form factor $F(K^2)$. To determine a breakdown of the theory in $e^+ + e^- \to \mu^+ + \mu^-$, according to the model of Eq. (XI-10) one has to measure the absolute cross section. The angular dependence, as we have seen, is independent of a possible breakdown as long as the one-photon channel dominates. For instance with

$$F(q^2) = \frac{1}{1 + (q^2/Q^2)}$$

the cross section takes on a factor

$$|F(-4E^2)|^2 \cong 1 + (8E^2/Q^2)$$

and for $8E^2/Q^2 \sim 10\%$ one can explore up to $Q \sim 9E$. For $E \sim 300$ MeV one can explore already up to $Q \lesssim 0.1$ fermi and for $E \sim 1$ GeV one can explore up to $Q \lesssim 0.03$ fermi. In view of its simpler feasibility, annihilation into a muon pair, $e^+ + e^- \to \mu^+ + \mu^-$, appears to be one of the most promising experiments with electron-positron colliding beams. The interpretation of the experiments will require an accurate evaluation of the radiative corrections. These have been discussed by Furlan et $al.$ (1964). Hard photon emission, $e^+ + e^- \to \mu^+ + \mu^- + \gamma$ has been discussed by Mosco (1964) and Longhi (1965). The graphs contributing to lowest order radiative corrections to $e^+ + e^- \to \mu^+ + \mu^-$ are given in Fig. 19. Initial and final vertex graphs are denoted by (V_i) and (V_f), respectively. Self-energy graphs are denoted by (SE_i) and (SE_f). Bremsstrahlung graphs are denoted by (B_i) and (B_f). The two-photon-exchange graphs are called (2γ). One has to add coherently the V, SE, and 2γ graphs to the lowest order graph and then add incoherently the bremsstrahlung contributions. A great simplification occurs if one is interested in experiments that treat symmetrically the final charges (total cross section, or any arrangement which does not distinguish between μ^+ and μ^-, etc.). In this case (experimentally the most interesting one) there is no interference between the lowest order graph (with only one photon exchanged) and the

2γ graph. Thus to the order e^6 in cross section one can entirely neglect for such situations the 2γ graphs. Furthermore, one can also neglect the interference between initial and final bremsstrahlung. The reason in both cases is the invariance under charge conjugation, which does not allow a photon to

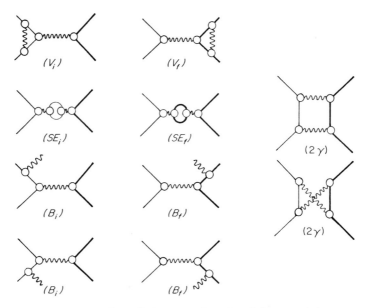

Fig. 19. Lowest order radiative corrections for $e^+ + e^- \rightarrow \mu^+ + \mu^-$.

transform virtually into two photons. One thus sees that one can talk consistently in these cases of an initial (interference of the lowest order graph with $V_i + SE_i$ plus the squared B_i contributions) and a final (same with $i \rightarrow f$) radiative correction.

5. *Effect of Virtual Strongly Interacting Particles*

Experimental investigations about the limits of validity of quantum electrodynamics may eventually run into the difficulty of having to deal with effects of the same order as the effects originating from virtual strongly interacting particles. These effects are hard to estimate accurately. It may be relevant to note that direct measurements of the production of strongly interacting particles in $e^+ - e^-$ collisions can be related directly to quantities that express the effect of virtual strongly interacting particles on the electrodynamical parameters. The modification to the photon propagator can be expressed through a function $\pi(K^2)$, additive with respect to the contributions from the various virtual states (Källen, 1958). The modified photon propagator can be written as

$$D'_{\mu\nu}(K) = \delta_{\mu\nu} \frac{1}{K^2} + \left(\delta_{\mu\nu} - \frac{K_\mu K_\nu}{K^2}\right) \int_0^\infty \frac{da\,\pi(-a)}{a(K^2 + a - i\varepsilon)} \qquad \text{(XI-11)}$$

where

$$\pi(K^2) = -\frac{(2\pi)^3}{3K^2} \sum_{P_z = K} \langle 0|J_\mu(0)|z\rangle\langle z|J_\mu(0)|0\rangle. \qquad \text{(XI-12)}$$

In Eq. (XI-12) J_μ is the current operator and the sum is extended over all physical states with momentum $p^z = K$. We consider the annihilation of $e^+ + e^-$ into a set of states Z and call $\sigma_Z(E)$ the total cross section for such annihilations. Similarly, we call $\pi_Z(-4E^2)$ the contribution to Eq. (XI-12) from the set of states Z. One can formally show that

$$\pi_Z(-4E^2) = \frac{E^2}{\pi^2\alpha} \sigma_Z(E). \qquad \text{(XI-13)}$$

Equation (XI-13) is obtained by direct comparison of the two expressions (XI-13) and the expression for $\sigma_Z(E)$.

6. Vacuum Polarization Effects in Positron-Electron Collisions

A suitable possibility for observing vacuum polarization effects is provided by electron-positron colliding beams. Relatively large vacuum polarization effects are expected in the neighborhood of a vector meson resonance with the same quantum numbers J, P, and C of the virtual photon into which the $e^+ - e^-$ pair annihilates. The $e^+ - e^-$ cross section into a final state that can be reached through the one-photon channel is modified by the vacuum polarization effect by a multiplicative factor which passes through a minimum at about $2E = M - \frac{1}{2}\Gamma$ and then reaches a maximum at about $2E = M + \frac{1}{2}\Gamma$, where M is the vector meson mass and Γ its width. The values at the maximum and minimum essentially depend on the branching ratio for decay of the vector meson into a pair $e^+ + e^-$. For the φ meson one can estimate, on the basis of an assumed branching ratio of $\sim 1 \times 10^{-3}$ for decay into $e^+ + e^-$, an effect of the order of 30% at the (approximately) symmetric maximum and minimum. A vacuum polarization effect of this order is much larger than indicated from the usual perturbation calculation. Its observation will require, among other things, a very narrow energy resolution, which should however be attainable with electron-positron colliding beams.

Kroll, Lee, and Zumino (1966) have recently produced a relation between the renormalized propagators of neutral vector mesons and the contribution to the photon propagator from virtual hadrons, valid to second electromagnetic order. The relation is obtained (among other remarkable results) in a

Lagrangian model where the electromagnetic current of the hadrons coincides with a linear combination of the vector meson fields.

XII. Discussion on Possible New Couplings

In the general framework of field theory, the description of possible deviations from quantum electrodynamics in terms of new couplings, rather than in terms of an essential modification of the mathematical formulation, appears more attractive and would sound more familiar to the theoretical physicists. In this section we shall present a discussion of the various coupling possibilities that have been discussed and in some cases subjected to experimental search.

We have thought it worthwhile to devote a whole section to the subject, as it seems to us that an analysis in terms of conjectured additional fields and couplings is the simplest and most natural way to frame the problem of possible breakdowns of electrodynamics (and perhaps the only one compatible with general principles). From such a viewpoint it will be useful if experimental results, bearing on the problem of validity of quantum electrodynamics will in the future be quantitatively interpreted, whenever possible, in terms of upper limits to new couplings and lower limits to intermediate masses rather than in terms of propagator and vertex cutoffs.

A. ABSENCE OF $\mu e \gamma$ COUPLING

The absence of a $\mu e \gamma$ coupling has been established to great accuracy. Such a coupling would directly give rise to processes (Feinberg, 1958; Gatto, 1959; Cabibbo and Gatto, 1959; Feinberg and Weinberg, 1959) such as

$$\mu^{\pm} \to e^{\pm} + \gamma \qquad\qquad\qquad \text{(XII-1)}$$

$$\mu^{\pm} \to e^{\pm} + e^{+} + e^{-} \qquad\qquad \text{(XII-2)}$$

$$\mu^{\pm} \to e^{\pm} + \gamma + \gamma \qquad\qquad \text{(XII-3)}$$

$$\mu^{-} + (\text{nucleus}) \to (\text{nucleus}) + e^{-}, \text{etc.} \qquad \text{(XII-4)}$$

The upper limit obtained by the Chicago group (Anderson et al., 1964) for the $\mu \to e + \gamma$ branching ratio is 2×10^{-8}, to 90% confidence level.

The decay mode (XII-2) would directly occur by internal conversion of the gamma ray from the hypothetical $\mu \to e + \gamma$ vertex. An upper limit of 1.5×10^{-7}, again to 90% confidence, was reported by Frankel et al. (1963a) for the branching ratio to this mode.

The same group (Frankel et al., 1963b) also reported an upper limit of 1.6×10^{-5} for the branching ratio to the decay mode (XII-3).

The capture process (XII-4), for a bound μ^{-}, would follow from the existence of a $(\mu e \gamma)$ vertex, by the induced $\mu - e$ transition in the nuclear Coulomb field. An upper limit of 2.5×10^{-7} (90% confidence level) was given by a group at CERN (Conversi *et al.*, 1962) for the branching ratio to this mode relative to ordinary muon capture.

The experimental results clearly indicate that processes such as (XII-1) to (XII-4), if they occur at all, have rates much smaller than the weak interaction rates. The simplest theoretical interpretation is in terms of a quantum number —muonic number—which is different for the electron and for the muon, and which is conserved either additively or multiplicatively.

B. Possible Couplings to Neutral Heavy Bosons

Couplings of the electrons and muons to heavy bosons have been considered many times on the basis of different motivations.

Couplings such as those responsible for ρ^0, ω^0, φ^0 decay into $e^+ + e^-$ or $\mu^+ + \mu^-$, or for the expected $\pi^0 \to e^+ + e^-$, $\eta^0 \to \mu^+ + \mu^-$, etc., certainly exist and can be described in terms of the ordinary coupling of the photon to the current of charge. The quantitative question whether such couplings do actually exhibit the exact strength implied by their theoretical description is however very hard to answer, particularly in the general absence of exact theoretical predictions for such strengths.

1. *A Hypothetical Coupling Responsible for the Muon Mass*

Strictly anomalous interactions of the muon with neutral boson fields, of various tensor character, have been discussed repeatedly in connection with the large muon mass as compared to the mass of the electron. The basic hope has always been to attribute the large muon mass to a specific interaction of the muon, which the electron does not possess.

The self-mass calculations are certainly not reliable enough to allow for a determination of the coupling strengths of such postulated anomalous interactions directly from the observed muon mass. The self-mass expressions of perturbation theory must be regularized by cutting off the divergent integrals.

If, for instance, the muon interacts with a massive neutral vector field, the self-mass computed in perturbation theory depends logarithmically on the cutoff mass.

Such a self-mass must be assumed to be comparable to the observed muon mass in the spirit of the model. For reasonable values of the cutoff, the coupling strength of the muon to the boson turns out to be larger than the electromagnetic strength.

However, a coupling of this sort would be incompatible with the present agreement of the measured $(g - 2)$ of the muon with quantum electrodynamics unless the mass of the hypothetical boson is assumed to be very large, of the order of ten nucleon masses or larger. Unfortunately, the significance of all such conclusions is deeply bound to the perturbation arguments used.

If the vector boson has the same quantum numbers as the photon, one may obtain a direct answer to these questions by a consistent exploration of the muon vertex in colliding beam processes such as

$$e^+ + e^- \rightarrow \mu^+ + \mu^-$$

$$p + \bar{p} \rightarrow \mu^+ + \mu^-.$$

The coupling to the e^+e^- pair or to the $p\bar{p}$ pair would arise at second electromagnetic order, as long as the hypothetical boson intermediate state has no direct interaction with the electrons and with the protons. However, for other assignments of quantum numbers to the boson the coupling would arise at higher orders.

2. *Search for Resonant Behavior*

Independently of the muon mass problem the search for resonant behaviors of $\mu^+\mu^-$ and also of e^+e^- pairs is certainly of great interest.

Electron-positron colliding beams and proton-antiproton annihilation will undoubtedly be very useful in this connection. Other processes giving $e^+ - e^-$ or $\mu^+ - \mu^-$ pairs, such as internal conversion of the virtual photon in inverse photoproduction

$$\pi^- + p \rightarrow n + e^+ + e^-,$$

and all the similar processes initiated by strongly interacting particles or by a photon, such as decays into Dalitz pairs, etc., will allow a study of possible resonant interactions of the lepton pair, by direct study of the invariant mass distribution of the pair.

Resonant terms to such distributions will be contributed by the vector meson resonances ρ^0, ω^0, φ^0 and it will be important to find out whether a simple picture can be obtained only in terms of such contributions.

In a recent paper on heavy electrons and muons by Low (1965) the possibility of a coupling of the electron to a boson b, of the form $g\bar{\psi}_e \Gamma_i \psi_e b_i$ is examined.

The mass of b might well lie in the region below 1 GeV provided the coupling strength g^2 is smaller than e^2.

The existence of the b particle may be observed in the trident reaction, $e + p \rightarrow e + p + e^+ + e^-$.

Unless the b meson is also coupled to nucleons, its existence will not affect any $e^+ - e^-$ production reaction from strong interacting particles. At the relevant mass value, the $e^+ - e^-$ mass distribution will pass through an extremely narrow peak.

Compton scattering on electrons would also be quantitatively insensitive to the new interaction, the detailed analysis depending on the specific tensor properties of b.

C. A Hypothetical Heavy Electron

1. Theoretical Implications

Low also discusses in detail the possible existence of a heavy electron e^*, with a magnetic coupling to the electron of the form $\lambda\bar{\psi}_e\sigma_{\mu\nu}\psi_e f_{\mu\nu} + \text{H.c.}$ For a mass of e^* of a few hundredths million electron volts, a coupling $\lambda \sim e/m_{e^*}$ may still be consistent with the present data.

The e^* could be emitted in weak decay processes in place of an ordinary electron whenever this is kinematically possible and depending on the nature of its weak couplings.

Its absence among weak decay products might however require that its mass be sufficiently large. Production of e^* would, most simply, be observed by detecting the recoil proton in

$$e + p \rightarrow e^* + p.$$

The e^* would appear in this reaction as a sharp missing mass peak in the distributions of the proton recoils.

The cross section can be evaluated in terms of the known proton form factors, which determine the coupling of the exchanged virtual photon to the proton, and of the postulated $e^*e\gamma$ vertex. The postulated magnetic interaction in this vertex is presumably to be considered as a low energy description of some renormalizable interaction, and for high values of the virtual photon momentum the coupling constant λ may be expected to fall down.

2. Experimental Search for e^*

An attempt to observe e^* in the mass range between 120 and 570 MeV has been made at the Orsay linear accelerator (Betourne et al., 1965). For masses between 570 and 240 MeV the authors of the experiment used a very sensitive maximum angle technique (Perez et al., 1963) which takes advantage of the most convenient kinematical situation. For lower masses the ordinary excitation technique is used.

The expected cross section is proportional to λ^2, which is assumed to be independent of the virtual photon momentum. The Orsay experiment provides for an upper limit for $|\lambda|$ for each given mass m^*.

With the more sensitive maximum angle technique $|\lambda|$ is found to be smaller than 1.5% of (e/m^*) for $m^* = 240$ MeV, and smaller than about 15% of (e/m^*) for the largest value m^* of the experiment, $m^* = 570$ MeV.

A new search for the hypothetical excited electron has been completed recently at DESY (Behrend *et al.*, 1966). Again, the possible reaction $e + p \rightarrow e + p$ was investigated in the search for $e*$ in the mass range 0.5 GeV $< m* <$ 1 GeV.

In this experiment two quadrupole spectrometers were employed to measure proton-electron coincidences.

The result provides an upper limit of 10^{-33} cm²/sr for the differential cross section for $e + p \rightarrow e* + p$ at laboratory angles of 7.5° and 10°.

3. *Further Remarks on e**

The presence of virtual $e*$ could also influence Compton scattering on electrons: A virtual $e*$ can be propagated in place of an ordinary electron.

By the same mechanism, the $e^+ - e^-$ pair production amplitude would be modified by the additional contributions from the graphs where the internal fermion line refers to a virtual $e*$. The modification would be of the kind reported in the wide-angle pair production experiment at Cambridge (Blumenthal *et al.*, 1965).

Direct production by photons of $e + e*$ pairs in a Coulomb field may reveal the presence of $e*$ as a missing mass if the photons are tagged for energy. Otherwise, one may measure the mass spectrum of the particles $e + \gamma$ from the decay of the hypothetical $e*$ and look for a peak in the distribution.

Low also discussed the implications of a possible coupling of the electron to an excited electron $e*$ and to a boson, such as $g\bar{\psi}_{e*}\Gamma_i\psi_e b_i$.

With this coupling alone, $e*$ and b would only be produced together. The lighter of them would be stable, except perhaps for weak interactions. One would then observe processes such as

$$e + p \rightarrow p + e* + b \rightarrow p + e* + e* + \bar{e}$$

if $e*$ is the stable one, or

$$e + p \rightarrow p + e* + b \rightarrow p + \bar{e} + b + \bar{b}$$

if b is stable.

By introduction of new particles and couplings, other modifications of quantum electrodynamics can be constructed in a variety of ways. The trident production experiments, like $e^{\pm} + p \rightarrow e^{\pm} + p + e^+ + e^-$ and $e^{\pm} + p \rightarrow e^{\pm} + p + \mu^+ + \mu^-$ offer possibility of studying final states $e^{\pm}e^{\pm}$, $e^{\pm}\mu^{\pm}$ in all their possible combinations of charges and of systematically looking for possible examples of resonant behavior.

XIII. Conclusions

We shall not attempt to summarize here the content of the preceding sections. Rather we shall mention some of those points which seem to us to deserve special attention (see Table I).

TABLE I

SUMMARY OF LATEST DATA BEARING ON THE PROBLEM
OF VALIDITY OF QUANTUM ELECTRODYNAMICS

	Theoretical value	Experimental value
Lamb shift $2S_{1/2}$-$2P_{1/2}$ in H	(1057 ± 0.11) Mc/sec[a]	(1057.77 ± 0.10) Mc/sec[b] (1058.05 ± 0.10) Mc/sec[c]
Hyperfine splitting in ground state of H	Ratio of theory to experiment[d] $r = 1 - (9 \pm 20) \times 10^{-6} + x$, $\quad \Delta\nu_H = 1,420,405,751.800 \pm 0.028$ cps[f] x depends on strong interactions: $x = 34 \times 10^{-6} + x_p$, where x_p is largely unknown polarizability correction[e]	
Value of α	From hyperfine splitting in muonium,[g] $\Delta\nu_M : \alpha^{-1} = 137.0388$ $(\pm 9$ ppm); same value from $2^2P_{3/2}$-$2^2P_{1/2}$ interval in deuterium.[h] Higher value of α from muonium suggested by new chemical shift correction.[i] Connection with Lamb shift and hyperfine structure problems	
Electron's gyromagnetic ratio	$\frac{1}{2}(g_e - 2)$ $= [(\alpha/2\pi) - 0.328(\alpha/\pi)^2]$[l,m] $+ [\text{estimated } 0.15(\alpha/\pi)^3]$[n]	$\frac{1}{2}(g_e - 2)$ $= [(\alpha/2\pi) - (0.327 \pm 0.05)(\alpha^2/\pi^2)]$[o]
Muon's gyromagnetic ratio	$\frac{1}{2}(g_\mu - 2) = (\alpha/2\pi) + 0.76(\alpha^2/\pi^2)$ $= 1165 \times 10^{-6}$[m,n]	$\frac{1}{2}(g_\mu - 2) = (1162 \pm 5) \times 10^{-6}$[p] $= (1165 \pm 3) \times 10^{-6}$[q]
e and μ scattering	$D^{-2} \gtrsim (1.9 \text{ GeV})^2$; where $D^{-2} = \Lambda_\mu^{-2} - \Lambda_e^{-2}$, Λ_μ and Λ_e are the cutoffs in μ and e vertex, respectively.[r]	
Wide-angle $e^+ - e^-$ production	Strong disagreement had been reported.[s] New experiment agrees with quantum electrodynamics.[t]	
Wide-angle $\mu^+ - \mu^-$ production	Absence of deviations for $\Lambda_\mu^{-1} > 0.23$ fermi, in μ propagator[u]; $\Lambda_\mu^{-1} = (0.16 \pm 0.08)$ fermi from latest experiment[v]	
Colliding $e^- - e^-$ beams	$-1.04 \leqslant \Lambda^{-2} \leqslant 3.26 \ (\text{GeV}/c)^2$ (99% confidence interval) and $\Lambda^{-2} = (0.83 \pm 0.83)(\text{GeV}/c)^2$ (68% confidence interval) for form-factor cutoff (photon propagator and vertex)[w]	
Heavy e^*	No evidence (upper limit $< 10^{-33}$ cm^2/sr for $e + p \rightarrow e^* + p$ at $7.5°$ and $10°$)[x,y]	

---

[a] Soto (1966)
[b] Dayhoff et al. (1953a)
[c] Robiscoe and Cosens (1966)
[d] Drell and Sullivan (1966)
[e] Iddings (1965)
[f] Crampton et al. (1963)
[g] Cleland et al. (1964)
[h] Dayhoff et al. (1953a)
[i] Rudermann (1966)
[l] Petermann (1957)
[m] Sommerfield (1957)
[n] Drell and Pagels (1966)

[o] Wilkinson and Crane (1963)
[p] Charpak et al. (1965)
[q] Farley et al. (1966)
[r] Cool et al. (1965)
[s] Blumenthal et al. (1965)
[t] Asbury et al. (1966)
[u] Alberigi-Quaranta et al. (1962)
[v] de Pagter et al. (1966)
[w] Barber et al. (1965)
[x] Betourne et al. (1965)
[y] Behrend et al. (1966)

1. *The Lamb Shift* (see Section II)

The latest theoretical value (Soto, 1966) for the $2S_{1/2}-2P_{1/2}$ Lamb shift in hydrogen is (1057.50 ± 0.11) Mc/sec. The experimental value of Dayhoff, *et al.* (1953a) is (1057.77 ± 0.10) Mc/sec. The latest measurements, however, by Robiscoe and Cosens (1966) give (1058.05 ± 0.10) Mc/sec. This discrepancy must be clarified.

2. *The Hyperfine Splitting in the Ground State of Hydrogen* (see Section III)

The hyperfine splitting is measured with a precision of two parts in 10^{11} (Crampton *et al.*, 1963). The ratio of the theoretical to the experimental value can be written (Drell and Sullivan, 1966) as $1 - (9 \pm 20) \times 10^{-6} + x$, where x depends on proton structure and in particular it contains an unknown polarizability correction x_p. Namely: $x = 34 \times 10^{-6} + x_p$ (Iddings, 1965). The problem is thus dependent on the theory of strong interactions.

3. *The Value of the Hyperfine Structure Constant* α (see Section IV)

Determination of α from the hyperfine splitting in muonium (Cleland *et al.*, 1964) gives $\alpha^{-1} = 137.0388(\pm 9$ ppm). The same value is obtained from the $2^2P_{3/2}\text{-}2^2P_{1/2}$ fine structure interval of deuterium (Dayhoff *et al.*, 1953a,b). A suggested reduction, by 20 ppm, in the μ^+ magnetic moment (Ruderman, 1966) destroys the agreement and leads to a higher value of α as determined from muonium. A higher value of α might indirectly be inferred from very tentative arguments based on the latest (not yet confirmed) value for the Lamb shift (Robiscoe, 1965) and would be of help in the problem of the hydrogen hyperfine structure. Further experimental and theoretical work is needed.

4. *The g Factor of the Electron* (see Section V)

The latest determination, by Wilkinson and Crane (1963) of the g factor of the electron, giving $\frac{1}{2}(g_e - 2) = (0.001159622 \pm 0.000000027)$, is in agreement with the theoretical prediction (Petermann, 1957; Sommerfield, 1957).

5. *The g Factor of the Muon* (see Section VI)

The CERN measurement (Charpak *et al.*, 1965) of the muon g factor, giving $\frac{1}{2}(g_\mu - 2) = 0.001162 \pm 0.000005$ is again in agreement with quantum electrodynamics, and constitutes an accurate test against modifications at small distances. ($\Lambda > 0.8$ GeV in the photon propagator; or $\Lambda > 1.1$ GeV in the vertex; or $\Lambda > 2$ GeV in the muon propagator.) New preliminary results at CERN give $\frac{1}{2}(g_\mu - 2) = 0.001165 \pm 0.000003$ (Farley *et al.*, 1966).

6. *Electron and Muon Scattering by Nucleons* (see Section VII)

From the results of a recent Brookhaven-Columbia-Rochester collaboration (Cool *et al.*, 1965) the electromagnetic couplings of e and of μ are seen to be identical down to very small distances $[D^{-2} \geqslant (1.9 \text{ GeV})^2$, where $D^{-2} = \Lambda_\mu^{-2} - \Lambda_e^{-2}$ and Λ_μ, Λ_e are the cutoffs in the μ and e vertex form factors, respectively].

7. *Wide-Angle Electron-Pair Production and Large-Angle Bremsstrahlung* (see Section VIII)

The experiment by Blumenthal *et al.* (1965) disagrees strongly from the prediction of quantum electrodynamics. A new experiment by Asbury *et al.* (1966) agrees with theory, contradicting the preceding result. It would also be of interest to measure and compare with theory large-angle bremsstrahlung.

8. *Wide-Angle Muon-Pair Production* (see Section IX)

An experiment at Frascati (Alberigi-Quaranta *et al.*, 1962) indicated absence of deviations from quantum electrodynamics down to small distances ($\Lambda_\mu^{-1} < 0.23$ fermi, in the muon propagator, for two standard deviations). The latest result from CEA (de Pagter *et al.*, 1966) suggests $\Lambda_\mu^{-1} = (0.16 \pm 0.08)$ fermi for two standard deviations. Further work is needed.

9. *Electron-Electron Storage-Ring Experiment* (see Section XI)

In terms of a form-factor cutoff Λ, the experiment gives: $-1.04 \leqslant \Lambda^{-2} \leqslant 3.26 \text{ (GeV}/c)^2$ for 99% confidence interval and $\Lambda^{-2} = (0.83 \pm 0.83) \text{ (GeV}/c)^2$ for 68% confidence interval (Barber *et al.*, 1965). Much progress is expected from this field as well as from electron-positron colliding beams.

10. *Absence of a Heavy Electron* (see Section XII)

No evidence for e^* has been found at Orsay (Betourne *et al.*, 1965) or Hamburg (Behrend *et al.*, 1966) and limits for its production cross section have been set.

We stress again the purely conventional significance of the cutoff limits of the above summary.

REFERENCES

Alberigi–Quaranta, A., De Pretis, M., Marini, G., Odian, A., Stoppini, G., and Tan, L. (1962). *Phys. Rev. Letters* **9**, 226.
Altarelli, G., and Buccella, F. (1964). *Nuovo Cimento* **34**, 1337.
Anderson, H. L., Parker, S., and Rey, C. (1964). *Phys. Rev.* **133**, B768.
Anderson, L. W., Pipkin, F. M., and Baird, J. C., Jr. (1960). *Phys. Rev.* **120**, 1279.

Andreassi, G., Budini, P., and Furlan, G. (1962). *Phys. Rev. Letters* **8**, 184.

Andreassi, G., Calucci, G., Furlan, G., Peressutti, G., and Cazzola, P. (1964). *Phys. Rev.* **128**, 1425.

Araki, G., Ohta, M., and Mano, K. (1959). *Phys. Rev.* **116**, 651.

Arnowitt R. (1953). *Phys. Rev.* **92**, 1002.

Aron, W., and Zuchelli, A. J. (1957). *Phys. Rev.* **105**, 1681.

Artru, X., Basdevant, J. L., and Omnes, R. (1966). To be published.

Asbury, J. G., Bertram, W. K., Becker, U., Joos, P., Rohde, M., Smith, A. J. S., Friedlander, S., Jordan, C., and Ting, C. C. (1966). Preprint.

Bailey, J., Brown, R. C. A., Fairley, F., Giesch, M., van der Meer, S., Picasso, E.,Whyte, N. (1965). *Intern. Conf. Elementary Particles, Oxford.*

Baranger, M., Dyson, F., Salpeter, E. (1952). *Phys. Rev.* **88**, 680.

Baranger, M., Bethe, H. A., and Feynman, R. (1953). *Phys. Rev.* **92**, 482.

Barber, W. C., Richter, B., Gittelman, B., and O'Neill, G. K. (1965). *Intern. Conf. Elementary Particles, Oxford.*

Bargmann, V., Michel, L., Telegdi, V. L. (1959). *Phys. Rev. Letters* **2**, 435.

Bayer, V. N., and Kheifets, S. A. (1963). *Nucl. Phys.* **47**, 313.

Bayer, V. N., and Galitsky, V. M. (1964). *Phys. Letters* **13**, 355.

Behrend, H. J., and Brasse, F. W., Engler, J., Gaussauge, E., Hultschig, H., Galster, S., Hartway, G., and Schopper, H. (1966). To be published.

Berestetskij, B., Krokhin, O. N., and Khlebnikov, A. K. (1958). *Zn. Exsperim. i Teor. Fiz.* **30**, 788.

Berg, R. A., and Lindner, C. N. (1961). *Nucl. Phys.* **26**, 259.

Berley, D., and Gidal, G. (1960). *Phys. Rev.* **118**, 1086.

Bernardini, C., Corazza, G. F., di Giugno, G., Hajssinki, O., Marin, P., Querzoli, R., and Touschek, B. (1964). Laboratori Nazionali Frascati, Frascati, Italy.

Bernardini, C., Merughetti-Vitale, L., Querzoli, R., Silvestrini, V., Troisi, I., Vandali, F., and Vitali, S. (1965). Private communication.

Bersohn, R., Weneser, J., and Kroll, N. (1953). *Phys. Rev.* **91**, 1257.

Bethe, H. A. (1947). *Phys. Rev.* **72**, 339.

Bethe, H. A., Brown, L. M., and Stehn, S. R. (1950). *Phys. Rev.* **77**, 370.

Betourne, C., Nguyen Ngoc, H., Perez, Y., Yorba, J., and Tran Thanh Van (1965). *Phys. Letters* **17**, 70.

Binnie, D. M., Duane, A., Jane, M. R., Jones, W. G., Meson, D. C., Newth, J. A., Potter, D. C., Rebman, I. U., Walters, J., Dickinson, B., Ellison, R. J., Herokham, A. E., Ibtsotson, M., Marshal, R., Templeman, R. F., and Wynroe, A. S. (1965). *Phys. Letters* **18**, 348.

Bjorken, J. D., and Drell, S. D. (1959). *Phys. Rev.* **114**, 1368.

Bjorken, J. D., Drell, S. D., and Frautschi, S. C. (1958). *Phys. Rev.* **112**, 1409.

Blumenthal, R. B., Ehn, D. C., Faissler, W. L., Joseph, P. M., Langerotti, L. J., Pipkin, F. M., and Stairs, D. G. (1965). *Phys. Rev. Letters* **14**, 660.

Bohr, A. (1948). *Phys. Rev.* **73**, 1109.

Borchi, E., and Gatto, R. (1965). *Phys. Letters* **14**, 352.

Boyarski, A., Glass, G., Chase, R. C., Gettner, M. (1965). *Phys. Rev. Letters* **15**, 835.

Breit, G. (1930). *Phys. Rev.* **35**, 1447.

Brochard, J., Chabbal, R., Chantrel, H., and Jacquinot, P. (1952). *J. Phys. Radium* **13**, 433.

Brodsky, S. J. (1966). To be published.

Brodsky, S. J., and Erickson, G. (1966). *Ann. Phys. N.Y.* on press.

Brodsky, S. J., and Sullivan, J. D. (1966). SLAC-PUB-242.

Brown, L. S. (1966). To be published.

Burleson, G. R., and Kendall, H. W. (1960). *Nucl. Phys.* **19**, 68.

Cabibbo, N., and Gatto, R. (1959). *Phys. Rev.* **116**, 1334.

Cabibbo, N., and Gatto, R. (1960). *Phys. Rev. Letters* **4**, 313.

Cabibbo, N., and Gatto, R. (1961). *Phys. Rev.* **124**, 1577.

Charpak, G., Farley, F. J. M., Garwin, R. L., Muller, T., Sens, J. C., and Zichichi, A. (1961). *Nuovo Cimento* **22**, 1043.

Charpak, G., Farley, F. J. M., Garwin, R. L., Muller, T., Sens, J. C., Telegdi, V. L., and Zichichi, A. (1961). *Phys. Rev. Letters* **6**, 128.

Charpak, G., Farley, F. J. M., Garwin, R. L., Muller, T., Sens, J. C., and Zichichi, A. (1962). *Phys. Letters* **1**, 16.

Charpak, G., Farley, F. J. M., Garwin, R. L., Muller, T., Sens, J. C., and Zichichi, A. (1965). *Nuovo Cimento* **37**, 1241.

Chen Mao-Chao (1962). *Phys. Rev.* **127**, 1844.

Cini, M., Ferrari, E., and Gatto, R. (1959). *Phys. Rev. Letters* **2**, 7.

Citron, A., Delorme, C., Fries, D., Goldzahl, L., Heintze, J., Michaelis, E. G., Richard, C. and Øveroas, H. (1962). *Phys. Letters* **1**, 175.

Cleland, N. E., Bailey, J. M., Eckhause, M., Hughes, V. W., Mobley, R. M., Prepost, R., and Rothberg, J. E. (1964). *Phys Rev. Letters* **13**, 202.

Cohen, E. R., and Dumond, J. W. M. (1965). *Rev. Mod. Phys.* **37**, 537.

Colegrove, K. D., Franken, P. A., Lewis, R. R., and Sands, R. H. (1958). *Phys. Rev. Letters* **3**, 420.

Cool, R., Maschke, A., Lederman, L. M., Tannenbaum, M., Ellsworth, R., Melissinos, A , Tinlot, J H., and Yamanouchi, T. (1965). *Phys. Rev. Letters* **14**, 724.

Conversi, M., di Lella, L., Penso, G., Toller, M., and Rubbia, C. (1962). *Phys. Rev. Letters* **8**, 125.

Crampton, S. B., Kleppner, D., and Ramsey, N. F. (1963). *Phys. Rev. Letters* **11**, 338.

Dashen, R., and Frautschi, S. C. (1964). *Phys. Rev.* **135**, B1190.

Davies, H. F. (1963). *Phys. Rev.* **131**, 2192.

Dayhoff, E. S., Triebwasser, S., and Lamb, W. (1953a). *Phys. Rev.* **89**, 98.

Dayhoff, E. S., Triebwasser, S., and Lamb, W. (1953b). *Phys. Rev.* **89**, 106.

de Pagter, J. K., Boyarski, A., Glass, G., Friedman, J. I., Kendall, H. W., Gettner, M., Larrabee, J. F., and Weinstein, R. (1964). *Phys. Rev. Letters* **12**, 739.

de Pagter, J. K., Friedman, J. I., Glass, G., Chase, R. C., Gettner, M., von Goeler, E., Weinstein, R., and Boiarski, A. M. (1966). *Phys. Rev. Letters* **17**, 767; *ibid* (1966) **16**, 35.

de Tollis, B. (1960). *Nuovo Cimento* **16**, 203.

Devons, S., Gidal, G., Lederman, L. M., and Shapiro, G. (1960). *Phys. Rev. Letters* **5**, 330.

Drell, S. D. (1958). *Ann. Phys. N.Y.* **4**, 75.

Drell, S. D. (1964). *Phys. Rev. Letters* **13**, 257.

Drell, S. D. (1965). *Proc. Intern. Symposium Electron Photon Interactions High Energies, Hamburg,* 1965, Deutsche Physikalische Gesellschaft, Hamburg, Germany.

Drell, S. D., and McClure, J. A. (1965). *Nuovo Cimento* **37**, 1638.

Drell, S. D., and Pagels, R. H. (1966). *Phys. Rev.* To be published.

Drell, S. D. (1966). Report at the XIII Conference on High Energy Physics, Berkeley, California.

Drell, S. D., and Sullivan, J. D. (1966). SLAC-PUB-204.

Drell, S. D., and Trefil, J. S. (1966). Unpublished.

Dumond, J. W. M. (1959). *Ann. Phys. N.Y.* **7**, 365.

Durand, L. (1962). *Phys. Rev.* **128**, 441.

Eisenhandler, E., Feigenbaum, J., Mistry, N. B., Mostek, P. J., Rust, D. R., Silverman, A., Sinclair, C. K., and Talman, R. M. (1966). *Bull. Am. Phys. Soc.* **11**, 20.

Erickson, G. and Yennie, D. (1966) *Ann. Phys. N.Y.* To be published.

Erikson, K. E. (1961). *Nuovo Cimento* **19**, 1044.

Erikson, K. E., and Petermann, A. (1960). *Phys. Rev. Letters* **5**, 446.

Euwema, R., and Wheeler, J. A. (1965). *Phys. Rev.* **103**, 803.

Farley, F. J. M., Bailey, J., Brown, R. C. A., Giesch, M., Jöstlein, H., van der Meer, S., Picasso, E., and Tannenbaum, M. (1966). Report at the XIII High Energy Physics Conference, Berkeley, California.

Feinberg, G. (1958). *Phys. Rev.* **110**, 1482.

Feinberg, G. (1958). *Phys. Rev.* **112**, 1637.

Feinberg, G., and Weinberg, S. (1959). *Phys Rev. Letters*, **3**, 111.

Feinberg, G., and Lederman, L. M. (1962). *Ann. Rev. Nucl. Sci.* 431.

Fenster, S., Köterle, and Nambu, Y. (1965). EFINS Report.

Fenster, S., and Nambu, Y. (1965). *Progr. Theoret. Phys.* (*Kyoto*), *Suppl.* 250.

Fermi, E. (1930). *Z. Physik*. **60**, 320.

Ferrari, E., and Thurnauer, P. G. (1966). To be published.

Feynman, R. P. (1949). *Phys. Rev.* **76**, 769.

Feynman, R. P. (1962). *Proc. Conf., Solvay*

Frankel, S., Frati, W., Halpern, J., Holloway, L., Wales, W., and Chamberlain, O. (1963a). *Phys. Rev.* **130**, 351.

Frankel, S., Frati, W., Halpern, J., Holloway, L., Wales, W., and Chamberlain, O. (1963b). *Nuovo Cimento* **27**, 894.

Franken, P., and Liebes, S. (1956). *Phys. Rev.* **104**, 1197.

French, J. B., and Weisskopf, V. (1949). *Phys. Rev.* **75**, 1240.

Fried, H., and Yennie, D. (1960). *Phys. Rev. Letters* **4**, 583.

Fukuda, H., Miyamoto, Y., and Tomonaga, S. (1949). *Progr. Theoret. Phys.* (*Kyoto*) **4**, 47, 121.

Fulton, T., and Martin, P., (1954). *Phys. Rev.* **95**, 811.

Furlan, G., Gatto, R., and Longhi, G. (1964). *Phys. Letters* **12**, 262.

Garwin, R. L., and Lederman, L. M. (1959). *Nuovo Cimento* **11**, 776.

Garybian, G. M. (1952). *Izv. Akad. Nauk. Arm. SSR* **5**, 3.

Gatto, R. (1959). *Fortschr. Physik*. **7**, 147.

Gatto, R. (1961). *Proc. Intern. Conf. Elementary Particles, Aix-en-Provence*, p. 487.

Gatto, R. (1965). *Proc. Intern. Symposium Electron Photon Interactions High Energy, Hamburg, 1965*, Deutsche Physikalische Gesellschaft, Hamburg.

Geiger, J. S., Hughes, V. W., and Radford, H. E. (1957). *Phys. Rev.* **105**, 183.

Gell-Mann, M. (1964). *Phys. Letters* **8**, 214.

Gell-Mann, M., and Goldberger, M. (1954). *Phys. Rev.* **96**, 1433.

Goldemberg, J., and Torizuka, Y. (1963). *Phys. Rev.* **129**, 2580.

Greenberg, D. A., and Foley, H. M. (1960). *Phys. Rev.* **120**, 1684.

Harriman, J. M., (1956). *Phys. Rev.* **101**, 594.

Heberle, J. W., Heskell, A., Reich, and Kusch, P. (1956) *Phys. Rev.* **101**, 612.

Heisenberg, W. (1934). *Z. Physik*. **90**, 209.

Hughes, V. W. Merder, S., and Wu, C. S. (1957). *Phys. Rev.* **106**, 934.

Hughes, V. W., Robinson, H., Theriot, D., and Ziock, K. (1966). To be published.

Hutchinson, D. P., Meues, J., Shapiro, G., and Patlach, A. M. (1963). *Phys. Rev.* **131**, 1351.

Iddings, C. K. (1965). *Phys. Rev.* **138**, B446.

Iddings, C. K., and Platzmann, P. (1959a). *Phys. Rev.* **113**, 192.

Iddings, C. K., and Platzmann, P. (1959b). *Phys. Rev.* **115**, 919.

Isaev, P. S., and Zlatev, I. S. (1959). *Nuovo Cimento* **13**, 1.

Isaev, P. S., and Zlatev, I. S. (1960). *Nucl. Phys.* **16**, 608.

Ivanenko, D. (1957). *Proc. Conf. Elementary Particles, Venice,* Soceità Italiana Fisica, Bologna.

Källen, G. (1958). Quantenelektrodynamik, "Handbuch der Physik," Vol. V, Part 1. Springer, Berlin.

Källen, G. (1952). *Helv. Phys. Acta* **25**, 417.

Källen, G., and Sabry, A. (1955). *Kgl. Danske Videnskab. Selskab. Mat.-Fys. Medd.* **29**, 17.

Karplus, R., and Klein, A. (1952a). *Phys. Rev.* **85**, 972.

Karplus, R., and Klein, A. (1952b). *Phys. Rev.* **87**, 848.

Karplus, R., and Kroll, N. (1950). *Phys. Rev.* **77**, 536.

Karplus, R., Klein, A., and Schwinger, J. (1952). *Phys. Rev.* **86**, 288.

Koenig, S. H., Prodell, A. G., and Kusch, P. (1952). *Phys. Rev.* **88**, 191.

Krass, A. (1965). *Phys. Rev.* **138**, B1628.

Kroll, N. (1966). CERN Preprint 66/430/5.

Kroll, N., and Lamb, W., Jr. (1949). *Phys. Rev.* **75**, 388.

Kroll, N., Lee, T. D., and Zumino, B. (1966). To be published.

Kroll, N., and Pollock, F. (1952). *Phys. Rev.* **86**, 876.

Kusch, P. (1955). *Phys. Rev.* **100**, 1188.

Lamb, W. (1952). *Phys. Rev.* **85**, 259.

Lamb, W. (1957). *Phys. Rev.* **105**, 559.

Lamb, W., and Retherford, R. C. (1947) *Phys. Rev.* **72**, 241.

Lamb, W., and Retherford, R. C. (1950). *Phys. Rev.* **79**, 549.

Lamb, W., and Retherford, R. C. (1951). *Phys. Rev.* **81**, 222.

Lamb, W., and Retherford, R. C. (1952). *Phys. Rev.* **86**, 1014.

Lathrop, J. F., Lundy, R. A., Pennman, S., Telegdi, V. L., Winston, R., and Yovanovitch, D. D. (1960a). *Nuovo Cimento* **17**, 114.

Lathrop, J. F., Lundy, R. A., Telegdi, V. L., Winston, R., and Yovanovitch, D. D. (1960b). *Nuovo Cimento* **17**, 109.

Layzer, A. S. (1960). *Phys. Rev. Letters.* **4**, 580.

Layzer, A. S. (1961). *Bull. Am. Phys. Soc.* **6**, 514.

Layzer, A. S. (1964). *Nuovo Cimento* **33**, 1538.

Lederman, L. M., and Tinlot, J. (1964). *12th Intern. Conf. High Energy Phys.*, Dubna.

Lee, T. D. (1962). *Phys. Rev.* **128**, 899.

Lee, T. D., and Yang, C. N. (1962). *Phys. Rev.* **128**, 885.

Lifschitz, J., and Sands, R. H. (1961). *Bull. Amer. Phys. Soc.* **6**, 424.

Lipworth, E., and Novick, R. (1957). *Phys. Rev.* **108**, 1434.

Lomon, E. L., *Phys. Letters* **21**, 555 (1966).

Longhi, G. (1965). *Nuovo Cimento* **35**, 1122.

Louisel, W. H., Pidd, R. W., and Crane, H. R. (1954). *Phys. Rev.* **94**, 7.

Low, F. E. (1950). *Phys. Rev.* **77**, 361.

Low, F. E. (1954). *Phys. Rev.* **96**, 1428.

Low, F. E. (1965). *Phys. Rev. Letters* **14**, 238.

Low, F, E., and Salpeter, E. (1951). *Phys, Rev.* **83**, 478.

Luttinger, J. (1957). *Phys. Rev.* **74**, 893.

Masek, G. E., Ewart, Tontonghi, and Williams, R. W. (1963). *Phys. Rev. Letters* **10**, 35.

Masek, G. E., and Panofsky, W. (1956). *Phys. Rev.* **101**, 1094.

Masek, G. E., Lazarus, A., and Panofsky, W. (1956). *Phys. Rev.* **103**, 374.

Masek, G. E., Haggje, L. D., Kim, Y. B., and Williams, R. W., (1961). *Phys. Rev.* **122**, 937.

Møller, C. (1932). *Ann. Physik* **14**, 568.

Mosco, U. (1964). *Nuovo Cimento* **33**, 115.

Nafe, J. E., and Nelson, E. B. (1948). *Phys. Rev.* **73**, 718.

Newcomb, W. A., and Salpeter, E. E. (1955). *Phys. Rev.* **97**, 1146.
Novick, R., Lipworth, E., and Yergin, P. (1956). *Phys. Rev. Letters* **100**, 1454.
Pekeris, C. L., Schiff, B., and Lifson, H. (1962). *Phys. Rev.* **126**, 1057.
Perez, Y., Yorba, J., and Bishop, G. R. (1963) in G. R. Bishop Stanford Linear Accelerator Report **25**.
Petermann, A. (1957). *Helv. Phys. Acta* **30**, 407.
Petermann, A., and Yamaguchi, Y. (1959). *Phys. Rev. Letters* **2**, 359.
Pichanick, P. M. J., Swift, R. D., and Hughes, V. W. (1964). *Bull. Am. Phys. Soc.* **9**, 90.
Pipkin, F. M. (1966). *Report to the XIII Intern. Conf. on High Energy Physics, Berkeley, California*.
Ramsey, N. F. (1950). *Phys. Rev.* **78**, 699.
Rich, A., and Crane, H. R. (1966). *Phys. Rev. Letters* **17**, 271.
Richter, B. (1958). *Phys. Rev. Letters* **1**, 114.
Robiscoe, R. T. (1965). *Phys. Rev.* **138**, A22.
Robiscoe, R. T., and Cosens, B. L. (1966). *Phys. Rev. Letters* **17**, 69.
Ruderman, M. A. (1966). *Phys. Rev. Letters* **17**, 794.
Russell, J. (1965). *Proc. Intern. Symposium Electron Photon Interactions High Energies, Hamburg, 1965*. Deutsche Physikalische Gesellschaft, Hamburg.
Salpeter, E. E. (1952). *Phys. Rev.* **87**, 328.
Salpeter, E. E. (1953). *Phys. Rev.* **89**, 92.
Salpeter, E. E. (1958). *Phys. Rev.* **112**, 1642.
Schiff, B., Pekeris, C. L., and Lifson, H. (1965). *Phys. Rev.* **137**, A1672.
Schupp, A. A., Pidd, R. W., and Crane, H. R. (1961). *Phys. Rev.* **121**, 1.
Schwartz, C. (1964). *Phys. Rev.* **134**, A1181.
Schwartz, C., and Tiemann, J. J. (1959). *Ann. Phys. N.Y.* **6**, 178.
Schwinger, J. (1948). *Phys. Rev.* **73**, 416.
Schwinger, J. (1949). *Phys. Rev.* **76**, 790.
Series, G. W. (1964). *Phys. Rev.* **136**, A684.
Sokolov, A. A., and Ternov, I. M. (1963). *Proc. Conf. Accelerator, Dubna*.
Sommerfield, C. (1957). *Phys. Rev.* **107**, 328.
Soto, M. F., Jr. (1966). *Phys. Rev. Letters* **17**, 1153.
Sternheim, M. (1963). *Phys. Rev.* **130**, 211.
Than Mynt, Kleppner, D., Ramsey, N., Robinson, H. (1966). *Phys. Rev. Letters* **17**, 405.
Traub, J., and Foley, H. M. (1959). *Phys. Rev.* **116**, 914.
Tsai, Y. S. (1960). *Phys. Rev.* **120**, 269.
Tsai, Y. S. (1965). *Phys. Rev.* **137**, 730.
Tsai, Y. S., Swanson, S. M., and Iddings, C. K. (1965). *Proc. Intern. Symposium Electron Photon Interactions High Energies, Hamburg, 1965*. Deutsche Physikalische Gesellschaft, Hamburg.
Uehling, E. A. (1953). *Phys. Rev.* **48**, 55.
Weinstein, R., Deutsch, M., and Brown, S. C. (1954). *Phys. Rev.* **94**, 758.
Weisskopf, V. (1936). *Kgl. Danske Videnskab. Selskab. Mat.-Fys. Medd.* **14**, No. 6.
Weneser, J., Bersohn R., and Kroll, N. M. (1953). *Phys. Rev.* **91**, 1257.
Wieder, J., and Lamb, W. E. (1957). *Phys. Rev.* **107**, 125.
Wilkinson, D. T., and Crane, H. R. (1963). *Phys. Rev.* **130**, 852.
Wittke, J. P., and Dicke, R. H. (1956). *Phys. Rev.* **103**, 620.
Zdanis, R. A., Madansky, L., Kraemer, R. W., and Hertzbach, S. (1965). *Phys. Rev. Letters* **14**, 721.
Zemach, A. C. (1956). *Phys. Rev.* **104**, 1771.
Zwanziger, D. (1961a). *Phys. Rev.* **121**, 1128.
Zwanziger, D. (1961b). *Bull. Am. Phys. Soc.* **6**, 514.
Zwanziger, D. (1964). *Nuovo Cimento* **34**, 77.

HIGH ENERGY STRONG INTERACTIONS OF ELEMENTARY PARTICLES

L. Bertocchi and E. Ferrari

This chapter was supposed to be written by Antonio Stanghellini. He was already ill when he began to fix the general structure of the paper, but his cruel illness prevented him from pursuing his work.

He died September 29, 1964.

We have tried to complete the paper following the designs he left, even if the development of the subject in this last year forced us to modify somewhat the original structure. We devote our modest work to his memory.

I. Introduction

During the past few years, the study of the strong interactions of elementary particles has been developed mainly by following two basic directions. The first one is the investigation and the classification of the numerous resonant states which are continuously being discovered. From the experimental point of view, this study does not require too large energies (once phase-space problems have been overcome), but rather it demands careful and ingenious analysis in order to determine the quantum numbers and the properties of such objects without ambiguity. From a theoretical point of view, the discovery of the new resonances has led to very important speculations, such as the introduction of symmetry groups for the classification of such particles [from the simplest one, SU(2), which classifies the particles according to their isotopic spin, to SU(3) and SU(6)].

The second direction of investigation which is being followed consists essentially of studying the dynamical properties of those few particles having a relatively long lifetime ($\geqslant 10^{-8}$ sec, say), for which experiments are feasible today. In this case, in order to get a thorough description of the related phenomena, one has to vary all that can be varied, i.e., the energy, the momentum transfer, and, generally, all the kinematical variables which can be easily studied in the observed reactions. This approach is a typical "high energy" approach, in the sense that the higher the energy available, the larger the amount of information which can be extracted from experiment. From the theoretical point of view, the description of the experimental facts is mainly phenomenological, and it is generally carried out with the aid of models which are directly suggested by the experimental evidence. Apart from a few well-established general principles, up to now one lacks a general framework (like the symmetry scheme) which can give a clue to the understanding of the dynamics of all particles. It is generally believed that only at very, very large energies do the general and simple laws characterize the basic features of the interactions of all particles. This is the philosophy of the so-called "asymptotic region," which is also supported by some general arguments and by a few experimental indications. However, at the energies presently available, such an optimistic situation seems to be still very far away.

The review of the experiments and of the theoretical ideas relevant to such a "dynamical" approach to the physics of strong interactions is the object of the present work. Of course, we do not underestimate the importance of the study of resonant state properties, and of their classification. However, at the present stage of our knowledge, the experimental and theoretical aspects of the two approaches are rather independent one of the other; thus, we can treat only one of them without a substantial loss of completeness. Therefore, we shall not discuss the basic properties of the various resonances, but we will suppose the reader to be sufficiently acquainted with them, so that we can refer to them, when needed, without further explanation.

From what has been said, we will consider only those "initial states" that are experimentally accessible, i.e., pp, np, $\bar{p}p$, $\pi^{\pm}p$, $K^{\pm}p$, and the reactions originated by them. A brief description of the experimental situation will open the work (Section II). A summary of the general properties of the scattering amplitude will follow (Section III), in order to make the understanding of the theoretical formalism easier. The basic models used for the description of the experimental facts will be presented in Sections IV and V. Finally, Section VI will deal specifically with the "asymptotic region" philosophy, which has led to several different theoretical speculations, though the experimental data are rather scanty.

II. Review of the Experimental Situation in High Energy Elementary Particle Collisions

A. Elastic Scattering

The reactions starting from a given initial state can be divided into elastic and inelastic processes. The importance of elastic scattering is well known. Both from the intuitive and the practical point of view, elastic scattering is the simplest two-body interaction that can be conceived, and also the easiest to study experimentally as well as theoretically. Today, the "basic" measurements which can be carried out in a process of elastic scattering at high energy is the determination of the shape of the center-of-mass (c.m.) angular distribution, $d\sigma/d\Omega$. More refined measurements, such as polarization, are much more difficult to perform systematically with the present techniques. Generally, in order to have a sensible comparison between experiments at different energies, it is customary to refer to the relativistically invariant quantity $d\sigma/dt$, where $-t$ is the four-momentum squared between final and initial state (Fig. 1):

$$t = (q_1 - p_1)^2 = (q_2 - p_2)^2. \tag{II-1}$$

In the c.m. system, we have

$$t = -2q^2(1 - \cos \Theta) \tag{II-2}$$

where q is the magnitude of the c.m. three-momentum, and Θ is the c.m. scattering angle.

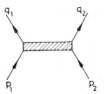

Fɪɢ. 1.   Schematic diagram of the elastic scattering. The four-momentum of the particles participating in the reaction is indicated by p_1, p_2, q_1, q_2. Subscript 1 refers to the incident particle, subscript 2 to the target particle (in the lab. system).

For physical scattering, t is always negative, and vanishes only in the forward direction. Sometimes it is convenient to introduce a positive quantity

$$\Delta^2 = -t = +2q^2(1 - \cos \Theta). \qquad \text{(II-3)}$$

We will use t or Δ^2 indifferently, by following the trend found in the literature. It can be easily obtained that

$$\frac{d\sigma}{d\Delta^2} = \frac{\pi}{q^2} \frac{d\sigma}{d\Omega}. \qquad \text{(II-4)}$$

The characteristic feature of high energy elastic scattering is the presence of a very pronounced forward peak in the angular distribution. This peak is understood in terms of the diffraction process, and is directly connected to the total cross section at the same energy through the optical theorem (Section III,A). This theorem follows directly from the conservation of probability, and states that the imaginary part of the scattering amplitude in the forward direction is directly proportional to the total cross section at the same energy:

$$\operatorname{Im} f(0) = \frac{q}{4\pi} \sigma_{\text{tot}} \qquad \text{(II-5)}$$

by defining $f(t)$ from the scattering amplitude in the customary way, i.e., such that

$$|f(t)|^2 = (d\sigma/d\Omega)_{\text{c.m.}}. \qquad \text{(II-6)}$$

In fact, the (extrapolated) value of the differential cross section in the forward direction is quite consistent with the value obtained from the right-hand side of Eq. (II-5). This shows that the dominant part of the scattering amplitude is given by its imaginary part, at least for small momentum transfers.

We shall focus our attention on the following problems:

(1) the behavior of the total cross sections as a function of the energy,
(2) the separation of the real and imaginary parts in the scattering amplitude in the forward direction,

(3) the study of the behavior of the width of the diffraction peak with energy ("shrinking" of the peak),

(4) the study of high momentum transfer events, and

(5) the measurement of polarization and of similar effects.

1. *Total Cross Sections*

The behavior of the total cross section as a function of the energy is connected to the elastic scattering through the optical theorem. Figure 2 (Lindenbaum, 1966; van Hove, 1966) presents the behavior of the total cross sections as a function of energy for the principal reactions at incident momenta between 6 and 22 GeV/c. It can be seen that the general trend is similar for all

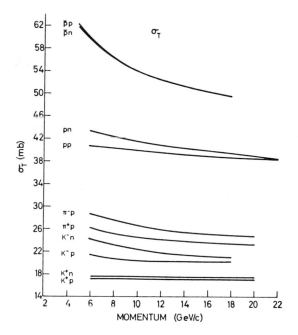

Fig. 2. Total cross sections for nucleon-nucleon and meson-nucleon scattering, reproduced from Lindenbaum (1966) and reported by van Hove (1966).

channels. The cross sections seem to tend to constant values as energy increases. Some of them are already nearly constant in the energy region under consideration (pp, K^+p, K^+n). The others are decreasing, more or less slowly. It should be noted that reactions on neutrons rapidly tend to have the same cross section as reactions on protons. Only the pion-nucleon cross sections exhibit a nearly constant difference of a certain size (about 2 mb). Note that for charge symmetry $\sigma(\pi^+n) = \sigma(\pi^-p)$ and $\sigma(\pi^-n) = \sigma(\pi^+p)$.

The latest review of the experiments on the total cross section can be found in a paper by Galbraith *et al.* (1965).

2. *The Real Part of the Scattering Amplitude*

Figure 3 shows a typical pattern of proton-proton elastic scattering at different energies for very small momentum transfers [$|t| \leqslant 0.14$ $(GeV/c)^2$]. The data shown are only an example of the results obtained from different experiments performed on this subject: Breitenlohner *et al.* (1963), Lohrmann *et al.* (1964), Kirillova *et al.* (1963, 1966), Dowell *et al.* (1964), Taylor *et al.* (1965), Bellettini *et al.* (1965a), and Foley *et al.* (1965a,b). The most interesting analysis that can be extracted from such data is the determination of the real part of the scattering amplitude, which may exist in addition to the large imaginary part implied by the optical theorem [Eq. (II-5)].

The investigation of the presence of a real part can be carried out by the analysis of the interference with Coulomb scattering, which is known to be important only at very small momentum transfers (the Coulomb scattering goes like e^2/t, where e is the electric charge, and its sign obviously depends on the signs of the charges of the scattering particles). By assuming that the imaginary part of the scattering amplitude behaves as a function of t like

$$f(t) = f(0) \exp\tfrac{1}{2}(bt + ct^2) \qquad \text{(II-7)}$$

[where $f(0)$ is taken from Eq. (II-5) and b, c are adjustable parameters (see Section IV,A)], it is possible to make an explicit calculation of the expected form of the angular distribution (diffraction + Coulomb + interference), and to look for the presence of a real part. The simplest evaluation is obtained by assuming the ratio of the real to the imaginary part to be t independent at fixed energy

$$\frac{\operatorname{Re} f(t)}{\operatorname{Im} f(t)} = \alpha. \qquad \text{(II-8)}$$

The value of α can be determined by fitting the experimental distributions. The results for proton-proton scattering give a negative value for α, of the order of -0.3 at all energies (constructive interference). It is important to note that the case of the absence of a real part ($\alpha = 0$) is clearly excluded. In Section IV,B the dependence of such conclusions will be discussed, to a certain extent, on a somewhat arbitrary assumption, i.e., that pp diffraction scattering is independent of the mutual orientation of the proton spins, and thus can be described by one scalar amplitude. However, a more definite indication of the existence of a nonnegligible real part in the scattering amplitude comes from pion-proton scattering, measured at very small momentum transfers (Foley *et al.*, 1965b). In this case, the spin-flip effect near the forward direction is very small (see Section IV,C), and the use of one

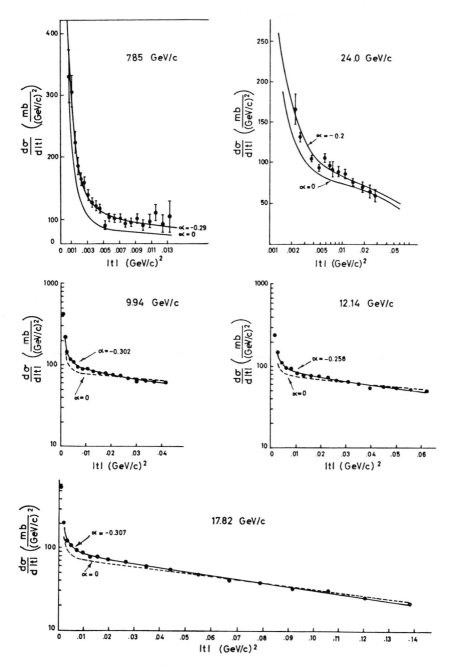

FIG. 3. Proton-proton elastic scattering distributions at different energies in the region of very small momentum transfers. Theoretical fits without real part ($\alpha = 0$) and with a suitable choice of α are shown. The data at 7.85 GeV/c are taken from Taylor *et al.* (1965); those at 24.0 GeV/c, from Lohrmann *et al.* (1964); the other data, from Foley *et al.* (1965b).

scalar amplitude is largely justified. Figures 4 and 5 report the relevant data for π^-p and π^+p collisions in the energy region below 16 GeV. It can be seen that the hypothesis of the absence of a real part is incompatible with the experimental data. The experiments on π^-'s have been carried out up to larger energies [$\leqslant 24$ GeV (Foley *et al.*, 1965b)]; there is an indication that the magnitude of α decreases rapidly toward zero, but further experimental evidence is needed in order to clarify the situation.

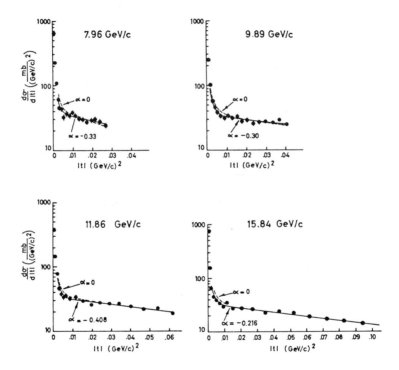

FIG. 4. π^--proton elastic scattering distribution at different energies in the region of very small momentum transfer [taken from Foley *et al.* (1965b)]. Theoretical fits without real part ($\alpha = 0$) and with a suitable choice of α are shown.

A measurement of α for np scattering has recently been attempted from the study of proton-deuteron collision (Bellettini *et al.*, 1965c). It is found that the values of α for pp and pn scattering at 19 GeV/c are nearly the same.

3. *The Diffraction Peak*

As has been already mentioned, the largest part of the elastic scattering events is contained in a narrow peak around the forward direction (the diffraction peak); the differential cross section $d\sigma/d|t|$ shows an exponential

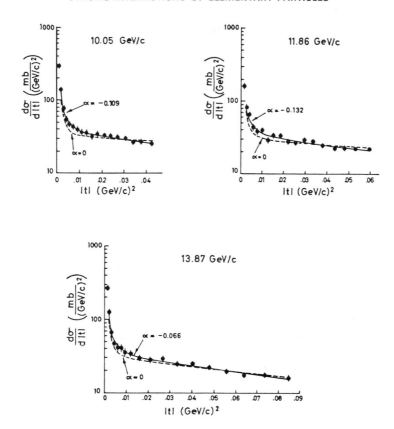

FIG. 5.   The same as in Fig. 4 for $\pi^+ p$ elastic scattering [taken from Foley *et al.* (1965b)].

decrease as a function of $|t|$; for the analysis of the peak structure one considers values of $|t|$ up to about 1 $(GeV/c)^2$. The experimental study of the diffraction peak in this range of momentum transfers has been performed by many authors.[1] The theoretical analysis of the peak structure is generally

[1] *For pp:*   Cork *et al.* (1957), Smith *et al.* (1961), Fickinger *et al.* (1962), Fujii *et al.* (1962), Diddens *et al.* (1962a), Foley *et al.* (1963a,b), Foley *et al.* (1965c), and Caldwell *et al.* (1964).

        The first three papers contain reference to other early work.

  For πp: Chretien *et al.* (1957), Lai *et al.* (1961), Cork *et al.* (1963), SOBB Collaboration (1963), Thomas (1960), Wang Chang Kang *et al.* (1960), Perl *et al.* (1962, 1963), ABBBHLM Collaboration (1964b), Brandt *et al.* (1963), Foley *et al.* (1963a,b,c), Foley *et al.* (1965c), and Caldwell *et al.* (1964).

  For Kp: Foley *et al.* (1963d), Cook *et al.* (1963a), Crittenden *et al.* (1964), and Foley *et al.* (1965c).

  For p̄p: Armenteros *et al.* (1960), Foley *et al.* (1963d), Escoubès *et al.* (1965), Ferbel *et al.* (1965a), and Foley *et al.* (1965c).

carried out by means of optical models (Section IV,A). Here we want to stress another experimental feature which has received considerable attention in the last few years; i.e., the study of the width of the diffraction peak as a function of energy, in the sense of an effective "shrinking" as energy increases.

The "width" of the diffraction peak can be described in terms of the coefficients b and c appearing in Eq. (II-7), in particular of the coefficient b which is the most important at low momentum transfers. By passing from the scattering amplitude to the differential cross section, Eq. (II-7) can be rewritten as

$$\frac{d\sigma}{d|t|} = \left(\frac{d\sigma}{d|t|}\right)_{t=0} \exp(bt + ct^2). \tag{II-9}$$

This fit has proved to be suitable for the description of the elastic scattering for all reactions, when $|t|$ is less than 1 $(GeV/c)^2$.

A theory which had some success some years ago, based on the concept of "Regge poles" (Section IV,D) and on the assumption that the "asymptotic region" was already shown at the energies presently available, predicted that the elastic peak for all processes of elastic scattering should shrink with energy in the same way (see, for example, Drell, 1962). With the increase of experimental knowledge it was shown that such a theory was not adequate, at least in the simple form in which it had been first proposed; however, interest in the behavior of the width of the diffraction peak as a function of energy has persisted. As an example, Fig. 6 gives a typical spectrum of the diffraction peak as a function of t, at different energies, for pp and $\pi^- p$ scattering.

It can be seen that in proton-proton scattering the diffraction peak shrinks, and in pion-proton scattering it keeps its width constant up to energies of 25 GeV (this happens also for π^+). For antiproton-proton and kaon-proton scattering the statistics are much poorer. There are definite indications, however, that in antiproton-proton scattering the diffraction peak expands, and in $K^+ p$ scattering it shrinks. For $K^- p$ scattering there seems to be no shrinkage, but better statistics are needed.

This complicated pattern is difficult to explain in terms of a simple theory. It is hoped that the situation will become more regular with increasing energy; however, the energy region where this can happen cannot be reached by existing machines. A more quantitative understanding of this point can be obtained by the analysis of the variation of the coefficients b and c of Eq. (II-9) with energy. The most significant cases are reported in Table I.

4. *Large Momentum Transfer Scattering*

The elastic scattering distribution in the momentum transfer region $|t| > 1$ $(GeV/c)^2$ has been measured by different experimental groups, both for pp (Diddens *et al.*, 1962b; Cocconi *et al.*, 1963; Baker *et al.*, 1964; Cocconi

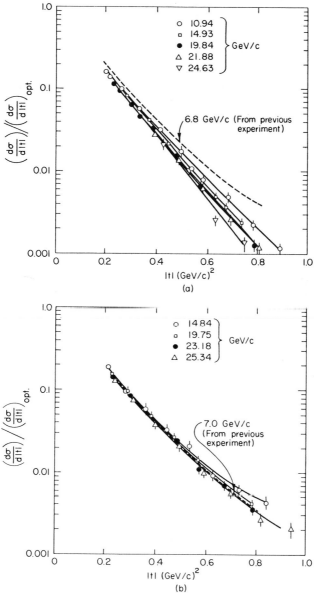

FIG. 6. Experimental distributions in the momentum transfer t in the region of the diffraction peak at different incident momenta: (a) for proton-proton and (b) for π^--proton elastic scattering [taken from Foley *et al.* (1965c)]. The cross sections are normalized to the optical value [right-hand side of Eq. (II-5)] in order to allow a better comparison at different energies. The lines connect points measured at the same energy, and exhibit the effect of shrinking or nonshrinking of the peak.

TABLE I.   Values of b and c [cf. Eq. (II-9)] as a Function of Energy, Measured from Fits over a Momentum Transfer Range Extending up to about 1 (GeV/c)^2

Reaction	p_{inc} (GeV/c)	b (GeV/c)$^{-2}$	c (GeV/c)$^{-4}$
pp	8.5	8.16 ± 0.28	0.84 ± 0.36[a]
	10.94	8.56 ± 0.47	1.20 ± 0.54[c]
	12.4	9.05 ± 0.34	1.41 ± 0.44[a]
	14.93	8.89 ± 0.52	0.98 ± 0.62[c]
	18.4	9.79 ± 0.63	1.53 ± 0.69[a]
	19.84	8.68 ± 0.39	0.70 ± 0.92[c]
	21.88	9.63 ± 0.78	1.56 ± 0.89[c]
	24.63	7.97 ± 1.56	0.82 ± 1.83[c]
$\pi^- p$	7.0	9.45 ± 0.25	2.75 ± 0.34[b]
	8.5	8.76 ± 0.22	2.20 ± 0.26[a]
	8.9	9.22 ± 0.21	2.54 ± 0.30[b]
	10.8	9.36 ± 0.23	2.45 ± 0.33[b]
	12.4	8.74 ± 0.21	1.94 ± 0.26[a]
	13.0	9.71 ± 0.26	3.02 ± 0.35[b]
	14.84	10.20 ± 0.96	4.02 ± 1.07[c]
	18.4	9.16 ± 0.46	2.44 ± 0.45[a]
	19.75	8.98 ± 0.65	2.44 ± 0.73[c]
	23.18	8.53 ± 0.74	1.79 ± 0.83[c]
	25.34	9.46 ± 0.71	2.83 ± 0.72[c]

Reaction	p_{inc} (GeV/c)	b (GeV/c)$^{-2}$	c (GeV/c)$^{-4}$
$\pi^+ p$	6.8	8.58 ± 0.23	2.24 ± 2.29[b]
	8.5	7.44 ± 0.37	0.81 ± 0.46[a]
	8.8	8.79 ± 0.23	2.38 ± 0.32[b]
	10.8	8.48 ± 0.25	1.79 ± 0.35[b]
	12.4	8.23 ± 0.78	2.20 ± 0.90[a]
	12.8	8.93 ± 0.27	2.36 ± 0.34[b]
	14.8	8.98 ± 0.31	2.27 ± 0.40[b]
	16.7	8.94 ± 0.35	2.82 ± 0.43[b]
$\bar{p}p$	4.0	13.0 ± 0.6	—[d]
	7.2	13.15 ± 0.47	—[e]
	8.9	12.84 ± 0.21	—[e]
	10.0	11.8 ± 2.9	—[e]
	11.8	12.33 ± 0.79	—[c]
	12.0	12.66 ± 0.29	—[e]
	15.9	8.78 ± 1.00	—[c]
$K^+ p$	6.8	6.13 ± 0.88	1.36 ± 0.77[e]
	9.8	6.23 ± 0.45	0.99 ± 0.55[e]
	12.8	6.93 ± 0.38	1.18 ± 0.45[e]
	14.8	7.06 ± 0.38	1.73 ± 0.42[e]
$K^- p$	7.2	10.2 ± 1.2	4.0 ± 0.9[e]
	8.9	10.5 ± 1.2	4.2 ± 1.0[e]
	11.8	7.67 ± 1.06	1.24 ± 1.27[c]
	15.9	7.85 ± 1.26	2.14 ± 1.35[c]

[a] Harting et al. (1965).   [b] Foley et al. (1963a,b).   [c] Foley et al. (1965c).   [d] Escoubès et al. (1965).   [e] Foley et al. (1965).

et al., 1965; Clyde *et al.*, 1964) and for $\pi^{\pm}p$ scattering (Perl *et al.*, 1962, 1963; ABBBHLM Collaboration, 1964b; Lai *et al.*, 1961; Cook *et al.*, 1963b; Perl *et al.*, 1965; Orear *et al.*, 1965). The most striking feature observed in this region is that the exponential decrease characterizing the forward peak is no longer maintained; the cross section tends to flatten, and the use of Eq. (II-7) with the values of b and c derived from the low momentum transfer region (Table I) would predict values enormously smaller than those observed. This situation is well summarized by Fig. 7, which refers to proton-proton

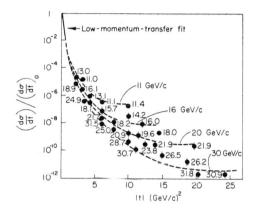

FIG. 7.   Differential cross section (normalized to the value in the forward direction) in proton-proton elastic scattering in the region of high momentum transfer (Cocconi *et al.*, 1965). The incident momentum is indicated for each experimental point. Dashed lines describe the experimental trend for fixed values of the incident momentum; each line ends at that value of t corresponding to a c.m. scattering angle of 90°.

scattering at momentum transfers extending up to 24 $(\text{GeV}/c)^2$. Another peculiar characteristic of high momentum transfer pp scattering is shown by Fig. 8, which exhibits the dependence of the cross section on the transverse momentum $p_{\perp} = q \sin \Theta$ (where q is the c.m. momentum, and Θ is the c.m. scattering angle).[2] Such a dependence seems to be exponential and energy independent. Section IV,C will discuss the theoretical interpretation of this behavior, which may be due to a mechanism different from that of diffraction.

At large momentum transfers, pion-proton scattering exhibits qualitatively the same features as proton-proton scattering; however, the absolute value of the cross section at high momentum transfers is smaller [the order of magnitude is of 0.1 $\mu\text{b}/(\text{GeV}/c)^2$ for πp and 1 $\mu\text{b}/(\text{GeV}/c)^2$ for pp, for $|t| \sim 3\text{--}4$

---

[2] It must be noted that at small momentum transfer $p_{\perp}^2$ is practically identical to $|t|$, since the two quantities differ by a factor $\cos^2 (\Theta/2)$.

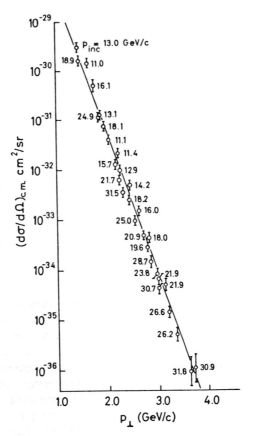

FIG. 8.   Dependence of the angular c.m. distribution $d\sigma/d\Omega$ on the transverse momentum $p_\perp$, for the experimental points of Fig. 7 (Cocconi *et al.*, 1965). The straight line fit is represented by $d\sigma/d\Omega = A \exp(-a p_\perp)$, where $A = 3.0 \times 10^{-26} \mathrm{cm}^2/\mathrm{sr}$ and $a^{-1} = 152$ MeV/c.

(GeV/c)² at an incident momentum of 8 GeV/c]. Furthermore, the πp-scattering distribution seems to present a small secondary maximum at about $|t| \sim 1.5$ (GeV/c)². Such a maximum is not observed in pp scattering. These arguments will again be discussed in Section IV,C.

In pion-proton scattering it is also possible to study the behavior of the angular distribution near the backward direction at high energies. A backward peak has been observed in $\pi^+ p$ scattering (ABBBHLM Collaboration, 1964d; ABC Collaboration, 1966).[3] A much smaller one has been observed in $\pi^- p$ scattering (Frisken *et al.*, 1965; Alikhanov *et al.*, 1965), after

---

[3] There exists also an experimental study of backward $\pi^- n$ scattering (Coffin *et al.*, 1965).

escaping detection in experiments with less statistics (ABBBHLM Collaboration, 1964b; Perl *et al.*, 1965). The shape of the c.m. angular distribution at 4 GeV/*c* is presented in Fig. 9.

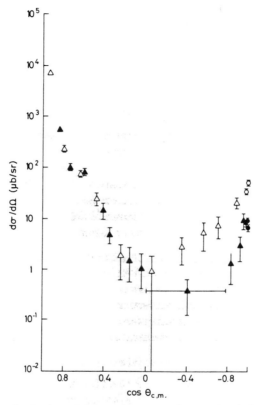

FIG. 9.   Angular distribution of pion-nucleon scattering at 4 GeV/*c* [taken from Frisken *et al.*, 1965], exhibiting the backward peaks. Also points from other experiments are reported. (▲) $\pi^- p$ 4 GeV/*c*, Coffin *et al.*, 1965; (△) $\pi^+ p$ 4 GeV/*c*, Harting *et al.*, 1965; and (●) $\pi^- p$ (○) $\pi^+ p$ 4 GeV/*c*, this experiment.

More recently, the structure of the backward peaks in $\pi^\pm p$ scattering has been determined with greater accuracy by Brody *et al.* (1966), at incident momenta between 4 and 10 GeV/*c*. The comparison between data at different energies is better made in terms of the dependence on the "crossed momentum transfer" u (for its definition, see Section III,A,2), which, near the backward direction, plays the same role as t does near the forward direction. The results obtained are shown in Fig. 10.

The problem of the interpretation of these effects will be discussed in Sections IV,C and IV,D,3.

5. *Polarization Measurements*

There are some recent measurements of polarization in *pp* scattering, using polarized targets (Kanavets *et al.*, 1966). The largest values of the maximum polarization occur at low energy (<1 GeV) and are of the order of 0.5. Then the value of the polarization drops to about 0.1 at energies of several GeV.

More extensive work has been recently performed in the measurement of the polarization in $\pi^{\pm}p$ scattering (Focardi *et al.*, 1965a; Borghini *et al.*, 1966a,b). The polarizations for π^+p and π^-p have a similar behavior as functions of *t*, but they are of opposite sign. Typical results are shown in Figs. 11 and 12. The most appealing explanation of these effects is currently provided by the so-called "Regge pole model" (Section IV,D); the theoretical curves predicted by this model have also been reported in the figures. This point will be further discussed in Section IV,D,3.

In order to have a complete reconstruction of the scattering matrix for *pp* scattering (and also to study the spin-dependent part of the interaction), it

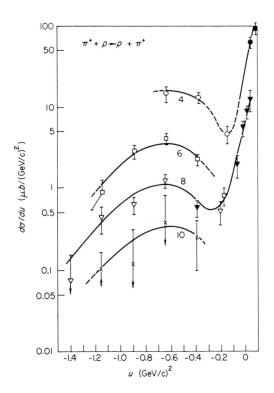

FIG. 10a.

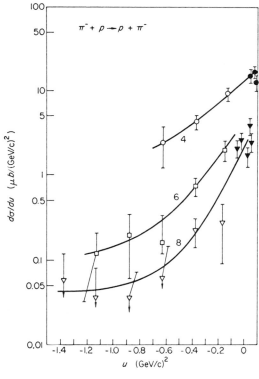

FIG. 10b.

FIG. 10. Plots showing the structure of the differential cross section near the backward direction: (a) for π^+p, (b) for π^-p scattering (taken from Brody *et al.*, 1966), as a function of the "crossed momentum transfer" u (see Section III,A,2). The curves connect points measured at the same incident momentum, and are labelled by its value (in GeV/c). (○), (□), (▽), (×): Brody *et al.* (1966). (▼), (●): Frisken *et al.* (1965).

will be necessary to perform experiments with polarized beams and polarized targets. For πp scattering only a polarized target is obviously required.

B. Charge Exchange Scattering

Charge exchange scattering can be considered as a particular case of elastic scattering, to which it is connected by charge independence. On the other hand, charge exchange scattering can also be considered as an example of inelastic process, insofar as the final state is not identical to the initial state.

For this reason, charge exchange scattering does not exhibit the characteristic enhancement in the forward direction due to diffraction scattering. Therefore its study can give useful information about the interaction mechanism that can be described in terms of "potential scattering," which, in elastic scattering, is overwhelmed by the huge contribution of diffraction.

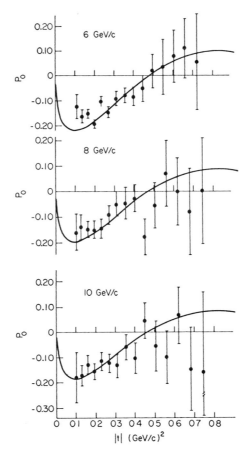

FIG. 11.   The behavior of the proton polarization P_0 as a function of the momentum transfer t for $\pi^- p$ elastic scattering at incident moments of 6, 8, and 10 GeV/c, as given by Borghini *et al.* (1966a). The theoretical curves represent a fit to the data, calculated by Chiu *et al.* (1966), using the Regge pole model.

High energy, charge exchange scattering has been measured experimentally for $\pi^- p$ (Borgeaud *et al.*, 1964; Bruyant *et al.*, 1964; Mannelli *et al.*, 1965; Stirling *et al.*, 1965; Sonderegger *et al.*, 1966), np (Larsen, 1960; Palevsky *et al.*, 1962; Friedes *et al.*, 1965; Manning *et al.*, 1966), and $K^- p$ collisions (Astbury *et al.*, 1965).

The reaction $\pi^- p \to \pi^0 n$ has been studied up to an incident momentum of 18 GeV/c. The characteristic feature of this process is the presence of a peak in the small momentum transfer region. Such a peak is not steeply decreasing from the forward direction, as is the diffraction peak, but rather it is flat up to $|t| \simeq 0.12$ $(\mathrm{GeV}/c)^2$, and then decreases with a slope similar to that of $\pi^\pm p$

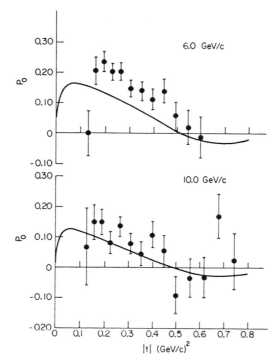

FIG. 12. The behavior of the proton polarization P_0 as a function of the momentum transfer t for π^+p elastic scattering at incident momenta of 6 and 10 GeV/c, as given by Borghini *et al.* (1966b). The theoretical curves represent the prediction by Chiu *et al.* (1966), on the basis of the Regge pole model.

elastic scattering. At high energy, there is indication (Mannelli *et al.*, 1965; Stirling *et al.*, 1965) of a dip at $t = 0$. A plot of the behavior of the differential cross section for $|t| \leqslant 0.5$ (GeV/c)^2 between 6 and 16 GeV/c is shown in Fig. 13.

Due to charge independence, the imaginary part of the charge exchange matrix element can be evaluated to within 10% by the optical theorem from the difference between π^-p and π^+p total cross sections. By comparison with experiment, it can be shown that for π^-p charge exchange scattering the real and imaginary parts are roughly of the same magnitude. It must be noted that the total cross section for charge exchange scattering decreases with energy roughly like $(p_{\text{inc}})^{-1}$, and in this energy range it is much smaller than the elastic cross sections (by a factor of 100 at $p_{\text{inc}} = 10$ GeV/c).

The polarization of the final neutron in π^-p charge exchange scattering has been recently measured (Bonamy *et al.*, 1966). Its behavior as a function of t at 6 and 11 GeV/c is shown in Fig. 14.

Neutron-proton charge exchange scattering (i.e., neutron-proton backward scattering) has been most widely studied in a rather low energy region [incident momenta up to 3.6 GeV/c (Larsen, 1960; Palevsky *et al.*, 1962; Friedes *et al.*, 1965)].

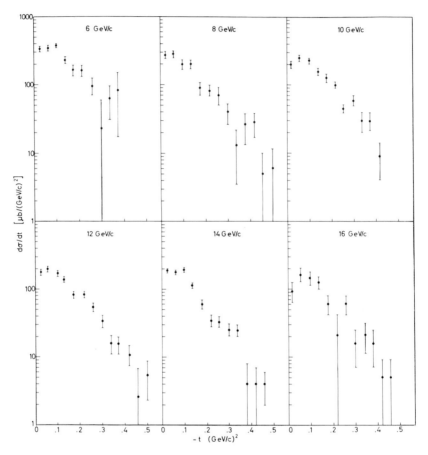

FIG. 13.   Differential $\pi^- p$ charge exchange cross section at various energies between 6 and 16 GeV/c [taken from Mannelli *et al.*, 1965].

Only a very recent experiment (Manning *et al.*, 1966) investigates this reaction at a higher momentum (8.15 GeV/c). Also, in this case, diffraction is not present, but a peak is exhibited in the forward direction; this peak shows a very fast decrease (faster than in elastic scattering) at very small momentum transfers [$|t| \leqslant 0.05$ (GeV/c)^2]; then the slope flattens out, and the behavior of the distribution becomes more similar to that of pp elastic scattering.

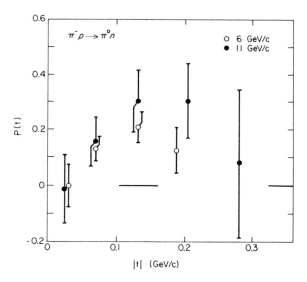

Fig. 14. The polarization $P(t)$ in $\pi^- p$ charge exchange scattering, as measured by Bonamy *et al.* (1966).

However, the measurement at 8 GeV/c shows that the slope for charge exchange scattering is flatter than for pp elastic scattering.[4] Figures 15 and 16 illustrate the situation.

Various theoretical models have been proposed in order to explain these effects; the relevant discussion can be found in Sections IV,A and IV,D.

Finally, $K^- p$ charge exchange scattering has been measured at 9.5 GeV/c (Astbury *et al.*, 1965). It presents the same characteristics observed in $\pi^- p$ charge exchange, i.e., a flat peak (with a possible dip at $t = 0$) extending up to $|t| \simeq 1$ (GeV/c)^2. It is not possible to draw definite conclusions for larger values of $|t|$ because of the large experimental errors.

It is interesting to note that the total cross sections for charge exchange (practically obtained by integrating the area under the forward peaks) decrease with energy in a different way for $\pi^- p$ and np: In the former case, the decrease goes like p_{inc}^{-1}; in the latter, it is faster, and goes roughly like p_{inc}^{-2}.

C. INELASTIC PROCESSES

The experimental information on inelastic processes at high energies is at present quite extensive, but far from systematic and exhaustive. As energy increases, a larger and larger number of open channels becomes important,

---

[4] A possible indication of the presence of a flat distribution at high momentum transfer also at 25 GeV is given by Steinrisser *et al.* (1962).

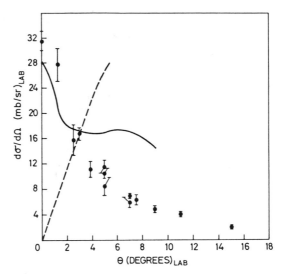

FIG. 15.   Differential *np*-charge exchange cross section at   3.00 GeV/*c* [taken from Friedes *et al.*, 1965]; (— — —) π-exchange model without absorption and (—) single π and ρ exchange with absorption (Henley and Muzinich, 1964).

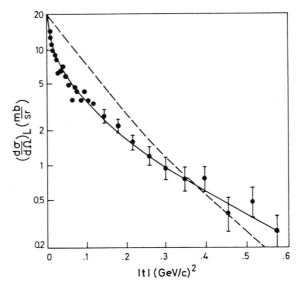

FIG. 16.   Charge exchange *np*-differential cross section at 8.15 GeV/*c* in the lab. system [taken from Manning *et al.* (1966)]. The solid line is the best fit; the broken line shows the results for *pp* scattering at 7.95 GeV/*c* [taken from Taylor *et al.* (1965)] normalized to the *np* result at $t = 0$, in the interval $0 \leq \Theta \leq 90$ mrad.

and only a very restricted sample of them has been studied experimentally in detail, generally for specific purposes. At present, the greatest importance of inelastic collisions lies in their use in studying resonant states. The study of inelastic collisions lies primarily in this direction, and the situation is still far from being clarified.

However, the discovery and the determination of the properties of resonant states is itself of fundamental importance to the understanding of the mechanism of inelastic processes. By grouping together the various final particles belonging to a resonant state and by considering them as a single entity, apparently complicated reactions can be reduced to a very simple form, and, among the numerous degrees of freedom which describe the final state, only those which are the most significant can be isolated and studied, by neglecting all the others. In this way, a dynamical analysis of the inelastic processes can be attempted, which is something more than a mere identification and classification of unknown objects. At present, this dynamical analysis is possible for those processes involving the most well-known resonances, such as the vector mesons or the excited baryons with spin $\frac{3}{2}$ and positive parity. In the following paragraphs we shall try to summarize what is known in this field. We shall have to unify many scattered results coming from the uncorrelated work of different laboratories.

It is experimentally demonstrated that in many cases of inelastic collisions at energies of some GeV (and to a smaller extent, also at higher energies), the final particles can be grouped in such a way as to leave only two objects (particles or resonances) as final products of the reaction. These "quasi-two-body processes" will occur more frequently when the multiplicity of the final state is low, i.e., when one or two additional particles are produced.

At high energy, a reaction of this type is also called a "quasi-elastic scattering."[5] The analogy consists of the fact that each of the two produced final "particles" can be associated (as in elastic scattering) with one of the initial particles, in the sense that it "shares" with it one or more quantum numbers (baryon number, strangeness, charge ...). Experiment shows that in analogy with elastic scattering each of the initial particles tends to transfer its state of motion to the corresponding final particle. Thus, an energetic incoming projectile will transform into an energetic final object (particle or resonance), whereas the target particle will give rise to a slowly moving final object. (In the c.m. system, this is the same as saying that the two final objects keep going in the forward and backward directions.) In other words, one of the incident particles, or both, are "excited" to a resonant state, but at high

---

[5] As a particular case of quasi-elastic scattering one can consider the production of two stable particles that are different from the initial ones, e.g., $\pi + N \rightarrow K + Y$. However, such reactions have a very small rate at high energy, and generally we will disregard them. [See, however, Daronian et al. (1966) and SOBB Collaboration (1966b).]

energy the excitation energy is small compared to the total energy available, and the motion of the two colliding particles is not much affected by the occurrence of the reaction.

In high energy quasi-elastic scattering, as in elastic scattering, small momentum transfers between intial and final particles are strongly preferred.

However, the dynamical reasons for such a behavior turn out to be quite different in the two cases. In elastic scattering, the large dominance of forward events is due to the process of diffraction, and the scattering amplitude is mainly imaginary. On the other hand, in quasi-elastic scattering the diffraction is absent, and the preference for low momentum transfers is due to other mechanisms of interaction which have a specific dynamic origin, and which generally produce a large (and even dominant) real part of the scattering amplitude. In a sense, quasi-elastic scattering is closer to charge exchange scattering than to elastic scattering. The interaction mechanisms which seem to be the most suitable for describing quasi-elastic scattering are mainly based on the so-called one-particle-exchange models, discussed in Section V (see also Chapter 3 by Hearn and Drell in this volume).

Quasi-elastic scattering is known to occur copiously as soon as phase space allows the production of the principal meson and nucleon resonances. The most important examples of quasi-elastic reactions are the following:

$$
\begin{array}{ll}
p + p \to N + N^* & \pi + p,\ \pi + n \to \rho + N \\
\qquad\quad\ N^* + N^* & \rho + N^* \\
& \pi + N^* \\
& \omega + N^* \\
K + p,\ K + n \to K^* + N & \omega + N \\
\qquad\qquad\quad\ K + N^* & \eta + N \\
\qquad\qquad\quad\ K^* + N^* & \eta + N^*.
\end{array}
$$

Here N^* indicates the first nucleon isobar ($T = J = \frac{3}{2}$, mass $= 1238$ MeV).

As the energy increases, the higher nucleon isobars, as well as the heavier boson resonances (f^0, A_2, ...) are also produced with increasing rate. However, we will not attempt a systematic review of their production, since the determination of the properties of such objects is still under way, and the knowledge about them is far from being complete.

Of course, $\overline{K}p$ and $\bar{p}p$ will produce the reactions analogous to those listed above, and, in addition, many others which are already open at very low energy (hyperon production for K^-, annihilation for $\bar{p}$).

D. The Experimental Status of High Energy Quasi-Elastic Interactions

1. $\pi^{\pm} p$ Interactions

High energy inelastic $\pi^{\pm} p$ interactions have been extensively studied in the last years, and a vast experimental literature is at present available.[6] The most accurate analyses have been performed with hydrogen bubble chamber techniques at energies not larger than 10 GeV [7]; they are mostly devoted to the study of final states containing a small number of secondary particles, and no more than one neutral reaction product. Such states can be analyzed in full detail with satisfactory statistics: Table II gives a list of such final states, and also indicates the most frequently occurring quasi-elastic channels. Of course, the quasi-elastic channels indicated in the table do not exhaust all possible cases of resonance formation in the final state. Some quasi-elastic channels, accessible in principle, are very rarely observed; a few examples will be discussed in the following.

There is also some work on inelastic $\pi^- p$ and π^- nucleus collisions at energies larger than 10 GeV [Goldsack et al. (1962) (16 GeV/c); Bellini et al. (1963, 1964) (6 and 18 GeV/c); and Jones (1965) (12 and 18 GeV/c)]. In such a case, the experimental analysis becomes much more difficult, and the situation is not so clear as at lower energies. We will not discuss the features of such very high energy collisions in this section.

Final states with many neutral particles cannot be studied in detail and are generally of more limited interest. However, in $\pi^- p$ interactions some supplementary information can be obtained by the analysis in $\pi^+ d$ collisions. Since corresponding final states originated in $\pi^- p$ and $\pi^+ n$ collisions contain

---

[6] We have omitted from the reference list all the works dealing only with the study of the resonances produced in the reactions; we have quoted only those works which contain the study of at least some "dynamical" elements of the processes, and then can be used as a support for the arguments discussed in Section V; also, we have not listed the works performed at incident momenta less than about 1.5 GeV/c. Copious additional references can be found in many of the papers mentioned here.

[7] $\pi^- p$ collisions: SOBB Collaboration (1962, 1963) (1.6 GeV/c); Daudin et al. (1963) (1.6 GeV/c); Carmony et al. (1962) (2.03 GeV/c); Satterblom et al. (1964) (2.1 GeV/c); Gutay et al. (1965) (2 GeV/c); SOBB Collaboration (1965a,b) (2.75 GeV/c); Derado et al. (1964, 1965) (4 GeV/c); ABBBHLM Collaboration (1964a,b) (4 GeV/c); Biswas et al. (1964) (10 GeV/c); and Fleury et al. (1962) (10 GeV/c).

$\pi^+ p$ collisions: Daronian et al. (1966) (1.6 GeV/c); Alff et al. (1962) (2.34, 2.62, and 2.90 GeV/c); Abolins et al. (1963, 1964) (3.54 GeV/c); Goldhaber et al. (1964) (3.65 GeV/c); SOBB Collaboration (1964, 1965c,d, 1966a) (2.75 GeV/c); Yamamoto et al. (1965) (2.77 GeV/c); ABBBHLM Collaboration (1964e, 1965) (4 GeV/c); and ABC Collaboration (1964, 1965a,b) (8 GeV/c).

TABLE II

THE PRINCIPAL REACTIONS ANALYZED IN $\pi^{\pm}p$ COLLISIONS, WITH THE INDICATION OF THE MOST FREQUENTLY OBSERVED QUASI-ELASTIC FINAL STATES[a]

Reaction No.[a]	Observed reaction	Quasi-elastic final states
(1a)	$\pi^+ p \to \pi^+ \pi^0 p$	$\pi^0 N^{*++}, \rho^+ p$
(1b)	$\pi^- p \to \pi^- \pi^0 p$	$\rho^- p$
(2a)	$\pi^+ p \to \pi^+ \pi^+ n$	
(2b)	$\pi^- p \to \pi^+ \pi^- n$	$\rho^0 n, f^0 n$
(3a)	$\pi^+ p \to \pi^+ \pi^+ \pi^- p$	$\pi^+ \pi^- N^{*++}, \rho^0 \pi^+ p, \rho^0 N^{*++}, A_2^+ p$
(3b)	$\pi^- p \to \pi^- \pi^- \pi^+ p$	$\rho^0 \pi^- p, \pi^- \pi^- N^{*++}, A_2^- p$
(4a)	$\pi^+ p \to \pi^+ \pi^+ \pi^- \pi^0 p$	$\pi^+ \pi^- \pi^0 N^{*++}, \omega \pi^+ p, \omega N^{*++}$
(4b)	$\pi^- p \to \pi^- \pi^+ \pi^- \pi^0 p$	$\omega \pi^- p, \pi^- \pi^- \pi^0 N^{*++}$
(5a)	$\pi^+ p \to \pi^+ \pi^+ \pi^+ \pi^- n$	
(5b)	$\pi^- p \to \pi^- \pi^+ \pi^- \pi^+ n$	

[a] Conventional reaction number given for reference in text.

a different number of neutral particles, some of them, which are not experimentally accessible in one case, can be studied in the other. We shall return to this point in Section D,2.

Strange particle production by pions has also been investigated[8]; the relevant cross sections are smaller by one order of magnitude than those for nonstrange final states. There exist some accurate analyses in hydrogen bubble chambers at rather low energy (see SOBB Collaboration, 1966b; Yamamoto et al., 1964; Wangler et al., 1965); at higher energy, the experimental situation becomes less clear.

Table III lists the values of cross sections measured at various incident momenta between 1.6 and 10 GeV/c, including the cross sections for the principal quasi-elastic channels. We have also plotted the above data for reactions (3b), (4b), and (5b), as well as for the quasi-elastic channels available in reaction (3b) [Figs. 17 and 18, taken from SOBB Collaboration, 1965a]. It

[8] SOBB Collaboration (1966b) $\pi^- p$ at 1.59 GeV/c
Yamamoto et al. (1964) $\pi^+ p$ at 2.77 GeV/c
Wangler et al. (1965) $\pi^+ p$ at 3 GeV/c
Bertanza et al. (1963) $\pi^- p$ at 4.65 GeV/c
Wang Kang Chang et al. (1961a,b) π^-'s of ~7 GeV/c
PCTP Collaboration (1963) π^-'s of 6, 11, and 18 GeV/c
Bigi et al. (1964) $\pi^- p$ at 10 GeV/c
Ferbel and Taft (1963) $\pi^- p$ at 11.4 GeV/c
Bartke et al. (1962) $\pi^- p$ at 16 GeV/c

can be seen that all these reactions, both inelastic and quasi-elastic, show a similar energy behavior increasing to a broad maximum and then slowly decreasing [cf. a similar analysis for $\pi^+ p$ collisions, performed by Daronian *et al.* (1966)]. Of course, for reasons of phase space, the increasing trend is slower for the many-particle reactions.

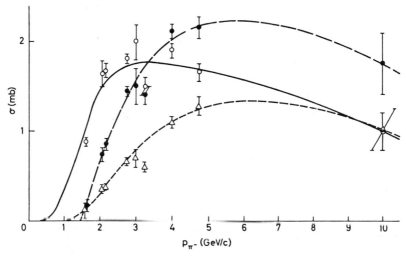

FIG. 17. Energy behavior of the cross sections for reactions (3b), (4b), (5b) of Table II [taken from SOBB Collaboration (1965a)]. See this paper for the experimental bibliography. ($\bigcirc$) $\pi^- p \to \pi^- p \pi^+ \pi^-$, ($\bullet$) $\pi^- p \to \pi^- p \pi^+ \pi^- \pi^0$, and ($\Delta$) $\pi^- p \to \pi^- n \pi^+ \pi^+ \pi^-$.

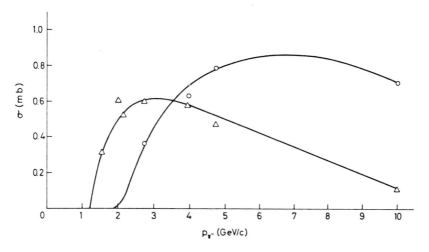

FIG. 18. Energy behavior of the cross sections for the principal quasi-elastic channels in the reaction $\pi^- p \to \pi^- \pi^+ \pi^- p$ [taken from SOBB Collaboration (1965a)]. See this paper for the experimental bibliography. ($\bigcirc$) $\pi^+ p \to p \pi^- \rho^0$ and (Δ) $\pi^- p \to N^{*++} \pi^- \pi^-$.

TABLE III

CROSS SECTIONS FOR THE PRINCIPAL INELASTIC REACTIONS AND THE MOST IMPORTANT QUASI-ELASTIC CHANNELS FROM $\pi^\pm p$ COLLISIONS AT VARIOUS INCIDENT MOMENTA BETWEEN 1.5 AND 10 GeV/c. ERRORS QUOTED ARE STATISTICAL.[a]

Reactions and principal quasi-elastic channels	Cross sections (mb)			
	$p_{inc} = 1.6$ GeV/c[b]	$p_{inc} = 2.75$ GeV/c[c]	$p_{inc} = 4$ GeV/c[d]	$p_{inc} = 10$ GeV/c[e]
$\pi^- p \rightarrow \pi^- \pi^- \pi^+ n$	6.45 ± 0.17	3.9 ± 0.1	3.16 ± 0.13	0.85 ± 0.12
$\rightarrow \rho^0 n$		(~ 1.1)	(0.75 ± 0.13)	
$\pi^- p \rightarrow \pi^- \pi^- \pi^0 p$	4.48 ± 0.15	2.8 ± 0.1	2.21 ± 0.10	0.47 ± 0.09
$\rightarrow \rho^- p$		(~ 0.75)	(0.45 ± 0.08)	
$\pi^- p \rightarrow \pi^- \pi^+ \pi^- p$	0.88 ± 0.04	1.81 ± 0.05	1.91 ± 0.08	1.01 ± 0.21
$\rightarrow \rho^0 \pi^- p$		(~ 0.36)	(~ 0.64)	(0.70 ± 0.10)
$\rightarrow N^{*++} \pi^- \pi^-$		(~ 0.61)	(~ 0.48)	(0.10 ± 0.04)
$\pi^- p \rightarrow \pi^+ \pi^- \pi^- \pi^0 p$	0.18 ± 0.02	1.44 ± 0.05	2.11 ± 0.09	1.77 ± 0.35
$\rightarrow N^{*++} \pi^- \pi^- \pi^0$			(~ 0.10)	(0.36 ± 0.08)
$\rightarrow \omega \pi^- p$			(0.26 ± 0.04)	(0.12 ± 0.05)
$\pi^- p \rightarrow \pi^- \pi^- \pi^- \pi^+ \pi^+ n$	0.12 ± 0.02	0.66 ± 0.03	1.47 ± 0.07	1.03 ± 0.24

	$p_{inc} = 1.6$ GeV/c[f]	$p_{inc} = 2.75$ GeV/c[g]	$p_{inc} = 4$ GeV/c[h]	$p_{inc} = 8$ GeV/c
$\pi^+ p \to \pi^+ \pi^0 p$	9.2 ± 0.2	2.79 ± 0.10	2.31 ± 0.06	0.60 ± 0.03
$\to N^{*++} \pi^0$	(1.25 ± 0.06)	(0.30 ± 0.03)	(0.29 ± 0.03)	(0.11 ± 0.01)
$\to \rho^+ p$	(2.0 ± 0.08)	(0.89 ± 0.10)	(~ 0.35)	(0.17 ± 0.04)
$\pi^+ p \to \pi^+ \pi^+ n$	3.7 ± 0.10	2.41 ± 0.15	1.44 ± 0.05	0.70 ± 0.03
$\pi^+ p \to \pi^+ \pi^- \pi^+ p$	3.3 ± 0.1	3.19 ± 0.17	3.09 ± 0.07	1.99 ± 0.05
$\to N^{*++} \pi^+ \pi^-$	(1.3 ± 0.07)		(~ 1.1)	
$\to \rho^0 \pi^+ p$			(~ 0.65)[l]	m
$\to N^{*++} \rho^0$	k	(~ 0.9)[f]	(0.60 ± 0.18)	(0.43 ± 0.04)
$\pi^+ p \to \pi^+ \pi^- \pi^+ \pi^0 p$	0.5 ± 0.1	3.35 ± 0.10	3.43 ± 0.07	2.10 ± 0.05
		3.87 ± 0.21[j]		
$\to N^{*++} \pi^+ \pi^- \pi^0$	(0.20 ± 0.03)	(1.01 ± 0.05)	(~ 1.1)	
$\to \omega \pi^+ p$	(0.10 ± 0.02)	(0.65 ± 0.02)	(~ 0.5)	
$\to \omega N^{*++}$	k	(~ 1.2)[-j]	(~ 0.35)	(0.10 ± 0.012)
$\pi^+ p \to \pi^+ \pi^+ \pi^+ \pi^- \pi^- n$	0.07 ± 0.02	0.33 ± 0.05[-j]	0.93 ± 0.04	0.75 ± 0.03

[a] The values of the cross sections for the quasi-elastic reactions have been enclosed in parentheses for convenience of reading.

[b] SOBB Collaboration (1963).

[c] SOBB Collaboration (1965a,b).

[d] ABBBHLM Collaboration (1964a,b).

[e] Biswas et al. (1964) and Fleury et al. (1962).

[f] Daronian et al. (1965).

[g] SOBB Collaboration (1964, 1965c,d) and Yamamoto et al. (1965).

[h] ABBBHLM Collaboration (1965).

[i] ABC Collaboration (1965a,c).

[j] Yamamoto et al. (1965).

[k] Below threshold

[l] pA_2^+: ~ 0.35.

[m] pA_2^+: 0.23 ± 0.04.

Generally, π^+p cross sections are larger than π^-p cross sections for analogous reactions, since the former show a strong excitation of the N^{*++} isobar, which cannot be produced in the latter by charge conservation. Actually, the formation of the N^{*++} isobar is one of the dominant features of π^+p interactions; only the formation of vector boson resonances (ρ, ω) can compete with it. Many-particle states originated in π^+p collisions show a remarkable amount of double-resonance production (N^{*++} + ρ, N^{*++} + ω). On the other hand, π^-p collisions are generally dominated by the formation of boson resonances, since isobar excitation is suppressed by isospin factors. However, reactions (3b) and (4b) show a clear evidence of N^{*++} formation, even though not accompanied by another boson resonance.

It has to be pointed out that, in some cases, some apparently "uncorrelated" events can be fitted by the production of heavier boson resonances; for example, it has been shown that a good fraction of the ρ^0 events not fitting the quasi-two-body final state ρ^0 N^{*++} in reaction (3a) can be interpreted as quasi-two-body final states of the type pA$_2{}^+$, where the resonance A$_2{}^+$ decays into $\rho^0\pi^+$ (Goldhaber *et al.*, 1964; Chung *et al.*, 1964; ABBBHLM Collaboration, 1964c; SOBB Collaboration, 1965e).

Five and more final particle states are less favorable for the observation of resonance production (with the exception of the ω meson, when it can be produced). Let us take the example of the $\pi^+\pi^-$ mass spectrum in reaction (5a) (Fig. 19), which in principle should exhibit ρ^0 formation. However, such

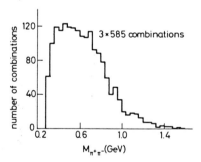

Fig. 19. Experimental distribution in the invariant mass of the systems ($\pi^+\pi^-$) produced in the reaction $\pi^+p \to \pi^+\pi^+\pi^+\pi^-n$ at 4 GeV/c [taken from ABBBHLM Collaboration (1965)].

a spectrum contains a large background, because several $\pi^+\pi^-$ combinations can be made up from the final state. Therefore, the few cases of ρ^0 formation are submerged by the sea of the other fictitious combinations, and their statistical significance is lost. From the analysis of the many-particle final states it can also be concluded that the production of two boson resonances ($\rho + \rho$, $\rho + \omega$) is very unlikely; the vector resonances observed seem to derive from the "excitation" of the incident pion, and likewise the nucleon isobars seem to derive from the excitation of the target nucleon.[9]

From this point of view it can also be understood why the nucleon isobar $N^{*-}(N^{*-} \rightarrow n + \pi^-)$ is rarely observed in reactions (5a,b) (compared to the large rate of production of the symmetric charge state N^{*++} in the other many-particle channels), and even less in reaction (2b).[10] This happens because the initial proton, in order to be excited to an N^{*-}, should transfer two units of charge to the other incident particle. Now, there seems to be evidence that such multiple charge transfers between the initial particles are not favored experimentally especially for the more simple reactions.[11]

There also exists experimental analysis of the many-charged particle systems (six or more in the final states) [Bardadin et al., 1963 (π^-p at 10 GeV/c)]. However, the large number of possible resonant combinations available makes it difficult to draw definite conclusions.

2. π^+d Collisions

Recent investigation has been performed on inelastic π^+d collisions, showing many-pion production with or without disintegration of the deuteron target [Cohn et al. (1965) (3.5 GeV/c); SOBB Collaboration (1965f) (4.5 GeV/c); and SOBBF Collaboration (1965) (4.5 GeV/c)]. In the most frequent case of deuteron disintegration, it is generally possible to consider one of the final nucleons as a "spectator," taking away very little energy, whereas the other nucleon acts as an effective target for the collision. In this way one obtains further information about π^+p interactions, and one can also study π^+n collisions; of course, the latter case is of more interest.

Table IV reports the reaction rates measured at 4.5 GeV/c. For the cases where a comparison can be made with the reaction rates on a "free" nucleon (the π^+n reactions are to be compared with the corresponding charge symmetric π^-p reactions), the cross sections measured in the deuteron reactions turn out to be appreciably lower [cf. the values at a nearby energy (4 GeV/c)

[9] This point is also confirmed by the poor ρ and ω production in nucleon-nucleon collisions (see, for example, Hart et al., 1962; Kidd et al., 1964). However, at 4 GeV/c there seems to be an appreciable ω production [$\sigma(pp \rightarrow pp\omega) \geqslant (0.14 \pm 0.06)$ mb] (Kidd et al., 1963).

[10] At 4 GeV/c, the cross section for N^{*-} production in reaction (2b) is (0.09 ± 0.03) mb (ABBBHLM Collaboration, 1964b); in reaction (5a), it is about 0.25 mb (ABBBHLM Collaboration, 1965). At 10 GeV/c, the cross section for N^{*-} production in reaction (5b) is (0.11 ± 0.05) mb (Biswas et al., 1964).

[11] In the philosophy of single-particle exchange models (see Section II,E and Section V), this fact can be understood in terms of the absence of a doubly charged resonance boson system, which can mediate the interaction. However, the suppression of double charge exchange processes seems to occur also when the exchanged system is a baryon, in spite of the existence of the doubly charged isobar N^{*++}, as in backward π^-p elastic scattering.

TABLE IV

THE PRINCIPAL REACTIONS ANALYZED IN $\pi^+ d$
COLLISIONS AT 4.5 GeV/c (SOBB Collaboration,
1965f; SOBBF Collaboration, 1965) WITH THE
VALUES OF THE MEASURED CROSS SECTIONS[a]

Reactions[b]	Cross sections (mb)
$\pi^+ d \quad \to d\pi^+\pi^+\pi^-$	0.26 ± 0.07
$\pi^+ p(n) \to p\pi^+\pi^+\pi^-(n)$	1.55 ± 0.15
$\pi^+ n(p) \to n\pi^+\pi^+\pi^-(p)$	1.26 ± 0.20
$\pi^+ n(p) \to p\pi^+\pi^-\pi^0(p)$	1.62 ± 0.24
$\pi^+ n(p) \to p\pi^+\pi^-(p)$	1.56 ± 0.04
$\pi^+ n(p) \to p(p) + \text{neutrals}$	0.49 ± 0.02

[a] See the experimental papers for the analysis of
the quasi-elastic channels.
[b] Spectator particle is shown in parentheses.

listed in Table III]. This difference may be due to experimental reasons connected with the difficulties of identifying the various channels correctly (such
as the necessity of a cutoff on the proton momentum, in order to allow
identification by ionization). Therefore, the study of the above-mentioned
reactions has been mainly devoted to the analysis of the many-pion resonances showing up in the mass spectra. Only the reaction $\pi^+ n \to \pi^+\pi^-\pi^0 p$ is of
interest for a dynamical analysis, because its counterpart in $\pi^- p$ collisions
cannot be observed. The most important quasi-elastic channel observed in
this reaction is $\pi^+ n \to \omega p$, studied in particular detail by Cohn et al. (1965).

3. $K^\pm p$ Interactions

In this case also, few-particle final states have been investigated in more
detail by means of hydrogen or deuterium bubble chamber analysis.[12] The
range of energy studied is, however, smaller than for pions (up to 5 GeV/c).

[12] $K^+ p$ collisions: Bettini et al. (1965) (1.45 GeV/c); Goldhaber et al. (1963) (1.96
GeV/c); Lynch et al. (1964) (2.97 GeV/c); Ferro-Luzzi et al.
(1965a,b) (2.97 GeV/c); Ferro-Luzzi et al. (1965c) (3, 3.5, and 5
GeV/c); and Goldhaber et al. (1965) (2.3 GeV/c; also, $K^+ n$);
(1966) (1.96 GeV/c).

$K^- p$ collisions: London et al. (1966) (2.24 GeV/c); Barlotaud et al. (1964) (3 GeV/c);
Focardi et al. (1965b) (3 GeV/c); Haque et al. (1965) (3.5 GeV/c);
and Badier et al. (1965a,b) (3 GeV/c).

Particular attention has been devoted to the reactions $K^{\pm}p \rightarrow K_1{}^0\pi^{\pm}p$, where strong production of the isobar K^* (or $\overline{K}^*$) is observed. For K^+p collisions, N^{*++} production is also very important. Also, four-particle final states have been investigated at low energies. The reaction $K^+p \rightarrow K^+p\pi^+\pi^-$ allows double resonance formation ($N^{*++}K^{*0}$, $K^{*0} \rightarrow K^+\pi^-$). There also exist data for other four-particle final states. Table V gives a survey of the situation for K^+p collisions at 3 GeV/c.

As can be seen from the table, quasi-elastic channels constitute the bulk of Kp inelastic interactions, and there is much less background than in πp collisions. This fact can be visualized from the plots shown in Fig. 20 [taken from Ferro-Luzzi *et al.* (1965a,b)]. Therefore, Kp collisions have so far been one of the favorite tests of the one-particle-exchange models (Sections II,E and V), which generally deal with the production of resonant states and do not account for the background events.

The K^-p interactions can also produce strange isobars (Y^*, Ξ^*, etc.). These reactions have a smaller cross section than the excitation processes of K^* and of nucleon isobars (Badier *et al.*, 1965a,b). It should be pointed out that in order to excite a nucleon to a strange isobar, strangeness must be transferred between the initial particles, and this mechanism might not be favored with respect to the exchange of nonstrange systems.

Processes with three strange particles in the final state (e.g., $K^+p \rightarrow K^+K^+\Lambda$) have an even smaller reaction rate (of the order of 10–20 μb), and have been investigated only in order to discover the possible existence of doubly strange boson resonances (Ferro-Luzzi *et al.*, 1965c).

4. pp and p̄p Interactions

The experimental situation for inelastic proton-proton (or proton-neutron) interactions shows quite a different aspect from that of the cases previously discussed. In fact, a systematic bubble chamber analysis of the same type as previously described for the other reactions is available only up to a rather low energy (incident kinetic energy of the order of 3 GeV),[13] probably because of a greater experimental difficulty in separating the different final states as energy increases. There are only a few bubble chamber works above 3 GeV, generally dealing with the study of particular channels [Alexander *et al.*, 1965b,c) (5.5 GeV/c); and Almeida *et al.* (1965) (10 GeV/c)]. On the

---

[13] *Single-pion production in pp collisions:* Bugg *et al.* (1964) (0.97 GeV kinetic energy (k.e.)); Fickinger *et al.* (1962) (2.0 GeV k.e.); Smith *et al.* (1961) (2.85 GeV k.e.); and Conte *et al.* (1964) (3.16 GeV k.e.).

Double- and multiple-pion production in pp collisions: Pickup *et al.* (1962) (2.0 GeV k.e.); Hart *et al.* (1962) (2.85 GeV k.e.); and Kidd *et al.* (1963, 1964) (4 GeV/c).

np collisions: Rushbrooke *et al.* (1964) (k.e. up to 0.97 GeV).

TABLE V

SUMMARY OF THE EXPERIMENTAL SITUATION FOR INELASTIC K^+p COLLISIONS[a]

Reactions	Incident momentum (GeV/c)	Cross sections (mb)	Quasi-elastic channels and relevant cross sections (mb)	
			$K^+p \to K^{*+}p$ ($K^{*+} \to K^0\pi^+$)	$K^+p \to K^0N^{*++}$
	0.91	1.98 ± 0.20	—	1.9 ± 0.2
	1.14	4.6 ± 0.3	0.9 ± 0.3	3.6 ± 0.5
	1.45	4.9 ± 0.2	2.1 ± 0.2	2.8 ± 0.1
$K^+p \to$ $K^0\pi^+p$	1.96	4.6 ± 0.6	~ 1.5	~ 3
	2.97	2.1 ± 0.3	0.8 ± 0.1	0.8 ± 0.1
	3.45	2.2 ± 0.3	0.8 ± 0.1	0.8 ± 0.1
	4.97	1.0 ± 0.2	0.3 ± 0.1	0.3 ± 0.1
			$K^+p \to K^{*0}N^{*++}$ ($K^{*0} \to K^+\pi^-$) ($K^{*0} \to K^0\pi^0$)	
$K^+p \to$ $K^+p\pi^+\pi^-$	1.96	1.7 ± 0.2		
	2.97	2.3 ± 0.3	1.2 ± 0.2	
$K^+p \to$ $K^0p\pi^+\pi^0$	1.96	1.3 ± 0.2		
	2.97	2.1 ± 0.2	0.46 ± 0.09	
				$K^+p \to K^{*+}N^{*+}$ ($K^{*+} \to K^0\pi^+$) ($N^{*+} \to p\pi^0$) ($N^{*+} \to n\pi^+$)
$K^+p \to$ $K^0n\pi^+\pi^+$	1.96	0.33 ± 0.1		0.18 ± 0.04
	2.97	0.6 ± 0.2		0.11 ± 0.05

[a] Data for three-particle final states taken from Ferro-Luzzi et al. (1965a). Data for four-particle final states taken from Ferro-Luzzi et al. (1965b). See Ferro-Luzzi et al. (1965a,b) for detailed experimental bibliography.

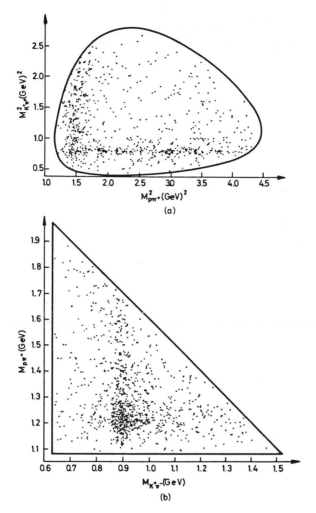

FIG. 20.   (a) Dalitz plot for the reaction $K^+p \to K^0\pi^+p$ at 3.0 GeV/c (747 events) [taken from Ferro-Luzzi *et al.* (1965a)]. The closed line indicates phase-space boundary. (b) "Scatter plot" of the effective masses of the two-particle systems $(p\pi^+)$ and $(K^+\pi^-)$ produced in the reaction $K^+p \to K^+\pi^+\pi^-p$ at 3.0 GeV/c (1009 events) [taken from Ferro-Luzzi *et al.* (1965b)]. The triangle corresponds to phase-space boundary.

other hand, counter experiments are much more productive for protons than for other projectiles, because of the very high intensity available in proton beams. Therefore, at present a good deal of experimental information on *pp* inelastic interactions is available under the form of fixed-angle momentum spectra of the scattered protons (or of other final particles), obtained from high statistics counter experiments.[14]

We shall then discuss separately the two energy regions below and above 3 GeV. In the first region, mainly studied through bubble chamber analysis, the dominating channel is $pp \to NN^*$, which absorbs a large fraction (more than 50% at 2.85 GeV) of the events of single-pion production, especially through the reaction $pp \to nN^{*++}$. The fraction of double isobar production events in the reactions of double-pion production is smaller, because charge conservation prevents the formation of two full isobars, and isospin factors depress the reaction rate. All the reactions of single-pion production and the principal features of the processes of double-pion production can be adequately described by the so-called one-pion-exchange model (Ferrari and Selleri, 1962) (see Sections V,B and V,D). In the reactions of double-pion production, there is no evidence for the formation of pionic resonances (Kidd et al., 1964), in agreement with the predictions of the one-pion-exchange model.

As the energy increases beyond 3 GeV, the experimental situation becomes less and less clear. We have already mentioned that experimental fixed angle proton momentum spectra are available. By the kinematics, a momentum spectrum at fixed angle in the laboratory system is equivalent to a doubly differential spectrum in the variables t and M^* (where t is the momentum transfer between the measured and the incident (or target) particle; and M^* is the mass of the "object" produced together with the measured proton). Thus the study of such spectra, even without separating the various final states, allows one to detect the excitation of nucleon isobars in reactions of the type $pp \to pN^{*+}$. (Here the N* must be singly charged for charge conservation, and can be any of the nucleon isobars.)

Such isobars appear as peaks in the momentum spectrum, and are generally superimposed on a large background; from their height it is possible to attempt a rough evaluation of the isobar production rate as a function of the energy and of the momentum transfer. We report here on experiments which have been performed at CERN in the energy range from 3 to 26 GeV (Cocconi et al., 1961a,b, 1964; Bellettini et al., 1965b), and with different values of the momentum transfer t.[15]

---

[14] Chadwick et al. (1962) (1.3, 2.1, and 2.9 GeV k.e.); Melissions et al. (1962) (2.85 GeV k.e.); Reay et al. (1966) (2.0, 2.4, and 2.85 GeV k.e.); Cocconi et al. (1961a,b) (9 to 26 GeV/c); Cocconi et al. (1964) (3.6 to 11.8 GeV/c); Bellettini et al. (1965b) (10.0, 19.3, and 26.4 GeV/c); and Ankenbrandt et al. (1965) (7.1 GeV/c).

[15] The results of experiments below 3 GeV are in agreement with the predictions of the one-pion-exchange model which fit the bubble chamber experiments (Ferrari et al., 1965).

At low energy, the production of N_{33}^{*+} is strongly observed.[16] However, as the energy and the momentum transfer increase the production rate drops very rapidly, and at incident energies around 8 GeV no enhancement of the N_{33}^{*} isobar above background is observed.[17] On the other hand, there is strong evidence for the production of the higher $T = \frac{1}{2}$ isobars, N_{13}^{*} and N_{15}^{*}, which, at an angle of 60 mrad in the lab. system, show up at all energies from 6 to 19 GeV [$|t|$ lies in the range between 0.1 and $1(GeV/c)^2$]. However, if the momentum transfer is made very small (scattering angle of a few milli-radians) the above-mentioned isobars, as well as the 33 resonance, are not clearly seen, and instead there appears a bump corresponding to an isobar mass of 1400 MeV probably belonging to an isobar N_{11}^{*} associated with a resonant behavior of the $P_{1/2}$ wave in pion-nucleon scattering (Bareyre et al., 1964, 1965; Roper, 1964; Auvil et al., 1964). The same effect is observed also in proton-deuteron inelastic collisions (Bellettini et al., 1965b).

There exist different theoretical interpretations of the appearance of this peak, which has also been conjectured to be a reflection of a kinematical effect (Ankenbrandt et al., 1965). However, the whole question of the production of nucleon isobars in inelastic pp collisions, with its strong dependence on energy and momentum transfer, is still not understood, and to our knowledge no successful predictions have been calculated from any "workable" theoretical model. In Fig. 21 we show some typical spectra of inelastically scattered protons showing the variations of the production rate for the various isobars, taken from Cocconi et al. (1964) and Bellettini et al. (1965b).

Strange particle production by protons turns out to be very weak at low energies [(Louttit et al. (1961) (2.85 GeV, kinetic energy); Alexander et al. (1964) (5.5 GeV/c)] (at about 3 GeV, the cross sections for the individual channels are of the order of some tens of μb). At higher energies, again the detailed investigation becomes more difficult [(Bartke et al., 1963) (24.5 GeV/c)].

For $\bar{p}p$ collisions, here we report only about the reactions where the antinucleon and the nucleon are still present in the final state, by neglecting the complex phenomenon of annihilation whose rate is strongly decreasing with energy. In principle, pion production in $\bar{p}p$ collisions should be described by the same mechanism as in pp and pn collisions, by taking into account the different isospin channels in the two cases. In particular, the one-pion-exchange model should be expected to give a good description of inelastic $\bar{p}p$ reactions. Experimental analysis has been performed up to an incident

[16] We have used the notation N_{ij}^{*} for a nucleon isobar having isospin $T = \frac{1}{2}i$ and spin $J = \frac{1}{2}j$. The isobar previously indicated by N^* is now called N_{33}^{*}.

[17] However, it must be mentioned that the bubble chamber experiment at 10 GeV/c (Almeida et al., 1965) still shows a strong formation of the doubly charged N^{*++} isobar.

momentum of 7 GeV/c, especially by bubble chamber techniques.[18] As far as the predictions of the one-pion-exchange model are concerned, there are some points of agreement and others of disagreement with experiment; the latter probably suggest a final state interaction. Section V,D contains a brief discussion of these effects.

Finally, we mention the interesting cases of strange baryon-antibaryon production in $\bar{p}p$ collisions, which present very peculiar features (the produced antibaryon and baryon keep going forward and backward in the c.m., respectively [Baltay *et al.* (1964b, 1965) (3.7 GeV/c); Böck *et al.* (1965) (5.7 GeV/c); and Musgrave *et al.* (1965) (3.0, 3.6, and 4.0 GeV/c)]. Also these reactions have been studied in terms of one-particle-exchange models, corrected for absorption (see chapter 3 by Hearn and Drell, this volume).

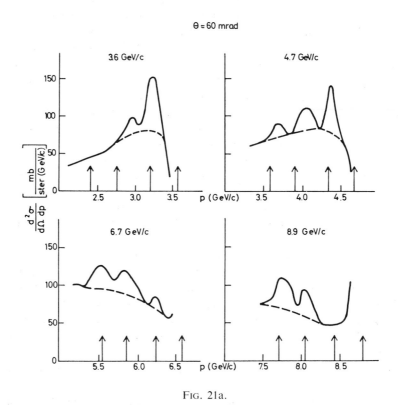

FIG. 21a.

[18] Lynch (1961) (1.61 GeV/c); Lynch *et al.* (1963) (1.61 GeV/c); Czyzewski *et al.* (1963) (3.0 and 4.0 GeV/c); Dehne *et al.* (1964a,b) (3.6 GeV/c); BHM Collaboration (1965) (3.6 and 5.7 GeV/c); Baltay *et al.* (1964a) (3.69 GeV/c); Ferbel *et al.* (1965b) (3.3 and 3.7 GeV/c); and Ferbel *et al.* (1965c,d) (7 GeV/c).

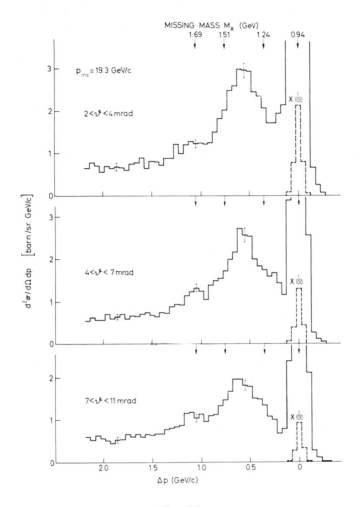

FIG. 21b.

FIG. 21. Examples of proton lab. momentum spectra at a fixed angle in the lab. system, measured in the CERN experiments of inelastic proton-proton scattering: (a) spectra at fixed angle and different incident momenta (indicated on top of the curves), showing the disappearance of the 33-resonance peak (Cocconi *et al.*, 1964); (b) spectra at fixed incident momentum and various angular ranges in the very small angle region, showing the enhancement of the 1400-MeV peak (Bellettini *et al.*, 1965b). The vertical arrows indicate the positions corresponding to the excitation of the isobars N_{15}^*, N_{13}^*, N_{33}^*, and to the position of the elastic peak (from left to right). The elastic peak is not shown in (a), where the dashed lines indicates the supposed behavior of the nonresonant background. In (b), the momentum scale is measured (toward the left) in terms of the distance from the elastic peak.

E. Characteristic Features of Quasi-Elastic Interactions

Among the quasi-elastic interactions previously discussed, quasi-two-body final states are the easiest to analyze. The most straightforward investigation which can be carried out in these cases is the study of the distribution in the momentum transfer t between one of the final isobars and the corresponding initial particle. This distribution is expected to be of particular interest also for quasi-two-body inelastic reactions, as it was for elastic and charge exchange scattering. Even in the many-particle quasi-elastic channels, where only one resonance is clearly excited [such as the final state $N^{*++}\pi^-\pi^-$ in reaction (3b) of Table II], it is possible to study the momentum transfer distribution between the produced isobar and the corresponding initial particle (such as the momentum transfer between N^{*++} and initial proton in the above-mentioned example).

The experimental analyses of such momentum transfer distributions always show a large accumulation of low momentum transfer events, which give rise to an appreciable "forward" peak especially in quasi-two-body reaction. Obviously, a diffractive picture (as in elastic scattering) cannot account for this effect[19] which must be ascribed to other mechanisms of interaction; the picture which has become the most popular in the last years accounts for the preference for low momentum transfers by assuming that the dominant mechanism of interaction is given by the exchange of a single virtual particle, stable or unstable, between the initial particles; in other words, by describing the quasi-two-body reactions as occurring through a graph of the type shown in Fig. 22. Especially when the exchanged particle is light (pion), it can be shown that this mechanism actually enhances the low momentum transfer events. At this point, we only say that the hypothesis of dominance of single-particle-exchange graphs has been worked out on the basis of models (one-particle-exchange models) which have to contain additional assumptions on the interaction mechanism in order to make practical calculations possible. In the frame of such models, besides the t distribution, the angular correlations among the decay products of the resonances also turn out to be particularly important (Gottfried and Jackson, 1964a). A brief discussion of the one-particle-exchange models and of their comparison with experiment is given in Section V. For a thorough treatment of this subject, see chapter 3 by Hearn and Drell, this volume. The agreement with experiment is generally good, with the limitations and the drawbacks which make a model different from a theory. In any case, it can be stated that so far one-particle-exchange effects seem to play a major role in the description of inelastic interactions.

---

[19] It should be noted, however, that the coherent droplet model of Byers and Yang (see Section IV,A) has been applied with good results to the quasi-two-body reactions from π^+p at 8 GeV/c (ABC Collaboration, 1964) by Białas (1966).

FIG. 22. One-particle-exchange diagram for the description of quasi-elastic processes: *a* and *b* represent the initial particles, *c* and *d* the final particles (stable or unstable); *e* is a virtual particle (stable or unstable) exchanged between *a* and *b*, and interacting with them so as to excite them to *c* and *d*.

Another possible explanation of isobar excitation at high energy is given by the so-called picture of the "diffraction dissociation" (Good and Walker, 1960) a brief account of which will be given in Section V,E.

F. INELASTIC PROCESSES WITH MANY-PARTICLE PRODUCTION

As we have already pointed out, the most characteristic features of high energy inelastic interactions are shown by the processes of resonance production. The analysis of the "nonresonant" background seems to have a limited interest. More interesting examples of many-particle production at low energy are provided by antiproton-proton annihilation, which can also be used for the study of the properties of the resonant states.[20]

As energy becomes very high (well beyond the limits at present reached by particle accelerators) since the average multiplicity is expected to increase, many-particle final states are expected to become of increasing importance. A preliminary insight into how very high energy inelastic reactions can look can be obtained from study of the collisions of ultra-energetic primary cosmic rays (which can attain energies of some hundreds or thousands of GeV). Such events are analyzed in nuclear emulsions exposed at a high altitude (ICEF Collaboration, 1963). The characteristic feature which seems to dominate such ultra-high energy reactions is the formation of the so-called "fireballs," i.e., groups of many particles apparently coming from an isotropic decay of a heavy "excited" object, originated from one of the initial particles. Section VI,A contains a brief discussion of these effects[21].

III. General Properties of the Scattering Amplitude

A. UNITARITY, CROSSING, AND ANALYTICITY

For the strong interactions at high energies there is really no theory; therefore, one has to use a more or less phenomenological approach based on a few general properties.

[20] See chapter by Armenteros and French in Volume III of this treatise.
[21] They are discussed more fully in this volume by Kidd.

The general properties, which are certainly or probably valid, are in decreasing order of likely validity: (1) unitarity, (2) crossing relation, and (3) analyticity properties.

We shall now briefly discuss the meaning and consequences of those properties that concern high energy hadron physics.

1. The Unitarity Condition

This expresses the general law of the conservation of probability, and can be mathematically realized by saying that the S operator is unitary, i.e.

$$SS^+ = 1. \tag{III-1}$$

Suppose there is a reaction transforming the initial state $|i\rangle$, which asymptotically contains two particles with four-momenta p_1 and p_2,[22] into a final state $|f\rangle$ containing n particles with four-momenta $p_3, p_4, \ldots, p_{n+2}$. If one defines the coefficients

$$n_p = \frac{(2p_0)^{1/2}(2\pi)^{3/2} \quad \text{for the bosons (p_0 is the energy of the boson)}}{(E/m)^{1/2}(2\pi)^{3/2} \quad \text{for the fermions (E is the energy of the fermion of mass m)}} \tag{III-2}$$

then one can define from the matrix element S_{if} of the S operator the scattering amplitude T_{if} by means of the relation[23]

$$S_{if} = \delta_{if} + (2\pi)^4 i \delta^{(4)}\left(p_1 + p_2 - \sum_{i=3}^{n+2} p_i\right) \frac{T_{if}}{n_{p_1} n_{p_2} n_{p_3} \cdots n_{p_{n+2}}}. \tag{III-3}$$

The unitarity condition for the scattering amplitude is then

$$T_{if} - T_{fi}^* = i \sum_n (2\pi)^4 \delta^{(4)}(p_1 + p_2 - p_n) T_{ni}^* T_{nf} / \Pi n_n^{\ 2}, \tag{III-4}$$

where the sum runs over all the possible intermediate states $|n\rangle$ with total four-momentum p_n, allowed by the energy-momentum conservation (expressed by the δ function) and the selection rules of the process.

If time reversal invariance is valid (as is usually assumed in strong interactions), one has ($T_{if} = T_{fi}$)

$$T_{if} - T_{fi}^* = 2i \text{ Im } T_{if}$$

[22] We shall use the metric $1, -1, -1, -1$.

[23] Here and in the following, symbols like S_{if}, $T_{in} \ldots$ will denote the matrix elements $\langle f|S|i\rangle$, $\langle n|T|i\rangle \ldots$. In the following equations, the symbols Πn_n, Πn_f will denote the product of the factors n_p (Eq.III-2) relevant to all the particles contained in the states $|n\rangle$, $|f\rangle$.

and the unitarity condition becomes

$$\text{Im } T_{if} = \tfrac{1}{2} \sum_n (2\pi)^4 \delta^{(4)}(p_1 + p_2 - p_n) \frac{T_{ni}^* T_{nf}}{\Pi n_n{}^2}. \qquad \text{(III-5)}$$

In general we shall denote the real and imaginary parts of the scattering amplitude by D and A: $T = D + iA$.

The importance of the T matrix lies in the fact that it is relativistically invariant; from it one can derive the cross section for the process connecting the initial state $|i\rangle$ and the final state $|f\rangle$ with total four-momentum p_f [24]

$$d\sigma_f = (2\pi)^4 \frac{\delta^{(4)}(p_1 + p_2 - p_f)(2\pi)^6 |T_{if}|^2}{n_1{}^2 n_2{}^2 \Pi n_f{}^2 |v_1 - v_2|} d_3 p_3 \dots d_3 p_f$$

$$= (2\pi)^4 \frac{\delta^{(4)}(p_1 + p_2 - p_f)|T_{if}|^2}{\Phi \cdot \Pi n_f{}^2} d_3 p_3 \dots d_3 p_f \qquad \text{(III-6)}$$

where $|v_1 - v_2|$ is the relative velocity of the initial particles, and we have written Φ for

$$\Phi = n_1{}^2 n_2{}^2 \frac{|v_1 - v_2|}{(2\pi)^6}. \qquad \text{(III-6a)}$$

In particular, if one considers the elastic reactions[25], one obtains the following expressions for the differential cross section in the c.m. system (where s is the square of the total energy in the c.m., m is the mass of the fermion,

---

[24] For more details, see any book of advanced quantum mechanics or, for instance, the review article of Gasiorowicz (1960); this form of the flux factor Φ is valid only for collinear scattering (into that category fall the laboratory and center-of-mass frames of references); in the general case one has the explicitly covariant form

$$\Phi = ((p_1 \cdot p_2)^2 - m_2{}^2 m_1{}^2)^{1/2} G$$

where

$$G = 2/m \quad \begin{array}{ll} 4 & \text{for (III-7a) and (III-7b)} \\ & \text{for (III-7c)} \\ 1/m^2 & \text{for (III-7d).} \end{array}$$

[25] Here the term *elastic* is meant in a general way as a two-particle into two-particle reaction:

Boson	+ Boson	→ Boson	+ Boson	B + B → B + B
Boson	+ Boson	→ Fermion	+ Antifermion	B + B → F + $\overline{\text{F}}$
Boson	+ Fermion	→ Boson	+ Fermion	B + F → B + F
Fermion	+ Fermion	→ Fermion	+ Fermion	F + F → F + F

and μ is the mass of the boson):

$$B + B \rightarrow B + B \qquad \frac{d\sigma}{d\Omega} = \frac{1}{(2\pi)^2} \frac{1}{16s} |T|^2 \qquad \text{(III-7a)}$$

$$B + B \rightarrow F + \bar{F} \qquad \frac{d\sigma}{d\Omega} = \frac{1}{(2\pi)^2} \left(\frac{s - 4m^2}{s - 4\mu^2}\right)^{1/2} \frac{m^2}{4s} |T|^2 \qquad \text{(III-7b)}$$

$$B + F \rightarrow B + F \qquad \frac{d\sigma}{d\Omega} = \frac{1}{(2\pi)^2} \frac{m^2}{4s} |T|^2 \qquad \text{(III-7c)}$$

$$\begin{matrix} F + F \rightarrow F + F \\ F + \bar{F} \rightarrow F + \bar{F} \end{matrix} \qquad \frac{d\sigma}{d\Omega} = \frac{1}{(2\pi)^2} \frac{m^4}{s} |T|^2. \qquad \text{(III-7d)}$$

In a concise way the truly elastic differential cross sections, Eqs. (III-7a), (III-7c), and (III-7d) can be represented as

$$\frac{d\sigma}{d\Omega} = \frac{1}{(2\pi)^2} \left(\frac{q}{\Phi}\right) |T|^2 \qquad \text{(III-8a)}$$

where q is the c.m. momentum and,

$$\Phi = \begin{cases} 4q\sqrt{s} & \text{for (III-7a)} \\ 2q(s/m)^{1/2} & \text{for (III7c)} \\ q(s/m^2)^{1/2} & \text{for (III-7d).} \end{cases} \qquad \text{(III-8b)}$$

It is also useful to introduce the scattering amplitude $f(q, \cos\Theta)$ such that

$$\frac{d\sigma}{d\Omega} = |f(q, \cos\Theta)|^2. \qquad \text{(III-9)}$$

One can verify immediately that the relation between the T amplitude and the f amplitude is

$$T = 2\pi(\Phi/q)f. \qquad \text{(III-10)}$$

From the general formula (III-6) one can derive the expression for the total cross section starting from the initial state $|i\rangle$

$$\sigma_T = \sum_f \frac{(2\pi)^4 \delta^{(4)}(p_1 + p_2 - p_f)|T_{if}|^2}{\Phi \cdot \Pi n_f^2}. \qquad \text{(III-11)}$$

Comparing Eq. (III-11) and the unitarity condition (III-5) taken for $|f\rangle = |i\rangle$ (elastic coherent scattering in the forward direction), one gets

$$A(\Theta = 0) = \text{Im } T_{ii} = \frac{1}{2} \sum_f (2\pi)^4 \delta^{(4)}(p_1 + p_2 - p_f) \frac{|T_{if}|^2}{\Pi n_f^2} = \frac{\Phi}{2} \sigma_T. \qquad \text{(III-12)}$$

This is the expression of the optical theorem, relating the imaginary part of the scattering amplitude in the forward direction at a given energy and the total cross section for the same initial state at the same energy. This important relation is solely a consequence of the conservation of probability.

One of the consequences of the optical theorem is that it sets a minimum to the value of the elastic cross section in the forward direction. In fact one has

$$\left(\frac{d\sigma}{d\Omega}\right)_{\Theta=0} = \left(\frac{q}{2\pi\Phi}\right)^2 (D^2 + A^2)_{\Theta=0} \geqslant \left(\frac{q}{2\pi\Phi}\right)^2 \cdot \left(\frac{\Phi\sigma_T}{2}\right)^2 = \left(\frac{q\sigma_T}{4\pi}\right)^2. \qquad \text{(III-13)}$$

The minimum value $(q\sigma_T/4\pi)^2$ of the forward differential cross section is usually referred to as the optical value.

2. The Crossing Relation

We shall now restrict ourselves to the case where two initial particles go into only two final particles. The T matrix for such a process is usually represented by the graph of Fig. 23.

FIG. 23.   Diagrammatic representation of the scattering amplitude: p_1 and p_2 are incoming, p_3 and p_4 outgoing four vectors.

The scattering amplitude T is a function of the two independent invariants one can form from the four four-vectors p_1, p_2, p_3, p_4, subjected to the condition of energy-momentum conservation

$$p_1 + p_2 = p_3 + p_4$$

and the mass shell conditions

$$p_i^2 = m_i^2; \qquad i = 1, 2, 3, 4$$

expressing the fact that the initial and final particles are physical ones.

In the channel in which the particles 1 and 2 are the initial particles of the scattering, one usually chooses as independent variables

$$s = (p_1 + p_2)^2 \qquad t = (p_1 - p_3)^2. \qquad \text{(III-14)}$$

It is important to notice that the threshold of the channel is given by the value $s_0 = (m_1 + m_2)^2$.

The meaning of these two invariants is very simple: s is equal to the square of the total energy (rest masses included) in the c.m., t is the momentum transfer between the particles 1 and 3.

In order to discuss the other two scattering channels and the crossing relation, it is useful to define the three Mandelstam variables

$$s = (p_1 + p_2)^2 \qquad t = (p_1 - p_3)^2 \qquad u = (p_1 - p_4)^2$$

connected by the relation

$$s + t + u = m_1{}^2 + m_2{}^2 + m_3{}^2 + m_4{}^2. \tag{III-15}$$

The three scattering channels are defined as:

Channel s: p_1 and p_2 are the four-momenta of the initial particles; s is a timelike invariant, t and u are spacelike; the threshold is $s_0 = (m_1 + m_2)^2$.

Channel t: p_1 and $-p_3$ are the four-momenta of the initial particles; t is timelike, s and u spacelike; the threshold is $t_0 = (m_1 + m_3)^2$.

Channel u: p_1 and $-p_4$ are the four-momenta of the initial particles; u is timelike, s and t spacelike; the threshold is $u_0 = (m_1 + m_4)^2$.

One can easily verify that the physical regions of the three channels (namely, the values of s, t, and u for which a physical process can take place) do not overlap.

The crossing relation connects the three channels and asserts that the same analytic function of the complex variables s, t, and u describes the scattering amplitude in all the three channels.[26]

3. *The Analyticity Properties*

In order to give a meaning to the crossing relation, it is necessary that the scattering amplitude satisfy some analyticity properties. In fact, as we have already said, the physical intervals of the variables s, t, and u for the scattering in the three channels are not connected; therefore, one must have a way of connecting up the scattering amplitudes in the three regions, which otherwise would not be the same analytic function in three different intervals of the variables (as the crossing relation asserts), but three completely disconnected functions.

One can list different kinds of analyticity properties of the scattering amplitudes, depending on the general postulates with which one starts.

(1) If one takes only the postulates of the axiomatic field theory (Bros

---

[26] This simple form of the crossing relation is valid when all the four particles 1–4 are spinless particles without internal degrees of freedom; when they possess spin or other internal variables one can easily analyze both the Lorentz and internal properties of the scattering amplitude.

et al., 1965a,b), it is possible to show that the scattering amplitude for the channel s, $T(s, t)$ is, for $t \leqslant 0$, the boundary value $\lim T(s + i\varepsilon, t)$ of an analytic function of the complex variable s, analytic in the complex upper-half-plane of s, *minus a finite region*. The physical region of the channel s

$$\left[\left(m_1{}^2 - \frac{t}{4} \right)^{1/2} + \left(m_2{}^2 - \frac{t}{4} \right)^{1/2} \right]^2 < s < \infty$$

lies entirely on the boundary of the domain.

Moreover, the analytic continuation of $T(s, t)$ to negative s is given by the relation

$$\lim_{\varepsilon \to 0} \left[T(s + i\varepsilon, t) = T^*(u - i\varepsilon, t) \right] \qquad \text{(III-16)}$$

where [see Eq. (III-15)]

$$u = \sum m_i{}^2 - t - s.$$

One still has the property that the physical region of the channel u lies on the boundary of the analyticity domain.

Therefore one arrives at the way to perform the analytic continuation from channel s to channel u through the analyticity domain; the relation (III-16) provides the mathematical expression to the crossing relation.

A similar property can be also shown to be valid between channels s and t at fixed u.

(2) One can enlarge the postulates by assuming analyticity properties so that a one-dimensional dispersion relation holds. Property (2) is, of course, more stringent than property (1); in fact, it requires the scattering amplitude to be analytic in all the upper half of the complex energy plane. Therefore, if one also makes the hypothesis that the scattering amplitude is polynomially bounded at infinity, one can write for $T(s, t)$ the integral representation

$$T(s, t) = \text{poles} + \frac{1}{\pi} \int_{s_0}^{\infty} \frac{\text{Im } T(s', t)}{s' - s} \, ds' + \frac{1}{\pi} \int_{u_0}^{\infty} \frac{\text{Im } T(u', t)}{u' - u} \, du' \qquad \text{(III-17)}$$

where the cuts lie on the real s axis, both on the positive and negative side, starting from the threshold s_0 and u_0 of the s and u channels. The poles are due to the stable bound states or particles which have the same quantum numbers as the s and u channels.

The one-dimensional dispersion relation, such as Eq. (III-17), can also be derived from axiomatic field theory for some processes (as, for instance, πp scattering) and for some limited values of the momentum transfer.

The dispersion relation takes the simple form (III-17) if the behavior of the function $T(s, t)$ at infinity in the upper half of the complex energy plane is limited by

$$\lim_{|s| \to \infty} s^\alpha T(s, t) = 0 \qquad \text{for any} \quad \alpha < 0.$$

If, on the contrary, we have only the less stringent condition on the growth of the amplitude

$$\lim_{|s| \to \infty} s^\alpha T(s, t) = 0 \qquad \text{for} \quad \alpha < -N \text{ (N positive integer)}$$

one can apply the Cauchy theorem to the function

$$T(s, t)/(s - s_1)^N$$

where s_1 is a fixed value, and one gets

$$T(s, t) = \text{poles} + \sum_{n=0}^{N-1} \frac{(s - s_1)^n}{n!} T^{(n)}(s, t)$$

$$+ \frac{(s - s_1)^N}{\pi} \int_{s_0}^\infty \frac{A(s', t)ds'}{(s' - s)(s' - s_1)^N}$$

$$+ \frac{(s - s_1)^N}{\pi} \int_{u_0}^\infty \frac{A(u', t)du'}{(u' - u)(s' - s_1)^N}. \qquad \text{(III-17a)}$$

One usually says that Eq. (III-17a) is an N-times subtracted dispersion relation, since one could reach the same result by assuming Eq. (III-17) to be (formally) valid and subtracting from it $T(s_1, t)$ and the first $N - 1$ derivatives $T^{(n)}(s_1, t)$.

(3) One can then be more optimistic and assume for $T(s, t)$ the maximal analyticity properties, expressed by the Mandelstam representation.

The Mandelstam representation is a spectral representation of the scattering amplitude, satisfying the following requirements:

(a) $T(s, t)$ is an analytic function of two independent variables (for instance, s and t);
(b) at the same time it satisfies unitarity in all the three channels, as is required by the crossing theorem;
(c) it possesses only those singularities which are required by the unitarity condition. The representation is mathematically written as

$$T(s, t, u) = \text{poles} + \frac{1}{\pi} \int_{s_0}^\infty \frac{\sigma_1(s')}{s' - s} ds' + \frac{1}{\pi} \int_{t_0}^\infty \frac{\sigma_2(t')}{t' - t} dt' + \frac{1}{\pi} \int_{u_0}^\infty \frac{\sigma_3(u')}{u' - u} du'$$

$$+ \frac{1}{\pi^2} \int_{s_0}^\infty \int_{t_0}^\infty \frac{\rho_{12}(s', t')}{(s' - s)(t' - t)} ds' dt'$$

$$+ \frac{1}{\pi^2} \int_{s_0}^\infty \int_{u_0}^\infty \frac{\rho_{13}(s', u')}{(s' - s)(u' - u)} ds' du'$$

$$+ \frac{1}{\pi^2} \int_{u_0}^\infty \int_{t_0}^\infty \frac{\rho_{23}(u', t')}{(u' - u)(t' - t)} du' dt'. \qquad \text{(III-18)}$$

(This is the nonsubtracted form.) In Eq. (III-18) the lower limits of integration of the simple and double spectral integrals are the thresholds of the channels s, t, and u. The spectral (real) functions σ_j and ρ_{ij} are the simple and double discontinuities across the cuts in the complex s and t (or u) plane.

The great usefulness of Eq. (III-18) is that it gives the most analytic form of the two-body scattering amplitude which is at the same time compatible with unitarity and crossing.

So far, the Mandelstam representation has not been derived from general principles; it has only been checked for many Feynman diagrams, although there are examples of Feynman diagrams exhibiting complex singularities which violate the Mandelstam representation.

B. THE GENERAL THEOREMS ON HIGH ENERGY SCATTERING

We now want to discuss some general theorems which can be derived for high energy hadron scattering as a consequence of the general properties we have already discussed.

The general theorems are essentially of three kinds:

(1) Theorems which assert that at high energy the total cross sections for the scattering on a given target of particles, which belong to a multiplet of a symmetry group, must be equal.

(2) Theorems relating at high energy the total cross sections for the scattering on a given target of a particle and its antiparticle.

(3) Upper and lower bounds on the high energy behavior of the scattering amplitude.

The first two kinds of theorems are known as Pomeranchuk-Okun and Pomeranchuk theorems, respectively; the prototype of a result of the third kind is the Froissart theorem, which concerns the high energy behavior of the total cross section. We shall now discuss separately the three kinds of theorems.

1. The Pomeranchuk-Okun Theorems

The theorem (Pomeranchuk, 1956; Okun and Pomeranchuk, 1956), which asserts that asymptotically the total cross sections on a given target of the particles belonging to the same multiplet of a symmetry group are equal, is based on the phenomenological observation that at high energies the total elastic cross section still constitutes an appreciable fraction of the total cross section, in spite of the large number of inelastic channels. Moreover, among the large number of inelastic reactions, any two-particle–two-particle reaction in which some quantum numbers are exchanged between the initial and final particles must have a cross section (which is only *a part* of the total inelastic cross section) negligible in comparison with the truly elastic one. From this fact, one deduces the asymptotic equality of the total cross sections for different initial particles.

In order to be definite, let us choose a particular example. If we consider πp scattering, we can list five processes with one pion and one nucleon in the final state:

$$
\begin{array}{ccc}
(1) & (2) & (3) \\
\pi^+ p \to \pi^+ p & \pi^0 p \to \pi^0 p & \pi^0 p \to \pi^+ n
\end{array}
$$

$$
\begin{array}{cc}
(4) & (5) \\
\pi^- p \to \pi^- p & \pi^- p \to \pi^0 n.
\end{array}
$$

(III-19)

Owing to isospin conservation, the two amplitudes T^1 and T^3, corresponding to a total isospin $T = \frac{1}{2}$ and $T = \frac{3}{2}$ describe the process, and we have

$$
\frac{d\sigma_1}{d\Omega} = |T^3|^2 \qquad\qquad \frac{d\sigma_3}{d\Omega} = \frac{d\sigma_5}{d\Omega} = \frac{2}{9}|T^3 - T^1|^2
$$

$$
\frac{d\sigma_2}{d\Omega} = \frac{1}{9}|2T^3 + T^1|^2 \qquad \frac{d\sigma_4}{d\Omega} = \frac{1}{9}|T^3 + 2T^1|^2.
$$

(III-20)

If we now compare processes (4) and (5) of Eq. (III-19) [or equivalently (2) and (3) of (III-19)], we see that process (5) of (III-19) is a charge exchange reaction; since it is only one of the many processes which are in competition in order to form the total inelastic $\pi^- p$ cross section, it is reasonable to believe that the charge exchange cross section (5) of (III-19) is only a small fraction of the total $\pi^- p$ inelastic cross section, and therefore also of the elastic cross section (4) of (III-19), which we know to be comparable with the total $\pi^- p$ cross section.

One must therefore have

$$
|T^3 - T^1| \ll |T^3 + 2T^1|
$$

which implies

$$
T^3 \simeq T^1.
$$

(III-21)

Of course, this relation should be better satisfied at larger energies, when more and more channels are opening; in order to indicate that a relation such as (III-21) is satisfied when the energy increases we shall write

$$
T^3 \rightleftharpoons T^1
$$

As a consequence of relation (III-21), all the amplitudes for the truly elastic reactions (III-19) become asymptotically equal

$$
T_{(1)} \rightleftharpoons T_{(2)} \rightleftharpoons T_{(4)}.
$$

(III-21′)

From this equality, by taking the imaginary parts in the forward direction and using the optical theorem one gets

$$\sigma_T(\pi^- p) \leqq \sigma_T(\pi^+ p) \leqq \sigma_T(\pi^0 p). \tag{III-22}$$

The same reasoning can also be applied to any member of an isotopic multiplet, and one obtains for instance

$$\sigma_{np}^T = \sigma_{pp}^T \tag{III-23}$$

(n and p: isotopic doublet).

If the interaction is supposed to be invariant with respect to a larger group, as for instance SU(3), one obtains the same result for all the particles belonging to the same multiplet (Amati *et al.*, 1964).

It is very interesting to consider the Pomeranchuk-Okun theorems from the point of view of the crossed channel (Amati *et al.*, 1964; Foldy and R. F. Peierls, 1963; van Hove, 1963b, 1965a,b).

In fact, as we have seen, the theorem is based on the assumption that the amplitude which dominates asymptotically all the processes is that amplitude for which all the particles retain their own quantum numbers.

Therefore, if one looks into the crossed channel, one can say that the object which is exchanged in the crossed channel does not transfer quantum numbers from the top to the bottom (see Fig. 24); it must therefore have the quantum numbers of the vacuum.

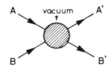

FIG. 24. Diagrammatic representation of the scattering amplitude with the vacuum quantum numbers in the crossed channel. Particles A and B are the initial particles for the scattering in the direct channel; A′ and B′ have the same quantum numbers as A and B, respectively.

Therefore the Pomeranchuk-Okun theorem can be expressed by saying that the crossed channel amplitude which dominates at high energies is the vacuum amplitude.

It is worthwhile mentioning that the Pomeranchuk-Okun theorem can simply be derived by assuming that one exchange amplitude dominates the others asymptotically, and moreover that it is not purely real in the forward direction; then, by using the optical theorem it can be shown that this amplitude must be the vacuum one.

In the section concerning the Regge pole theory (Section IV,D) we shall see the great importance of the Pomeranchuk-Okun theorem.

2. *The Pomeranchuk Theorem*

The Pomeranchuk-Okun theorem we have just discussed relates only to particles in the same symmetry multiplet; it cannot say anything about the total cross sections on a given target of a particle and its antiparticle[27] as, for instance, for pp and $\bar{p}p$ or K^+p and K^-p processes.

By using the assumptions that

(1) a forward dispersion relation is valid, and
(2) the total cross sections $\sigma_T(pp)$ and $\sigma_T(\bar{p}p)$ tend asymptotically to constant (*a priori* different) values,

Pomeranchuk (1958; see also Amati *et al.*, 1960) was able to show that these two constants must be equal.

The same result can now be obtained under weaker assumptions.

In fact, the analyticity properties which follow from axiomatic field theory, together with some reasonable assumptions concerning the asymptotic behaviors of the cross sections, are enough to derive both the Pomeranchuk and other related results. This is done by using a mathematical theorem of the theory of analytic functions, such as the Phragmèn-Lindelöf theorem, as was shown for the first time by Meiman (1962). Here we shall follow the somewhat more general treatments of Logunov *et al.* (1964) and van Hove (1963a; 1964; 1965a,b).

Let us first recall the Phragmèn-Lindelöf theorem (Titchmarsh, 1958).

Theorem

Let us define in the upper half of the complex s plane an (open) region R with boundary B defined by $|s| > s_0 > 0$.

If a function $f(s)$ satisfies the following properties:

(a) it is analytic in R;
(b) it is continuous on B and is bounded there, $|f(s)| \leqslant c$.
(c) $\lim \sup [s^{-1} \log f(s)] < 0$;
(d) $f(s)$ has finite limits for $|s| \to \infty$ on the real axis

$$\lim_{s \to \infty} f(s) = a \qquad \lim_{s \to -\infty} f(s) = b$$

then $a = b$.

In order to apply the Phragmèn-Lindelöf theorem to the scattering amplitude, we define, following Logunov *et al.* (1964), an admissible function $\Phi(s)$ by the following requisites:

(a) the function $1/\Phi(s)$ is analytical and less than any exponent $e^{\varepsilon(s)}$, $\varepsilon > 0$, as $|s| \to \infty$ in the upper-half-plane;

---

[27] Except, of course, when particle and antiparticle belong to the same multiplet, as in the case of π^+ and π^-.

(b) it is continuous along the real axis;

(c) $\lim\limits_{s \to \infty} \dfrac{\Phi(s, t)}{\Phi(-s, t)} = e^{-i\pi\delta(t)}$

where $\delta(t)$ is a real function, but otherwise arbitrary.

Let us now suppose that the amplitudes $T(s, t)$ and $\overline{T}(s, t)$ for the direct and crossed reaction actually satisfy the properties of being:

(a) analytic in the upper half s plane, minus a finite region;
(b) continuous on the real s axis;
(c) $\limsup [s^{-1} \ln |T(s, t)|] \leqslant 0$;

(d) $\lim\limits_{s \to \infty} \dfrac{T(s, t)}{\Phi(s, t)} = V_1(t) \qquad \lim\limits_{s \to \infty} \dfrac{T(-s, t)}{\Phi(-s, t)} = V_2(t)$ \hfill (III-24)

where $\Phi(s, t)$ is an admissible function, and $V_1(t)$ and $V_2(t)$ are *a priori* different.

Properties (a) and (b) follow from the axiomatic field theory; (c) is the hypothesis that $T(s, t)$ is a tempered distribution, namely, that it is polynomially bounded at infinity in the upper half plane; property (d) means that along the real axis $T(s, t)$ does not show an oscillatory behavior.

We can now apply the Phragmèn-Lindelöf theorem to the function

$$V(s, t) = \frac{T(s, t)}{\Phi(s, t)}$$

obtaining

$$V_1(t) = V_2(t)$$

and hence

$$|T(s, t)| \equiv |\overline{T}(s, t)| \qquad \frac{d\sigma(s, t)}{d\Omega} \equiv \frac{d\overline{\sigma}(s, t)}{d\Omega} \qquad \text{(III-25)}$$

where $d\overline{\sigma}/d\Omega$ is the reaction in which we have replaced, by the crossing theorem, one initial particle with its antiparticle.

If now we make the specific assumption (van Hove, 1965a,b)

$$\Phi(s, t) = s^{\alpha(t)}(\ln s)^{\beta(t)}(\ln \ln s)^{\gamma(t)} \cdots$$

we get $\overline{V}_1(t) = V_1(t)e^{-i\pi\alpha(t)}$, namely, the phase of $V_1(t)$ depends only on $\alpha(t)$. Moreover, if we take $\alpha(0) = 1$, then applying the optical theorem which for large s reads

$$A(s, 0)/s = \sigma_T(s) = \text{const}$$

we finally get

$$\sigma_T(s) \equiv \overline{\sigma}_T(s) \qquad \text{(III-26)}$$

that is, we have obtained the Pomeranchuk theorem on the asymptotic equality of the particle and antiparticle cross section.

Furthermore, since in this case

$$\lim_{s \to \infty} \frac{T(s, 0)}{T^*(s, 0)} = -1 \qquad \text{(III-27)}$$

the scattering amplitude in the forward direction becomes asymptotically purely imaginary, and

$$\lim_{s \to \infty} \frac{D(s, 0)}{A(s, 0)} = 0. \qquad \text{(III-28)}$$

Therefore one must reach asymptotically the optical theorem limit

$$\left(\frac{d\sigma}{d\Omega}\right)_0 = \left(\frac{q\sigma_T}{4\pi}\right)^2.$$

It is interesting to note that, whereas in the original Pomeranchuk derivation it was necessary to assume analyticity in the complete upper half s plane and the asymptotic constancy of the cross sections, by means of the Phragmèn-Lindelöf theorem it is enough to assume the analyticity properties, which follow from axiomatic field theory, and one can allow a logarithmic increase of the total cross sections

$$\sigma_T \simeq \text{const}(\ln s)^\beta (\ln \ln s)^\gamma \cdots. \qquad \text{(III-29)}$$

These results are true in this simple form if the particles are scalar. By the same method one can prove in the physical cases the following results (Logunov *et al.*, 1965):

(a) Asymptotic equality of differential cross sections:

$$
\begin{aligned}
\pi^+ + p &\to \pi^+ + p &\rightleftharpoons \pi^- + p &\to \pi^- + p \\
K^+ + p &\to K^+ + p &\rightleftharpoons K^- + p &\to K^- + p \\
\pi^+ + p &\to K^+ + \Sigma^+ &\rightleftharpoons K^- + p &\to \pi^- + \Sigma^+ \\
\pi^- + p &\to K^0 + \Lambda^0 &\rightleftharpoons \overline{K}^0 + p &\to \pi^+ + \Lambda^0 \\
K^- + p &\to K^0 + \Xi^0 &\rightleftharpoons \overline{K}^0 + p &\to K^+ + \Xi^0 \\
\Sigma^+ + \text{He} &\to p + \text{He}_\Lambda &\rightleftharpoons \bar{p} + \text{He} &\to \overline{\Sigma^+} + \text{He}_\Lambda \qquad \text{(III-30)} \\
p + p &\to p + p &\rightleftharpoons \bar{p} + p &\to \bar{p} + p \\
\Sigma^+ + p &\to \Sigma^+ + p &\rightleftharpoons \overline{\Sigma^+} + p &\to \overline{\Sigma^+} + p \\
\Sigma^- + p &\to \Lambda^0 + n &\rightleftharpoons \overline{\Lambda^0} + p &\to \overline{\Sigma^-} + n \\
\Sigma^+ + p &\to p + \Sigma^+ &\rightleftharpoons \bar{p} + p &\to \overline{\Sigma^+} + \Sigma^+ \\
\Sigma^- + p &\to n + \Lambda^0 &\rightleftharpoons \bar{n} + p &\to \overline{\Sigma^-} + \Lambda^0
\end{aligned}
$$

(b) In the first five processes listed above, the recoil fermion polarizations are equal in magnitude and opposite in sign for $s \to \infty$.

(c) Asymptotic equality of the total cross sections:

$$\sigma_T(\pi^+ + p) \rightleftharpoons \sigma_T(\pi^- + p)$$

$$\sigma_T(K^+ + p) \rightleftharpoons \sigma_T(K^- + p)$$

$$\sigma_T(\bar{p} + p) \rightleftharpoons \sigma_T(p + p) \qquad \text{(III-30')}$$

$$\sigma_T(\Sigma^- + p) \rightleftharpoons \sigma_T(\Sigma^+ + p)$$

C. Upper and Lower Bounds on the Asymptotic Behavior of the Scattering Amplitude

Starting from the general properties discussed in Section III,A, one can also set upper or lower bounds on the high energy behavior of the scattering amplitude both in the forward direction and for $t \neq 0$. Many of these bounds give too weak constraints to be compared with the actual behavior of the cross sections; nevertheless, it is interesting to give a review of these results, since they are obtained as a consequence of very general hypotheses and therefore are examples of the kinds of results that can be obtained without any detailed assumption about the specific form of the interaction.

Since all the derivations present, in general, mathematical difficulties that are too complicated to be discussed here, we shall limit ourselves to listing the results which have been obtained under various specific assumptions.[28]

We shall follow the review article of Martin (1965b,d).

(1) Consequences of the analytic properties derived from the axiomatic field theory, together with boundedness conditions inside the analyticity domain:

For the scattering amplitude one has the upper bound in the forward direction (Greenberg and Low, 1962)

$$|T(s, \cos \Theta = 1)| < C s^2 \log^2 s \quad \text{(Greenberg-Low bound).} \qquad \text{(III-31)}$$

For nonforward directions one gets

$$|T(s, |\cos \Theta| \neq 1)| < C s^{3/2} \log^{3/2} s. \qquad \text{(III-32)}$$

In the forward direction one obtains also a lower bound (Jin and Martin, 1964; Wit, 1965a,b)

$$\lim \sup s^2 |T(s, t = 0)| > 0 \qquad \text{(III-33)}$$

namely, the amplitude cannot decrease faster than $1/s^2$.

---

[28] In the form in which we shall present them, the results are valid for the scattering of scalar particles; the presence of spin introduces no further complications, apart from kinematical factors (Cornille, 1964).

(2) If one assumes further analyticity properties, by requiring that the nearest singularity of the scattering amplitude should correspond to the mass of the lowest physical state with the quantum numbers of the channel, one obtains the upper bound (Froissart, 1961; Martin, 1963a)

$$|T(s, \cos \Theta = 1)| < C\, s \log^2 s \quad \text{(Froissart bound)}. \qquad \text{(III-34)}$$

This result is of extreme importance, since by applying the optical theorem one gets an upper limit for the growth with the energy of the total cross section

$$\sigma_T(s) < C \log^2 s \qquad \text{(III-35)}$$

namely, the total cross section can only increase logarithmically.

For nonforward angles one gets

$$|T(s, |\cos \Theta| \neq 1)| < C\, s^{3/4} \log^{3/2} s. \qquad \text{(III-36)}$$

One obtains also a lower bound on the total elastic cross section (Martin, 1963b)

$$\sigma_{el}(s) > C\, \frac{\sigma_T^{\,2}(s)}{(\log s)^2}. \qquad \text{(III-37)}$$

In the backward direction, if a pole is present in the physical sheet near $\cos \Theta = -1$ (as, for instance, the neutron pole in high energy $\pi^+ p$ scattering) the backward scattering amplitude cannot decrease faster than a power s^{-n} (Gribov and Pomeranchuk, 1962a).

(3) By postulating as analyticity properties the Mandelstam representation, one does not gain anything in the forward direction, but one improves the result for $\cos \Theta \neq 1$ (Martin, 1965b,d; Kinoshita $et\ al.$, 1963, 1964)

$$|T(s, |\cos \Theta| \neq 1)| < C\, \frac{(\log s)^{3/2}}{\sin^2 \Theta}. \qquad \text{(III-38)}$$

One obtains also an interesting lower bound for any angular interval $\Theta_1 < \Theta < \Theta_2$ (forward and backward directions excluded) (Cerulus and Martin, 1964; Kinoshita, 1964)

$$\lim_{\Theta_1 < \Theta < \Theta_2} \sup |T(s, \cos \Theta)| > \exp[-C\, s^{1/2} \log s]. \qquad \text{(III-39)}$$

It was noticed by Khuri and Kinoshita (1965a) that in the derivations of the bounds we have just discussed, not all the properties of the scattering amplitude were used. In fact, one only uses the analyticity properties in the t variable and the unitarity condition, whereas the other properties, such as analyticity in s and crossing, are not exploited.

They have, moreover, stressed that by an appropriate introduction of those last properties one can further improve the Greenberg-Low [(III-31)] or the Froissart [(III-34)] bound.

We shall review their results here. We consider for definiteness pion-nucleon scattering, and we concentrate on the symmetric amplitude:

$$T^{(s)}(s, t) = \tfrac{1}{2}(T_{\pi^+ p} + T_{\pi^- p}).$$

If one starts from the analyticity properties which follow from axiomatic field theory, then as already mentioned one obtains the Greenberg-Low bound

$$|T^{(s)}(s, 0)| < Cs^2 \log^2 s. \qquad \text{(III-40)}$$

Adding the further hypothesis that the scattering amplitude in the forward direction does not become relatively real at high energies,[29] and more precisely that there must exist a positive α so that

$$\left| \frac{A^{(s)}(s, 0)}{D^{(s)}(s, 0)} \right| \geq \tan \pi\alpha \qquad 0 < \alpha < \tfrac{1}{2} \qquad \text{(III-41)}$$

holds for relatively large energies, Khuri and Kinoshita (1965b,c), by exploiting the information given by the crossing and the analyticity in the s variable,[30] have shown that

$$\lim_{s \to \infty} \int_{s_0}^{s} \frac{T^{(s)}(s', 0)}{s'^3} \qquad \text{(III-42)}$$

exists.

This result is extremely important; in fact, with the Greenberg-Low bound it would be possible that three subtractions are required in a dispersion relation [since (III-42) is not necessarily valid]; from (III-42) one deduces instead that in any case one does not need more than two subtractions.

If, moreover, one adds the physical requirement that the scattering amplitude does not show violent oscillations for $s \to \infty$, one can be more precise and obtain the bound

$$|T^{(s)}(s, 0)| < Cs^{2 - \alpha/2}. \qquad \text{(III-43)}$$

If one starts from the analyticity properties underlying the Froissart bound,

$$\sigma_T(s) \underset{s \to \infty}{<} C \log^2 s$$

[29] This is a reasonable feature in a theory in which, when $s \to \infty$, an infinite number of inelastic channels are open.

[30] All the results of Khuri and Kinoshita have been obtained in a general way by applying theorems on analytic univalent functions; for details we refer to the end of Section IV,B, where further results of these theorems will be discussed.

with the same technique, and adding the hypothesis that the scattering amplitude does not oscillate with large amplitude for large s, one can show that

(a) if as $s \to \infty$

$$\left| \frac{D^{(s)}(s, 0)}{A^{(s)}(s, 0)} \right| \geqslant \tan \pi \alpha \qquad 0 < \alpha < \tfrac{1}{2} \tag{III-44}$$

then

$$\sigma_T(s) < s^{-\alpha/2}$$

(b) if as $s \to \infty$

$$\left| \frac{D^{(s)}(s, 0)}{A^{(s)}(s, 0)} \right| \geqslant (\log s)^{-a} \qquad 0 < a < 1 \tag{III-45}$$

then

$$\sigma_T(s) < (\log s)^{-\lambda}$$

where λ can be chosen arbitrarily large;

(c) if as $s \to \infty$

$$\left| \frac{D^{(s)}(s, 0)}{A^{(s)}(s, 0)} \right| \cdot \log s \to 0$$

the total cross section is bounded by

$$\sigma_T(s) < C \log^\varepsilon s \tag{III-46}$$

where ε is an arbitrarily small number.

Therefore in all these cases the Froissart bound can be improved; the only
case in which this is not possible is that where

$$\left| \frac{D^{(s)}(s, 0)}{A^{(s)}(s, 0)} \right| \sim \frac{\pi}{\log s}.$$

We want to stress that the general conclusion of the Khuri-Kinoshita
results is that there is a strict connection between the asymptotic behavior
of $|D(s, 0)/A(s, 0)|$ and that of $|T(s, 0)|$; this is the consequence of the fact
that at the same time the amplitude must satisfy many constraints (unitarity,
crossing, analyticity in s and t).

A few words now about the experimental verification of the high energy
theorems.

Concerning the Pomeranchuk-Okun and the Pomeranchuk theorems, at
the highest measured energies none of them is satisfied; in fact, still at
20 GeV the total $\pi^- p$ cross section has a value of about 28 mb, which is
2 mb larger than the $\pi^+ p$ cross section (see Fig. 2).

The situation is still worse for $\bar{p}p$ and pp scattering; in fact the $\bar{p}p$ total cross section has a rapidly decreasing slope for all the measured energies, but at 20 GeV it has a value of about 50 mb, which is larger than the pp total cross section at the same energy, i.e., $\sigma_{pp} \simeq 40$ mb.

The situation of pn and pp scattering is better; the pn total cross section, which is larger than the pp cross section at lower energies, seems to be equal to σ_{pp} at the highest measured energy, $p_{inc} = 22$ GeV/c, at a value of 40 mb.

The obvious conclusion is that if the asymptotic theorems are true, the presently available machines have not yet reached the asymptotic region of the energy. A tentative conclusion could also be that for NN reactions the asymptotic region starts at higher energies than for πN[31]; this not only because at 20 GeV the $\sigma_{\bar{p}p} - \sigma_{pp}$ difference is much larger than the $\sigma_{\pi - p} - \sigma_{\pi + p}$, but also because at 20 GeV the ratio $D(s, 0)/A(s, 0)$ remains still large and constant for pp, whereas it decreases toward zero for $\pi^{\pm}p$ (see Section II,A).

Concerning the bounds, none is violated till now; all the total cross sections show a slowly decreasing behavior consistent with the Froissart bound, whereas at angles different from zero the experiments are too far from the theoretical limits.

As we shall see in Section IV,C, at large angles the lower limit (III-39) seems to be saturated; therefore a tentative conclusion could be that in some cases the upper bounds (total cross sections) or the lower bounds (large-angle scattering) are saturated.

IV. The Elastic Scattering

As we have seen in Section II,A, the elastic cross section for the processes pp, $\pi^{\pm}p$, $\bar{p}p$, and $K^{\pm}p$ at energies larger than ~ 1 GeV is mostly contained within a forward peak $[-t \leqslant 1 \,(\text{GeV}/c)^2]$; for some processes ($\pi^{\pm}p$ scattering in the range from 1.5 to 12.4 GeV/c of incident momentum) there appears also a secondary maximum at a momentum transfer of the order of -1.5 $(\text{GeV}/c)^2$. There is no indication of such a secondary maximum in pp scattering.

At larger angles $[1 < -t \,(\text{GeV}/c)^2]$ the differential cross section becomes flatter both for pp and for $\pi^{\pm}p$ scattering, while at fixed angle it decreases

[31] A useful parameter for the characterization of the asymptotic region could be the value of the cosine of the angle in the crossed channel for elastic scattering (van Hove, 1965b, p. 67).

$$\cos \Theta_t = \frac{s - m_1{}^2 - m_2{}^2}{2 \, m_1 m_2} \qquad (t = 0).$$

One can see, for instance, that it has the same value at 28 GeV for pp and at 4 GeV for πp scattering.

very rapidly with the energy. There are also indications for a backward peak in both $\pi^\pm p$ scattering whose value is much larger for $\pi^+ p$ than for $\pi^- p$.

In this section we shall discuss:

(1) the description of the forward peak in terms of an optical model,

(2) the problem of the real part of the scattering amplitude in the forward direction and its connection with the forward dispersion relations,

(3) the proposed models for the large-angle scattering and the backward peak, and

(4) we shall then end the section with a discussion of the Regge pole theory.

A. THE OPTICAL MODEL

In nuclear physics,[32] when one studies the high energy scattering of a nucleon on a complex nucleus,[33] one observes that the mean free path of the nucleon in nuclear matter becomes just of the order of the nuclear radius. In this case it is therefore reasonable to describe the effect of the nucleus on the incident particle by an effective potential, and to treat the passage of the nucleon through the nucleus in strict analogy with the passage of the light through a medium with a refractive index.

Since the nucleon can be both scattered elastically and absorbed, giving rise to nuclear reactions, the refractive index will also have an imaginary part (absorption coefficient). In this optical analogy the nucleus, as we shall see, is described by a complex potential. Such a description has been shown to be useful in nuclear physics, giving a good description of the elastic scattering and also of the polarization (Frahn and Venter, 1964; Hufner and de Shalit, 1965).

When we pause to consider, for instance, the elastic scattering of pions on protons above 2 GeV, we see that the value of the total cross section corresponds to the square of the pion Compton wavelength which, from the Hofstadter experiments, turns out to be just the value of the proton electromagnetic radius. The mean free path of the pion inside the nucleon at those energies is therefore of the order of the nucleon dimensions.

This fact and the peaked behavior of the small-angle elastic cross section suggest that one can try to apply the optical model also for the description of high energy hadron scattering.

We shall now briefly treat the already classical theory of the optical model (Serber, 1964; Glauber, 1959). In order to understand the relation between the elastic scattering and the absorption, we shall treat first the simplest case of the scattering of a plane wave of momentum k by a partially absorbing disk of radius R and thickness T.

---

[32] Fernbach et al. (1949), Brown (1957), Feshbach (1958), and Lock (1960).

[33] In nuclear physics "high energy" means, for instance, 100 MeV or above.

The variation of the amplitude of an incoming plane wave, e^{-ikz}, after passing the disk, is

$$a = \exp[-(K/2 - ik_l)T] \tag{IV-1}$$

where K is the absorption coefficient and k_l the momentum inside the disk.

The absorption cross section is given by the product of the surface (πR^2) by the difference between the incoming and transmitted fluxes

$$\sigma_a = \pi R^2(1 - |a|^2) = \pi R^2(1 - e^{-KT}). \tag{IV-2}$$

The corresponding elastic cross section is

$$\sigma_{el} = \pi R^2|1 - a|^2 = \pi R^2(1 - 2e^{-KT/2} \cos k_l T + e^{-KT}). \tag{IV-3}$$

In this derivation we have neglected the reflection at the surface of the disk.

It is easy to see that for a completely absorbing disk $(K \to \infty)$ we get $\sigma_a = \sigma_{el} = \pi R^2$, and we obtain the well-known result that the total cross section is twice the geometrical one.

The same procedure can also be applied to a sphere with uniform density (see, for example, Lock, 1960, p. 108).

It is more interesting to compute the angular distribution of the differential cross section.

Owing to the fact that at high energies many partial waves are scattered, one can apply the impact parameter method by substituting the discrete sum over the partial waves by an integral over the impact parameter.[34]

Remembering that the scattering amplitude can be written

$$f(k, \cos \Theta) = \sum_l (2l + 1) \frac{a_l - 1}{2ik} P_l(\cos \Theta) \tag{IV-4}$$

where in presence of absorption $|a_l| \leqslant 1$, one makes the following substitutions:

$$l + \tfrac{1}{2} = kb \ (kdb = dl)$$

so converting the sum into an integral

$$f(k, \cos \Theta) = (1/ik) \int_0^R kb \ kdb(a_l - 1)P_l(\cos \Theta) \tag{IV-5}$$

where the integral runs from the origin to the maximum value R of the impact parameter (optical radius).

[34] The conditions under which this substitution is valid have been recently investigated (Luming and Predazzi, 1966).

For small values of Θ one can approximate the Legendre polynomials by the Bessel function

$$P_l(\cos\Theta) = J_0[(l + \tfrac{1}{2})\sin\Theta] = J_0(kb\sin\Theta)$$

and one finally gets

$$f(k,\cos\Theta) = \frac{k}{i}\int_0^R b\,db\,J_0(kb\sin\Theta)[a(b) - 1]. \qquad \text{(IV-6)}$$

This is the general expression of the optical model. The various particular models can be obtained by giving special forms to the dependence of the scattering coefficient $a(b)$ on the impact parameter b. This amounts to choosing the potential in which the scattering particle moves.[35]

In fact, if the particle is subjected to a potential

$$U = U(r) + iV(r) \qquad \text{(IV-7)}$$

the relation between the local wave vector $\mathbf{k}'(r)$ in the presence of the interaction and the free wave vector $\mathbf{k}$ is given by the energy conservation (remember we are treating relativistic particles)

$$(k^2 + m^2)^{1/2} = (k'^2(r) + m^2)^{1/2} + U(r) + iV(r). \qquad \text{(IV-8)}$$

Since by definition $\mathbf{k}$ is a real vector, one sees that an imaginary part of the potential induces also an imaginary part of the interaction wave vector $\mathbf{k}'(r)$.

The main problem of the scattering is to obtain the phase $\varphi(r)$ of the amplitude; in the small wavelength approximation, which is our approximation at high energies, $\varphi(r)$ satisfies the eikonal equation

$$\nabla_2\varphi(r) = k'^2(r). \qquad \text{(IV-9)}$$

The further approximation is to find the solution of Eq. (IV-9) for only small deflections of the incident particle from its line of flight, which is

$$\varphi(r) = \int_{-\infty}^r \mathbf{k}'\cdot d\mathbf{z} \qquad \text{(IV-10)}$$

where the integration runs over the straight line parallel to the incident momentum $\mathbf{k}$, namely, over the optical path of the particle.

From Eqs. (IV-8) and (IV-10) we get the asymptotic wave function[36]

$$\psi(\mathbf{k},\mathbf{r}) = \exp(i\mathbf{k}'\cdot\mathbf{r}) = \exp(i\mathbf{k}\cdot\mathbf{r})\cdot\exp\left\{-i\int_{-\infty}^{+\infty} dz[U(z) + iV(z)]\right\} \qquad \text{(IV-11)}$$

[35] For this treatment see, for example, van Hove (1965b).

[36] For simplicity we have introduced in Eq. (IV-11) the solution of Eq. (IV-8) for $\mathbf{k} - \mathbf{k}'$ by neglecting the mass m; of course, one could also introduce the true solution of Eq. (IV-8) or also a different form, if one assumes nonrelativistic energy conservation; the only important point is that the logarithm of $a(b)$ can be expressed as an integral over a function of the potential.

and in terms of the distance of closest classical approach b

$$\psi(\mathbf{k}, \mathbf{r}) = \exp(i\mathbf{k} \cdot \mathbf{r}) \cdot \exp\left\{ -2i \int_b^\infty r'dr' \frac{[U(r') + iV(r')]}{(r'^2 - b^2)^{1/2}} \right\}. \qquad \text{(IV-11}')$$

The partial scattering amplitude $a_l = a(b)$ is therefore given by

$$e^{2i\delta} = a(b) = \exp\left\{ -2i \int_b^\infty \frac{r'dr'}{(r'^2 - b^2)^{1/2}} [U(r') + iV(r')] \right\}. \qquad \text{(IV-12)}$$

Giving the potential one can therefore compute from Eqs. (IV-6) and (IV-12) the scattering amplitude and the differential cross section.

The comparison between the potential and the scattering amplitude can be made easier by inverting the Bessel transform (IV-6) and therefore expressing the partial scattering amplitude $a(b)$ in terms of $f(k, \cos \Theta)$.

By defining $(-t)^{1/2} = k \sin \Theta$ one gets for the inversion

$$a(b) = 1 - \frac{1}{ik} \int_0^\infty J_0[b(-t)^{1/2}](-t)^{1/2}d[(-t)^{1/2}]f(k, \cos \Theta). \qquad \text{(IV-13)}$$

As we have already said, when one applies the optical model to physical processes one assumes an ad hoc potential [or, what is the same, an ad hoc $a(b)$] in order to fit and correlate the various experimental facts. In this way one has the advantage that it is not necessary to have a very detailed knowledge of the mechanism which produces the scattering, but a few parameters of a smooth function, the potential, are enough. It is evident that in the same fact lies also the limitation of the optical model, since it is not able to discriminate between different detailed "elementary" mechanisms.

Of course, a more physical approach to an optical model would consist not in giving a priori the imaginary part of the potential in order to fit the elastic scattering data, but in deriving it from the properties of the inelastic scattering, which at very high energies consists mainly in the production of particles; in this way one would simply explain the elastic scattering as the shadow of the absorption of the incident wave into the inelastic channels.

In order to construct such a theory, one must therefore have a knowledge of the mean behavior of the general properties of the production phenomena. Up to now this procedure can be applied only at very high energies. Similar approaches, which do not necessarily need the introduction of the concept of a potential, will be treated in Section VI.

We can now discuss the various models which have been proposed in order to explain high energy hadron scattering.

The crudest one is the black uniform sphere; the target is represented by a completely absorbing sphere for distances less than a radius R, and therefore

$$a(b) = 0 \qquad \text{for} \quad b \leqslant R$$

whereas

$$a(b) = 1 \qquad \text{for} \quad b > R.$$

$$\qquad \text{(IV-14)}$$

Introducing this hypothesis into Eq. (IV-6) one gets

$$f(k, \cos \Theta) = \frac{iR}{\sin \Theta} J_1(kR \sin \Theta) \qquad \frac{d\sigma}{d\Omega} = \frac{R^2}{\sin^2 \Theta} J_1{}^2(kR \sin \Theta). \qquad \text{(IV-15)}$$

For the total cross section, using the optical theorem and remembering that

$$J_1(kR \sin \Theta) \underset{\Theta \to 0}{\to} \frac{kR \sin \Theta}{2}$$

one gets

$$\sigma_T = (4\pi/k) \operatorname{Im} f(k, \Theta = 0) = 2\pi R^2 \qquad \text{(IV-16)}$$

namely, twice the geometrical cross section.

Of course one can take as model not a "black" but a "gray" sphere, namely, a sphere which, for $b \leqslant R$, is only partially absorbing

$$a(b) = a \quad b \leq R \qquad (0 < a < 1)$$

$$a(b) = 1 \quad b > R. \qquad \text{(IV-17)}$$

The opacity factor $(1 - a)$ is therefore different from 1, and the differential and total cross sections are

$$\frac{d\sigma}{d\Omega} = \frac{R^2}{\sin^2 \Theta} (1 - a)^2 J_1{}^2(kR \sin \Theta)$$

$$\sigma_T = 2\pi R^2 (1 - a). \qquad \text{(IV-18)}$$

It is worthwhile to note that in this model, since $a(b)$ is purely real, the potential is purely imaginary [see Eq. (IV-12)]; therefore all the elastic scattering is due to the shadow of the inelastic processes.

If one now compares Eq. (IV-18) with the phenomenological fit of the angular distribution for high energy hadron scattering

$$\frac{d\sigma}{d(-t)} = \frac{d\sigma}{d(-t)_{t=0}} \cdot \exp(bt + ct^2) \qquad \text{(IV-19)}$$

(see Section II,A), we get the following values for the optical radius R (see Table VI), using the data of Table I.[37] Summarizing (Lindenbaum, 1965) the experimental situation for the optical radius and opacity factor of the proton,

---

[37] The relation between R, $(1 - a)$, $d\sigma/d(-t)_{t=0}$, and b can immediately be found by expanding the Bessel function; one gets

$$R^2 = 4b \qquad (1 - a)^2 = \frac{1}{4\pi b^2} \left(\frac{d\sigma}{d(-t)} \right)_{t=0}$$

TABLE VI

OPTICAL MODEL RADIUS FOR pp, $\bar{p}p$, π^+p, π^-p, K^-p, K^+p

Reaction	p_{inc} (GeV/c)	R (Fermi)	Reaction	p_{inc} (GeV/c)	R (Fermi)
pp	8.5	1.14 ± 0.02	π^-p	7.0	1.21 ± 0.02
	10.94	1.15 ± 0.04		8.5	1.17 ± 0.02
	12.4	1.18 ± 0.03		8.9	1.19 ± 0.02
	14.93	1.18 ± 0.04		10.8	1.21 ± 0.02
	18.4	1.23 ± 0.04		12.4	1.16 ± 0.02
	19.84	1.16 ± 0.05		13.0	1.23 ± 0.02
	21.88	1.22 ± 0.05		14.84	1.26 ± 0.06
	24.63	1.11 ± 0.10		18.4	1.19 ± 0.03
				19.75	1.18 ± 0.04
$\bar{p}p$	4.0	1.44 ± 0.04		23.18	1.15 ± 0.05
	7.2	1.45 ± 0.03		25.34	1.21 ± 0.05
	8.9	1.41 ± 0.01			
	10.0	1.35 ± 0.02	K^+p	6.8	0.98 ± 0.07
	11.8	1.40 ± 0.04		9.8	0.98 ± 0.04
	12.0	1.44 ± 0.02		12.8	1.04 ± 0.03
	15.9	1.17 ± 0.07		14.8	1.05 ± 0.03
π^+p	6.8	1.15 ± 0.02	K^-p	7.2	1.26 ± 0.08
	8.5	1.08 ± 0.03		8.9	1.28 ± 0.08
	8.8	1.19 ± 0.02		11.8	1.09 ± 0.07
	10.8	1.15 ± 0.02		15.9	1.15 ± 0.08
	12.4	1.14 ± 0.05			
	12.8	1.18 ± 0.02			
	14.8	1.18 ± 0.02			
	16.7	1.18 ± 0.03			

we can say that for incident protons R increases with the energy (the forward peak shrinks), but the rate of increase tends to decrease at higher energies; for incident antiprotons, R decreases with the energy (the peak expands); R increases also for incident K^+, whereas it is independent of the energy for incident K^-, π^+, π^-. The projectile for which the proton is the most opaque is the antiproton: $(1 - a) = 0.83 \pm 0.07$, with the proton next: $(1 - a) = 0.74 \pm 0.22$, followed by pions and K mesons, $(1 - a) = 0.55 \pm 0.04$.

This simple model of a partially absorbing uniform nucleon presents many difficulties:

(1) The scattering amplitude in the forward direction is purely imaginary, whereas the experiments indicate that also at the highest explored energies there is a definite nonzero real part of the amplitude (see Section IV,B).

(2) By expanding the Bessel function in power series, we can obtain a relation between the coefficients b and c of formula (IV-19), namely,

$$c = -b^2/12.$$

Although c is not well determined experimentally, this result is definitely wrong in sign and magnitude.

(3) The Bessel function $J_1(kR \sin \Theta)$ shows zeros, which reflect into the angular distribution (IV,18); the first zero is for $kR \sin \Theta = 3.8$. The experiments do not show this feature. The root of this difficulty is to be found in the fact that the (partially) absorbing sphere shows a sharp boundary, which is responsible for the oscillations in the angular distribution.[38]

Whereas in the literature there are (to our knowledge) no attempts to modify the simple optical model in order to overcome the first two difficulties,[39] the validity of the third objection has been questioned. In particular, Dar et al. (1964a) have tried to fit the secondary maxima, which appear in $\pi^\pm + p$ elastic scattering at a momentum transfer $-t = 1.5$ (GeV/c)^2 in the range of incident momentum between 1.5 to 12.4 GeV/c with the simple optical model. In the same way they have also obtained a fit to the inelastic two-body processes (1964b), as $p\bar{p} \to n\bar{n}$ at 900 MeV/c, and $p\bar{p} \to \Lambda^0 \bar{\Lambda}^0$ at 3.3 GeV/c, and to the polarization (Alexander et al., 1965a) in $\pi^\pm p$ scattering at 690 and 980 MeV.

An essentially identical remark was made by Simmons (1964). He still treats the simple optical model with a potential which vanishes beyond a fixed value of the impact parameter, but instead of replacing the sum over the Legendre polynomials by an integral over a Bessel function, he limits the sum over the values of the angular momentum to a finite number of partial waves. Of course the angular distribution still shows a series of maxima and minima.

The same model (Marshall and Oliphant, 1965) has also been applied to fit the $K^- p$ angular distribution at 2 GeV/c (Crittenden et al., 1964).

As a general remark, we can say that these approaches give reasonable fits when the incident energy is not too high (of the order of a few GeV); but it seems inadequate at higher energies. In fact, when the energy increases, the secondary maximum of πp scattering more likely becomes an inflection, and tends to disappear (Caldwell et al., 1964; Harting et al., 1965; Coffin et al.,

---

[38] A model with nonsharp boundary has been proposed by Armenteros et al. (1960) where it has been taken that

$$a(b) = 1 - \exp\left[\frac{-(b^2 - R^2)}{R_1^2}\right] \qquad (b > R).$$

[39] Although it should be noted that an impact parameter model, strictly related to the optical model, has been proposed by Durand and Greider (1963); in their model a nonzero real part in the forward direction is allowed.

1965); therefore, there is no evidence for minima of the angular distribution at higher energies.

More refined optical models have been proposed by Serber (1963) and Krisch (1963) in order to explain also the scattering at larger momentum transfer $[-t \geqslant 1 \ (\text{GeV}/c)^2]$. They consist essentially of assuming a purely imaginary potential, whose radial distribution has a Yukawian form.

Since in this way the interaction at small distances is stronger than that given by the uniform sphere, one gets a larger cross section for large values of the momentum transfer, which corresponds to the experimental situation both in πp and pp scattering.

The t dependence of the differential cross section for $-t \leqslant 1 \ (\text{GeV}/c)^2$ is practically the same as that given by the simple uniform sphere, while for $1 < -t < 10 \ (\text{GeV}/c)^2$ it gives a t^{-5} law, which fits the pp experiments. The same model has also been applied to elastic and charge exchange $K^- p$ scattering at 2 GeV/c (Lindenbaum, 1965), and to πp elastic scattering (Aly *et al.*, 1963).

A somewhat similar approach is that of Henley and Muzinich (1964). They have avoided the introduction of a potential by directly parametrizing the partial wave scattering amplitude by taking

$$1 - a_l = 1 - \exp(2i\delta_l) = C \, \frac{\exp(RA^{-1}\{1 - [1 + (l^2/k^2R^2)]^{1/2}\})}{[1 + (l^2/k^2R^2)]^{1/2}} \qquad \text{(IV-20)}$$

where $C \leqslant 1$, A, and R are adjustable parameters. In this way they are able to fit both the small and large momentum transfer regions in the πp, pp, and Kp angular distribution.

They also predict the angular distribution for $pn \to np$, $\pi^- p \to \pi^0 n$, and $K^- p \to \overline{K}{}^0 n$ charge exchange reactions; although the very high energy data are rather scarce, their results are not in good agreement with the experiment.

Very recently an interesting paper by Byers and Yang (1966) appeared, in which they suggest an essentially optical model that unifies the treatment of both the elastic and charge (or nucleon) exchange peaks for small values of the momentum transfer.

They start from the phenomenological observation that the forward elastic peaks in pp, $\bar{p}p$, πp, and Kp differential cross sections; the peaks in $\pi^- p \to \pi^0 n$ for $0.1 \leqslant -t \leqslant 0.6 \ (\text{GeV}/c)^2$, in $K^- p$ charge exchange, and in pn charge exchange for incident momentum between 1.37 and 15 GeV/c (see Section II,B); as well as the backward peaks in $\pi^{\pm} p$ (see below, Section IV,C), are all well represented by the formula

$$\frac{d\sigma}{d(-t)} = \left(\frac{d\sigma}{d(-t)}\right)_{t=0} e^{\gamma t} \qquad \text{(IV-21)}$$

where γ is always of the same order of magnitude $\sim 10 \ (\text{GeV}/c)^{-2}$.

The existence of large peaks for small values of the momentum transfer, independent of the possibility that in the reaction quantum numbers have been exchanged, leads to the conclusion that whereas large momentum transfers are difficult to realize, it is relatively easy to transfer in a coherent way (since t is small) quantum numbers such as charge, strangeness, and nucleon number.

The universality of the form of the peaks suggests, moreover, that the mechanisms of all those coherent phenomena have to be related to each other.

To support this interpretation, one should note that in the charge exchange reactions, such as $\pi^- p \to \pi^0 n$, $K^- p \to K^0 n$, it is impossible to have good fits with the one-particle-exchange model even if the form factor and absorption corrections are included (see Hearn and Drell, in this volume).

One can therefore conclude that in charge exchange reactions the "diffraction scattering" (as the Regge pole exchange is, essentially) is preferred with respect to the "potential scattering" (as the peripheral mechanism). In figurative language, Byers and Yang say that at high energy the reaction time is so short that there is not enough time to exchange the peripheral particle.

They therefore suggest an impact parameter model both for the elastic and (for instance) $\pi^- p \to \pi^0 n$ charge exchange scattering.

The non-spin-flip partial amplitude $a^{ex}(b) - 1$ for the charge exchange is related to the truly elastic partial amplitude $a(b) - 1$ by the relation

$$a^{ex}(b) - 1 = K^{ex} \, a(b) \ln a(b) \qquad \text{(IV-22)}$$

where K^{ex} is a complex constant, independent of b but dependent on the energy. The factor $\ln a(b) = 2i\delta(b)$ has the following origin: The charge exchange amplitude is proportional to the thickness of the target, which in the eikonal approximation is proportional to $\delta(b)$; namely, the phase shift measures the optical path of the incident particle inside the target.

For the spin-flip part of the exchange amplitude, $\beta^{ex}(b) - 1$, a similar hypothesis is made, adding a factor b^2 in order to obtain the high b dominance experimentally found in the spin-flip experiments

$$\beta^{ex}(b) - 1 = K^{ex}_{flip} a(b) \cdot b^2 \ln a(b). \qquad \text{(IV-23)}$$

Deriving $a(b)$ from the elastic experiments, which turns out to be of the form

$$a(b) = 1 - 0.58 \, e^{-b^2/20} \quad (b \text{ in } (\text{GeV}/c)^{-1}) \qquad \text{(IV-24)}$$

it is possible to predict in terms of the only parameter K^{ex}_{flip}/K^{ex} both the form of the small t charge exchange angular distribution and the polarization of the final neutron perpendicular to the scattering plane. In this approach the observed positive slope of the charge exchange differential cross section for

$t = 0$ is attributed to an important contribution of the spin-flip amplitude in this region.

A few words now about the theoretical justification of the optical models in describing high energy scattering.

It has been shown by Omnès (1965) that whenever a scattering amplitude satisfies the Mandelstam representation,[40] it is possible to find a potential which, treated in the eikonal approximation, gives the amplitude up to multiplicative corrections of the order of $1/k$ for finite values of the momentum transfer; the eikonal function is essentially determined by the discontinuity of the scattering amplitude across the cut in the complex t plane. The potential which is obtained is, in general, an energy dependent one, whose behavior at the origin is of the form of

$$V(r, s) \underset{r \to 0}{\simeq} c_1 \frac{\log(kr)}{r} + \frac{c_2}{r}$$

and whose behavior at infinity is

$$V(r, s) \underset{r \to \infty}{\to} e^{-\mu_0 r}$$

namely, it is determined by the nearest singularity in the t plane. Therefore the notion of an optical potential can be based on general properties, and it is meaningful also when the amplitude has an asymptotic Regge behavior (see Section IV,D below).

B. THE REAL PART OF THE SCATTERING AMPLITUDE

One of the characteristics of the optical model, as is usually applied to high energy physics, is that the scattering amplitude, at least at small angles, where the model is applied, is purely imaginary; in such a theory the diffraction peak is interpreted as being due only to the shadow of the inelastic processes.

This hypothesis is in definite contradiction to the experiments, both for pp and πp elastic scattering (see Section II,A).

The absolute value of the real part of the scattering amplitude in the forward direction can be obtained by the measurement of the value of the differential cross section at zero degrees; its sign can be deduced from the interference at small angles of the strong interaction part of the scattering amplitude with the Coulomb amplitude, which is due to the electromagnetic interaction between the two scattering charged particles.

---

[40] In fact, not all the analyticity properties of the Mandelstam representation are needed, but it is enough (Chadan, 1965) to assume analyticity inside an ellipse in the cos Θ plane, having the nearest Mandelstam singularity on his boundary.

In fact, when one writes

$$T(s, t) = D(s, t) + iA(s, t)$$

one can obtain the value of $A(s, 0)$ from the optical theorem

$$A(s, 0) = (\Phi/2)\sigma_T(s) \tag{III-12}$$

where we remember that

$$\Phi = \frac{q\sqrt{s}}{m^2} \text{ for } pp \to pp, \qquad \Phi = \frac{2q\sqrt{s}}{m} \text{ for } \pi p \to \pi p$$

and therefore

$$\left(\frac{d\sigma}{d\Omega}\right)_{\Theta=0} = \frac{q^2\sigma_T^2(s)}{16\pi^2}\left[1 + \frac{D^2(s, 0)}{A^2(s, 0)}\right]. \tag{IV-25}$$

In this way, from the knowledge of the total cross section and of the extrapolation at zero degrees of the differential elastic cross section one can get the absolute value of the ratio

$$\alpha(s) = D(s, 0)/A(s, 0). \tag{IV-26}$$

One can moreover get the sign of $D(s, 0)$ [and therefore also of $\alpha(s)$, since $A(s, 0)$ is definite positive] by noting that the Coulomb scattering amplitude is, in the Born approximation, purely real, its sign depending on the relative sign of the electric charges of the two scattering particles.

Therefore the complete scattering amplitude can be written

$$T(s, t) = D_{\text{nucl}}(s, t) + D_{\text{Coul}}(s, t) + iA_{\text{nucl}}(s, t) \tag{IV-27}$$

and the differential cross section

$$\frac{d\sigma}{d\Omega}(s, t) = \frac{q^2}{(2\pi\Phi)^2}\left[D_{\text{nucl}}^2 + D_{\text{Coul}}^2 + 2D_{\text{nucl}}D_{\text{Coul}} + A_{\text{nucl}}^2\right]. \tag{IV-28}$$

From the measurement of the nuclear cross section and the calculation of D_{Coul}, one finds that D_{nucl} and D_{Coul} become comparable in the high energy region for a momentum transfer of the order of $t \simeq 0.002$ $(\text{GeV}/c)^2$.

The sign of the interference term $2D_{\text{nucl}}D_{\text{Coul}}$ depends, of course, on the sign of D_{nucl}[41]; more precisely, one must have:

For pp, π^+p (like charges): constructive interference in the differential cross section if $D_{\text{nucl}} < 0$, namely, if the strong interaction is repulsive;

For π^-p: destructive interference if $D_{\text{nucl}} < 0$,

and, of course, the reversed situation if $D_{\text{nucl}} > 0$.

[41] With the usual definition, D_{Coul} is negative for like charges (repulsion) and positive for unlike charges (attraction).

The analysis of the experiments shows in a definite way that $\alpha(s) < 0$ for pp, π^+p, and π^-p. Very recently, the ratio $\alpha(s)$ has also been obtained for pn scattering, by extracting the information from proton-deuteron scattering; also in this case $\alpha(s)$ turns out to be negative.

The experimental results for $\alpha(s)$ in the various reactions are shown in Table VII.

TABLE VII

THE RATIO $\alpha(s) = D(s, 0)/A(s, 0)$ FOR pp, π^+p, π^-p, np

Reaction	p_{inc} (GeV/c)	$\alpha(s)$	Reaction	p_{inc} (GeV/c)	$\alpha(s)$
pp	1.7^a	-0.007 ± 0.07	π^+p	10.05^g	$-0.109\,^{+0.069}_{-0.115}$
	2.8^b	-0.13 ± 0.07			
	4.8^b	-0.39 ± 0.1		11.86^g	$-0.132\,^{+0.071}_{-0.131}$
	6.8^b	-0.32 ± 0.07			
	7.85^c	-0.29 ± 0.03		13.87^g	$-0.063\,^{+0.099}_{-0.156}$
	7.92^d	$-0.247\,^{+0.082}_{-0.075}$			
	8.9^b	-0.32 ± 0.07	π^-p	7.96^g	$-0.330\,^{+0.113}_{-0.067}$
	9.2^b	-0.34 ± 0.07			
	9.94^d	$-0.302\,^{+0.071}_{-0.069}$		9.89^g	$-0.300\,^{+0.144}_{-0.086}$
	10.00^e	-0.33 ± 0.035			
	10.11^e	-0.43 ± 0.043		11.86^g	$-0.408\,^{+0.107}_{-0.058}$
	10.8^b	-0.27 ± 0.06			
	12.14^d	$-0.258\,^{+0.066}_{-0.067}$		15.84^g	$-0.216\,^{+0.127}_{-0.069}$
	17.82^d	$-0.307\,^{+0.065}_{-0.060}$		20.04^g	$-0.106\,^{+0.158}_{-0.081}$
	19.33^e	-0.33 ± 0.033		23.95^g	$-0.001\,^{+0.151}_{-0.091}$
	24.0^f	-0.19 ± 0.09			
	26.42^e	-0.32 ± 0.033	np	6.9^b	-0.06 ± 0.19
				8.9^b	-0.45 ± 0.20
				10.9^b	-0.40 ± 0.17
				19.3^h	-0.35 ± 0.05

[a] Dowell et al. (1964).
[b] Kirillova et al. (1963, 1966).
[c] Taylor et al. (1965).
[d] Foley et al. (1965a).

[e] Bellettini et al. (1965a).
[f] Lohrmann et al. (1964).
[g] Foley et al. (1965b).
[h] Bellettini et al. (1965b).

In order to extract $\alpha(s)$ from the experimental data, one usually makes the following simplifying hypotheses:

(1) At small angles the elastic scattering amplitude for pp and for πp scattering is spin independent;

(2) The ratio $\alpha(s, t) = D(s, t)/A(s, t)$ is, for small intervals of t, independent of the momentum transfer t: $\alpha(s, t) \simeq \alpha(s)$.

The first hypothesis is more justified for πp scattering, since pion-nucleon scattering is described by only two independent amplitudes, which can be chosen in the c.m. system as

$$T(s, t) = T_0(s, t) + T_1(s, t)\boldsymbol{\sigma} \cdot (\boldsymbol{q}_{\text{in}} \times \boldsymbol{q}_{\text{fin}}). \qquad \text{(IV-29)}$$

In the forward direction $(\boldsymbol{q}_{\text{in}} \times \boldsymbol{q}_{\text{fin}})$ vanishes, and therefore, unless $T_1(s, t)$ is singular for $t = 0$ (which is a very implausible situation), the spin-flip contribution is very small near $t = 0$.

The situation may be different for pp scattering where five independent amplitudes are present, and one can form with the spins of the two protons two spin-dependent terms, which do not vanish in the forward direction (van Hove, 1965b), in addition to the spin-independent amplitude.

Nevertheless, the hypothesis of spin independence near $t = 0$ is the simplest one; it can be justified a posteriori from the fact that in this way one obtains a good agreement with the forward dispersion relations (see below).[42]

The second hypothesis, that $\alpha(s, t) = D(s, t)/A(s, t)$ is t independent in the range of interference between the strong and Coulomb amplitude, has no justification a priori, but it can be considered as a first-order approximation in a power series expansion.

From the consideration of Table VII, one can notice that in all the cases one obtains a negative $\alpha(s)$ (repulsive interaction); in the first approximation all the values have the same order of magnitude $\alpha(s) = -0.3$. This general feature is certainly an important one, which has to be explained in any detailed theory. Moreover, in $\pi^- p$ scattering the general trend for $\alpha(s)$ is to decrease with the energy and, within the experimental errors, $\alpha(\pi^- p)$ seems to show a dip at 12 GeV/c and then to vanish at the highest measured momentum, $p_{\text{inc}} = 24$ GeV/c.

The results for $D(s, 0)$, obtained from the experiment, can be compared with the predictions of the forward dispersion relations (FDR) in order to test the validity of the general principles underlying the derivations of the FDR.

It is easy to make this comparison for πp scattering, since the only ingredients one needs are:

---

[42] It was shown by Bellettini et al. (1965a) that with a purely imaginary spin-dependent amplitude one cannot fit the experimental distributions. The situation in which complex spin-dependent amplitudes are present is so complicated that more information than simple scattering angular distributions is needed (as, for example, polarization experiments).

(1) the πN-coupling constant f^2;

(2) the scattering lengths for πN scattering in the total isospin states $T = \frac{1}{2}$ and $T = \frac{3}{2}$, a_1 and a_3;

(3) $D(s, 0)$ at the experimental energies;

(4) the values of the measured total cross sections $\sigma_T(\pi^{\pm}p)$ for energies which range from 0 to the maximum energy allowed by the existing accelerators ($E \simeq 20$ GeV); and

(5) a hypothesis on the behavior of the total cross sections $\sigma_T(\pi^+ p)$ and $\sigma_T(\pi^- p)$ for energies larger than 20 GeV, where no experiments have been possible up to now.

The only critical point, at least at high energies, is the last one.

Höhler *et al.* (1964) have assumed an asymptotic behavior for the total cross sections above 5 GeV of the form

$$\frac{\sigma_T(\pi^+ p) + \sigma_T(\pi^- p)}{2} = \sigma_\infty + \frac{b^+}{p_{inc}^\alpha}; \qquad \frac{\sigma_T(\pi^- p) - \sigma_T(\pi^+ p)}{2} = \frac{b^-}{p_{inc}^\beta}, \qquad \text{(IV-30)}$$

which is the form suggested by the Regge theory, including the ρ, P, and P' trajectories (see Section IV,D).

The values for the parameters they used are (in units $\hbar = c = m_\pi = 1$)

$$\alpha = \beta = 0.5 \quad \sigma_\infty = 1.050; \qquad b^+ = 2.21; \qquad b^- = 0.340 \quad \text{(IV-30')}$$

which give good agreement for not too high energies.

At higher energies, the experiments at 8, 10, and 12 GeV/c give a value for the real part of the $\pi^- p$ scattering which is much larger than that predicted by the calculations of Höhler *et al.* (1964) and also by a similar calculation by Barashenkov and Dedyu (1964) (Fig. 25).*

Nevertheless, this fact must not necessarily mean that FDR are not valid.

In fact, a completely pragmatic point of view has been taken by Lautrup and Olesen (1965) and Lautrup *et al.* (1965), who have tried to avoid any assumption regarding the behavior of the total cross sections in the unknown region above 20 GeV.

By using the experiment at 10 GeV/c, where both $D^+(s, 0)$ and $D^-(s, 0)$ have been measured, as a calibration point, they have obtained sum rules from the FDR for the total cross sections above 20 GeV, which have then been used to compute the values of $D^-(s, 0)$ at 8, 12, and 16 GeV/c, to be compared with the experimental results.

Their conclusion is that although the agreement is rather bad, the experimental errors, mostly on the real parts, are too large to allow definite

---

* *Note added in proof:* At the American Physical Society Meeting (New York, January 1967) new experimental results of measurements of the real parts for $\pi^{\pm}p$ scattering have been presented by the Lindenbaum group. The experimental results of $D^+(s, 0)$ and $D^-(s, 0)$ are in very good agreement with FDR in the range of incident momenta between 8 and 26 GeV/c.

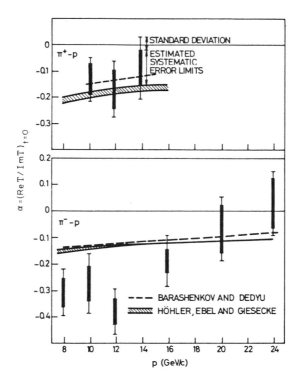

FIG. 25. The ratio $\alpha(s) = D(s, 0)/A(s, 0)$ as a function of the incident momentum for $\pi^+ p$ and $\pi^- p$ scattering. The dotted line is the calculation of Barashenkov and Dedyu (1964) the continuous line that of Höhler *et al.* (1964) (the shaded area corresponds to the estimated error in the calculation). The solid rectangles represent the estimated limits of the systematic errors; the flags add one standard deviation of the statistical errors [taken from Foley *et al.* (1965b)].

conclusions. Other possible sources of errors are the errors on a_1, a_3, and f^2, which are quite important; and possible structures in the total cross sections *below* 20 GeV, which are known only at intervals of 2 GeV.

Instead of looking for violations of causality, the FDR at high energies seem therefore to be rather a tool for obtaining some information about the behavior of the total cross sections in the region above 20 GeV.

By adopting this kind of philosophy, one can conclude that from the behavior of the antisymmetric amplitude

$$T^{(A)} = \tfrac{1}{2}[T_{\pi^- p} - T_{\pi^+ p}]$$

at 10 and 12 GeV/c, it is likely (Lautrup *et al.*, 1965; Olesen, 1966) that the antisymmetric total cross section

$$\sigma^{(A)} = \tfrac{1}{2}[\sigma_{\pi^- p} - \sigma_{\pi^+ p}]$$

which is positive below 20 GeV, changes its sign above; namely, that in this energy region the $\sigma_{\pi+p}$ total cross section becomes larger than the $\sigma_{\pi-p}$ cross section.[43] (Of course, this does not mean that the Pomeranchuk theorem is violated, since we have no compelling reason to think that the asymptotic energy is reached at 20, rather than at, say, 50 GeV.)

One can also conclude that in order to fit the symmetric amplitude

$$T^{(s)} = \tfrac{1}{2}[T_{\pi-p} + T_{\pi+p}]$$

the simple behavior

$$\sigma_T{}^{(s)} = \sigma_\infty + \frac{b^{(s)}}{p_{inc}{}^\alpha}$$

does not seem to have enough flexibility to describe the experimental situation (Höhler et al., 1966a; Höhler and Baacke, 1965); in fact, the data on $D^{(s)}(s, 0)$ seem to suggest that $\sigma_T{}^{(s)}$ has to show a minimum around 20 GeV, and to increase (at least for a limited interval of energy) above this minimum.

It should be noticed, however, that the experimental errors, mostly on the difference $D^- - D^+$, are still too large to allow precise and definite conclusions.

In order to be complete, one can also say that the real part of the anti-symmetric amplitude (or, at least, its absolute value) can also be obtained from the forward value of the charge exchange differential cross section

$$\pi^- p \to \pi^0 n.$$

The results of the experiments (Section II,B) performed at incident momenta up to 18 GeV/c are in substantial agreement with the values of $D^{(A)}$ obtained from the interference experiments,[44] apart from the two points at 10 and 12 GeV/c, where the interference experiments show very large errors.[45]

[43] It should be noticed, however, that the charge exchange data up to 18 GeV/c contradict this prediction (Höhler et al., 1964, 1966a; Höhler and Baacke, 1965).

[44] In the charge exchange experiments the errors on the real part are, in general, considerably smaller than in the Coulomb interference experiments, since (see Section II,B) the real part in the forward direction is of the same order as the imaginary part. One has nevertheless the disadvantage that the sign of the real part cannot be determined, and is usually fixed from the dispersion relation.

[45] This is a critical point concerning the reliability of the experimental results for D^- at 8, 10, and 12 GeV/c, which seem to contradict the predictions of FDR (Fig. 25). In fact, if one compares the values of $D^{(A)} = \tfrac{1}{2}(D^- - D^+)$ and of $-D^{ex}/\sqrt{2}$ (which from charge independence must be equal to $D^{(A)}$), one gets (Höhler and Baacke, 1965), for the only energies where both D^- and D^+ are available

p_{inc}(GeV/c)	$\tfrac{1}{2}(D^- - D^+)$	p_{inc}(GeV/c)	$-D^{ex}/\sqrt{2}$
10	$-0.75 \begin{smallmatrix}+0.9\\-0.5\end{smallmatrix}$	9.8	$+0.27 \pm 0.06$
11.86	$-1.26 \begin{smallmatrix}+1.0\\-0.5\end{smallmatrix}$	13.3	$+0.39 \pm 0.06$

It seems therefore worthwhile to wait for a clarification of the experimental situation before drawing definite conclusions on possible violations of causality or charge independence.

The situation is more complicated for pp scattering; here, besides the πN-coupling constant and the total pp and $\bar{p}p$ cross sections, one needs the analytic continuation of the $\bar{p}p$ total cross section from $s = 4m^2$ below to $s = 4\mu^2$ (the unphysical region contribution). The reason for the appearance of the unphysical region is that in the $\bar{p}p$ channel there are physical states (the lightest is the two-pion state) having the same quantum numbers as the $\bar{p}p$ state; therefore, the application of the unitarity condition in the $\bar{p}p$ channel says that the imaginary part of the scattering amplitude in this channel starts to be different from zero at $s = 4\mu^2$, whereas the physical threshold of the channel (above which one can apply the optical theorem) is $s = 4m^2$.

In the last years two different approaches have been proposed in order to compare the experimental real parts with the FDR.

Söding (1964), using a once-subtracted dispersion relation, has replaced the continuum contribution to the forward imaginary amplitude in the unphysical region by discrete resonance contributions; in this way one introduces the values of the coupling constants between those resonances and the proton as unknowns in the FDR. For the total cross sections above 30 GeV he makes an hypothesis similar to that of Höhler for πp scattering, namely, (by calling q the incident momentum),

$$\sigma_T = \sigma_\infty + Aq^\alpha$$

where

$$\sigma_\infty = 39 \text{ mb}, \qquad \alpha_{pp} = -2.5, \qquad \alpha_{\bar{p}p} = -0.72$$

which fits the experimental values of the cross sections in the range 10 GeV/c $< q <$ 30 GeV/c.

In this way one has still assumed the Pomeranchuk theorem, since

$$\sigma_\infty(pp) = \sigma_\infty(\bar{p}p).$$

The unknowns introduced by the values of the real parts at the subtraction point and of the coupling constants between the resonances and the proton have been eliminated in the following way: From the assumed behavior of the total cross section, one has that for the symmetric amplitude

$$T^{(s)} = \frac{T_{pp} + T_{\bar{p}p}}{2}$$

the total cross section has the behavior

$$[\sigma_T^{(s)}(q) - \sigma_T^{(s)}(\infty)]_{q \to \infty} \to \text{const} \cdot q^\alpha \qquad \text{with} \quad -1 < \alpha < 0 \qquad \text{(IV-31)}$$

and therefore (Lehmann, 1962)

$$D^{(s)}(q) \underset{q \to \infty}{\to} \text{const} \cdot q^{1+\alpha}. \qquad \text{(IV-32)}$$

The imaginary part of the antisymmetric amplitude

$$T^{(A)} = \tfrac{1}{2}[T_{pp} - T_{\bar{p}p}]$$

owing to the Pomeranchuk theorem, does not tend to zero for $q \to \infty$ and therefore one imposes as an extra condition[46]

$$\left(\frac{D^{(A)}}{A^{(A)}}\right)_{q \to \infty} \to 0 \ . \tag{IV-33}$$

This constraint eliminates one of the unknowns. The others are eliminated by requiring a fit of the FDR in the range $68 \leqslant E^{pp}_{\text{lab}} \leqslant 310$ MeV, where the real part of the scattering amplitude can be obtained with great precision from the phase shift analysis.

In this way, Söding shows that for a good parametrization the poles of the ρ, ω, and η mesons are enough.

The main predictions are: The D_{pp} real part in the forward direction is positive for $E < 1.7$ GeV and then changes its sign; the ratio $D(s, 0)/A(s, 0)$ ranges between -0.2 and -0.4 between 2 and 30 GeV.

The curve predicted in this way is in good agreement with the experimental values of D_{pp} in the energy range $1 \leqslant E \leqslant 30$ GeV (Fig. 26); only the CERN points (Bellettini $et\ al.$, 1965a) are lower than the predicted curve, and seem to indicate a flatter behavior up to 26 GeV/c.

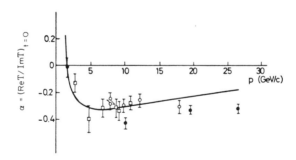

FIG. 26.   The ratio $\alpha(s) = D(s, 0)/A(s, 0)$ as a function of the incident momentum for pp scattering. The continuous curve is the calculation of Söding [taken from Kirillova $et\ al.$ (1966)].

An approach similar to that of Lautrup and Olesen (1965) for πp scattering has been taken by Levintov and Adelson-Velsky (1964); they have tried to avoid any assumption about the unphysical region and the high energy

[46] The situation in which $\lim_{q \to \infty} D^{(A)}/A^{(A)} \neq 0$ would be highly unphysical, for it would mean that in a scattering process with an infinite number of open inelastic channels the amplitude for elastic scattering is relatively real (Khuri and Kinoshita, 1965b); see also the end of Section III,C.

behavior of the total cross sections by using a twice-subtracted dispersion relation, where the subtractions are chosen in the region of 1080–1380 MeV, in order to parametrize the high energy contribution, and by choosing a calibration point at 24.5 GeV, in order to parametrize the unphysical region contribution.

Their results coincide practically with those of Söding.

The analysis of forward dispersion relations is not the only way to test the general principles (as analyticity and causality or crossing) by means of the experiments on the real part of the scattering amplitude.

In fact, it was shown first by Khuri and Kinoshita (1965a–d) that from the general properties of the scattering amplitude one can derive relations for the real part of the scattering amplitude itself, where, unlike the case for the FDR, the range of integration runs only over finite values of the energy; in this way one gets rid of the difficulty of the FDR, where one is forced to assume some properties of physical quantities (such as the total cross section) in that region of energy where experiments cannot yet be done.

The general way in which to achieve these results is to construct from the symmetrized[47] part of the scattering amplitude in the forward direction

$$T^{(s)}(E) = \tfrac{1}{2}[T(E) + T(-E)] \tag{IV-34}$$

an auxiliary function which can be shown to be an analytic univalent function in the upper-half-plane of the complex energy plane, Im $E > 0$, namely, an analytic function which does not take any value more than once in the upper half E plane.

The great advantage is that univalent functions satisfy many sharp inequalities; most of these are a consequence of mathematical theorems by Koebe (see Hayman, 1958, Chapter 1) and Ahlfors (see Nevanlinna, 1953, p. 93).

Here we do not intend to obtain the inequalities by the use of the theory of univalent functions, for which we refer to the original papers; following Khuri and Kinoshita (1965c,d) we shall derive directly an inequality for the real part of the scattering amplitude by exploiting the information given by the fact that $T^{(s)}(E)$ satisfies a twice-subtracted dispersion relation (see Section III,C)

$$T^{(s)}(E) - T^{(s)}(0) = \frac{2E^2}{\pi} \int_\mu^\infty \frac{dE' \; \text{Im} \; T^{(s)}(E')}{E'(E'^2 - E^2)} \qquad (\text{Im } E \geqslant 0). \tag{IV-35}$$

---

[47] As done by Khuri and Kinoshita, we shall refer here to πp scattering; then $T^{(s)}(E)$ is the symmetric amplitude after subtracting the nucleon pole term

$$T^{(s)}(E) = \tfrac{1}{2}[T_{\pi+p}(E) + T_{\pi-p}(E)] - \text{nucleon pole.}$$

In Eq. (IV-35) we have chosen as subtraction point the origin $E = 0$. [For symmetry reasons the first derivative $T^{(s)'}(0) = 0$.]

If we now consider the function

$$g(E) = \int_0^E \frac{T^{(s)}(E') - T^{(s)}(0)}{E'^2} \, dE', \qquad (IV\text{-}36)$$

by using Eq. (IV-35) and taking the real part one gets

$$\text{Re } g(E) = \frac{1}{\pi} \int_\mu^\infty dE' \, \frac{\text{Im } T^{(s)}(E')}{E'^2} \ln \left| \frac{E' + E}{E' - E} \right|; \qquad 0 < \arg E < \pi.$$

$$(IV\text{-}37)$$

From the fact that $\text{Im } T^{(s)}(E) > 0$ for $E > \mu$ (optical theorem) it follows that $\text{Re } g(E) > 0$ for all E, such that $0 \leqslant \arg E \leqslant \pi/2$.

In particular, for positive real E one gets

$$\int_0^E \frac{\text{Re } T^{(s)}(E') - T^{(s)}(0)}{E'^2} \, dE' = \frac{1}{\pi} \int_\mu^\infty dE' \, \frac{\text{Im } T^{(s)}(E')}{E'^2} \ln \left| \frac{E' + E}{E' - E} \right|.$$

$$(IV\text{-}38)$$

The integrand on the right-hand side is always positive. If the integration is cut off at the maximum energy E_m for which experimental data are available, one obtains an inequality which should be satisfied regardless of the actual value of the total cross section at super-high energies

$$\int_0^E \frac{\text{Re } T^{(s)}(E') - T^{(s)}(0)}{E'^2} \, dE' \geqslant \frac{1}{\pi} \int_\mu^{E_m} \frac{\text{Im } T^{(s)}(E')}{E'^2} \ln \left| \frac{E' + E}{E' - E} \right| dE'.$$

$$(IV\text{-}39)$$

It is clear from this inequality that if the real part $\text{Re } T^{(s)}(E)$ at high energies remains negative and larger than $T^{(s)}(0)$, the inequality (IV-39) could be violated.

The inequality (IV-39) presents the disadvantage that for its actual computation one needs the value of $T^{(s)}(0)$ and of $T^{(s)}(E)$ in the unphysical region $0 < E < \mu$. A way to compute these unknown quantities would just be to use the ordinary dispersion relations, since one knows that they work well in the low energy region.[48]

[48] Also if one "subtracts" the inequality (IV-39), by getting

$$\int_{E_1}^E \frac{\text{Re } T^{(s)}(E') - T^{(s)}(0)}{E'^2} \, dE' \geqslant \frac{1}{\pi} \int_\mu^{E_m} \frac{\text{Im } T^{(s)}(E')}{E'^2} \ln \left| \frac{(E' + E)(E' - E_1)}{(E' - E)(E' + E_1)} \right|$$

one still has to know $T^{(s)}(0)$.

A way to overcome this difficulty was proposed by Martin (1965c), who suggested the use of another (univalent) function, namely,

$$g'(E^2) = \int_{\mu^2}^{E^2} dz' \frac{\text{Re } T^{(s)}(z) - T^{(s)}(\mu^2)}{(E^2 - \mu^2)^{3/2}} \tag{IV-40}$$

getting the inequality

$$\int_{\mu^2}^{E^2} \frac{\text{Re } T^{(s)}(z) - T^{(s)}(\mu^2)}{(z - \mu^2)^{3/2}} \, dz$$

$$\geq \frac{1}{\pi} \int_{\mu^2}^{E_m^2} dz' \frac{\text{Im } T^{(s)}(z')}{(z' - \mu^2)^{3/2}} \log \left| \frac{(z' - \mu^2)^{1/2} + (E^2 - \mu^2)^{1/2}}{(z' - \mu^2)^{1/2} - (E^2 - \mu^2)^{1/2}} \right|. \tag{IV-41}$$

It was later shown by Wit (1965c) that this result is true only if the condition $\sigma_T^{(s)}(E) > \sigma_T^{(s)}(\mu)$ is true for all the energies $E > \mu$. This condition for πp scattering is actually true for all energies $E \leqslant 30$ GeV; but, of course, to suppose that it is true also for larger, not yet experimentally available, energies is just an hypothesis on the super-high energy region, which one wants to avoid.

Until now no explicit check of the validity of the inequality (IV-39) and of others, which can be obtained by the use of univalent functions, has been published.

C. THE LARGE-ANGLE SCATTERING

1. Proton-Proton Scattering

At high energies (from 11 to 31.8 GeV/c) measurements (Section II,A,4) of the proton-proton elastic cross section have shown that for momentum transfers larger than ~ 1 (GeV/c)^2 the differential cross section can no longer be represented by the expression

$$\frac{d\sigma}{d(-t)} = \exp(a + bt + ct^2) \tag{IV-42}$$

but it remains much larger than one could expect from its low momentum transfer behavior (see Fig. 7).

The principal characteristics of the large momentum transfer differential cross section are the following:

(1) At fixed energy, for angles larger than about 65°–90°, the differential cross section in the c.m. system seems to be isotropic.

(2) In this region, at fixed momentum transfer, the differential cross section decreases very rapidly when the energy increases; the energy depend-

ence becomes more pronounced the higher the momentum transfer considered. At fixed angle, $d\sigma/d\Omega$ varies as

$$d\sigma/d\Omega \propto \exp(-a\sqrt{s}).$$

(3) If the data are plotted versus the transverse momentum

$$p_\perp = p \sin \Theta,$$

most of the energy dependence is removed, and all the data tend to show a simple behavior of the form (Orear, 1964a; Narayan and Sarma, 1963) (see Fig. 8)

$$d\sigma/d\Omega = A \exp(-ap_\perp). \tag{IV-43}$$

This simple law seems to be valid for all the values of the measured incident momentum and momentum transfer, which range from

$$11 \text{ GeV}/c \leqslant p \leqslant 31.8 \text{ GeV}/c; \qquad 2.25 \leqslant -t \leqslant 24.39 \text{ (GeV}/c)^2.$$

In Section IV,A we have already described the explanations of the large-angle pp scattering as due to sophisticated forms of optical models.

We add here only a few general remarks.

If the optical potential one chooses is an absorptive regular potential at the origin $r = 0$ (namely, a potential which for is $r \to 0$ less singular than $1/r^2$), it is impossible to get an exponential decrease of the differential cross section for large t [we remember that for Θ not too large $p \sin \Theta \simeq \sqrt{|t|}$ and therefore the Orear plot (IV-43) can be approximately written as $d\sigma/d\Omega = A \exp(-a\sqrt{|t|})$]. As we have seen in Section IV,C, by a suitable superposition of Yukawa potential, Serber (1963) was able to get a t^{-5} law for large t, which can also represent a parametrization of the experimental distribution. But if we want an exponential behavior at large t, the absorptive potential has to be strongly singular at the origin, behaving as r^{-n}, with $n > 2$. It should be noticed, however, that this is not the only solution of the problem. In fact, it has been shown (see, for instance, Cottingham and Dombey, 1966) that the same exponential behavior for large t can be reproduced both by a strongly singular absorptive potential and by a very smooth (real or complex) potential, namely, a potential which is analytic in r for all values of r.

The fact that for angles greater than $60°$ in the c.m. system the differential cross section becomes practically isotropic has led many people to give a completely different explanation of that part of the angular distribution.

As for the optical model, one still uses nuclear physics as a guide. In nuclear physics, a practically isotropic differential cross section is present whenever the reaction proceeds via an intermediate compound state, which then decays statistically in any of the possible final states (including elastic and inelastic) with a probability proportional to the phase space. It is therefore under-standable that in this case one could get an isotropic angular distribution (although this is not necessarily a consequence of a statistical model).

With this analogy in mind, many people[49] have applied a statistical model to large-angle ($\geqslant 60°$) pp scattering.

We have already discussed how this model describes the flattening of the angular distribution; the spectacular exponential decrease with the energy of the differential cross section can also be obtained by thermodynamical arguments, and comes essentially from the Boltzmann factor $\exp(-E/KT)$ (remember that the total energy in the c.m. system is connected with s by $E = \sqrt{s}$).

In fact (Hagedorn, 1965), let P_0 be the statistical weight for an elastic central collision (and therefore with large momentum transfer), and ΣP_j, $j \neq 0$, the sum of the statistical factors of all the inelastic channels. The central elastic cross section $\sigma_{cen,el}$ will be proportional to P_0

$$\sigma_{cen,el} = \alpha P_0 \qquad (IV-44)$$

It is not possible to write directly a similar relation between σ_{in} and ΣP_j, since most of the inelastic cross section comes from noncentral collisions. We may, however, write

$$\sigma_{cen} = \alpha \Sigma P_j \qquad (IV-45)$$

and

$$\sigma_{in} = \frac{\sigma_{in}}{\sigma_{cen}} \cdot \sigma_{cen} = \frac{\sigma_{in}}{\sigma_{cen}} \alpha \Sigma P_j. \qquad (IV-46)$$

Now, assuming isotropy, and adding a factor 2 due to the identity of the protons, we can write

$$\frac{d\sigma}{d\Omega} = \frac{2}{4\pi} \alpha P_0 = \frac{2}{4\pi} \sigma_{in} \left(\frac{\sigma_{cen}}{\sigma_{in}}\right) \frac{P_0}{\Sigma P_j}. \qquad (IV-47)$$

One must now compute both $P_0/\Sigma P_j$ and σ_{cen}/σ_{in}; $P_0/\Sigma P_j$ can be computed by calculating the ratio of the elastic and inelastic phase spaces at energy E, and one gets (Orear, 1964b; Fast et al.,1963)

$$\left(\frac{P_0}{\Sigma P_j}\right)_{pp} = \exp[-3.25(E - 2)] \qquad (IV-48)$$

where E is $\sqrt{s}$ in nucleon masses.

[49] Fast and Hagedorn (1963), Fast et al. (1963), Cocconi (1964), Jones (1964), Hagedorn (1965), and Białas and Weisskopf (1965).

For the ratio $\beta = \sigma_{cen}/\sigma_{in}$ Hagedorn (1965) adopts the model of a nucleon without hard core and asks under what conditions a collision can be considered as central; that is, a collision in which thermal equilibrium can be established. By picturing the nucleons as extended Lorentz-contracted objects, and the interaction as a sort of shock wave, thermal equilibrium will be established if during the time Δt of contact the shock wave can travel at least once to the end of the nucleons and back. This is so if the unshaded part of the nucleons in Fig. 27 is less than the contracted radius along the line of flight

$$\rho \leqslant \rho_0 = \frac{\Delta t}{2} = \frac{r}{\gamma} = \frac{2mr}{E} \qquad (\text{IV-49})$$

where r is the nucleon radius, $\gamma = E/2m$ the Lorentz factor.

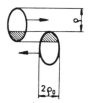

FIG. 27. Pictorial definition of central collisions in the c.m. system [taken from Jones (1964)].

If one now assumes that the ratio between the central and the inelastic cross sections is given by the ratio between the central geometric cross section $\pi\rho_0^2$, for which the above condition is made, and the total geometric cross section πr^2, then

$$\frac{\sigma_{cen}}{\sigma_{in}} = \frac{\pi\rho_0^2}{\pi r^2} = \frac{4m^2}{E^2}, \qquad (\text{IV-50})$$

one finally gets

$$\frac{d\sigma}{d\Omega} = \frac{\sigma_{in}}{2\pi} \frac{4m^2}{E^2} \exp[-3.25(E-2)]. \qquad (\text{IV-51})$$

One can notice that the hypothesis (IV-50) is not so crucial for the result, since the most important part of (IV-51) is the exponential decrease.

Formula (IV-51) gives a very good agreement with the experimental data for angles between $80°$ and $90°$, with $\sigma_{in} = 3 \times 10^{-26}$ cm^2.

If this explanation is correct, then one could also try to explain the intermediate part of the angular distribution (outside the diffraction peak but before $60°$) by adding the diffraction contribution (which depends only on t) and the large-angle statistical contribution (which depends only on s) (Minami,

1964a,b). That this is not the case was shown by Bethe (1964); in fact, even after subtracting the statistical contribution in the intermediate region [for instance, at $-t = 6\ (\text{GeV}/c)^2$], the cross section is still strongly dependent on the energy and cannot be explained by a pure diffraction pattern.

Therefore, the explanation of the intermediate region remains rather mysterious, unless one accepts the refined optical models we have discussed in Section IV,A.

The only assertion one can safely make is that the small-angle and the large-angle angular distribution might probably be explained by different mechanisms, of which the most popular are the optical and the statistical models; the connecting region is, of course, a competing region, which is more difficult to understand (see also below).

An interesting speculation about the large-angle pp scattering was put forward by Wu and Yang (1965). Impressed by the exponential decrease of the differential cross section with the transverse momentum and by the great number of excited states of the nucleon above an excitation energy of 300 MeV, they have argued that "… the difficulty in making large transverse momentum transfers could naturally be due to the difficulty in accelerating the various parts of a nucleon without breaking it up. If this is the case, such a difficulty is presumably present in all high energy collisions. Furthermore, the dominant effect of such a difficulty is to contribute a rapidly decreasing factor to the appropriate differential cross section independent of the specific process."

As a consequence, apart from slowly varying power factors, any process of the form

$$p + p \rightarrow A + B,$$

where A and B are excited states of the nucleon, must decrease at fixed angle exponentially with the same law.

Moreover, one can connect the large-angle pp scattering with the nucleon electromagnetic form factor; in fact, in large-angle pp scattering, both of the final protons receive large $p_\perp$ without breaking up. In ep scattering it is difficult for the proton to receive large momenta, but the electron does not show this difficulty; therefore one can assume that for large momentum transfer the electromagnetic form factor should behave as

$$F(t) \propto A\ \exp(-\tfrac{1}{4}a\sqrt{|t|}) \tag{IV-52}$$

where a is the numerical factor which fits large-angle pp scattering, $a^{-1} = 0.15$ GeV/c. The factor $\tfrac{1}{4}$ comes from the fact that in pp there are two protons, instead of one in ep (which gives a relative factor 2), and moreover in the angular distribution the scattering amplitude has to be squared (which gives another factor 2).

Assumption (IV-52) is not in disagreement with the data.

Therefore it seems that the exponential behavior of the differential cross section with respect to $p_\perp$ could be a very general feature and have a deeper meaning; it is worth mentioning that in $pn \to np$ charge exchange the large-angle scattering (Section II,B) (up to $p \sin \Theta = 0.8$ GeV/c) follows the same law $d\sigma/d\Omega = A \exp(-ap_\perp)$, with a value for the constant $a^{-1} = 0.165$ Gev/c, to be compared with the value for pp, $a^{-1} = 0.15$ Gev/c. Moreover, other processes (Orear, 1964b), such as $\pi p \to \pi p$ and $pp \to \pi d$, follow the same simple law, and also does the transverse momentum distribution of the secondaries produced in pp scattering from 10 to 10^5 GeV:

$$\frac{dN}{dp_\perp} \propto p_\perp \exp(-ap_\perp) \qquad \text{(IV-53)}$$

with $a^{-1} = 160$ MeV/c, namely, the same value which fits pp and πp experiments.

Formula (IV-53) can easily be derived, in the elastic scattering case, from the behavior $d\sigma/d\Omega = A \exp(-ap_\perp)$ of the differential cross section (Cocconi, 1964).

Another interesting remark concerning the large-angle scattering has been made by Kinoshita (1964). He added the physically extremely plausible hypothesis that the total cross section is constant with the energy to the conditions used by Cerulus and Martin (see Section III,C) in obtaining the lower bound on the scattering amplitude, namely:

(a) $T(s, t)$ is analytic and bounded by s^N in a certain domain of the cut $\cos \Theta$ plane;

(b) $|T(s, t)| \leqslant \exp[\varphi_a(s)]$ on the segment of the real axis

$$-a \leqslant \cos \Theta \leqslant a \qquad \text{(IV-54)}$$

where $\varphi_a(s)$ is a positive function of s and $0 < a < 1$.

Then he gets the result

$$|T(s, \cos \Theta)| \geqslant \exp(-[M(\cos \Theta)p \sin \Theta \ln s + N \ln s] \qquad \text{(IV-55)}$$

where $M(\cos \Theta)$ is a complicated, but known function, which for angles not too near to 90° can be written as

$$|T(s, \cos \Theta)| \geqslant \exp\left(-\left[\frac{2(N-1)}{(t_0)^{1/2}} p \sin \Theta \ln s + N \ln s\right]\right) \qquad \text{(IV-56)}$$

(t_0 is the nearest singularity in the t plane).

This formula, apart from the logarithmic term $\ln s$ which multiplies the transverse momentum $p \sin \Theta$, is not very different from the Orear (1964a) fit

$$d\sigma/d\Omega = A \exp(-ap_\perp). \tag{IV-43}$$

One observes therefore that at large angles the scattering at very high energies takes place with the minimum amplitude consistent with the analyticity requirements.

This argument has been put forward by Martin (1965a), who has shown also that a behavior at large t of the form factor proposed by Wu and Yang is consistent with the fastest asymptotic decrease allowed by its analyticity and boundedness properties.

Moreover, if one takes a form for the scattering amplitude factorized in the s and t dependence, as

$$T(s, t) = sf(t) \tag{IV-57}$$

which can fit the diffraction peak, then, if the large-angle cross section is consistent with its lower bound, one gets at fixed angle a behavior of the Orear form (IV-43).

In this way one links together the small- and large-angle behavior of the differential cross section; the plateau of the angular distribution at large angles is therefore a consequence of the diffraction peak, in the sense that, in order to satisfy the general theorems, the cross section cannot decrease too fast.

This explanation is not necessarily in contrast with the statistical model; in fact, in Martin's words (Martin, 1965a):

"In the statistical approach particles are created freely and move freely inside a certain 'volume of interaction.' This volume of interaction is what remains of that force that you cannot suppress unless the scattering amplitude is identically zero. Now, if particles move freely and therefore obey the simple laws of statistical mechanics, this means the interaction is minimal."

2. Pion-Proton Scattering

We have already remarked in Section IV,A on the optical model, that in the momentum range between 1.5 and 18 GeV/c both $\pi^\pm p$ angular distributions show a characteristic shoulder in the differential cross section, lying always at about $-t = 1.5$ (GeV/c)^2.[50]

This shoulder has been generally explained as a secondary maximum in the diffraction pattern. It shows a remarkable feature; namely, as the incident momentum increases the relative magnitude of the maximum decreases;

---

[50] The same bump is also present in the $\pi^- p \to \pi^0 n$ charge exchange angular distribution. (Sonderegger *et al.*, 1966).

whereas at 1.58 GeV/c it behaves like a bump, at 12.5 GeV/c (if it is present) it shows only as an inflection in the angular distribution (Fig. 28).

If the secondary diffraction model has to be retained this characteristic cannot be explained unless some peculiar energy dependence of the opacity factor is assumed. Moreover, it is likely that spin effects and real part effects are important in the energy region where the secondary peak is large (Coffin et al., 1965).[51]

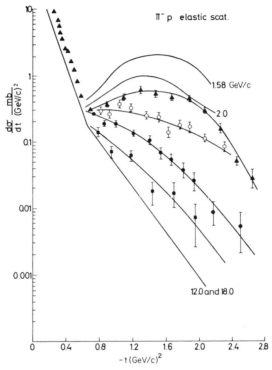

FIG. 28. $d\sigma/d|t|$ versus $-t$ for π^-p-elastic scattering in the secondary maximum region; the smooth curves refer to previous experiments, the points to the experiment of Coffin et al. (1965) from whose paper figure is taken. 1.58 GeV/c, Duke et al. (1965); 2.0 GeV/c, Damouth et al. (1963), and Suwa et al. (1965); (▲) 2.5 GeV/c, (○) 3.0 GeV/c, (●) 4.0 GeV/c, and (■) 6.0 GeV/c, this experiment; 12.0 and 18.0 GeV/c, Orear et al. (1965) and Harting et al. (1965).

The largest angle $\pi^\pm p$ scattering shows a feature similar to pp scattering, namely, the differential cross section changes its diffraction character and flattens.

[51] That spin-flip terms are important whenever they are not overwhelmed by the diffraction peak is shown by the peculiar behavior of the charge exchange differential cross section for $|t| < 0.2$ (see Section II,B), which can only be explained by a spin-flip term.

A remarkable fact, noticed by Perl *et al.* (1965), Orear *et al.* (1965), Caldwell *et al.* (1964), and Coffin *et al.* (1965) is that, whereas inside the principal maximum the *pp*- and *πp*-differential cross sections are always of the same order of magnitude, starting from $-t \cong 2.5$ $(\text{GeV}/c)^2$ the *pp* cross section remains much larger than the $\pi^{\pm} p$ cross sections, which are very similar to each other.

This feature could perhaps give an explanation of the fact that there is no evidence of the secondary maximum in the *pp* angular distribution. In fact, if the flat angular distribution at large *t* is due to some mechanism other than diffraction, as discussed above, the large flat background which is present in *pp* could not allow the observation of a small effect, such as the secondary maximum, which can instead be seen in $\pi^{\pm} p$, due to the much smaller value of the flat background. A difficulty in this interpretation is that, as we have said, in *πp* scattering the secondary maximum tends to disappear at high energies, where the absolute value of the flat part diminishes.

However, the most interesting interpretation of the secondary maximum in *πp* collisions is provided by the Regge pole theory, and will be discussed in Section IV,D,3.

An interesting representation which connects at the same time the small and large *t* behavior of the elastic differential cross section, both for *pp* and *πp* scattering, has been proposed by Contogouris (1966); starting from an iteration in the *s* channel of a Regge-like amplitude (see Section IV,D), he gets an impact-representation scattering amplitude of the form

$$1 - e^{2i\delta} = 1 - a(b) = \frac{A \exp(-\mu^2 b^2)}{1 - RA \exp(-\mu^2 b^2)}$$

where A, μ, and R are three parameters, which can be expressed in terms of the total cross section, the width of the diffraction peak, and the ratio $\sigma_{\text{el}}/\sigma_{\text{tot}}$. In this way, having fixed the parameters in such a way to fit the small-*t* part of the angular distribution, one gets a rather good fit of the large-*t* distribution; moreover, the smaller value of the *πp* scattering at large *t* in comparison with the *pp* scattering is explained in terms of the lower value of the ratio $\sigma_{\text{el}}/\sigma_{\text{tot}}$.

Another interesting feature of the $\pi^{\pm} p$ angular distribution is the behavior of the differential cross section near the backward direction in the center-of-mass system.

The angular distribution for $\pi^{+} p$ scattering in the energy range between 3 and 8 GeV/c (Section II,A) definitely shows a backward peak which is much smaller than the forward peak; the height of the differential cross section at 180° is about 2×10^{-3} times the height of the forward differential cross section at 4 GeV/c.

Concerning the shape of the backward angular distribution, it can be fitted with a formula similar to that used for the diffraction peaks, where one obviously substitutes u for t

$$\frac{d\sigma}{d(-u)} = \exp(a + bu).$$

For the backward peak, the experimental results give values of b ranging from 17 ± 3 $(\text{GeV}/c)^{-2}$ at 8 GeV/c to 11.6 $(\text{GeV}/c)^{-2}$ at 4 GeV/c, where the values of b for the forward peak are of the order of 8 $(\text{GeV}/c)^{-2}$. Therefore the backward peak is narrower than the forward diffraction peak.

The situation is slightly more complicated for $\pi^- p$. In fact in many experiments there is no evidence for a backward peak, although it is found in other experiments (Section II,A); in any case if it is present, it is much smaller (from 4 to 7 times) than the corresponding peak in $\pi^+ p$. (Perhaps this is the reason which has prevented it being found in experiments which are not sufficiently accurate.)

Many arguments have been used in the attempt to explain the backward peak. The simplest (Blokhintsev, 1962, 1966; Perl et al., 1963) is to treat the backward region by an optical model, by applying to the small values of the angle

$$\Theta' = 180° - \Theta$$

the same approximations as one does for the forward peak. In this way one gets for the backward peak the formula

$$(d\sigma/d\Omega)_{\Theta'} = (1 - a)^2 \, R^2 [B(kR\Theta')]^2 \qquad \text{(IV-58)}$$

where $B(kR\Theta)$ is a function which is more peaked than $J_1(kR \sin \Theta)$ and whose first terms in the series expansion are

$$B = \tfrac{1}{2}[1 - (kR\Theta/2)^2]. \qquad \text{(IV-59)}$$

In this way one correctly obtains a narrower angular distribution for the backward peak in comparison with the forward peak. A great difficulty in this theory is that it predicts a backward differential cross section independent of the energy, whereas experimentally it decreases by a factor of 3 in passing from 4 to 8 GeV/c. Moreover, this simple model does not give any explanation of the differences between $\pi^+ p$ and $\pi^- p$ scattering.

A mechanism which could explain this difference is neutron exchange, which gives a pole near the backward direction in $\pi^+ p$ but is absent in $\pi^- p$ (Fig. 29). If the contribution of this Feynman diagram is calculated without corrections for the form factor in the $pn\pi$ vertex and for the absorption, it gives a contribution which is too large. By taking into account these corrections, the shape of the $\pi^+ p$ backward peak comes out right, but the magnitude is still too large at energies of some GeV (Białas, 1965).

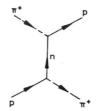

FIG. 29.   The neutron exchange Feynman diagram.

Another explanation in terms of Regge poles will be discussed in Section IV,D,3.

D. THE REGGE POLE MODEL

None of the models we have discussed so far for the elastic scattering (optical model, statistical model) use in a specific way the general properties of the scattering amplitude discussed in Section III.

On the other hand, models such as the strip approximation (Chew and Frautschi, 1961a,b,c; Amati *et al.*, 1961) or the Regge pole theory make full use of the analyticity properties.

Since the strip approximation contains many difficulties (mainly concerning the asymptotic behavior of the amplitude) which are overcome by the Regge pole theory, we shall limit ourselves to presenting here the basic theory and the applications of this last approach.

We are aware of the fact that today no physicist, even the most optimistic, still has the illusion that all the features of high energy elastic scattering can be explained in terms of only one dominant Regge trajectory (at least at the energies available with the present machines); nevertheless, in terms of Regge poles one can give a rather simple explanation of some phenomena, such as the charge exchange reactions, and relate some characteristics of high energy scattering, such as the behavior of the total cross sections, the phase of the forward scattering amplitude, and the polarization.

Our line of work will be first a brief review of the Regge theory in non-relativistic scattering and its extension to relativistic scattering; then the unsuccessful analysis of high energy scattering in terms of the dominant Regge trajectory alone, and finally the present phenomenology of high energy scattering in terms of a relatively small number of families of known elementary particles.

1. *Potential Theory*

Let us consider the partial wave expansion of the scattering amplitude

$$f(E, \cos \Theta) = \sum_{l=0}^{\infty} (2l + 1)P_l(\cos \Theta)f_l(E). \qquad \text{(IV-60)}$$

By using the Sommerfeld-Watson transform (Sommerfeld, 1949, p. 279; Morse and Feshbach, 1953, Chapter 4), the expansion (IV-60) can be rewritten as an integral in the complex plane of the angular momentum variable

$$f(E, \cos \Theta) = \frac{i}{2} \int_{C_1} \frac{(2l+1)}{\sin \pi l} f(l, E) P_l(-\cos \Theta) \, dl \qquad \text{(IV-61)}$$

where the contour C_1 is shown in Fig. 30.

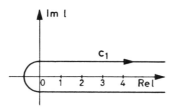

FIG. 30.   The complex path of integration for the Sommerfeld-Watson transform.

Now, it was shown by Regge (1960; also, Bottino et al., 1962) that, for a potential which is a superposition of Yukawa potentials, the integration path can be deformed along the straight line parallel to the imaginary l axis through $l = -\frac{1}{2}$; in this way the scattering amplitude can be expressed as an integral along that line (the so-called background integral) plus the sum of the residues of the poles, which can be present in the right half l plane

$$f(E, \cos \Theta) = \frac{i}{2} \int_{-1/2-i\infty}^{-1/2+i\infty} \frac{2l+1}{\sin \pi l} f(l, E) P_l(-\cos \Theta) \, dl$$

$$+ \sum_{n=1}^{N} \frac{C_n(E)}{\sin \pi l_n(E)} P_{l_n(E)}(-\cos \Theta). \qquad \text{(IV-62)}$$

We can now look for the physical meaning of these poles and their relation with the bound states.

When, for $\cos \Theta$ fixed, the energy E varies, the position of any pole $l_n(E)$ describes a trajectory in the complex l plane (Regge trajectory).

It is shown in the articles quoted above that for $E < 0$ (namely, in the bound-state region), one has

$$\text{Im } l_n(E) = 0 \qquad \left(\frac{dl_n(E)}{dE} \right)_{E=0} > 0. \qquad \text{(IV-63)}$$

The connection with the bound states arises whenever the real part of $l_n(E)$ passes through a positive integer (the physical values of the angular momentum). In fact, if one takes for simplicity only the term corresponding to one trajectory

$$f_n(E, \cos \Theta) = \frac{C_n(E)}{\sin \pi \, l_n(E)} \, P_{l_n(E)}(-\cos \Theta) \qquad \text{(IV-64)}$$

and projects out of it the lth partial wave, one gets

$$f_n(l, E) = \frac{1}{\pi} \frac{C_n(E)}{(l_n + l + 1)(l_n - l)}. \qquad \text{(IV-65)}$$

Suppose now there is a value E_0 of the energy E, such that

$$l_n(E_0) = L + i\alpha$$

where L is a positive integer (or 0). Then, for $E \approx E_0$, one has

$$f_n(L, E) = \frac{\gamma_n}{E - E_0 + i\Gamma} \qquad \gamma_n = \frac{C_n(E_0)}{\pi(2L + 1)(d \operatorname{Re} l_n(E)/dE)_{E=E_0}}$$

$$\Gamma = \frac{\alpha}{(d \operatorname{Re} l_n(E)/dE)_{E=E_0}}. \qquad \text{(IV-66)}$$

In the region $E < 0$ (see IV-63) $\alpha = 0$ and therefore $\Gamma = 0$. Then the scattering amplitude shows a pole for a real negative value of the energy, namely, a bound state with angular momentum L.

In the region $E > 0$ (scattering region), $\Gamma \neq 0$, and we have a Breit-Wigner form of the scattering amplitude for a resonance with angular momentum L.

It is clear, therefore, that a single Regge trajectory can at the same time describe a group of bound states and resonances, which of course must have the same quantum numbers, apart from the angular momentum which turns out to be a function of the energy E of the real or complex energy levels of the bound states and resonances.

If now one interprets all the existing particles (Chew and Frautschi, 1961d, 1962), stable or unstable, as Regge poles, then they must all lie on Regge trajectories which are characterized by quantum numbers, specific to the trajectory itself.

2. Regge Poles and High Energy Scattering

What is now the relevance of Regge poles for the high energy (Frautschi *et al.*, 1962) scattering of the elementary particles? It comes when one adds the crossing relation to the hypothesis that the Regge pole theory is also valid in field theory.[52]

---

[52] Although until now it has not been possible to prove that in an exact field theory this hypothesis is true, it was shown (Bertocchi *et al.*, 1962; Amati *et al.*, 1962a) that a large class of Feynman diagrams show an asymptotic Regge behavior (see also Section VI,C,2). Nevertheless, the validity of the Regge theory in field theory has to be considered as a postulate.

In fact, in potential theory Regge was able to show that the background integral for cos $\Theta \to \infty$ vanishes at least as $(\cos \Theta)^{-1/2}$, and therefore is dominated by the pole contribution, which behaves as $(\cos \Theta)^{l_n(E)}$ [remember that $P_l(\cos \Theta)$ is a polynomial of order l].

If now we pass to relativistic scattering in the channel in which s has the meaning of the square of the energy and t of the momentum transfer, one can perform the analytic continuation in the complex angular momentum of the crossed t channel; therefore, the contribution of one Regge pole to the scattering amplitude becomes of the form

$$\frac{C_n(t)}{\sin \pi \, \alpha_n(t)} \, P_{\alpha_n(t)}(-\cos \Theta_t) \qquad \text{(IV-67)}$$

where we have denoted by $\alpha_n(t)$ the complex angular momentum in the t channel, and cos Θ_t is related to s and the masses m_1 and m_2 of the two initial particles (in the s channel) by

$$\cos \Theta_t = [s + (t/2) - m_1{}^2 - m_2{}^2]/2\{[t/4 - m_1{}^2][t/4 - m_2{}^2]\}^{1/2}. \qquad \text{(IV-68)}$$

If, at fixed t, we let s go to infinity, we see that for $s \to \infty$ also cos $\Theta_t \to \infty$; if also in field theory the pole terms dominate asymptotically, and if the Regge poles are the only singularities[53] in the right-hand half of the complex l plane, the asymptotic behavior of the scattering amplitude for $s \to \infty$ will be of the form

$$T(s, t) \underset{s \to \infty}{\to} \sum_n \frac{\beta_n(t)(-s)^{\alpha_n(t)}}{\sin \pi \, \alpha_n(t)}. \qquad \text{(IV-69)}$$

We can now recognize two great differences between potential and relativistic scattering:

(1) Whereas in potential scattering the region in which Regge poles represent the dominant term of the amplitude, namely, cos $\Theta \to \infty$, is highly unphysical (the physical region running, of course, between $+1$ and -1), in relativistic scattering the values $s \to \infty$, $t \leqslant 0$ are physical values, characterizing the high energy scattering in the s channel. This important feature can be understood by noticing that in potential theory there are only two intervals

---

[53] One should, of course, note that it was shown by Mandelstam (1963) on the basis of the properties of particular Feynman diagrams, and by Gribov *et al.* (1965) by the analysis of multiparticle terms of the unitarity condition in the t channel, that very likely there are also moving branch points in the angular momentum plane, in the physical sheet. The position of those branch points is the same as found first by Bertocchi *et al.* (1962) for the branch points in the unphysical sheets by iterating in the s channel the Regge amplitude of the multiperipheral model (see also Section VI,C,2). Nevertheless, one can hope that the contributions of these cuts in the angular momentum will not be very important, at least in an energy region that is not too high.

of E, namely, the scattering region, $E > 0$, and the bound-state region, $E < 0$. In field theory, owing to the crossing property the intervals are three, since the bound-state interval is finite, running from t_0 (the threshold of the t channel) down to zero; for $t > t_0$ one encounters the scattering region of the t channel (where t has the meaning of an energy squared), while $t \leqslant 0$ belongs to the scattering in the s channel (and t has now the meaning of a momentum transfer).

(2) The second difference, connected, as the first one, with the crossing property, says that since unitarity has to hold not only in the t channel (where the analytic continuation of the partial wave expansion was performed) but also in the s channel, the power $\alpha_n(t)$ has, for $t \leqslant 0$, an upper limit $\alpha_n(t) \leqslant 1$ (Froissart limit, see Section III,C).

In analogy with potential theory, one assumes that in relativistic scattering also $\alpha(t)$ is real for $t < t_0$; moreover, $\alpha'(0) > 0$[54]; in general, one assumes $\alpha'(t) > 0$ for the whole interval $-\infty < t < t_0$.

The intercepts of Re $\alpha(t)$ with positive integers correspond to stable particles (for $0 < t < t_0$) or resonances ($t > t_0$).

Another minor difference, which is nevertheless very important for the high energy phenomenology, is:

(3) Whereas in potential theory one can have a direct potential without an exchange potential, in field theory the presence of the crossed u channel always introduces an exchange amplitude (Frautschi et al., 1962).

Therefore one must divide the amplitude in the symmetric and antisymmetric parts with respect to the exchange $s \rightarrow u$, with

$$T_n^{\pm}(s, t) = \beta_n^{\pm}(t) \frac{(-s)^{\alpha_n(t)} \pm (-u)^{\alpha_n(t)}}{2 \sin \pi \alpha_n(t)}. \qquad \text{(IV-70)}$$

Since, for $s \rightarrow \infty$, $u \rightarrow -s$, we obtain from the analytic continuation of the Legendre polynomial to positive values of s the form of the dominant term

$$T_n^{\pm}(s, t) = \beta_n^{\pm}(t) \cdot s^{\alpha_n(t)} \cdot \left\{ \frac{\exp[-i\pi\alpha_n(t)] \pm 1}{2 \sin \pi \alpha_n(t)} \right\}, \qquad \text{(IV-71)}$$

where $\beta_n^{\pm}(t)$ is real for $t \leqslant 0$ (Frautschi et al., 1962; Barut and Zwanziger, 1962).

The factor

$$\frac{\exp[-i\pi\alpha_n(t)] \pm 1}{2 \sin \pi \alpha_n(t)} = \xi_n^{\pm}(t) \qquad \text{(IV-72)}$$

is called the signature.

[54] This property is valid in some models of Regge poles in field theory (see Bertocchi et al., 1962).

It can now be shown that the trajectory, which in the diffraction region $t \leqslant 0$ has the maximum possible value of $\alpha(t)$ [namely, $\alpha(0) = 1$], must have positive signature, if one imposes the condition that the real part of the amplitude cannot diverge for $s \to \infty$.

In fact, for even signature, we have[55]

$$A^+(s, t) \xrightarrow[s \to \infty]{} -\tfrac{1}{2}\beta^+(t)s^{\alpha(t)} \tag{IV-73}$$

and therefore

$$\sigma_T(s) \propto \frac{A(s, 0)}{s} = \frac{|\beta^+(0)|}{2} s^{\alpha(0)-1}$$

behaves as a constant if $\alpha(0) = 1$:

$$D^+(s, t) \xrightarrow[s \to \infty]{} \frac{\beta^+(t)}{2} \left[\frac{\cos \pi \alpha(t) + 1}{\sin \pi \alpha(t)} \right] s^{\alpha(t)} \xrightarrow[\alpha(0) \to 1]{} 0. \tag{IV-74}$$

If we had taken odd signature, we would still have obtained (IV-73), but instead of (IV-74) we would get

$$D^-(s, t) \xrightarrow[s \to \infty]{} \frac{\beta^-(t)}{2} \left[\frac{\cos \pi \alpha(t)}{\sin \pi \alpha(t)} \frac{1}{} \right] s^{\alpha(t)} \xrightarrow[\alpha(0) \to 1]{} \infty. \tag{IV-75}$$

If therefore the ratio $D(s, 0)/A(s, 0)$ is not to diverge for $s \to \infty$, the dominant trajectory must have positive signature. This result is a special form of the general result obtained in Section III, where we have shown that if $D(s, 0)/A(s, 0)$ does not diverge for $s \to \infty$, the dominant amplitude must have the quantum numbers of the vacuum in the t channel, and therefore positive signature. In accordance with this alternative form of the Pomeranchuk-Okun theorem, it is assumed (Chew et al., 1962; Gribov, 1961; Lovelace, 1962) that there exists a Regge trajectory which crosses $\alpha = 1$ for $t = 0$ (in order to get constant asymptotic cross sections) and moreover has all the quantum numbers of the vacuum.

This trajectory, which controls the asymptotic limit of all the total and elastic cross sections, is called the Pomeranchuk trajectory (P).

3. Phenomenology of High Energy Scattering

Let us now suppose that the asymptotic behavior of the scattering amplitude is controlled by the Regge poles.

If at the energies available with the present machines the asymptotic region is already reached, the elastic scattering will be controlled by the only Pomeranchuk pole. The only difference between different physical processes

---

[55] Note that $\beta^+(0)$, as defined here, must be negative.

will then consist in different residue functions $\beta(t)$. Therefore the amplitude for a particular elastic scattering, which shall be distinguished by a suffix i, will be

$$T^{(i)}(s, t) = \beta_i(t)s^{\alpha_P(t)}\xi^+. \tag{IV-76}$$

For the total and differential cross sections one gets

$$\sigma_T^i(s) \propto |\beta_i(0)|s^{\alpha_P(0)-1} = \text{const}$$

$$\frac{d\sigma^i(s, t)}{dt} \propto \beta_i^2(t)s^{2[\alpha_P(t)-1]}\left[1 + \cot^2\frac{\pi\alpha_P(t)}{2}\right]. \tag{IV-77}$$

The main predictions of these formulas are (Chew *et al.*, 1962):

(1) The diffraction peak of each differential cross section must shrink with increasing energy, because

$$\frac{d\sigma^i(s_1, t)}{d\sigma^i(s_2, t)} \to \left(\frac{s_1}{s_2}\right)^{2[\alpha_P(t)-1]} \tag{IV-78}$$

is smaller than 1 for $t \lesssim 0$ and $s_1 > s_2$, since $\alpha'_P(t) > 0$ and $\alpha_P(0) = 1$.

(2) The ratio of the differential cross sections of two different processes at the same energy is only a function of t

$$\frac{d\sigma^i(s_1, t)}{d\sigma^j(s_1, t)} \to f(t). \tag{IV-79}$$

(3) The total cross sections for NN, πN, and $\pi\pi$ must be related by

$$\sigma_{\pi N}^2(s) = \sigma_{NN}(s)\sigma_{\pi\pi}(s). \tag{IV-80}$$

This last relation is a consequence of the factorization of the residues (Gell-Mann, 1962; Gribov and Pomeranchuk, 1962b,c); namely, the coupling of each Regge pole with the two incident particles, which can be diagrammatically described as in Fig. 31, is the product of a factor which refers only to the upper particle, with a factor which refers only to the lower one.

As we have seen in Section II these very simple predictions are not satisfied by the experiment, both for the different behaviors of the total and differential cross sections with energy and for the different energy dependence of the diffraction peaks in various processes, of which some shrink, some remain constant, and some others expand; the third prediction cannot be tested experimentally, since $\pi\pi$ cross sections at high energy have not yet been measured either directly or indirectly.

We are therefore forced to conclude that if the Regge approach has something to do with nature, we are not yet in the asymptotic region where the dominant Pomeranchuk pole is sufficient to explain the scattering amplitude.

In such a situation, if one wants to preserve the Regge pole theory, one is forced to consider other contributions coming from lower lying trajectories which could be important at intermediate energies.

Of course, the physically relevant trajectories must be chosen only on phenomenological grounds, by trying to fit the experimental data either by means of trajectories to which some physical particles or resonances do belong, or by postulating the existence of some further trajectories which are

FIG. 31. Schematic representation of the exchange of a Regge pole, (drawn as a spring) in the description of the reaction $a + b \rightarrow a' + b'$.

needed to explain experiments. It is interesting that all the trajectories which have been predicted only to fit experiments have then been associated with some resonances, which sometimes have been experimentally discovered only after their theoretical prediction.

Besides the P trajectory, whose quantum numbers are

$$T = 0, \qquad P = +, \qquad G = +, \qquad \text{positive signature,}$$

and to which one may associate the f^0 resonance (2^{++}); in this case the trajectory should pass through the points

$$J = 1 \quad \text{at} \quad t = 0 \qquad \text{and} \quad J = 2 \quad \text{at} \quad t = (m_{f_0})^2 = (1253 \text{ MeV})^2,$$

the natural candidates for nonstrange boson Regge trajectories (which can be useful for explaining the low momentum transfer scattering) are the ρ trajectory (1^{-+}) and the the ω trajectory (1^{--}).

In all the reasonable fits, as we shall see, all these trajectories have $\alpha(0) > 0$ and could then be useful for explaining high energy scattering (for instance, the π trajectory, which crosses $J = 0$ at 140 MeV, must have $\alpha'(t) > 0$, $\alpha(0) < 0$, and is therefore too low to be observed).

Nevertheless, it has been very quickly recognized that these three trajectories are not enough to explain the high energy data.

The first new trajectory, which was proposed on theoretical grounds by Igi (1962, 1963), is a trajectory which has the same quantum numbers of the vacuum as the Pomeranchuk trajectory P, and is usually called P'.

The reason for the need of the P' is as follows:

If the Pomeranchuk trajectory is the only singularity with the quantum numbers of the vacuum and with $\alpha(0) > 0$, then one can use an unsubtracted dispersion relation for the symmetric part of the forward πp scattering (after having subtracted the contribution of the P pole), since what remains of the amplitude goes to 0 for $s \to \infty$. One therefore gets (Igi, 1962) the simple sum rule for the scattering length $a^+ = \frac{1}{3}(a_1 + 2a_3)$:

$$\left(1 + \frac{1}{m}\right)a^+ + \frac{f^2}{m}\frac{1}{1 - 1/(4m^2)} = \frac{1}{2\pi^2}\int_0^\infty dk'[\sigma_T^{(s)}(k') - \sigma_T^{(s)}(\infty)]. \qquad \text{(IV-81)}$$

Here all quantities are expressed in units of the pion mass; the meaning of the symbols used can be found in Section IV,B.

If one inserts the experimental data, the left-hand side has a value of ~ 0.014, while the right-hand side gives 2.2. Therefore, if the Regge poles are the only contributions at high energies, there must exist another trajectory with the quantum numbers of the vacuum (the only ones which can contribute to the symmetric amplitude at $t = 0$) and $\alpha(0) = 0.5$.

In recent years a resonance has been discovered, the f' (Barnes et al., 1965), which has a mass $m = 1500$ MeV and the quantum numbers (2^{++})

$$J = 2, \qquad T = 0, \qquad P = +, \qquad G = +,$$

and which could therefore be a good candidate for lying on the P' trajectory.

The spectrum of the nonstrange boson trajectories with $\alpha(0) > 0$ is completed by another trajectory, with the quantum numbers

$$T = 1, \qquad P = +, \qquad G = -, \qquad \text{positive signature.}$$

This trajectory, usually called R, was first suggested by Pignotti (1964) on the basis of SU(3) and bootstrap arguments; afterward it was shown (Ahmadzadeh, 1964) that its introduction is needed to explain the pp and np total cross sections and the np charge exchange angular distribution, as well as the Kp and Kn (Phillips and Rarita, 1965a) total cross sections and the $K^-p \to \overline{K}^0n$ charge exchange data. It might be associated with the $T = 1$, $J = 2$, $P = +$ A_2 meson (mass = 1300 MeV).

Table VIII gives the Regge trajectories, with baryon number and strangeness equal to zero, which are relevant to the interpretation of high energy data. We do not think it useful either to trace trajectories as straight lines or something else, or to report trajectories which are not required to explain high energy scattering, and therefore whose existence as Regge trajectories is not based on experimental evidence.

We shall now present a brief review of the experimental facts which can be fitted by using the previous five trajectories; our line will be to start from the simplest reactions (namely, those which need the least number of trajectories, for reasons of selection rules) and then to pass to the more complicated ones.

One further complication in the Regge pole theory when applied to physical processes is due to the spin of the scattering particles. This means

TABLE VIII

REGGE TRAJECTORIES RELEVANT TO INTERPRETATION OF HIGH ENERGY DATA

Trajec- tory	Isospin T	Parity P	Parity G	Signa- ture	$\alpha(0)^a$	$\alpha'(0)^a$	Particles associated with the trajectory		
							Name	Spin	(MeV) mass
P	0	+	+	+	1	0.34	f^0	2	1250
P'	0	+	+	+	0.5	0.34	f'	2	1500
ρ	1	−	+	−	0.54	0.65	ρ	1	765
ω	0	−	−	−	0.52	0.60	ω	1	782
R	1	+	−	+	0.32	0.80	A_2	2	1300

^{a} Taken from the first solution of Table IX.

that whenever the nucleon enters into the game one has to consider the possibility of helicity flip. This fact has the consequence that the number of couplings between the Regge trajectories and the scattering particles becomes greater; a systematic treatment of the spin effects in πN scattering has been given by Singh (1963), and in NN scattering by Wagner (1963).

The simplest reaction which can be explained by the five Regge trajectories of Table VIII is pion-nucleon charge exchange scattering.

In fact, the quantum numbers of the t channel are

$$T \geqslant 1, \qquad N = 0, \qquad G = +, \qquad P = (-1)^J$$

where J is the exchanged spin. Among the five trajectories, only the ρ satisfies those requirements.

The differential cross section is given by (Phillips and Rarita, 1965b)

$$\frac{d\sigma}{dt}(s, t) = \frac{1}{\pi s}\left(\frac{m}{4k}\right)^2\left\{\left(1 - \frac{t}{4m^2}\right)|A|^2 + \frac{t}{4m^2}\left(s - \frac{s + p^2}{1 - (t/4m^2)}\right)|B|^2\right\} \quad \text{(IV-82)}$$

where A is the nonhelicity flip amplitude

$$A = -C_\rho \frac{\exp(-i\pi\alpha_\rho) - 1}{\sin \pi \alpha_\rho}\left(\frac{E}{E_0}\right)^{\alpha_\rho} \quad \text{(IV-83)}$$

and B the helicity-flip amplitude

$$B = -D_\rho \frac{\exp(-i\pi\alpha_\rho) - 1}{\sin \pi \alpha_\rho}\left(\frac{E}{E_0}\right)^{\alpha_\rho - 1} \quad \text{(IV-84)}$$

(k is the c.m. system momentum, p the pion lab. momentum, m the nucleon mass, E the total pion lab. energy, E_0 an arbitrary scale parameter, and C and D the residues).

This formula gives a good fit (Logan, 1965a) to the experiment (Section II,A) in the interval of t from 0 to -0.32 $(\text{GeV}/c)^2$, for energies ranging between 6 and 16 GeV/c (Fig. 32; see also Desai, 1966). The best fit for $\alpha_\rho(t)$ gives a straight line[56]

$$\alpha_\rho(t) = 0.64 \pm 0.02 + (0.64 \pm 0.04)t. \qquad \text{(IV-85)}$$

Another case in which only one trajectory can contribute is the reaction

$$\pi^- p \to \eta^0 n$$

in which only the R trajectory can contribute (Phillips and Rarita, 1965c). The forward peak $[0 \leqslant -t \leqslant 1 \; (\text{GeV}/c)^2]$ has been analyzed (Guisan *et al.*, 1965)

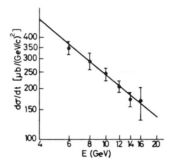

FIG. 32. Differential cross section $d\sigma/dt$ as a function of the incident energy for the reaction $\pi^- p \to \pi^0 n$ between 6 and 16 GeV. The continuous line is the ρ trajectory fit [taken from Logan (1965a)].

at 10 GeV/c by taking the same parameters of the R trajectory as derived by Phillips and Rarita (1965b) from the analysis of πp and Kp experiments (see below). The slope of the differential cross section, together with the small-angle dip, is well reproduced, and the fit is rather good except for two experimental points between 0 and 0.2 $(\text{GeV}/c)^2$ (Fig. 33).

---

[56] A value of $\alpha_\rho(0)$ of the order of 0.5 is in agreement with the observed behavior of the integrated charge exchange cross section, proportional to

$$\frac{1}{p} \sim \frac{1}{s} \simeq s^{-2 + 2\alpha(0)}/\log s.$$

Moreover, the behavior for $|t| < 0.2$ of the charge exchange differential cross section (see Section II,B) can be qualitatively understood by noticing that the spin-flip term vanishes for $t = 0$, due to the kinematical factor t, is different from zero for $t \neq 0$, but it has to vanish again for $\alpha(t) = 0$ (namely, for $|t| \simeq 1$) due to the signature factor $(e^{-i\pi\alpha} - 1)$. [In other words, when the trajectory has $\alpha(t) = 0$, the spin of the Reggeized ρ is zero, and therefore only one coupling with the proton is left.]

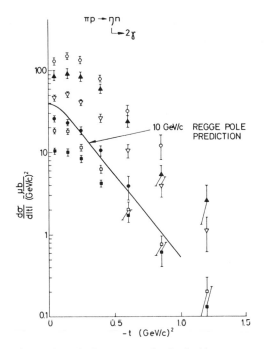

FIG. 33.   The experimental results for $\pi^- p \to \eta^0 n$, for incident momentum between 2.91 and 18.2 GeV/c. The solid line is the Regge pole prediction on the basis of the R trajectory exchange, as calculated by Phillips and Rarita (1965c) [taken from Guisan et al., 1965]. Data (in GeV/c) are as follows: (O) 2.91, (▲) 3.72, (▽) 5.9, (●) 9.8, (□) 13.3, and (■) 18.2.

A further confirmation of the Regge pole theory for the reaction $\pi^- p \to \pi^0 n$ is found in the analysis by Höhler $et\,al$. (1966b). In this paper, both the old data of the Saclay group (Stirling et al., 1965) for $\pi^- p \to \pi^0 n$, and new data from the same group (Sonderegger et al., 1966), for incident momenta between 4.83 and 18.2 GeV/c are analyzed up to a momentum transfer $|t| = 2$ (GeV/c)^2 on the basis of the Regge pole theory. A good fit is obtained by taking

$$\alpha_\rho(0) = 0.57 \pm 0.02 \qquad \alpha_\rho{}'(0) = 0.87 \pm 0.05 \, (\text{GeV}/c)^{-2}.$$

One therefore gets a remarkable shrinking of the peak; moreover, the non-spin-flip and the spin-flip amplitudes turn out to have the same energy dependence.

Also for the reaction $\pi^- p \to \eta n$, an analysis of the data at all the measured energies has been recently performed by Phillips and Rarita (1965f). They get parameters for the R trajectory in agreement with those previously obtained.

In order to see which combination of cross sections is a function of only two trajectories, it is useful to write the amplitudes for various processes, involving π mesons, K mesons, nucleons, and antinucleons, in terms of the Regge trajectories which can contribute

$$(1) \quad T(\pi^+ p \to \pi^+ p) = T_P + T_{P'} - T_\rho$$

$$(2) \quad T(\pi^- p \to \pi^- p) = T_P + T_{P'} + T_\rho$$

$$(3) \quad T(\pi^- p \to \pi^0 n) = -\sqrt{2}\, T_\rho$$

$$(4) \quad T(K^- p \to K^- p) = T_P + T_{P'} + T_\rho + T_\omega + T_R$$

$$(5) \quad T(K^- n \to K^- n) = T_P + T_{P'} - T_\rho + T_\omega - T_R$$

$$(6) \quad T(K^+ p \to K^+ p) = T_P + T_{P'} - T_\rho - T_\omega + T_R$$

$$(7) \quad T(K^+ n \to K^+ n) = T_P + T_{P'} + T_\rho - T_\omega - T_R \qquad \text{(IV-86)}$$

$$(8) \quad T(K^- p \to \overline{K}^0 n) = \qquad\qquad + 2T_\rho \qquad + 2T_R$$

$$(9) \quad T(K^+ n \to K^0 p) = \qquad\qquad - 2T_\rho \qquad + 2T_R$$

$$(10) \quad T(pp \to pp) = T_P + T_{P'} - T_\rho - T_\omega + T_R$$

$$(11) \quad T(\bar{p}p \to \bar{p}p) = T_P + T_{P'} + T_\rho + T_\omega + T_R$$

$$(12) \quad T(pn \to pn) = T_P + T_{P'} + T_\rho - T_\omega - T_R$$

$$(13) \quad T(pn \to np) = \qquad\qquad - 2T_\rho \qquad + 2T_R.$$

These relations are valid for the amplitudes, but, from the optical theorem, they are also valid for the total cross sections.

We can therefore obtain relations which are functions of only two Regge trajectories.[57]

$$(a) \quad \sigma_T(\pi^+ p) + \sigma_T(\pi^- p) \propto \text{Im}(T_P + T_{P'})_0$$

$$(b) \quad \sigma_T(K^- p) - \sigma_T(K^- n) \propto \text{Im}(T_\rho + T_R)_0$$

$$(c_1) \quad \sigma_T(K^+ n) - \sigma_T(K^+ p) \propto$$
$$\qquad\qquad\qquad\qquad\qquad \text{Im}(T_\rho - T_R)_0$$
$$(c_2) \quad \sigma_T(pn) - \sigma_T(pp) \quad \propto$$

$$(d_1) \quad \sigma_T(K^- p) - \sigma_T(K^+ p) \propto$$
$$\qquad\qquad\qquad\qquad\qquad \text{Im}(T_\rho + T_\omega)_0 \qquad \text{(IV-87)}$$
$$(d_2) \quad \sigma_T(\bar{p}p) - \sigma_T(pp) \quad \propto$$

$$(e) \quad \sigma_T(K^- n) - \sigma_T(K^+ n) \propto \text{Im}(T_\omega - T_\rho)_0$$

$$(f) \quad \sigma_T(K^- n) - \sigma_T(K^+ p) \propto \text{Im}(T_\omega - T_R)_0$$

$$(g_1) \quad \sigma_T(K^- p) - \sigma_T(K^+ n) \propto$$
$$\qquad\qquad\qquad\qquad\qquad \text{Im}(T_\omega + T_R)_0$$
$$(g_2) \quad \sigma_T(\bar{p}p) - \sigma_T(pn) \quad \propto$$

[57] The only combination which is a function of only one Regge trajectory, namely, $\sigma_T(\pi^- p) - \sigma_T(\pi^+ p)$, which contains only the ρ trajectory, from charge independence gives the same information as $\pi^- p$ charge exchange.

Of course, the same information which comes out from (b) and (c) can also be obtained, for $t \neq 0$, from reactions (8), (9) and (13) of (IV-86).

The evidence for the R trajectory now arises from the fact that the ρ trajectory alone cannot fit at the same time (Ahmadzadeh, 1964) the energy dependence of the difference $\sigma_{pp} - \sigma_{np}$ and of the $[d\sigma(np)/d\Omega]_{\text{ch exch}}$ where the ρ parameters are taken, for instance, from $\pi^- p \to \pi^0 n$ charge exchange. Other evidence comes from the analysis of (b) and (c_1) in (IV-87) and reaction (8) in (IV-86) which cannot be explained by the ρ trajectory alone (Phillips and Rarita, 1965a).

Nevertheless, it should be noticed that Roy (1965), using the same parameters for the ρ trajectory as derived by Logan (1965a) from the $\pi^- p \to \pi^0 n$ charge exchange, and computing from those the $\rho \overline{K}^0 K^-$ coupling constant by means of SU(3) symmetry, has been able to fit the $K^- p \to \overline{K}^0 n$ charge exchange data (Section II,A).

In the last months a general analysis of all the πN and KN reactions by means of the five Regge trajectories of Table VIII has been performed by Phillips and Rarita (1965b); their results are shown in Table IX where the

TABLE IX

ANALYSIS OF πN AND KN REACTIONS BY MEANS OF FIVE REGGE TRAJECTORIES

Soln.	α'_P	$\alpha_{P'}$	$\alpha'_{P'}$	α_ρ	α'_ρ	α_R	α'_R	α_ω	α'_ω
1	0.34	0.50	0.34	0.54	0.65	0.32	0.80	0.52	0.60
2	0.34	0.50	0.34	0.53	0.71	0.30	0.55	0.50	0.60
3	0.34	0.50	0.34	0.54	0.78	0.30	0.75	0.52	0.60
4	0.34	0.50	0.34	0.53	0.75	0.31	0.55	0.52	0.50

values of $\alpha_i(0)$ and $\alpha_i'(0)$ [in units $(\text{GeV}/c)^{-2}$] are reported for the five trajectories $[\alpha_P(0) = 1]$, for four different solutions, which are all similar to each other.

With the same parameters one also explains the following experimental facts:

(1) At zero momentum transfer the $\pi^- p$ differential cross section is slightly greater than the $\pi^+ p$, at each energy. For larger t, however, the $\pi^+ p$ cross section is larger (crossover effect). The crossover point occurs at $t = -0.12 \pm 0.10$ for the energy range 6–10 GeV/c (Logan, 1965b). The same phenomenon occurs also for $K^\mp p$ scattering.

These effects are explained (Phillips and Rarita, 1965b) if the ρ-pole nonhelicity flip term A_ρ and the helicity flip term B_ρ give interference with the P

and P' contributions which are of opposite sign, and A_ρ goes through zero at the crossover point.

(2) As we have already said, the elastic $\pi^\pm p \to \pi^\pm p$ and the charge exchange $\pi^- p \to \pi^0 n$ angular distributions show a dip at $t \simeq -0.6$, followed by a secondary maximum. A nice explanation of the dip in the charge exchange process can be obtained from the vanishing at that point of the helicity flip amplitude (Höhler et al., 1966b; Arbab and Chiu, 1966). In fact, one has to notice that the ρ trajectory reaches the value $\alpha_\rho(t) = 0$ for $t \simeq -0.6$, namely at the dip. Therefore, for this value of t, the ρ trajectory behaves as a 0^+ meson, which cannot produce a helicity flip. The helicity flip amplitude, which is zero at $t = 0$, is thus predicted to vanish again at $t = -0.6$. Now, from the tendency of the differential cross section $d\sigma/d|t|$ to rise at very small $|t|$ before the exponential fall-off sets in, one may infer that the helicity flip amplitude is much larger than the non-helicity-flip amplitude. Thus the zero of the helicity flip amplitude leads to a minimum in the angular distribution.

It has been proposed by Frautschi (1966) that also trajectories of even signature give vanishing helicity flip amplitudes when they verify $\alpha(t) = 0$. Since the P' trajectory vanishes also at about $t = -0.6$, in this way one explains the existence of the dip also in the elastic $\pi^\pm p$ and $\bar{p}p$ angular distributions. Moreover, the relative importance of the contributions from the P' and ρ trajectories over that from the P trajectory decreases as the energy increases; one can then explain in a natural way the disappearance of the dip at high energies in elastic $\pi^\pm p$ scattering.

(3) A third prediction concerns the phase of the scattering amplitude in the forward direction. In fact, if the amplitude is written as a superposition of some Regge poles, and the trajectories $\alpha_i(t)$ and the residues $\beta_i(t)$ are known from the analysis of the experiments, the amplitudes in the forward direction can, of course, be computed exactly, and also the ratio $\alpha(s) = D(s, 0)/A(s, 0)$.

It is a very remarkable fact that by taking three poles for $\pi^\pm p$ (P, P' and ρ) and four poles for pp (P, P', ρ, ω, discarding the R contribution, which seems to be small), it is possible to give predictions (Phillips and Rarita, 1965d) which for πp agree with experiments in sign, magnitude, and in giving a larger value of $\alpha(s)$ for $\pi^+ p$ than for $\pi^- p$ (Section IV,B).

For pp the agreement is rather bad for $E < 10$ GeV, but it is very good for $E > 10$ GeV (remember that it is likely that the asymptotic region for pp starts at higher E than for πp).

(4) It is also possible to give general predictions for the polarization (Phillips and Rarita, 1965e). For elastic $\pi^\pm p$ scattering, the polarization is due to the interference between the contribution from the P and P' trajectories, and the contribution from the ρ trajectory; therefore it must have opposite sign in $\pi^+ p$ and $\pi^- p$ scattering, because of the isospin 1 of the ρ [cf. Eqs.

(IV-86)]. This prediction is verified experimentally, as illustrated by the data shown in Figs. 11 and 12 (Section II), together with the Regge pole predictions by Chiu *et al.* (1966).

Recent data on the polarization in the charge exchange reaction $\pi^- p \to \pi^0 n$, as shown in Fig. 13 (Section II), indicate that a nonvanishing polarization is present both at 6 and 11 GeV/c. This is a difficulty for the simplest form of the Regge pole model, where only the ρ trajectory contributes to this reaction, and therefore gives zero polarization, because the spin-flip and the non-spin-flip amplitudes have the same phase. A nonzero polarization can be explained either by the introduction of another Regge pole ρ' with the same quantum numbers as the ρ but with an intercept $\alpha_{\rho'}(0) = -0.63$ (Högaasen and Frisk, 1966; Högaasen and Fischer, 1966); or by the contribution of s-channel resonances (Phillips, 1966; Logan and Sertorio, 1966). All these theories predict a rapid decrease of the polarization with increasing energy; until now, the data at 11 GeV/c have too large errors to allow definite conclusions.

The general conclusion about the theory of Regge poles is that by using the five trajectories P, P', ρ, ω, R, one can get good fits and, moreover, relate various experimental facts such as the shape of the diffraction peaks, the energy behavior of the total cross sections, and the phase of the forward amplitudes.

This result is something more than a test that the high energy amplitude can be written as a sum of terms of the form

$$T(s, t) = \sum_i \beta_i(t) s^{\alpha_i(t)} \xi_i(t) \tag{IV-88}$$

since one makes the precise assumption that the complete amplitude is a sum of a few terms, each proportional to a power of the energy, and *each having a simple isospin and G parity in the crossed channel.*

Of course, this is far from being a proof of the Regge theory in its more general form, namely, that *all* the elementary particles lie on Regge trajectories; in fact, from high energy scattering nothing can be learned about particles whose (possible) trajectories have too low an intercept at $t = 0$.

The Regge pole theory can be also applied to backward $\pi^{\pm} p$ scattering (Frautschi *et al.*, 1962; Gribov, 1962) by taking into account the Regge trajectories exchanged in the u channel.

The new feature is that now the u channel has baryonic number 1; therefore the dominant trajectories which can be expected to be present are the neutron and the $\frac{3}{2}$, $\frac{3}{2}$ resonance trajectories in $\pi^+ p$ scattering (where the u channel has the quantum numbers of $\pi^- p$ scattering), but only the $\frac{3}{2}$, $\frac{3}{2}$ resonance in $\pi^- p$ scattering.

Therefore, $\pi^- p$ scattering would be an example of a reaction with only one dominant Regge trajectory, the most useful situation in which to test the Regge pole hypothesis.

One interesting feature of the fermion trajectory exchange is that (Gribov, 1962) one should find rapid oscillations in the angular distribution near 180° modulating the dominant Regge behavior; these are due to the interference effect between the two complex conjugate trajectories of opposite parity, which correspond to the same fermion trajectory in the region $t < 0$.

A qualitative analysis of backward $\pi^- p$ scattering (Section II,A,4) has recently been attempted by Chew and Stack (1965), in order to obtain the intercept of the N^*_{33} trajectory at $u = 0$; their result is $\alpha_{N^*}(0) \simeq -0.3$. The data on backward $\pi^+ p$ scattering have been analyzed by Chiu and Stack (1966), who have shown that they can be explained essentially in terms of the only N trajectory (the N^*_{33} contribution turns out to be very small). The intercept of the N trajectory at $u = 0$ has been determined as $\alpha_N(0) = -0.34$.

The explanation of the backward peak in $\pi^+ p$ scattering as due to the N trajectory alone has also allowed to give an explanation of the dip which is present in the $\pi^+ p$ angular distribution at $u \simeq -0.2$, but is absent in the corresponding $\pi^- p$ angular distribution (cf. Fig. 10). In fact, for this value of u, $\alpha_N(u) = -\frac{1}{2}$; since the N trajectory has even signature, the N contribution has to vanish for this value of u, thus giving rise to a dip in the $\pi^+ p$ angular distribution. Since the N^*_{33} trajectory has odd signature, its contribution does not vanish for $\alpha_{N^*}(u) = -\frac{1}{2}$, and therefore no dip is present in the $\pi^- p$ angular distribution.[58]

V. Models for the Inelastic Interactions

A. EARLY ATTEMPTS: THE STATISTICAL MODEL, THE ISOBAR MODEL

As mentioned in Section II, interest in the inelastic processes has considerably increased in the last years, after the discovery of the new resonances. Previously, the apparent complexity of such reactions had discouraged people from attempting a thorough study of the dynamics of these processes. The first and also the simplest interpretation of the experimental data was based on the assumption that the occurrence of a certain final state is proportional to the amount of phase-space available to that state (statistical hypothesis). This approach, of an immediate application, was first proposed by Fermi (1950, 1953, 1954), and subsequently it received some attention (Hagedorn 1960; Fast and Hagedorn, 1963). For certain reactions (e.g., in $\bar{p}p$ annihilation) the statistical hypothesis fitted the experimental distributions rather well. However, in many cases (e.g., in nucleon-nucleon collisions at energies of a few GeV) marked deviations from the statistical predictions were found in the experimental spectra.

---

[58] The N^*_{33} contribution would vanish for a value of u such that $\alpha_{N^*}(u) = -\frac{3}{2}$, which is completely outside the backward peak.

A definite improvement in the understanding of the inelastic processes came from the work of Lindenbaum and Sternheimer (Lindenbaum and Sternheimer, 1957; Sternheimer and Lindenbaum, 1958, 1961). They pointed out that the features of low energy pion-nucleon interaction (dominated by the formation of the 33 resonance) were expected to show up also in the inelastic final states, whenever a pion and a nucleon were produced with the proper value of their relative energy. In particular, Lindenbaum and Sternheimer postulated that in inelastic nucleon-nucleon and pion-nucleon collisions, one or both nucleons are excited to an "isobar state" of various mass (preferentially, the isobar N_{33}^*), which subsequently decays without interaction with the other produced particles. Since the production of a virtual isobar state occurs also in pion-nucleon elastic scattering, the probability of formation of an isobar with mass m_1 should reflect the behavior of the total elastic pion-nucleon cross section $\sigma(m_1)$ as a function of m_1, i.e., of the total c.m. energy. This probability is therefore assumed to be of the form

$$dP_{\text{single}} = aF\sigma(m_1)\,dm_1 \tag{V-1}$$

$$dP_{\text{double}} = a'F'\sigma(m_1)\,\sigma(m_2)\,dm_1\,dm_2 \tag{V-2}$$

for the excitation of one or two isobars, respectively. Here a and a' are normalization constants (for nucleon-nucleon collisions, their ratio fixes the ratio of single- to double-pion production); F and F' are kinematical (phase-space) factors associated with the process of isobar production. [The expression of such factors has been discussed in detail (Sternheimer and Lindenbaum, 1961; Bergia et al., 1960).] The early version of this model considered only the formation of the N_{33}^* isobar; the model has been further extended so as to include the higher resonances. We recall here also a paper by Bergia et al. (1960), where the problem of the interferences between different processes of isobar formation is studied. It must be pointed out that, in principle, the mechanism of isobar production should not be specified; the simplest applications (Lindenbaum and Sternheimer, 1957; Sternheimer and Lindenbaum, 1958) treat it as statistical, but it is always possible to modify the model by inserting further assumptions (e.g., by postulating a particular angular distribution for isobar production and for its polarization). However, certain distributions, like energy distributions in the c.m. system are, in fact, dominated by the very fact of the formation of the isobar, and their shape is due to the factors $\sigma(m_1)$, $\sigma(m_2)$ appearing in Eqs. (V-1) and (V-2), almost independently of the mechanism of production. Such factors predict sharp peaks in the above-mentioned distributions, especially at energies larger than 1.5 GeV. Such peaks have been observed experimentally and the data have been fitted by a proper choice of the parameters contained in the models, in all cases where the current statistical picture failed.

Of course, the spirit of the isobar model can be applied to any process of quasi-elastic scattering. However, it has been practically applied only to the production of nucleon isobars, because the other existing resonances have been discovered after the advent of the one-pion-exchange model.

B. The Chew-Low Extrapolation and the One-Pion-Exchange Model

In spite of its success, the isobar model suffers from an intrinsic limitation; that is, it can be applied without ambiguity only in those cases where the mechanism of isobar production has practically no influence on the shape of the spectra, as occurs for c.m. energy spectra. If, however, one wishes to explain other experimental distributions, like angular c.m. or energy lab. spectra, as well as the total cross sections, one is forced to introduce some assumptions about the mechanism of isobar production, whose justification is not clear. In particular, the simplest assumption (statistical isobar production) is inadequate to explain the strong forward and/or backward peaking of certain reaction products in the c.m. system. In order to obtain such effects, a very strongly anisotropic angular distribution has to be assumed for isobar production.

This difficulty has been overcome by the advent of the one-pion-exchange model (see chapter by Hearn and Drell, this volume; see also Ferrari and Selleri, 1962) which might be considered as an isobar model with a specific mechanism of isobar production. The first idea underlying the development of the one-pion-exchange model is contained in the work by Chew and Low (1959). However, these authors did not aim to establish a theory of inelastic interactions; they merely wanted to extract from the knowledge of inelastic processes some information about elastic scattering of unstable particles (such as pion-pion scattering), which could not be obtained by laboratory measurements. Taking for definiteness pion production in pion-nucleon collisions:

$$\pi + N \to \pi + \pi + N, \qquad (V\text{-}3)$$

the Chew-Low approach can be described as follows. Among all possible Feynman graphs contributing to reaction (V-3), let us single out the one represented in Fig. 34, where a single pion (the lightest strongly interacting

Fig. 34.   The one-pion-exchange diagram describing reaction (V-3). Full lines represent nucleons, wavy lines represent pions. Letters denote four-momenta.

particle) is exchanged between the initial particles. This graph contains a singularity in the variable Δ^2 [by defining $\Delta^2 = -t = -(q_2 - p_2)^2$, the momentum transfer to the nucleon], of the type $(\Delta^2 + \mu^2)^{-1}$ (where μ is the pion mass); this singularity is the nearest to the physical region. Physical values of Δ^2 are always in the range $\Delta^2 > 0$. However, in the unphysical point $\Delta^2 = -\mu^2$ this graph will become infinite, and therefore it will rigorously overwhelm all the possible other contributions. If, in some way, it is possible to "extrapolate" the experimental data as a function of Δ^2, from the physical region ($\Delta^2 > 0$) to the unphysical point $\Delta^2 = -\mu^2$, the result of this extrapolation will be computable in terms of the graph of Fig. 34 alone. If we disregard the structure of the upper vertex, and describe it through a matrix element $T_1(q, p_1, q_1, q_1')$ relevant to the reaction (pion-pion scattering)

$$q + p_1 \rightarrow q_1 + q_1' \tag{V-4}$$

(with the incident pion q off-mass-shell), from the definition of the T matrix (III-3) it can be realized immediately that the T-matrix element coming from the graph of Fig. 34 has the following general structure:

$$T - G \, \frac{[\bar{u}(q_2)\gamma_5 u(p_2)] \cdot T_1(q, p_1, q_1, q_1')}{\Delta^2 + \mu^2} \, K'(\Delta^2) K(\Lambda^2) \tag{V-5}$$

where G is the renormalized pion-nucleon coupling constant and $K(\Delta^2)$, $K'(\Delta^2)$ are form factors relevant to the proper vertex part (πNN) and to the pion propagator. Further Δ^2 dependence (off-shell effects) occurs in the scattering matrix element T_1. As $\Delta^2 \rightarrow -\mu^2$, K, and K' go to 1 (by definition), and the off-shell matrix element T_1 goes to the value describing a physical pion-pion scattering, such as would be obtained by using a pion target.

By passing, through Eq. (III-6), from the matrix element to the cross section, by summing over the spins of the nucleons and integrating over the internal degrees of freedom of q_1, q_1', and by multiplying the resulting expression by the factor $(\Delta^2 + \mu^2)^2$, one finally obtains the Chew-Low formula:

$$\lim_{\Delta^2 \rightarrow -\mu^2} \left[(\Delta^2 + \mu^2)^2 \, \frac{d\sigma}{d\Delta^2} \right] = \frac{1}{8\pi} \frac{1}{\Phi^2} \left(\frac{G^2}{4\pi} \right) \Delta^2 k \omega \sigma_1(\omega) \, d\omega^2. \tag{V-6}$$

Here $\omega^2 = (q_1 + q_1')^2$ is the mass squared of the final two-pion system, $\sigma_1(\omega)$ is the pion-pion scattering cross section at total c.m. energy ω, k is the c.m. momentum [in the case considered ($\pi\pi$ scattering), $k = (\frac{1}{4}\omega^2 - \mu^2)^{1/2}$], and Φ is the invariant flux factor of the initial state, which, e.g., can be given in the laboratory system as $p_{inc} M$ (where M is the target mass).

It is easily realized that by selecting those events contained in narrow bands of the variable ω, and by plotting the left-hand side of Eq. (V-6) as a function of Δ^2, it is possible in principle to extrapolate the (finite) left-hand side to the unphysical point $\Delta^2 = -\mu^2$, and then to obtain an evaluation of the unknown quantity $\sigma_1(\omega)$. The elegance and the rigor of this method have been quickly recognized; however, practical applications have proved to be very difficult, even in the cases where the unphysical point $\Delta^2 = -\mu^2$ is very close to the physical region. In fact, in spite of the accuracy of the measurements, the form of the fit to the experimental points is generally uncertain enough to allow a large error on the value reached by the extrapolation. Nevertheless, such a procedure has been tried in some cases, by using linear or quadratic fits[59,60] to the left-hand side of Eq. (V-6) as a function of Δ^2 (Anderson *et al.*, 1961; Carmony and van de Walle, 1962). However, it was soon realized that it was much more profitable to work directly in the physical region, even by giving up some of the rigor contained in the Chew-Low derivation. Many theorists [first of all Goebel (1958), Drell (1960a,b), Bonsignori and Selleri (1960), and Salzman and Salzman (1960a,b, 1961)] pointed out that if the pole is close to the physical threshold for Δ^2, a diagram of the type of Fig. 34 is likely to be dominant also in the physical region near the pole, and then the T-matrix element derived from this graph is expected to give the main features of the reaction for the events where Δ^2 is small. Let us consider a generalized one-pion-exchange graph, by allowing more than one particle to come out from both vertices (Fig. 35). It is immediately seen that Eq. (V-5) is rewritten in the following form

$$T = \frac{T_1(q, p_1, Q_1) \cdot T_2(-q, p_2, Q_2)}{\Delta^2 + \mu^2} K'(\Delta^2) \tag{V-7}$$

where T_1 describes the reaction $q + p_1 \rightarrow Q_1$ and T_2 the reaction $-q + p_2 \rightarrow Q_2$ (the exchanged particle traveling from vertex 2 to 1 is equivalent to its

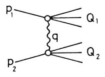

FIG. 35. The most general one-pion-exchange diagram; Q_1 and Q_2 represent the total four-momenta of the particles coming out from one of the vertices.

[59] If the left-hand side were equal to the right-hand side also off the extrapolation point, the fit would have to be linear and to pass through zero at $\Delta^2 = 0$. The deviations from such a behavior (off-shell effects, Δ^2-dependent limits of integration over the range of ω considered) are supposed to be negligible, or at most to add a further term in Δ^2, in the region close to the pole.

[60] An example of extrapolation to a known value ($\pi^+ p$ scattering cross section) can be found in a paper by Smith *et al.*, 1960.

antiparticle traveling from vertex 1 to 2)[61]. The expression for the cross section $d\sigma/d\Delta^2$, once integration over the internal degrees of freedom has been performed, becomes

$$\frac{d\sigma}{d\Delta^2} = \frac{1}{8\pi} \frac{1}{\Phi^2} \left(\frac{G^2}{4\pi}\right) \frac{\Delta^2 K^2(\Delta^2) K'^2(\Delta^2)}{(\Delta^2 + \mu^2)^2} k(\Delta^2, \omega)\omega\sigma_1(\Delta^2, \omega)\, d\omega^2 \quad \text{(V-8)}$$

for a graph containing a three-particle nucleon-nucleon-pion vertex like that of Fig. 34 and

$$\frac{d\sigma}{d\Delta^2} = \frac{1}{16\pi^3} \frac{1}{\Phi^2} \frac{K'^2(\Delta^2)}{(\Delta^2 + \mu^2)^2} k_1(\Delta^2, \omega_1)\omega_1\sigma_1(\omega_1) k_2(\Delta^2, \omega_2)\omega_2\sigma_2(\omega_2)\, d\omega_1^2\, d\omega_2^2$$

$$\text{(V-9)}$$

for a graph containing two many-particle vertices, of mass ω_1 and ω_2, respectively, like that of Fig. 35. In the above formulas, we have taken into account that in the physical region for the inelastic process, the intermediate meson q is off-mass-shell. Such off-mass-shell effects can be seen in the presence of the form factors K and K', and in the dependence of the flux factors $k_1\omega_1$, $k_2\omega_2$ and of the cross sections σ_1, σ_2 on Δ^2. In general, the behavior of K and K' and the dependence of σ_1 on Δ^2 are not known. For "small" values of Δ^2 (of the order of μ^2, say), it is reasonable to suppose that all these quantities are not too drastically different from their on-shell values $(\Delta^2 = -\mu^2)$; therefore, a sensible way of applying the one-pion-exchange model in the region of very small momentum transfers is to put $\Delta^2 = -\mu^2$ everywhere, except in the rapidly varying factor $\Delta^2(\Delta^2 + \mu^2)^{-2}$. In this way, one is led to use the Chew-Low formula also in the physical region.[62] This procedure is known under the name of "pole approximation." It has been used in many cases, e.g., in order to determine the behavior of the pion-pion cross section in the resonant ($\pi^+\pi^-$, $\pi^\pm\pi^0$) and nonresonant ($\pi^+\pi^+$, $\pi^-\pi^-$)

[61] In the case of a pion-nucleon vertex, $T_2 = GK(\Delta^2)[\bar{u}(q_2)\gamma_5 u(p_2)]$ and we obtain again Eq. (V-5).

[62] One can wonder why the known dependence of the factors k_1 and k_2 on Δ^2 is not retained in this approach. In fact, the prescription given for the evaluation of the one-pion-exchange contribution is, in a sense, arbitrary, and other prescriptions can be equally acceptable (see, for example, the Born term approach, described in the next section). For very small $\Delta^2(\Delta^2 \approx \mu^2)$, the Δ^2 dependence of the k's is irrelevant, but as Δ^2 increases to values of the order of 10–$15\,\mu^2$, which are still small compared with the extension of the physical region, this Δ^2 dependence becomes important, and, for the same reason, the same should be expected from the other neglected off-shell effects. When the reaction occurring in a many-particle vertex is an elastic scattering, the pole approximation procedure described above amounts to stating that the partial wave amplitudes describing the scattering process are independent of Δ^2. [See Ferrari and Selleri (1962) for a discussion of this point.]

states from the analysis of suitable reactions.[63] With reference to what has been said in the previous section, we want to point out that the one-pion-exchange model represents an improvement, rather than a replacement of the isobar model, and can easily account for the success of the latter in describing nucleon-nucleon and pion-nucleon collisions. In fact, the (pion-nucleon scattering) cross sections σ_1 and σ_2 in formulas (V-8) and (V-9) (calculated in the pole approximation) remind one of the simpler formulas (V-1) and (V-2). In fact, if we look only at the mass distributions (ω_1 and/or ω_2) we have to integrate the distributions (V-8) and (V-9) over Δ^2; in this way we lose the characteristic effect of dominance of low momentum transfer events, and the basic shape of the spectrum is given by the behavior of the cross section, as in (V-1) or (V-2). The phase factors may be different in the two cases, but in the resonance region they vary much less rapidly than the cross section, and do not produce an appreciable distortion of the spectrum shape. Therefore the mass spectra look similar in the two models. We can say that the one-pion-exchange model "contains" the isobar model; the same statement obviously holds for any model which explicitly considers the formation of resonances. In addition, the one-pion-exchange model predicts a very peculiar Δ^2 dependence, which appears to be in good agreement with experiment (Bonsignori and Selleri, 1960).

C. Modifications and Extensions of the One-Pion-Exchange Model: Peripheral Models

The one-pion-exchange model, in the pole approximation, has been applied to simple reactions of the type (V-3), in order to deduce the pion-pion scattering cross section from the analysis of the low momentum transfer events. However, it was soon realized that, when comparing the experimental and the theoretical distributions in Δ^2, the theory tends to predict more events than observed already at momentum transfers which are small compared to the extension of the physical region ($\Delta^2 \simeq 10 \div 15 \ \mu^2$), and where there is still a remarkable number of events. In other words, the collimation of the reaction products is stronger than expected from the rapidly decreasing factor $(\Delta^2 + \mu^2)^{-2}$. As an example, if one arbitrarily postulates the validity of the model in the whole physical region, the predicted total cross sections for

---

[63] The $\pi^+\pi^-$, $\pi^\pm\pi^0$ cross sections have been deduced from the study of the reactions $\pi^-p \to \pi^+\pi^-n$, $\pi^\pm p \to \pi^\pm\pi^0 p$, by selecting the events where the momentum transfer between final nucleon and initial proton is small (SOBB Collaboration, 1963). The $\pi^-\pi^-$ cross section has been derived from the analysis of the reaction $\pi^-p \to N^{*++}\pi^-\pi^-$, again by a selection of events with low momentum transfer between N^* and p (Schmitz, 1964; SOBB Collaboration, 1965a). The equivalent $\pi^+\pi^+$ cross section has been deduced in a similar way from the reaction $\pi^+p \to \pi^+\pi^+n$ and it has been shown to be consistent with the $\pi^-\pi^-$ scattering data. See the discussion and the relevant plots in SOBB Collaboration (1965a), ABBBHLM Collaboration (1965), and Daronian et al. (1966).

single-pion production in nucleon-nucleon collisions are larger than the experimental ones by a factor of 2 or 3 at energies of a few GeV (Da Prato, 1961).

We get an even worse disagreement if we try to extend the description in terms of a single-particle-exchange interaction to other classes of quasi-elastic processes observed experimentally. Taking the diagram of Fig. 34 as an example, we note that the main contribution to it comes from the configuration where the two outgoing pions are in a resonant state (ρ meson, f^0 meson). Therefore, the same diagram can practically be represented under the form of a Born term diagram (Fig. 36) where the final (unstable) particle c is understood to decay subsequently into the observed final products. The four-particle vertex in Fig. 34 is now replaced by a three-particle vertex involving

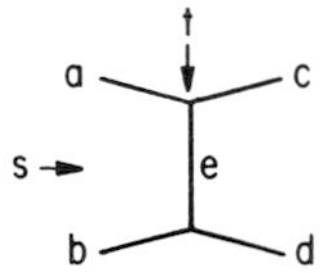

FIG. 36.   The most general diagram of single particle exchange interaction (Born term). Letters denote particles. The direct and crossed channels (s and t channels) are also indicated.

one unstable particle; the relevant coupling constant can be inferred from the width of the physical decay $c \rightarrow a + e$ (in this case, $\rho \rightarrow \pi\pi$). In the same way, many other quasi-two-body processes can be described by a diagram having the structure of a Born term, where generally any of the final particles c, d, as well as the intermediate particle e, can be unstable. One must allow also the exchange of unstable objects, because a strong collimation in the Δ^2 distribution is observed also when the exchange of a pseudoscalar object (like the pion) is forbidden by selection rules. Such is the case of the reaction $\pi^+ p \rightarrow \pi^0 N^{*++}$ (Fig. 37). If we want to ascribe the enhancement observed at low Δ^2 to the exchange of a single particle, chosen among those experimentally known, we are quite naturally led to the exchange of a ρ meson. Generally speaking, all quasi-elastic reactions occurring most frequently can be described by Born terms involving the exchange of a pseudoscalar and/or a vector meson. Baryon exchange is generally not considered (except for a few special cases, like backward pion-nucleon elastic scattering), because its contribution to the dominant low momentum transfer peak is always very small.

Now, the general Born term, as shown in Fig. 36, can be evaluated by the standard Feynman techniques. However, in this way, when high spin ($J \geqslant 1$) resonances are produced, additional kinematic factors enter in the couplings at the vertices, and these factors are generally increasing functions of Δ^2. As an example, for pion exchange such factors behave like k_{off}^l, where $k_{off} = k(\Delta^2, \omega)$ is the off-shell momentum of the exchanged pion at the resonance

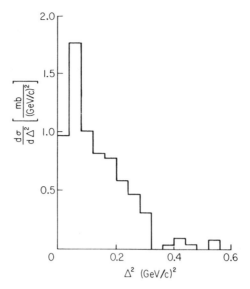

Fɪɢ. 37. Δ^2-distribution for the reaction $\pi^+ p \rightarrow \pi^0 N^{*++}$ at 4 GeV/c [taken from ABBBHLM Collaboration (1964f)].

energy ω, as defined in Eq. (V-8), and l is the angular momentum in which the exchanged pion and the initial particle are bound into the produced resonance. Therefore, in spite of the rapidly decreasing denominator $(\Delta^2 + m_e^2)^{-2}$ the contribution of a Born term to the cross section does not show the characteristic collimation of low momentum transfer events, but has a slowly decreasing or even an increasing behavior, in gross disagreement with experiment, both in shape and magnitude.

Therefore, it becomes apparent that the peripheral model must be "modified" in some way, by taking into account effects neglected in the simple Born terms. The development of this idea and its application to inelastic processes at high energies has become such a large and developing subject that a whole chapter of the present book is devoted to it (Hearn and Drell, this volume). The reader is therefore referred to this chapter for a detailed discussion of this field. Here, we will only summarize the essential points very briefly, especially in connection with the experimental facts discussed in Section II,C to E. Of course, the references we quote are far from being exhaustive.

The approaches followed to provide a suitable modification of the peripheral model are (presented in chronological order):

(1) The form factor approach, where the corrections damping the peripheral contributions at high Δ^2 are introduced by modifying the interaction at the vertices of the single-particle-exchange diagram, because of the "virtuality" of the intermediate particle. The main corrections come from

unknown Δ^2-dependent form factors (playing the same role as the electro-magnetic form factors in photon exchange) which are fitted by comparison with the experiment. The description of the form factor model and its principal applications are found in the works by Ferrari and Selleri (1961, 1962, 1963). For a theoretical discussion of the need for such form factors, see Dürr and Pilkuhn (1965).

(2) The absorption approach, where account is taken of the initial and final state interactions giving rise to a rescattering of the initial and final particles (Fig. 38). It can be shown that this effect provides a large absorption in the

FIG. 38. The most general form of peripheral diagram with rescattering in the initial and final states.

lowest partial waves, and therefore a collimation of the reaction products. In principle, the parameters of the model can be obtained from the knowledge of the elastic scattering in the initial and final states. However, elastic scattering of unstable particles is not known, and its fitting involves a certain number of hypotheses. Slowly varying form factors at the vertices may also be included. Pioneer work in this field has been done by Sopkovich (1962), and by Dar and collaborators (Dar, 1964; Dar *et al.*, 1964b; Dar and Tobocman, 1964). A systematic treatment of the subject has been provided by Durand and Chiu (1964, 1965a,b) and by Jackson and collaborators (Gottfried and Jackson, 1964b; Jackson, 1965; Jackson *et al.*, 1965).

(3) The unitarized models, where the requirements imposed by unitarity (badly violated by Born term contributions, still giving trouble in the form factor and absorption models) are taken into account since the beginning. The theoretical basis for such models is the analysis of the scattering amplitude through the N/D method (Chew and Mandelstam, 1960, 1961). The resulting models are usually called "K-matrix models" (Arnold, 1964; Dietz and Pilkuhn, 1965a,b; Trefil, 1966). Even a qualitative description of the mathe-matical structure of these models would be exceedingly complicated for the purposes of this chapter; the reader is referred to Section V of the chapter by Hearn and Drell, page 248 of this volume.

In addition to the collimation obtained at low Δ^2 (which in most cases is produced, however, not by the exchange mechanism itself but by the correc-tions superimposed on it), the assumption of a dominating single-particle-exchange contribution has also another important consequence. Indeed, such a hypothesis implies the exchange of the sharply defined quantum number belonging to the intermediate particle through the crossed channel (*t* channel) of the quasi-two-body reaction under consideration. In certain cases, the exchange of such quantum numbers can be independently tested from the experimental data. In particular, the spin and parity of the exchanged particle will influence the angular correlations among the decay products of the resonances produced (cf. Section IV,B of chapter by Hearn and Drell, page 238). The first proposal of a study of angular correlations in order to test pion exchange has been made by Treiman and Yang (1962). More recently, Gottfried and Jackson (1964a) have discussed this problem extensively.

D. Qualitative Discussion of the Peripheral Models

The peripheral models mentioned in the previous section have given, on the whole, a good agreement with experiment, even surprisingly good if one considers how weak is the theoretical basis supporting the hypothesis of single-particle-exchange dominance. Therefore, the limitations and inadequacies appearing when the comparison with experiment is carried out in greater detail, are, in a sense, to be expected (see a relevant discussion by Hearn and Drell, this volume). There may be also some concern about the validity of the methods used in order to modify the " unadorned " Born term contributions. In this respect, the unitarized models are believed to be the most reliable; however, the great complexity of the calculations needed for their practical application has somewhat restricted their use so far. Instead, the earlier versions of the peripheral model (i.e., the form factor and the absorption model) have been tested experimentally in a large number of reactions. Therefore, it is possible to present a somewhat comparative discussion of them.

As far as the observed low momentum transfer collimation is concerned, both procedures can generally fit the experimental data; indeed, they produce as their ultimate result, a cutoff function which depends strongly on Δ^2 and turns out to be independent of energy (also in the absorption model). Therefore, the various effects can hardly be separated, if one considers only the Δ^2 distributions, because the predictions of both models involve a certain degree of arbitrariness. However, the absorption model provides a natural explanation of the observed angular correlations, which cannot be predicted by the only insertion of form factors at the vertices. This is, in the authors' opinion, the main reason for the large popularity of the absorption model, which is also believed to have a better theoretical foundation. [However, the theoretical ideas on which the absorption approach is based have been recently criticized by Selleri (1966)]. Indeed, the absorption approach is much more flexible than the form factor method; it can be applied in principle to any type of quasi-two-body reactions, and it can be extended to higher energies, whereas the form factor approach seems to be applicable only to pion exchange and to be restricted to a "medium-energy" region ($\leqslant 4$ GeV). On the other hand, the form factor model, just because of its more "empirical" character, can be a useful tool for fitting reactions which the absorption model is unable to reach; for example, the cases where no double resonance production occurs and, however, peripheral effects are clearly present. Such is the case of the reaction $\pi^+ p \to N^{*++}\pi^-\pi^-$, or of a large fraction of the events observed in double-pion production in proton-proton collisions (Ferrari, 1963). In general, all inelastic reactions from proton-proton collisions below 4 GeV are very well fitted by the form factor model. Figure 39 gives an example of the agreement obtained by using a unique, "universal" form factor. At higher energies, where the model fails, the experimental results for inelastic pp collisions have not yet received a convincing explanation.

It should also be mentioned that, in some particular cases, suitable final state interactions can be added to the insertion of form factors. We quote the

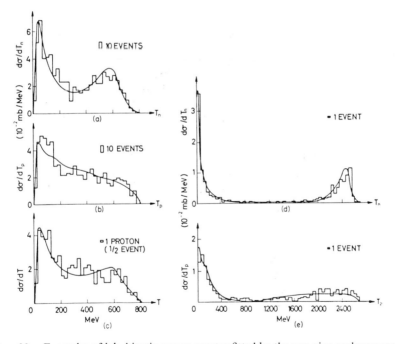

FIG. 39. Examples of lab. kinetic energy spectra fitted by the one-pion-exchange model with form factors [taken from Ferrari and Selleri (1963), which also contains the experimental bibliography.] (a) Neutrons from $pp \to pn\pi^+$, (b) protons from $pp \to pn\pi^+$, (c) protons from $pp \to pp\pi^0$ (at an incident energy of 970 MeV), (d) neutrons, and (e) protons from $pp \to pn\pi^+$ (at 2.85 GeV), where only events in which the system $p\pi^+$ is in the region of the resonance N^{*++} have been selected.

calculation of the reaction rate for $pp \to \pi^+ d$ at low energy, through a mechanism of one-pion exchange followed by a final state interaction binding the final proton and neutron into a deuteron (Fig. 40) (Chaoud et al., 1963, 1966; Yao, 1964).

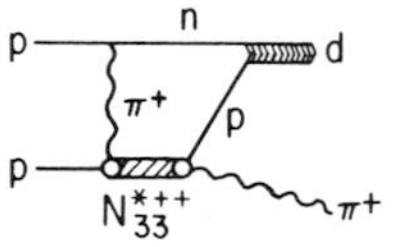

FIG. 40.   A possible mechanism for the reaction $pp \to \pi^+ d$.

Finally, we mention the interesting case provided by low energy inelastic $\bar{p}p$ collisions, where a nucleon and an antinucleon are still present in the final state. The identity of the relevant peripheral graphs with those describing inelastic pp collision could let one believe that also such reactions should be well fitted by the form factor model. On the other hand, initial and final state interactions are much stronger than in the pp case, and therefore absorption effects not observed in pp collisions should be detected. The experimental evidence on this subject is somewhat contradictory. A clear indication of a final state interaction is given by the comparison of the single-pion production processes; the cross sections for $\bar{p}p$ collisions are reduced by a factor of two with respect to the values expected from the data for pp collisions (Czyzewski et al., 1963). On the other hand, double-pion production in $\bar{p}p$ collisions is fairly well described by the same mechanism governing the corresponding pp reactions (Ferbel et al., 1965b,d). The absorption model, applied to the channel $\bar{p}p \to N^{*++}\overline{N^{*++}}$ overestimates the total cross section, though providing an explanation for the angular correlations experimentally observed (Svensson, 1965).

E. Diffraction Dissociation

Under the name of " diffraction dissociation " it is customary to indicate a particular phenomenon, which may occur in high energy particle interaction, as a source of quasi-elastic events. The most favorable conditions for its detection are given by scattering on complex nuclei. It is well known that elastic scattering on complex nuclei exhibits an extremely sharp diffraction peak, due to the coherent action of all the nucleons of the target (see, for example, Bellettini et al., 1966). Under such conditions, the nucleus acts as a single diffractive center and does not break up even in very high energy interactions. In fact, the momentum absorbed by the nucleus is generally very small, so that there is practically no energy transfer, and the nucleus cannot attain the excited or the continuum state.

An extension of this idea to the case of inelastic elementary particle collisions has been formulated by Good and Walker (1960; see also Good, 1961), following also the direction of investigation of several Russian physicists, who had studied various effects of this kind [such as diffraction disintegration of the deuteron and electromagnetic radiation in diffraction scattering (Feinberg and Pomeranchuk, 1951)]. The basic idea underlying these studies is that in the process of diffraction other states can be produced which are not equal to the original one. When there is an energy degeneration, this fact is experimentally well known: The most striking example is the K_1^0 regeneration by nuclear scattering of a K_2^0 beam. Here the different absorption of the K^0, $\overline{K}^0$ components in nuclear matter creates some K_1^0 amplitude in the unscattered beam, while the scattering nucleus remains unchanged. When the energy is high, one can believe this process also occurs for the production of states which are not really degenerate in energy, but rather can be produced through a "virtual dissociation" of the incoming particle, such as $N \to N\pi$, $N \to YK$ and $\pi \to \pi\pi\pi$. The mass M^* of the states produced is different from the mass M of the projectile: however, if we want such a process to occur through a diffraction-like mechanism, neither exciting nor breaking up the target nucleus, we must again require the recoil momentum of the nucleus to be small. For forward scattering, the transverse momentum taken by the nucleus is small anyway: We must require the longitudinal momentum $q_\parallel$ to be also negligible with respect to the inverse of the nuclear radius, $R \sim A^{1/3}/m_\pi$ (where A is the atomic number and m_π the pion mass). Since in first approximation $q_\parallel$ is given by

$$q_\parallel = \frac{M^{*2} - M^2}{2p_{\text{inc}}}, \tag{V-10}$$

the condition $q_\parallel R \ll 1$ also reads as

$$p_{\text{inc}} \gg p_{\text{thres}} = \frac{M^{*2} - M^2}{2m_\pi} A^{1/3} \tag{V-11}$$

where the right-hand side is a sort of "threshold" for diffraction dissociation, depending on the mass M^* of the dissociation products.

It must be noted that when Eq. (V-11) is satisfied, the incoming and outgoing states can be considered as practically degenerate with respect to the nucleus, because inside the nucleus the number of oscillations of the wave functions of the two systems is practically the same (the phase difference being of the order of $p_{\text{thres}}/p_{\text{inc}}$)

In terms of quantum mechanical considerations, the "selective absorption" which gives rise to the creation of new states can be easily understood. Take for definiteness a nucleon projectile: the incident wave $|I\rangle$ will be given by

$$|I\rangle = \exp(ip_{\text{inc}}z)|N\rangle \tag{V-12}$$

where $|N\rangle$ is the state describing a physical nucleon, with a well-defined set of quantum numbers (spin, parity, isospin, etc.). Let $|N\rangle$ be developed as the superposition of a complete set of states $|C_i\rangle$, in such a way that they have definite absorption rates in nuclear matter[64]

$$|N\rangle = \sum_i c_{ni}|C_i\rangle \qquad (V\text{-}13)$$

(the index "n" labels the physical nucleon state).

After traversing the nucleus, the amplitude of the states $|C_i\rangle$ will be reduced by a factor η_i (with $|\eta_i| \leqslant 1$) and thus the transmitted wave $|T\rangle$ at $z = 0$ (i.e., immediately behind the nucleus) will be given by

$$|T\rangle = \sum_i c_{ni}\eta_i|C_i\rangle. \qquad (V\text{-}14)$$

Now, reexpand the $|C_i\rangle$'s in terms of the physical states $|D_k\rangle$

$$|C_i\rangle = \sum_k d_{ik}|D_k\rangle. \qquad (V\text{-}15)$$

Comparison of Eq. (V-13) with Eq. (V-15) shows that

$$\sum_i c_{ni}\, d_{ik} = \delta_{kn}. \qquad (V\text{-}16)$$

Then we will obtain the following expression for the scattered wave $|S\rangle = |I\rangle - |T\rangle$ (at $z = 0$)

$$|S\rangle = \sum_{i,k} (1 - \eta_i)c_{ni}\, d_{ik}|D_k\rangle = (1 - \bar{\eta})|N\rangle + \sum_{k \neq n} \bar{\eta}_k|D_k\rangle \qquad (V\text{-}17)$$

by using Eq. (V-16), and the definitions

$$\bar{\eta} = \sum_i \eta_i c_{ni}\, d_{in} \qquad \bar{\eta}_k = \sum_i \eta_i c_{ni}\, d_{ik}. \qquad (V\text{-}18)$$

It can be seen that, through diffraction, scattering states $|D_k\rangle$ that are different from the initial one can also be produced in the scattering wave. Only if all $|C_i\rangle$'s are absorbed by the same amount (in particular, for complete absorption, all η_i's equal to zero), will the scattered wave contain the initial state only. Therefore, a semitransparent nucleus is more suitable for the occurrence of the phenomenon.

It must be pointed out that the nucleus parameters have not been called into play in the above derivation, because the nucleus was thought to remain in its ground state. Therefore, since nuclear interaction conserves quantum numbers, only the states $|D_k\rangle$ having the same quantum numbers as the

[64] In the article by Good (1961) the $|C_i\rangle$'s are incorrectly identified with "bare" particle states. However, a further specification of such states is, for our purposes, irrelevant.

initial state can originate in the diffraction process.[65] It can also be seen directly that the angular momentum transfer Δl is zero (since Δl is of the order of $q_{\parallel} R$), and transfer of other quantum numbers cannot occur insofar as the target nucleus remains in its ground state. Experimentally, at high energy one should observe the production of inelastic states whose total momentum and energy are as close as possible to those of the incident projectile; the momentum transfer distribution of such events should have the same form as that for elastic scattering. Resonant systems produced by such a mechanism should have the same quantum numbers as the incident particle. In order to avoid fake events accompanied by a slight excitation of the target nucleus, nuclei with ground state far from the nearest excited states (such as ^{4}He or ^{12}C) are to be preferred.

In the case of a nucleon target, the argument becomes less clear.

In this case, the target can suffer large recoils without being excited or broken, and a certain transfer of angular momentum can be admitted (with or without parity change), as well as spin flip. Under such conditions, the phenomenon of diffraction dissociation is perhaps better represented in terms of graphs such as those in Fig. 41, referring to single-pion production in nucleon-nucleon scattering. Diagram (a) can be visualized as diffraction scattering of the incident projectile on a pion of the cloud of the target nucleon (or vice versa).

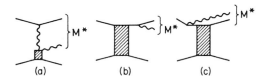

FIG. 41.   The diagrams illustrating diffraction dissociation in the process of single pion production in nucleon-nucleon scattering. Full lines represent nucleons, wavy lines represent pions. The box indicates diffraction scattering. M^* is the total mass of the dissociation products, as explained in the text.

A specific model of this kind has been developed by Drell and Hiida (1961), in order to explain the salient features of the recoil proton spectra observed in inelastic proton-proton collisions at 16 GeV/c (Cocconi et al., 1961a,b) (see Section II,D). It should be noted that both before and after the diffraction scattering, the pion-nucleon system (of mass M^*) originated by nucleon dissociation must have the same isospin ($T = \frac{1}{2}$) as the initial nucleon. Therefore, this model can explain why the excitation of the 33 isobar is not observed

---

[65] This argument does not apply to charge conjugation or G parity, because the target nucleus is *not* an eigenstate of C or G. Hence, an incident pion can give rise to any number of pions, even or odd (except two, from spin-parity considerations).

at high energy. However, the Drell-Hiida model does not reproduce the experimental situation at lower energies (Ferrari *et al.*, 1965).

In Fig. 42 we report an interesting plot, taken from an early CERN work (Cocconi *et al.*, 1964), where the experimental momentum transfer distribution for nucleon isobar production between 3.6 and 11.8 GeV/c is tentatively derived. For the two $T = \frac{1}{2}$ resonances, the observed behavior is roughly similar to that of the elastic scattering, in agreement with the predictions of the diffraction dissociation mechanism. However, the energies studied are not sufficiently high: the value of p_{thres} calculated from Eq. (V-11) is of the order of 5 and 7 GeV/c for the two isobars in question. Perhaps the mechanism of diffraction dissociation can better explain the huge excitation of the "1400 MeV object" at high energy and small momentum transfer (Section II,D,4; Fig. 17b), which probably has all quantum numbers equal to those of the nucleon.

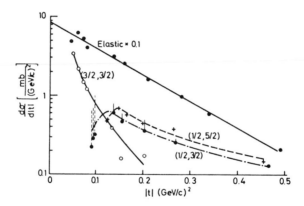

FIG. 42.   Momentum transfer distribution for the production of the first nucleon isobars [indicated by (T, J)] as deduced from the experiments of Cocconi *et al.* (1964), (from which diagram is taken), performed at a fixed lab. angle of 60 mrad and with different incident momenta from 3.6 to 11.8 GeV/c. The shape of the distribution for elastic scattering, measured in the same conditions, is shown for comparison.

More interesting results have been obtained from the analysis of $\pi^- p$ collisions on carbon nuclei at incident momenta of 6 and 18 GeV/c (Bellini *et al.*, 1963). It has been shown that a certain class of events (with three fast-charged secondaries going forward in the c.m. system) is not observed at 6 GeV/c, but is observed in 36% of the cases at 18 GeV/c. The features of the distribution of these secondaries are quite consistent with the picture of diffraction dissociation discussed above. In particular, the recoil momentum of the carbon nucleus calculated according to Eq. (V-10) has been found in almost all cases to stay below the limit $A^{1/3}/m_\pi \simeq 60$ MeV/c, required in order that the process can take place.

VI. The Models for Very High Energies

All the models discussed in Sections IV and V for the elastic and inelastic scattering are based on experiments which have been performed with the presently existing accelerators. In this section we want to discuss some models based on the experimental evidence coming from cosmic ray experiments, which can be therefore applied at higher energies.

We recall here briefly the general features of very high energy inelastic collisions, as derived from cosmic ray events up to 10^{14} eV (see Kidd, this volume):

(1) The multiplicity of the particles produced is large (of the order of 20) and increases slowly with the energy.

(2) Most of the particles produced are pions (pionization); the percentage of heavy particles produced is 10–20%.

(3) The average transverse momentum of the particles produced (namely, the projection of the momentum on the plane perpendicular to the line of flight of the initial particles) is *small*, of the order of 0.4–0.5 GeV/c, and almost *constant* with the energy and emission angle of the secondaries. As a consequence, the angular distribution in the c.m. system is concentrated in two narrow cones around the initial forward and backward direction. In the lab. system this structure shows up as a narrow cone around the direction of the line of flight (corresponding to the forward cone in the c.m.) surrounded by a diffuse cone (corresponding to the backward cone in the c.m.) (jet structure).

(4) The inelasticity K, defined as

$$K = \frac{\text{total energy of created particles}}{\text{total energy at disposal in the c.m. system}}$$

has an average value of 0.5, and is nearly constant with the energy. Therefore the two initial particles are still very energetic after the collision.

We do not intend here to review the many kinds of theories which have been proposed in order to explain these characteristics, such as the multiple production theory (Lewis *et al.*, 1949), the statistical theory (Fermi, 1950), the Heisenberg model (Heisenberg, 1952), the Landau hydrodynamical model (Landau, 1953), and many others.

We shall only briefly discuss a model which is very popular among cosmic ray physicists, namely, the two-fireball model, and then focus our attention on two models, which have some field-theoretical roots, the van Hove uncorrelated particle model and the multiperipheral model. In the last two models the features of the inelastic processes are strictly connected to the properties of elastic scattering via the unitarity condition; as a matter of fact, both models for inelastic phenomena arose from considerations about the elastic scattering. We shall discuss these points later when treating the models.

A. THE TWO-FIREBALL MODEL

In order to describe the two-cone structure of many of the high energy nucleon-nucleon inelastic events, it has been proposed (Ciok *et al.*, 1958a,b; Cocconi, 1958; Niu, 1958) that, in the process of scattering, two highly excited centers or "fireballs" are emitted, which then decay in an isotropic way in their own center of mass. The mass of the two fireballs is nearly the same (and therefore the number of decay particles of each fireball is approximately equal), and they travel in the c.m. system with the same velocity but in opposite directions, along a line of flight which for simplicity is assumed to be the same as that of the two initial nucleons. An important point in the model is that the fireballs are distinct from the final nucleons, which, as we have said, retain much of their initial energy.

The name "fireball" is due to the fact that the two excited centers decay in a very large number of particles (as we have said, the multiplicity is large).

The two-cone structure, or in general any anisotropy of the secondary distribution in the center-of-mass system, can be easily investigated by the use of a particular plot, the so-called log tan plot.

For this, let us define as $F(\Theta_L)$ the fraction of the total number of particles which in the laboratory system are produced at angles smaller than or equal to Θ_L; if we now plot log $\{F/(1 - F)\}$ versus log tan Θ_L, it is easy to show (see, for instance, Cocconi, 1958) that:

(1) If the c.m. distribution of the secondaries is isotropic, it corresponds to a straight line of slope 2.

(2) If the c.m. distribution is not isotropic, but symmetric with respect to $\Theta_{c.m.} = \pi/2$ and *different* from zero for $\Theta_{c.m.} = \pi/2$, then the plot distribution is not very far from a straight line, with a slope (in general) different from 2.

(3) The situation is completely different when the angular distribution, besides being anisotropic and symmetric, vanishes for $\Theta_{c.m.} = \pi/2$. In that case the log tan plot consists of a curve similar to that of Fig. 43.

The two-fireball model, which produces an anisotropic, symmetric angular distribution, will show up as a plot of the kind shown in Fig. 43. If now one analyzes the experimental data, a great number of high energy jets, containing a great number of charged observed secondaries, give rise to a plot in which the particles are distributed into two distinct straight lines.

The fact that the mean slope of each of the two lines is near to 2 means that the angular distribution of the secondaries in the center-of-mass system of each of the two groups is nearly isotropic.

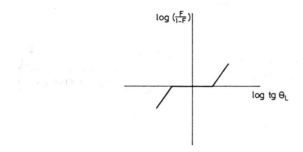

FIG. 43. Plot of the quantity log $F/(1 - F)$ versus log tan Θ_L (see text), illustrating the situation for a symmetric, strongly anisotropic distribution in the c.m. system.

In the two-fireball model in order to get small transverse momenta one is forced to assume that the energy of the secondaries in the center-of-mass system of the fireball is also limited (of the order of 1 GeV).

An interesting point has been recently stressed by Fukuda and Iso (1966); if one computes the high energy elastic scattering as a shadow of the inelastic scattering, one cannot reproduce from the fireball model the observed features of the elastic angular distribution, unless one assumes an unreasonably long lifetime of the fireball.

There is also some evidence (Hasegawa, 1961; Hayakawa, 1963) that the number of fireballs is greater than two (some experiments can be analyzed with four or six fireballs). For further discussion of the experimental position relative to interactions at very high energy the reader is referred to the chapter by Kidd in this volume.

B. THE RELATION BETWEEN SCATTERING AND ABSORPTION

In Section IV,A we have discussed the explanation of the forward elastic peak in terms of the optical model, where a purely imaginary potential is used to derive the properties of the elastic scattering.

In other terms, in the optical model the elastic scattering is considered as the shadow of the inelastic processes, which are described as the effect of a purely imaginary potential.

Nevertheless, the introduction of a potential is not necessary in order to understand the relation between scattering and absorption, which can be easily found on the basis of the unitarity condition.

We can rewrite the unitarity condition (III-5), by separating on the right-hand side the elastic and inelastic contribution

$$\operatorname{Im} T(q, \cos \Theta) = E(q, \cos \Theta) + I(q, \cos \Theta). \qquad \text{(VI-1)}$$

Here, $E(q, \cos \Theta)$ is the contribution of the intermediate state containing the same two particles as in the initial and final states, Θ_1 and Θ_2 are the scattering angles between the initial and intermediate direction (Θ_1) and the intermediate and final direction in the c.m. system (Θ_2), such that the angle between the initial and final direction be Θ; $I(q, \cos \Theta)$ is the contribution of all the inelastic intermediate states. (For simplicity we treat here the equal-mass case; the general case is an immediate extension.)

$$E(q, \cos \Theta) = \frac{1}{32\pi^2} \frac{q}{\sqrt{s}} \int d\Omega_1 \, T(q, \cos \Theta_2) T^*(q, \cos \Theta_1) \qquad \text{(VI-2')}$$

$$I(q, \cos \Theta) = \frac{1}{2} \sum_{n_{in}} (2\pi)^4 \delta^{(4)}(p_1 + p_2 - p_{n_{in}}) \frac{T^*_{n_{in}i} T_{n_{in}f}}{\prod n^2_{n_{in}}}. \qquad \text{(VI-2'')}$$

If we suppose now (as it is reasonable, within 30%) that the elastic scattering amplitude at high energy and at small angles is purely imaginary $[T(q, \cos \Theta) = iA(q, \cos \Theta)]$, we get

$$A(q, \cos \Theta) = +\frac{1}{32\pi^2} \frac{q}{\sqrt{s}} \int d\Omega_1 A(q, \cos \Theta_2) A(q, \cos \Theta_1) + I(q, \cos \Theta).$$

$$\text{(VI-3)}$$

From this (nonlinear) relation one can calculate $A(q, \cos \Theta)$ once the inelastic contribution $I(q, \cos \Theta)$ is known. Now the sum in (VI-2'') runs over all the states $|n_{in}\rangle$ which are different from the initial state $|i\rangle$ (the kind or number of particles in $|n_{in}\rangle$ is different from that in $|i\rangle$ and $|f\rangle$); $\langle i|T|n_{in}\rangle$ is therefore the production amplitude starting from the initial state $|i\rangle$. The relation (VI-3) allows one to compute the elastic (shadow) scattering in terms of the parameters of the production amplitudes.

It is also possible to understand qualitatively why the diffraction peak has a steep behavior. In fact, let us take once again the unitarity condition (III-5)

$$\text{Im } T_{if} = \frac{1}{2} \sum_n (2\pi)^4 \delta^{(4)}(p_1 + p_2 - p_n) \frac{T^*_{ni} T_{nf}}{\prod n_n^2}.$$

In the forward direction $|f\rangle = |i\rangle$ each term of the sum (being a modulus squared) is positive definite, and therefore all the contributions of the intermediate states $|n\rangle$ add up in a coherent way to build up the forward coherent imaginary amplitude (remember the optical theorem!).

If we remember now the jet structure of the production amplitude, we can say that $\langle i|T|n_{in}\rangle$ will be different from zero only when the angle between the initial and the intermediate directions is small; since the same is also valid for $\langle n_{in}|T|f\rangle$, the product

$$\langle f|T|n_{in}\rangle \langle n_{in}|T^+|i\rangle$$

will vanish very rapidly as the angle Θ increases. The law of decrease for $A(q, \cos \Theta)$ as a function of Θ depends, moreover, also on the angular dependence of the phase of the production amplitudes $\langle i|T|n_{in}\rangle$. The precise angular dependence of the shadow scattering depends therefore on the production mechanism.

It is therefore interesting to see whether the experimental knowledge on the inelastic processes allows reconstruction, via the unitarity condition, of the general features of the elastic peaks.

The relation between scattering and production can be made clearer by passing to partial waves (van Hove, 1963c, 1964, 1965b).

Expanding in the usual way the scattering amplitude $f(q, \cos \Theta)$ [related to $T(q, \cos \Theta)$ by $T(q, \cos \Theta) = 8\pi\sqrt{s}f(q, \cos \Theta)$, Eq. (III-10)]

$$f(q, \cos \Theta) = \frac{i}{2q} \sum_{l=0}^{\infty} (2l + 1)\eta_l P_l(\cos \Theta) \qquad \text{(VI-4)}$$

(η_l is connected to the complex phases shift δ_l by $i(\eta_l/2) = \exp(i\delta_l)\sin\delta_l$) and analyzing in the same way the inelastic contribution

$$I(q, \cos \Theta) = \frac{2\pi\sqrt{s}}{q} \sum (2l + 1)f_l P_l(\cos \Theta) \qquad \text{(VI-5)}$$

we get

$$\text{Re } \eta_l = \frac{|\eta_l|^2}{2} + f_l. \qquad \text{(VI-6)}$$

If the scattering amplitude is purely imaginary, η_l is real, and we have

$$\eta_l - (\eta_l^2/q) = f_l \qquad \eta_l = 1 \pm (1 - 2f_l)^{1/2}. \qquad \text{(VI-7)}$$

Since $\eta_l = 1 - a_l$, the unitarity condition $|a_l| \leqslant 1$ puts the limit

$$|1 - \eta_l| < 1; \qquad 0 \leqslant f_l \leqslant \tfrac{1}{2}. \qquad \text{(VI-8)}$$

In order to choose the root in Eq. (VI-7), we impose the physical condition that there will be no scattering as the impact parameter $b = (l/q) \to \infty$; therefore

$$\eta_l \underset{l \to \infty}{\to} 0; \qquad f_l \underset{l \to \infty}{\to} 0.$$

This condition forces us to choose

$$\eta_l = 1 - (1 - 2f_l)^{1/2} \qquad \text{(VI-9)}$$

This equation allows one to compute the elastic partial wave once the inelastic contribution f_l is known. Remember that this simple result is only true when the elastic amplitude is purely imaginary.

The inelastic contribution $I(q, \cos \Theta)$ has a simple physical interpretation in the center-of-mass system.

In our case (elastic coherent scattering) the final state $|f\rangle$ is identical to the initial one $|i\rangle$, with the only difference that the vectors $\boldsymbol{q}_a + \boldsymbol{q}_b = 0$ and $\boldsymbol{q}_{a'} + \boldsymbol{q}_{b'} = 0$ of the initial and final particles are rotated through the scattering angle Θ; $I(q, \cos \Theta)$ of (VI-2″) is therefore the sum of the overlapping of the matrix element leading from $|i\rangle$ to $|n_{in}\rangle$, with the same matrix element leading from the rotated state $|f\rangle$ to the same $|n_{in}\rangle$. Now, if we define the projection operator on the inelastic state Q by

$$Q|i\rangle = Q|f\rangle = 0; \qquad Q|n_{in}\rangle = |n_{in}\rangle$$

we can construct the inelastic part of the final wave function as

$$QT|i\rangle = \delta^{(4)}(P - p_a - p_b)|f(\boldsymbol{q})\rangle$$

(T is the T operator whose matrix elements give the T matrix, P is the total four-momentum operator). Therefore we have

$$I(q, \cos \Theta) = \langle f(\boldsymbol{q}')|\delta^{(4)}(P - p_a - p_b)|f(\boldsymbol{q})\rangle \cdot \pi^2 s. \qquad \text{(VI-10)}$$

The physical interpretation of $I(q, \cos \Theta)$ is therefore given by the overlapping of the inelastic part of the final wave function in the direction $\boldsymbol{q}$ with the same wave function in the direction $\boldsymbol{q}'$.

It is now possible to solve the following problem: giving the angular dependence of the overlap function $I(q, \cos \Theta)$, derive the corresponding form of the elastic angular distribution $d\sigma/dt$.

It has been shown by van Hove (1963c, 1964, 1965b) that, if the overlap function is Gaussian in the angle

$$I(q, \Theta) = I(q, 0)e^{At} \qquad \text{(VI-11)}$$

($t \propto \Theta^2$ for small Θ), then the angular distribution of the elastic shadow scattering has the form

$$\frac{d\sigma}{dt} = \left(\frac{d\sigma}{dt}\right)_{t=0} \exp(bt + ct^2)$$

which is in accord with experiment (see Section II,A,3).

In fact, from Eq. (VI-11) one can calculate f_l by an impact parameter method

$$f_l = f_0 \exp[-(l^2/4Aq^2)] = f_0 \exp[-(\rho^2/4A^2)] \qquad \text{(VI-12)}$$

($\rho = l/q$ is the impact parameter). Then the total and inelastic cross sections are

$$\sigma_{tot} = 16\pi A\{\log[\tfrac{1}{2} + \tfrac{1}{2}(1 - 2f_0)^{1/2}] + 1\}$$
$$\sigma_{in} = 8\pi A f_0. \qquad \text{(VI-13)}$$

As a consequence, the ratio σ_{el}/σ_{tot} is independent of the form of the overlap function

$$\frac{\sigma_{el}}{\sigma_{tot}} = 1 - f_0/2\{\log[\tfrac{1}{2} + \tfrac{1}{2}(1 - 2f_0)^{1/2}] - (1 - 2f_0)^{1/2} + 1\} = g(f_0). \qquad \text{(VI-14)}$$

Moreover, since f_0 is limited by $0 \leqslant f_0 \leqslant \tfrac{1}{2}$, we get the limitation[66]

$$0 \leqslant (\sigma_{el}/\sigma_{tot}) \leqslant g(\tfrac{1}{2}) = 0.185. \qquad \text{(VI-15)}$$

For the angular distribution we get, for small f_0

$$\frac{d\sigma}{dt} = \left(\frac{d\sigma}{dt}\right)_{t=0} e^{2At} \qquad \text{(VI-16)}$$

namely, the elastic scattering amplitude has the same t dependence as the overlap function.

More generally, one gets

$$\frac{d\sigma}{dt} = \left(\frac{d\sigma}{dt}\right)_{t=0} \exp(bt + ct^2) \qquad \text{(VI-17)}$$

where $b = 2a_1 A$, $c = 2a_2 A^2$, and a_1 and a_2 are known functions of f_0.

This model has been applied to high energy pp and πp scattering by Cottingham and Peierls (1965).

For pp scattering it is plainly not adequate in this simple form, for at least two reasons:

(1) even at the highest measured energies the real part of the scattering amplitude is not negligible (see Section IV,B);

(2) the ratio σ_{el}/σ_{tot} has the value 0.24 at 19 GeV/c, and therefore the limit (VI-15) is violated.

Nevertheless, by modifying the model with the introduction of a real part but preserving the Gaussian form of the overlap function, Cottingham and Peierls have fitted both the small- and large-angle part of the pp angular distribution; in their calculation the ratio $D(s, 0)/A(s, 0)$ is used as a parameter to fit the data. It is remarkable that the value of $D(s, 0)/A(s, 0)$ which gives agreement between theory and experiment is of the same order of magnitude as found in the interference experiments.

For πp scattering, the model seems to be more adequate since $D(s, 0)/A(s, 0)$ tends rapidly to zero and, moreover, $\sigma_{el}/\sigma_{tot} = 0.16 < 0.185$ at 17 GeV/c. The

[66] This result has to be compared with that of the uniform absorbing sphere $\sigma_{el}/\sigma_{tot} = \tfrac{1}{2}$. In our case the "target" is still completely absorbing (the amplitude is purely imaginary), but not in a uniform way.

values of the parameters A and f_0, extracted from the analysis of πp scattering at 17 GeV/c are

$$f_0 = 0.455 \qquad A = 5 \; (\text{GeV}/c)^{-2}.$$

More recently, the model has also been applied to the elastic $\bar{p}p$ scattering for energies between 4 and 12 GeV/c (Kokkedee, 1966); both the antishrinking of the elastic peak and the fact that the ratio $\sigma_{\text{el}}/\sigma_{\text{tot}}$ exceeds the maximum allowed value 0.185 are explained here as an effect of the annihilation channels.

C. Models for Very High Energy Inelastic Scattering

The theory we have discussed in the previous section explains the form of the diffraction angular distribution as the shadow of inelastic processes, whose overlap function is of a Gaussian form.

Of course, the theory would be complete when it is possible to obtain a Gaussian overlap function from a theory of the production processes.

We shall not examine in this respect all the models we have quoted in Section VI,A, nor the two-fireball model; we shall only briefly discuss two models, both giving a Gaussian overlap function: the uncorrelated particle model (van Hove, 1963c, 1964, 1965b) and the multiperipheral model (Amati et al., 1962b).

1. The Uncorrelated Particle Model

The model assumes that in very high energy collisions there is no correlation between the produced secondaries in the final state, except the obvious one which corresponds to the general conservation of energy and momentum.

The precise mathematical definition is as follows: let us divide the longitudinal momentum q_l of each secondary in $n \gg 1$ subintervals

$$q^{(j-1)} \leqslant q_l \leqslant q^{(j)}; \quad j = 1, \ldots, n \tag{VI-18}$$

where the energy-momentum conservation imposes the limitation

$$q^{(0)} = -q < q^{(1)} < \cdots < q^{(n)} = q \tag{VI-19}$$

(q is the incident momentum).

For the inelastic part of the final wave function one takes the *ansatz*

$$|f(\boldsymbol{q})\rangle = \prod_{j=1}^{n} g_j(\boldsymbol{q}) |0\rangle \tag{VI-20}$$

where $|0\rangle$ is the vacuum state and $g_j(\boldsymbol{q})$ is a polynomial in creation operators of particles with longitudinal momenta in the interval (VI-18).

One has therefore to study the angular dependence for large n of the function [cf. Eq. (VI-10)]:

$$F(q, \Theta) = \langle 0| \prod_{j'} g_{j'}^*(q') \, \delta^{(4)}(P - p_a - p_b) \prod_j g_j(q)|0\rangle. \qquad \text{(VI-21)}$$

If one now makes the simplifying hypothesis that $g_j(q')$ only creates particles within the same momentum region as $g_j(q)$, then[67] one has only to compute

$$F(q, \Theta) = \int \delta^{(4)}\left(\sum_j P_j - p_a - p_b\right) \prod_j f_j(P_j^\mu, \Theta) d_4 P_j \qquad \text{(VI-22)}$$

where

$$f_j(P_j^\mu, \Theta) = \langle 0|g_j^*(q') \, \delta^{(4)}(P - p_a - p_b)g_j(q)|0\rangle. \qquad \text{(VI-23)}$$

and a notation like $f(p^\mu)$ means that f is a function of the four-vector $p^\mu (\mu = 0, 1, 2, 3)$.

The behavior for large n of Eq. (VI-22) can be computed by using methods of probability theory (see van Hove, 1964a) obtaining

$$F(q, \Theta) = F(q, 0) \exp[-A\Theta^2] \qquad A = -\sum_j [\partial \ln \tilde{f}_j(u_\mu, \Theta)/\partial \Theta^2]_{\Theta=0}. \qquad \text{(VI-24)}$$

$[\tilde{f}_j(u^\mu, \Theta)$ is the four-dimensional Fourier transform of $f_j(p^\mu, \Theta)$,

$$\tilde{f}_j(u_\mu, \Theta) = \int d_4 p \, \exp(iu_\mu p^\mu) f_j(p^\mu, \Theta)]. \qquad \text{(VI-25)}$$

One therefore gets the Gaussian form (VI-11).

If, moreover, one assumes that the transverse momentum distribution is independent of the incident energy and there is no correlation between the longitudinal and transverse momentum, then the energy dependence of A/q^2 is determined by the dependence on the initial energy of the energy distribution $W(q_0)$ of the secondaries. There is a strict correlation between the energy dependence of A/q^2 and that of the multiplicity of produced particles $N(q)$.

The general result is that A/q^2 can never increase with q; shrinking of the elastic peak is not allowed. Furthermore, when the energy dependence of $W(q_0)$ is such as to give $N(q) \to \infty$ for $q \to \infty$, then A/q^2 will in general tend to zero as $q \to \infty$, unless very special forms of $W(q_0)$ are postulated. For instance, if one takes

$$W(q_0) = C(q)q_0^{-\alpha} \quad \text{for} \quad q_0 \leqslant q; \qquad W(q_0) = 0 \quad \text{for} \quad q_0 > q$$

[67] This hypothesis is justified empirically from the jet structure of the particles produced.

with the normalization condition

$$\int W(q_0)\, dq_0 = 1,$$

then one finds

$$A/q^2 \to \text{const} \qquad N \propto \ln q \qquad \text{for} \quad \alpha = 1$$

$$\to \text{const} \qquad \propto q^{\alpha - 1} \qquad \text{for} \quad 1 < \alpha < 2$$

$$\propto (\ln q)^{-1} \qquad \propto q/\ln q \qquad \text{for} \quad \alpha = 2.$$

The general remark is that in the uncorrelated particle model one always gets constancy of the diffraction peak whenever the multiplicity $N(q)$ increases slowly with the incident energy.

2. *The Multiperipheral Model*

The total inelastic cross section calculated from the peripheral model increases with energy (see Hearn and Drell, this volume); therefore constant asymptotic cross sections are inconsistent with the simple peripheral model of Fig. 44.

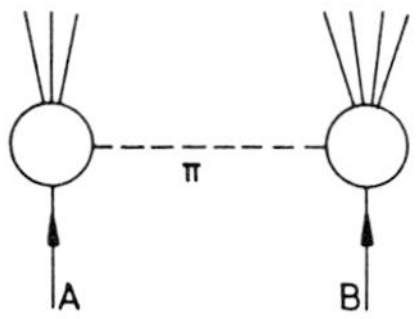

FIG. 44. Schematic diagram of multiparticle production in the peripheral model at high energies; the particles produced are emitted only from the two upper and lower "centers."

This inconsistency can be eliminated if one assumes that whenever the relative energy between one of the incident particles, say, A, and the virtual exchanged pion becomes large, the scattering amplitude $T_{A\pi}$ is again dominated by the one-pion-exchange mechanism.

As the energy increases each of the two bubbles in the upper and lower vertices of Fig. 44 must therefore show an internal peripheral structure, and this process of degradation of the energy in the bubbles continues, via the increase of the number of bubbles, toward the situation when each bubble becomes a low energy scattering amplitude, which is then dominated by the resonance phenomena. In other words, the production amplitude is as peripheral as possible (Fig. 45); the multiperipheral model (Amati *et al.*, 1962b) assumes that the dominant inelastic mechanism at high energy is

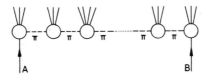

FIG. 45. Schematic diagram of multiparticle production in the multiperipheral model at high energies. The exchanged particle is a pion, but the particles produced can be emitted as groups of low energy particles from many "centers," whose number increases with the incident energy.

represented by a chain of low energy amplitudes, linked by virtual pions. The basic assumptions of the model are therefore:

(1) the dominance of one-pion exchange at high energies, and
(2) the negligible dependence of the low energy amplitudes on the mass of the virtual pion.

The main features of the model for the production processes, which are independent of the details of the model (such as the form of the low energy amplitudes or the nature of secondaries) but depend only on its essential properties, are:

(a) The multiplicity of the secondaries increases logarithmically with energy.
(b) The average energy carried out by the primary after the reaction is proportional to the initial energy; therefore, the inelasticity is constant.
(c) The spectra of transverse momenta of the secondaries is independent of the initial energy and of the energies of the secondaries; both the energies and transverse momenta of the secondaries are limited to small values.

By computing the shadow of the multiperipheral model, one can get both the total cross section and the elastic diffraction scattering.

Concerning the total cross section, it can be shown (Ceolin *et al.*, 1962) that the forward imaginary scattering amplitude off the mass shell $A(s, u)$ (u is the mass of the virtual pion) has the asymptotic behavior

$$A(s, u) = s^{\alpha} \varphi_{\alpha}(u) \tag{VI-26}$$

where $\varphi_{\alpha}(u)$ satisfies the homogeneous Fredholm integral equation

$$\varphi_{\alpha}(u) = \frac{1}{16\pi^3} \int ds_0 \, A_R(s_0) \int_0^1 dx \, x^{\alpha} \int_{u_0'}^{\infty} du' \, \frac{\varphi_{\alpha}(u')}{(u' + \mu^2)^2} \tag{VI-27}$$

where $A_R(s_0)$ is the low energy scattering amplitude, represented by each sub-bubble in Fig. 45, $u_0' = x[u + s_0/(1 - x)]$, and s_0 is integrated over its physical range. The physical scattering amplitude is given by the mass-shell condition $A(s, u = -\mu^2)$.

Since Eq. (VI-27) is an homogeneous Fredholm equation, it is an eigenvalue equation for the exponent α, which can therefore be determined as a function of the low energy input $A_R(s_0)$. It is possible therefore to obtain constant total cross sections, when the equation (VI-27) admits the eigenvalue $\alpha = 1$.

Concerning the elastic shadow of the multiperipheral model, one has:

(a) that simply neglecting elastic effects as compared with the inelastic ones, namely, writing

$$A(s, t) \propto \sum_{n_{in}} T_{n_{in}i} T^*_{n_{in}f} , \tag{VI-28}$$

the elastic scattering amplitude has the asymptotic Regge behavior (Bertocchi et al., 1962)

$$T(s, t) = C(t)s^{\alpha(t)}\xi(t) \tag{VI-29}$$

where $\alpha(t)$ is still the eigenvalue of an homogeneous Fredholm integral equation: this amounts to computing the elastic scattering as the iteration in the t channel of the ladder graph of Fig. 46;

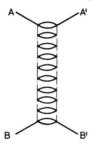

FIG. 46.   The shadow graph of the multiperipheral model, showing an asymptotic Regge behavior for the elastic scattering amplitude.

(b) if one also takes into account the elastic contribution to the unitarity condition (Amati et al., 1963), the forward behavior is still of the Regge form, but for $t \neq 0$ the multiple elastic scattering effects become important; the shrinking of the peak is predicted to decrease with the energy, and the large-angle differential cross section has the behavior

$$\frac{d\sigma}{dt} \propto \frac{\exp[-c(-t)^{1/2}]}{t^2} .$$

REFERENCES

Aachen-Berlin-Birmingham-Bonn-Hamburg-London (I.C.)-Munich Collaboration (1964a). *Nuovo Cimento* **31**, 485.
Aachen-Berlin-Birmingham-Bonn-Hamburg-London (I.C.)-Munich Collaboration (1964b). *Nuovo Cimento* **31**, 729.

Aachen-Berlin-Birmingham-Bonn-Hamburg-London (I.C.)-Munich Collaboration (1964c). *Phys. Letters* **10**, 226.

Aachen-Berlin-Birmingham-Bonn-Hamburg-London (I.C.)-Munich Collaboration (1964d). *Phys. Letters* **10**, 248.

Aachen-Berlin-Birmingham-Bonn-Hamburg-London (I.C.)-Munich Collaboration (1964e). *Phys. Letters* **11**, 167.

Aachen-Berlin-Birmingham-Bonn-Hamburg-London (I.C.)-Munich Collaboration (1964f). *Nuovo Cimento* **34**, 495.

Aachen-Berlin-Birmingham-Bonn-Hamburg-London (I.C.)-Munich Collaboration (1965). *Phys. Rev.* **138**, B897.

Aachen-Berlin CERN Collaboration (1964a). *Phys. Letters* **12**, 356.

Aachen-Berlin-CERN Collaboration (1965a). *Phys. Letters* **18**, 351.

Aachen-Berlin-CERN Collaboration (1965b). *Phys. Letters* **19**, 608.

Aachen-Berlin-CERN Collaboration (1965c). Private communication from the CERN group.

Aachen-Berlin-CERN Collaboration (1966). *Proc. 12th Intern. Conf. High Energy Phys.*, *Dubna*, 1964, **1**, 514. Atomisdat, Moscow, 1966.

Abolins, M., Lander, R. L., Mehlhop, W. A. W., Xuong, N. H., and Yager, P. M. (1963). *Phys. Rev. Letters* **11**, 381.

Abolins, M., Carmony, D. D., Hoa, D. N., Lander, R. L., Rindfleisch, C., and Xuong, N. H. (1964). *Phys. Rev.* **136**, B195.

Ahmadzadeh, A. (1964). *Phys. Rev.* **134**, B633.

Alexander, G., Benary, O., Kidron, N., Shapira, A., Yaari, R., and Yekutieli, G. (1964). *Phys. Rev. Letters.* **13**, 355 a.

Alexander, G., Dar, A., and Karshon, U. (1965a). *Phys. Rev. Letters* **14**, 918.

Alexander, G., Benary, O., Reuter, B., Shapira, A., Simopoulou, E., and Yekutieli, G. (1965b). *Phys. Rev. Letters* **15**, 207.

Alexander, G., Benary, O., Kidron, N., Haber, B., Shapira, A., Yekutieli, G., and Gotsman, E. (1965c). *Nuovo Cimento* **40**, A839.

Alff, C., Berley, D., Colley, D., Gelfand, N., Nauenberg, U., Miller, D., Schultz, J., Steinberger, J., Tan, T. H., Brugger, H., Kramer, P., and Plano, R. (1962). *Phys. Rev. Letters* **9**, 322.

Alikhanov, A. I., Bayatyan, G. L., Brachman, E. V., Galaktionov, Yu. V., Joch, F. A., Landsberg, L. G., Lyubimov, V. A., Pavlovski, F. A., Sidorov, I. V., Yeliseev, G. P., and Zel'dovich, O. Ya. (1965). *Phys. Letters* **19**, 345.

Almeida, S. P., Atherton, H. W., Byer, T. A., Dornan, P. J., Forson, A. G., Sharenguivel, J. H., Sendall, D. M., and Westwood, B. A. (1965). *Phys. Letters* **14**, 240.

Aly, H. H., Lurie, D., and Rosendorff, S. (1963). *Phys. Letters* **7**, 198.

Amati, D., Fierz, M., and Glaser, V. (1960). *Phys. Rev. Letters*, **4**, 589.

Amati, D., Fubini, S., Stanghellini, A., and Tonin, M. (1961). *Nuovo Cimento* **22**, 569.

Amati, D., Fubini, S., and Stanghellini, A. (1962a). *Phys. Letters* **1**, 29.

Amati, D., Stanghellini, A., and Fubini, S. (1962b). *Nuovo Cimento* **26**, 896.

Amati, D., Cini, M., and Stanghellini, A. (1963). *Nuovo Cimento*, **30**, 193.

Amati, D., Foldy, L. L., Stanghellini, A., and van Hove, L. (1964). *Nuovo Cimento* **32**, 1685.

Anderson, J. A., Bang, V. X., Burke, P. G., Carmony, D. D., and Schmitz, N. (1961). *Phys. Rev. Letters*, **6**, 365.

Ankenbrandt, C. M., Clyde, A. R., Cork, B., Keefe, D., Kerth, L. T., Layson, W. M., and Wenzel, W. A. (1965). *Nuovo Cimento* **35**, 1052.

Arbab, F., and Chiu, C. B. (1966). Preprint, Univ. of California Radiation Lab., 16686.

Armenteros, R., Coombes, C. A., Cork, B., Lambertson, G. R., and Wenzel, C. A. (1960). *Phys. Rev.* **119**, 2068.

Arnold, R. C. (1964). *Phys. Rev.* **136**, B1388.

Astbury, P., Finocchiaro, G., Michelini, A., Websdale, D., West, C. H., Beusch, W., Gobbi, B., Peppin, M., Pouchon, M. A., and Polgor, E. (1965). *Phys. Letters* **16**, 328.

Auvil, P., Donnachie, A., Lea, A. T., and Lovelace, C. (1964). *Phys. Letters* **12**, 76.

Badier, J., Demoulin, M., Goldberg, J., Gregory, B. P., Pellettier, C., Rouge, A., Ville, M., Barlotaud, R., Leveque, A., Louedec, C., Meyer, J., Schlein, P., Verglas, A., Holtuizen, D. J., Hoogland, W., and Tenner, A. G. (1965a). *Phys. Letters* **16**, 171.

Badier, J., Demoulin, M., Goldberg, J., Gregory, B. P., Pellettier, C., Rouge, A., Ville, M., Barlotaud, R., Leveque, A., Louedec, C., Meyer, J., Schlein, P., Verglas, A., Holtuizen, D. J., Hoogland, W., Kluyver, J. C., de Lijser, E., and Tenner, A. G. (1965b). Report CEA (Commissariat à l'Energie Atomique) N-532.

Baker, W., Jenkins, E., Read, A., Cocconi, G., Cocconi, V. T., Krisch, A., Orear, J., Rubinstein, R., Scarl, D., and Ulrich, B. (1964). *Phys. Rev. Letters* **12**, 132.

Baltay, C., Ferbel, T., Sandweiss, J., Taft, H. D., Culwick, B. B., Fowler, W. B., Gailloud, M., Kopp, J. K., Louttit, R. I., Morris, T. W., Sandford, J. R., Shutt, R. P., Stonehill, D. L., Stump, R., Thorndike, A. M., Webster, S., Willis, W. J., Bachman, A. H., Baumel, P., and Lea, R. M. (1964a). *Proc. Intern. Conf. Nucleon Structure, Stanford, 1963*, p. 267. Stanford Univ. Press, Stanford, California.

Baltay, C., Sandweiss, J., Taft, H. D., Culwick, B. B., Fowler, W. B., Kopp, J. K., Louttit, R. I., Sandford, J. R., Shutt, R. P., Stonehill, D. L., Thorndike, A. M., and Webster, M. S. (1964b). *Phys. Rev. Letters* **11**, 32, 346.

Baltay, C., Sandweiss, J., Taft, H. D., Culwick, B. B., Kopp, J. K., Louttit, R. I., Shutt, R. P., Thorndike, A. M., and Webster, M. S. (1965). *Phys. Rev.* **140**, B1027.

Barashenkov, V. S., and Dedyu, V. I. (1964). Preprint JINR P-1598, Dubna.

Bardadin, M., Michejda, L., Otwinowski, S., and Sosnowski, R. (1963). *Proc. Intern. Conf. Elementary Particles, Sienna* **1**, 628. Società Italiana di Fisica, Bologna.

Bareyre, P., Bricman, C., Valladas, G., Villet, G., Bizard, J., and Seguinot, J. (1964). *Phys. Letters* **8**, 137.

Bareyre, P., Bricman, C., Stirling, A. V., and Villet, G. (1965). *Phys. Letters* **18**, 342.

Barlotaud, R., Leveque, A., Louedec, C., Meyer, J., Schlein, P., Verglas, A., Badier, J., Demoulin, M., Goldberg, J., Gregory, B. P., Kresbich, P., Pellettier, C., Ville, M., Gelsema, E. S., Hoogland, J., Kluyver, J. C., and Tenner, A. G. (1964). *Phys. Letters* **12**, 352.

Barnes, V. E., Culwick, B. B., Guidoni, P., Kalbfleisch, G. R., London, G. W., Palmer, R. B., Radojcic, D., Rahm, D. C., Rau, R. R., Richardson, C. R., Samios, N. P., Smith, J. R., Goz, B., Horwitz, N., Kikuchi, T., Leitner, J., and Wolfe, R. (1965). *Phys. Rev. Letters* **15**, 322.

Bartke, J., Budde, R., Cooper, W. A., Filthuth, H., Goldschmidt-Clermont, Y., McLeod, G. R., de Marco, A., Minguzzi-Ranzi, A., Montanet, L., Morrison, D. R. O., Nilsson, S., Peyrou, C., Sosnowski, R., Bigi, A., Carrara, R., Franzinetti, C., Mannelli, I., Brautti, G., Ceschia, M., and Chersovani, L. (1962). *Nuovo Cimento* **24**, 876.

Bartke, J., Cooper, W. A., Czapp, B., Filthuth, H., Goldschmidt-Clermont, Y., Montanet, L., Morrison, D. R. O., Nilsson, S., Peyrou, C., Sosnowski, R., Bigi, A., Carrara, R., Franzinetti, C., and Mannelli, I. (1963). *Nuovo Cimento* **29**, 8.

Barut, A. O., and Zwanziger, D. E. (1962). *Phys. Rev.* **127**, 974.

Bellettini, G., Cocconi, G., Diddens, A. N., Lillethun, E., Pahl, J., Scanlon, J. P., Walters, J., Wetherell, A. M., and Zanella, P. (1965a). *Phys. Letters* **14**, 164.

Bellettini, G., Cocconi, G., Diddens, A. N., Lillethun, E., Scanlon, J. P., Shapiro, A. M., and Wetherell, A. M. (1965b). *Phys. Letters* **18**, 167.

Bellettini, G., Cocconi, G., Diddens, A. N., Lillethun, E., Matthiae, G., Scanlon, J. P., and Wetherell, A. M. (1965c). *Phys. Letters* 19, 341.

Bellettini G., Cocconi, G., Diddens, A. N., Lillethun, E., Matthiae, G., Scanlon, J. P., and Wetherell, A. M. (1966). *Nucl. Phys.* 79, 609.

Bellini, G., Fiorini, E., Herz, A. J., Negri, P., and Ratti, S. (1963). *Nuovo Cimento* 29, 896.

Bellini, G., Fiorini, E., Negri, P., Hennessy, J., Veillet, J. J., Crussard, J., Ginestet, J., and Anh Ha Tran (1964). *Phys. Letters* 10, 126.

Bergia, S., Bonsignori, F., and Stanghellini, A. (1960). *Nuovo Cimento* 16, 1073.

Bertanza, L., Culwick, B. B., Lai, K. W., Mittra, I. S., Samios, N. P., Thorndike, A. M., Yamamoto, S. S., and Lea, R. M. (1963). *Phys. Rev.* 130, 786.

Bertocchi, L., Fubini, S., and Tonin, M. (1962). *Nuovo Cimento* 25, 626.

Bethe, H. A. (1964). *Nuovo Cimento* 33, 1167.

Bettini, A., Cresti, M., Limentani, S., Peruzzo, L., Santangelo, R., Locke, D., Crennell, D. J., Davies, W. T., and Jones, P. B. (1965). *Phys. Letters* 16, 83.

Białas, A. (1965). Private communication.

Białas, A. (1966). *Phys. Letters* 19, 604.

Białas, A., and Weisskopf, V. F. (1965). *Nuovo Cimento* 35, 1211.

Bigi, A., Brandt, S., de Marco-Trabucco, A., Peyrou, C., Sosnowski, R., and Wroblewski, A. (1964). *Nuovo Cimento* 33, 1249, 1265.

Biswas, N. N., Derado, I., Schmitz, N., and Shephard, W. D. (1964). *Phys. Rev.* 134, B901.

Blokhintsev, D. I. (1962). *Nuovo Cimento* 23, 1061.

Blokhintsev, D. I., (1966). *Nuovo Cimento* 41, A481.

Röck, R. K., Cooper, W. A., French, B. R., Kinson, J. B., Levi-Setti, R., Revel, D., Tallini, B., and Zylberajch, S. (1965). *Phys. Letters* 17, 166.

Bonn-Hamburg-Milano Collaboration (1965). *Phys. Letters* 15, 356.

Bonamy, P., Borgeaud, P., Brehin, S., Bruneton, C., Falk-Vairant, P., Guisan, O., Sonderegger, P., Caverzasio, C., Guilland, J. P., Schneider, J., Yvert, M., Mannelli, I., Sergiampietri, F., and Vincelli, M. L. (1966). *Proc. 13th Intern. Conf. High Energy Phys.*, Berkeley, 1966, to be published.

Bonsignori, F., and Selleri, F. (1960). *Nuovo Cimento* 15, 465.

Borgeaud, P., Bruneton, C., Ducros, Y., Falk-Vairant, P., Guisan, O., Mouchet, J., Sonderegger, P., Stirling, A., Yvert, M., Tran, A. H., and Warshaw, S. D. (1964). *Phys. Letters*, 10, 134.

Borghini, M., Coignet, C., Dick, L., Di Lella, L., Michailowicz, A., Macq, P. C., and Olivier, J. C. (1966a). *Phys. Letters* 21, 114.

Borghini, M., Coignet, C., Dick, L., Kuroda, K., Di Lella, L., Michailowicz, A., Macq, P. C., and Olivier, J. C. (1966b). *Proc. 13th Intern. Conf. High Energy Phys.*, Berkeley 1966, to be published.

Bottino, S., Longoni, A., and Regge, T. (1962). *Nuovo Cimento* 23, 954.

Brandt, S., Cocconi, V. T., Morrison, D. R. O., Wroblewski, A., Fleury, P., Kayas, G., Muller, F., and Pellettier, C. (1963). *Phys. Rev. Letters* 10, 413.

Breitenlohner, P., Egli, P., Hofer, H., Koch, W., Nikolic, M., Pahl, J., Pallinger, A., Schneeberger, M., Schneeberger, R., Winzeler, H., Czabek, G., and Kellner, G. (1963). *Phys. Letters* 7, 73.

Brody, H., Lanza, R., Marshall, R., Niederer, J., Selove, W., Shochet, M., and Van Berg, R. (1966). *Phys. Rev. Letters* 16, 828.

Bros, J., Epstein, H., and Glaser, V. (1965a) *Comm. Math. Phys.* 1, 240.

Bros, J., Epstein, H., and Glaser, V. (1965b). "High Energy Physics and Elementary Particles," p. 85. IAEA, Vienna.

Brown, G. E. (1957). *Proc. Phys. Soc. (London)* A70, 361.

Bruyant, F., Goldberg, M., Vegni, G., Winzeler, H., Fleury, P., Huc, J., Lestienne, R., de Rosny, G., and Vanderhagen, R. (1964). *Phys. Letters* **12**, 278.

Bugg, D. V., Oxley, A. J., Zoll, J. A., Rushbrooke, J. G., Barnes, V. E., Kinson, J. B., Dodd, W. P., Doran, G. A., and Riddiford, L. (1964). *Phys. Rev.* **133**, B1017.

Byers, N., and Yang, C. N. (1966). *Phys. Rev.* **142**, 976.

Caldwell, D. O., Elsner, B., Harting, D., Helmholtz, A. C., Middelkoop, W. C., Powell, P., Zacharov, B., Zanella, P., Dalpiaz, P., Focacci, M. N., Focardi, S., Giacomelli, G., Monari, L., Beaney, J. A., Donald, R. A., Mason, P., and Jones, L. W. (1964). *Phys. Letters* **8**, 288.

Carmony, D. D., and van de Walle, R. T. (1962). *Phys. Rev.* **127**, 959.

Carmony, D. D., Grard, F., van der Walle, R. T., and Xuong, N. H. (1962). *Proc. 11th Intern. Conf. High Energy Phys.*, CERN, Geneva, p. 44.

Ceolin, C., Duimio, F., Fubini, S., and Stroffolini, R. (1962). *Nuovo Cimento* **26**, 247.

Cerulus, F., and Martin, A. (1964). *Phys. Letters* **8**, 80.

Chadan, K. (1965). *Nuovo Cimento* **37**, 658.

Chadwick, G. B., Collins, G. B., Duke, P. J., Fujii, T., Hien, N. C., Kemp, M. A. R., and Turkot, F. (1962). *Phys. Rev.* **128**, 1823.

Chaoud, J., Russo, G., and Selleri, F. (1963). *Phys. Rev. Letters* **11**, 506.

Chaoud, J., Russo, G., and Selleri, F. (1966). *Nuovo Cimento* **45**, A38.

Chew, G. F., and Frautschi, S. C. (1961a). *Phys. Rev. Letters* **5**, 589.

Chew, G. F., and Frautschi, S. C. (1961b). *Phys. Rev.* **123**, 1478.

Chew, G. F., and Frautschi, S. C. (1961c). *Phys. Rev.* **124**, 264.

Chew, G. F., and Frautschi, S. C. (1961d). *Phys. Rev. Letters* **7**, 394.

Chew, G. F., and Frautschi, S. C. (1962). *Phys. Rev. Letters* **8**, 41.

Chew, G. F., and Low, F. E. (1959). *Phys. Rev.* **113**, 1630.

Chew, G. F., and Mandelstam, S. (1960). *Phys. Rev.* **119**, 467.

Chew, G. F., and Mandelstam, S. (1961). *Nuovo Cimento* **19**, 752.

Chew, G. F., and Stack, J. D. (1965). Preprint, Univ. of California Radiation Lab., 16293.

Chew, G. F., Frautschi, S. C., and Mandelstam, S. (1962). *Phys. Rev.* **126**, 1202.

Chiu, C. B., and Stack, J. D. (1966). Preprint, Univ. of California Radiation Lab., 16745.

Chiu, C. B., Phillips, R. J. N., and Rarita, W. (1966). Preprint, Univ. of California Radiation Lab., 16940.

Chretien, M., Leitner, J., Samios, N. P., Schwartz, M., and Steinberger, J. (1957). *Phys. Rev.* **108**, 383.

Chung, S. U., Dahl, O. I., Hardy, L. M., Hess, R. I., Kalbfleisch, G. R., Kirz, J., Miller, D. H., and Smith, G. A. (1964). *Phys. Rev. Letters* **12**, 621.

Ciok, P., Coghen, T., Gierula, J., Holynski, R., Jurak, A., Miesowicz, M., Saniewska, T., Stanisz, O., and Pernegr, J. (1958a). *Nuovo Cimento* **8**, 166.

Ciok, P., Coghen, T., Gierula, J., Holynski, R., Jurak, A., Miesowicz, M., Saniewska, T., and Pernegr, J. (1958b). *Nuovo Cimento* **10**, 741.

Clyde, A. R., Cork, B., Keefe, D., Kerth, L. T., Layson, W. M., and Wenzel, W. A. (1964). Preprint, Univ. of California Radiation Lab., 11441.

Cocconi, G. (1958). *Phys. Rev.* **111**, 1699.

Cocconi, G. (1964). *Nuovo Cimento* **33**, 643.

Cocconi, G., Diddens, A. N., Lillethun, E., and Wetherell, A. M. (1961a). *Phys. Rev. Letters* **6**, 231.

Cocconi, G., Diddens, A. N., Lillethun, E., Manning, G., Taylor, A. E., Walker, J. G., and Wetherell, A. M. (1961b). *Phys. Rev. Letters* **7**, 450.

Cocconi, G., Cocconi, V. T., Krisch, A., Orear, J., Rubinstein, R., Scarl, D., Baker, W., Read, A., and Jenkins, E. (1963). *Phys. Rev. Letters* **11**, 499.

Cocconi, G., Lillethun, E., Scanlon, J. P., Stahlbrandt, C. A., Ting, C. C., Walters, J., and Wetherell, A. M. (1964). *Phys. Letters* **8**, 134.

Cocconi, G., Cocconi, V. T., Krisch, A. D., Orear, J., Rubinstein, R., Scarl, D. B., Ulrich, B. T., Baker, W. F., Jenkins, E. W., and Read, A. L. (1965). *Phys. Rev.* **138**, B165.

Coffin, C., Dikman, N., Ettlinger, L., Meyer, D., Saulys, A., Terwilliger, K., and Williams, D. (1965). *Phys. Rev. Letters* **15**, 838.

Cohn, H. O., Bugg, W. M., and Condo, G. T. (1965). *Phys. Letters* **15**, 344.

Conte, F., Dameri, M., Grosso, C., Kidd, J., Mandelli, L., Pelosi, V., Ratti, S., Tallone, L., and Tomasini, G. (1964). Preprint, Univ. of Milano.

Contogouris, A., (1965). Private communication.

Cook, V., Keefe, D., Kerth, L. T., Murphy, P. G., Wenzel, W. A., and Zipf, T. F. (1963a). *Phys. Rev.* **129**, 2743.

Cook, V., Cork, B., Holly, W., and Perl, M. L. (1963b). *Phys. Rev.* **130**, 762.

Cork, B., Wenzel, W. A., and Causey, C. W. (1957). *Phys. Rev.* **107**, 859.

Cork, B., Holly, W., and Perl, M. L. (1963). *Phys. Rev.* **130**, 762.

Cornille, H. (1964). *Nuovo Cimento* **31**, 1101.

Cottingham, W. N., and Dombey, N., (1966). *Nuovo Cimento* **43**, A397.

Cottingham, W. N., and Peierls, R. F. (1965). *Phys. Rev.* **137**, B147.

Crittenden, R., Martin, H. J., Kernan, W., Leipuner, L., Li, A. C., Ayer, F., Marshall, L., and Stevenson, M. L. (1964). *Phys. Rev. Letters* **12**, 429.

Czyzewski, O., Escoubès, B., Goldschmidt-Clermont, Y., Guinea-Moorhead, M., Hofmokl, T., Lewisch, R., Morrison, D. R. O., Schneeberger, N., and de Unamuno, S. (1963). *Proc. Intern. Conf. Elementary Particles, Sienna* **1**, 271. Società Italiana di Fisica, Bologna.

Damouth, D. E., Jones, L. W., and Perl, M. L. (1963). *Phys. Rev. Letters* **11**, 287.

Da Prato, G. (1961). *Nuovo Cimento* **22**, 123.

Dar, A. (1964). *Phys. Rev. Letters* **13**, 91.

Dar, A., and Tobocman, W. (1964). *Phys. Rev. Letters* **12**, 511.

Dar, A., Kugler, M., Dothan, J., and Nussinov, S. (1964a). *Phys. Letters* **11**, 265.

Dar, A., Kugler, M., Dothan, J., and Nussinov, S. (1964b). *Phys. Rev. Letters* **12**, 82.

Daronian, P., Daudin, A., Jabiol, M. A., Lewin, C., Kochowski, C., Ghidini, B., Mongelli, S., and Picciarelli, V. (1966). *Nuovo Cimento* **41**, A503.

Daudin, A., Jabiol, M. A., Kochowski, C., Lewin, C., Selleri, F., Mongelli, S., Romano, A., and Waloschek, P. (1963). *Phys. Letters* **5**, 125.

Dehne, H. C., Lohrmann, E., Raubold, E., Söding, P., Teucher, H. W., and Wolf, G. (1964a). *Phys. Letters* **9**, 185.

Dehne, H. C., Lohrmann, E., Raubold, E., Söding, P., Teucher, H. W., and Wolf, G. (1964b). *Phys. Rev.* **136**, B843.

Derado, I., Schmitz, N., and Shephard, W. D. (1964). *Phys. Rev. Letters* **13**, 505.

Derado, I., Kenney, V. P., Poirier, J. A., and Shephard, W. D. (1965). *Phys. Rev. Letters* **14**, 872.

Desai, B. R. (1966). *Phys. Rev.* **142**, 976.

Diddens, A. N., Lillethun, E., Manning, G., Taylor, A. E., Walker, T. G., and Wetherell, A. M. (1962a). *Phys. Rev. Letters* **9**, 108.

Diddens, A. N., Lillethun, E., Manning, G., Taylor, A. E., Walker, T. G., and Wetherell, A. M. (1962b). *Phys. Rev. Letters* **9**, 111.

Dietz, K., and Pilkuhn, H. (1965a). *Nuovo Cimento* **37**, 1561.

Dietz, K., and Pilkuhn, H. (1965b). *Nuovo Cimento* **39**, 928.

Dowell, A. D., Homer, R. J., Khan, Q. H., McFarlane, W. K., McKee, J. S. C., and O'Dell, A. W. (1964). *Phys. Letters* **12**, 252.

Drell, S. D. (1960a). *Phys. Rev. Letters* **5**, 278.

Drell, S. D. (1960b). *Phys. Rev. Letters* **5**, 342.

Drell, S. D. (1962). *Proc. 11th Intern. Conf. High Energy Phys.* CERN, Geneva, p. 897.

Drell, S. D. and Hiida, K. (1961). *Phys. Rev. Letters* **7**, 193.

Duke, P. J., Jones, D. P., Kemp, M. A. R., Murphy, P. G., Prentice, J. D., Thresher, J. J., and Atkinson, H. H. (1965). *Phys. Rev. Letters* **15**, 468.

Durand, L., III and Chiu, Y. T. (1964). *Phys. Rev. Letters* **12**, 399.

Durand, L., III and Chiu, Y. T. (1965a). *Phys. Rev.* **137**, B1530.

Durand, L., III and Chiu, Y. T. (1965b). *Phys. Rev.* **139**, B646.

Durand, L., III, and Greider, K. R. (1963). *Phys. Rev.* **132**, 1217.

Dürr, H. P., and Pilkuhn, H. (1965). *Nuovo Cimento* **40**, A236.

Escoubès, B., Federighini, A., Goldschmidt-Clermont, Y., Guinea-Moorhead, M., Hofmokl, T., Lewisch, R., Morrison, D. R. O., Schneeberger, M., and de Unamuno-Escoubès, S. (1965). *Phys. Letters* **15**, 188.

Fast, G., and Hagedorn, R. (1963). *Nuovo Cimento* **27**, 208.

Fast, G., Hagedorn, R., and Jones, L. W. (1963). *Nuovo Cimento* **27**, 856.

Feinberg, E. L., and Pomeranchuk, I. Ya. (1951). *Nuovo Cimento Suppl.* **3**, 652.

Ferbel, T., and Taft, H. (1963). *Nuovo Cimento* **28**, 1214.

Ferbel, T., Firestone, A., Sandweiss, J., Taft, H. D., Gailloud, M., Morris, T. W., Bachman, A. H., Baumel, P., and Lea, R. M. (1965a). *Phys. Rev.* **137**, B1250.

Ferbel, T., Firestone, A., Sandweiss, J., Taft, H. D., Gailloud, M., Morris, T. W., Willis, W. J., Bachman, A. H., Baumel, P., and Lea, R. M. (1965b). *Phys. Rev.* **138**, B1528.

Ferbel, T., Firestone, A., Johnson, J., Sandweiss, J., and Taft, H. D. (1965c). *Nuovo Cimento* **38**, 12.

Ferbel, T., Firestone, A., Johnson, J., Sandweiss, J., and Taft, H. D. (1965d). *Nuovo Cimento* **38**, 19.

Fermi, E. (1950). *Progr. Theoret. Phys.* (*Kyoto*) **5**, 570.

Fermi, E. (1953). *Phys. Rev.* **92**, 452.

Fermi, E. (1954). *Phys. Rev.* **93**, 1435.

Fernbach, S., Serber, R., and Taylor, T. B. (1949). *Phys. Rev.* **75**, 1352.

Ferrari, E. (1963). *Nuovo Cimento* **30**, 240.

Ferrari, E., and Selleri, F. (1961). *Phys. Rev. Letters* **7**, 387.

Ferrari, E., and Selleri, F. (1962). *Nuovo Cimento Suppl.* **24**, 453.

Ferrari, E., and Selleri, F. (1963). *Nuovo Cimento* **27**, 1450.

Ferrari, E., Gennarini, S., and Lariccia, P. (1965). *Nuovo Cimento* **39**, 169.

Ferro-Luzzi, M., George, R., Goldschmidt-Clermont, Y., Henri, V. P., Jongejans, B., Leith, D. W. G., Lynch, G. R., Muller, F., and Perreau, J. M. (1965a). *Nuovo Cimento* **36**, 1101.

Ferro-Luzzi, M., George, R., Goldschmidt-Clermont, Y., Henri, V. P., Jongejans, B., Leith, D. W. G., Lynch, G. R., Muller, F., and Perreau, J. M. (1965b). *Nuovo Cimento* **39**, 417.

Ferro-Luzzi, M., George, R., Goldschmidt-Clermont, Y., Henri, M. P., Jongejans, B., Leith, D. W. G., Lynch, G. R., Muller, F., and Perreau, J. M. (1965c). *Phys. Letters* **17**, 155.

Feshbach, H. (1958). *Ann. Rev. Nucl. Sci.* **8**, 49.

Fickinger, W. J., Pickup, E., Robinson, D. K., and Salant, E. O. (1962). *Phys. Rev.* **125**, 2082.

Fleury, P., Kayas, G., Muller, F., and Pellettier, C. (1962). *Proc. 11th Intern. Conf. High Energy Phys.*, CERN, Geneva, p. 597.

Focardi, S., Giacomelli, G., Monari, L., and Serra, P. (1965a). *Nuovo Cimento* **39**, 829.

Focardi, S., Minguzzi-Ranzi, A., Serra, P., Monari, L., Herrier, S., and Verglas, A. (1965b). *Phys. Letters* **16**, 351.

Foldy, L. L., and Peierls, R. F. (1963). *Phys. Rev.* **130**, 1585.

Foley, K. J., Lindenbaum, S. J., Love, W. A., Ozaki, S., Russell, T. T., and Yuan, L. C. L. (1963a). *Phys. Rev. Letters* **10**, 376.

Foley, K. J., Lindenbaum, S. J., Love, W. A., Ozaki, S., Russell, T. T., and Yuan, L. C. L. (1963b). *Phys. Rev. Letters* **11**, 425.

Foley, K. J., Lindenbaum, S. J., Love, W. A., Ozaki, S., Russell, T. T., and Yuan, L. C. L. (1963c). *Phys. Rev. Letters* **10**, 543.

Foley, K. J., Lindenbaum, S. J., Love, W. A., Ozaki, S., Russell, T. T., and Yuan, L. C. L. (1963d). *Phys. Rev. Letters* **11**, 503.

Foley, K. J., Gilmore, R. S., Jones, R. S., Lindenbaum, S. J., Love, W. A., Ozaki, S., Willen, E. H., Yamada, R., and Yuan, L. C. L. (1965a). *Phys. Rev. Letters* **14**, 74.

Foley, K. J., Gilmore, R. S., Jones, R. S., Lindenbaum, S. J., Love, W. A., Ozaki, S., Willen, E. H., Yamada, R., and Yuan, L. C. L. (1965b). *Phys. Rev. Letters* **14**, 862.

Foley, K. J., Gilmore, R. S., Lindenbaum, S. J., Love, W. A., Ozaki, S., Willen, E. H., Yamada, R., and Yuan, L. C. L. (1965c). *Phys. Rev. Letters* **15**, 45.

Frahn, W. E., and Venter, R. H. (1964). *Ann. Phys. (N.Y.)* **27**, 135.

Frautschi, S. C. (1966). *Phys. Rev. Letters* **17**, 722.

Frautschi, S. C., Gell-Mann, M., and Zachariasen, F. (1962). *Phys. Rev.* **126**, 2204.

Friedes, J. L., Palevsky, H., Stearns, R. L., and Sutter, R. J. (1965). *Phys. Rev. Letters* **15**, 38.

Frisken, W. R., Read, A. L., Ruderman, H., Krisch, A. D., Orear, J., Rubinstein, R., Scarl, D. B., and White, D. H. (1965). *Phys. Rev. Letters* **15**, 313.

Froissart, M. (1961). *Phys. Rev.* **123**, 1053.

Fujii, T., Chadwick, G. B., Collins, G. B., Duke, P. J., Hien, N. C., Kemp. M. A. R., and Turkot, F. (1962). *Phys. Rev.* **128**, 1836.

Fukuda, H., and Iso, C. (1966). *Nuovo Cimento* **43**, A43.

Galbraith, W., Jenkins, E. W., Kycia, T. F., Leontic, P. A., Phillips. R. H., Read, A. L., and Rubinstein, R. (1965). *Phys. Rev.* **138**, B913.

Gasiorowicz, S. (1960). *Fortschr. Phys.* **8**, 665.

Gell-Mann, M. (1962). *Phys. Rev. Letters* **8**, 263.

Glauber, R. (1959). "High-Energy Collision Theory, Lectures in Theoretical Physics." Wiley (Interscience), New York.

Goebel, C. (1958). *Phys. Rev. Letters* **1**, 337.

Goldhaber, G., Chinowski, W., Goldhaber, S., Lee, W., and O'Halloran, T. (1963). *Phys. Letters* **6**, 62.

Goldhaber, G., Brown, J. L., Goldhaber, S., Kadyk, J. A., Shen, B. C., and Trilling, G. H. (1964). *Phys. Rev. Letters* **12**, 336.

Goldhaber, S., Brown, J. L., Butterworth, I., Goldhaber, G., Hirata, A. A., Kadyk, J. A., and Trilling, G. H. (1965). *Phys. Rev. Letters* **15**, 737.

Goldhaber, S., Chinowski, W., Goldhaber, G., and O'Halloran, T. (1966). *Phys. Rev.* **142**, 913.

Goldsack, S. J., Riddiford, L., Tallini, B., French, B. R., Neale, W. W., Norbury, J. R., Skillicorn, I. O., Davies, W. T., Derrick, M., Mulvey, J. H., and Radojcic, D. (1962). *Nuovo Cimento* **23**, 941.

Good, M. L. (1961). *Proc. Intern. Conf. Theoretical Aspects of Very High Energy Phenomena*, CERN, Geneva, Report 61–22, p. 263.

Good, M. L., and Walker, W. D. (1960). *Phys. Rev.* **120**, 1857.

Gottfried, K., and Jackson, J. D. (1964a). *Nuovo Cimento* **33**, 309.

Gottfried, K., and Jackson, J. D. (1964b). *Nuovo Cimento* **34**, 735.

Greenberg, O., and Low, F. E. (1962). *Phys. Rev.* **124**, 2047.

Gribov, V. N., (1961). *Zh. Eksperim. i Teor. Fiz.* **41**, 1962.

Gribov, V. N., (1961). *Zh. Eksperim. i Teor. Fiz.* **41**, 1962; (1962). *Soviet Phys. JETP* (*English transl.*) **14**, 1395.

Gribov, V. N. (1962). *Zh. Eksperim. i Teor. Fiz.* **43**, 1529; (1963). *Soviet Phys. JETP* (*English transl.*) **16**, 1080.

Gribov, V. N., and Pomeranchuk, I. Ya. (1962a). *Nucl. Phys.* **33**, 516.

Gribov, V. N., and Pomeranchuk, I. Ya. (1962b). *Phys. Rev. Letters* **8**, 346.

Gribov, V. N., and Pomeranchuk, I. Ya. (1962c). *Phys. Rev. Letters* **8**, 412.

Gribov, V. N., Pomeranchuk, I. Ya., and Ter-Martirosyan, K. A. (1965). *Phys. Rev.* **139**, B184.

Guisan, O., Kirz, J., Sonderegger, P., Stirling, A. V., Borgeaud, P., Bruneton, C., Falk-Vairant, P., Amblard, B., Caverzasio, C., Guillaud, J. P., and Yvert, M. (1965). *Phys. Letters* **18**, 202.

Gutay, L., Lannutti, J. E., and Tuli, S. K. (1965). *Nuovo Cimento* **39**, 381.

Hagedorn, R. (1960). *Nuovo Cimento* **15**, 434.

Hagedorn, R. (1965). *Nuovo Cimento* **35**, 216.

Haque, N., Scotter, D., Musgrave, B., Blair, W. M., Grant, A. L., Hughes, I. S., Negus, P. J., Turnbull, R. H., Ahmad, A. A. Z., Baker, S., Celnikier, L., Misbahuddin, S., Sherman, H. J., Skillicorn, I. O., Atherton, A. R., Chadwick, G. B., Davies, W. T., Field, J. H., Gray, P. M. D., Lawrence, D. E., Loken, J. G., Lyons, L., Mulvey, J. H., Oxley, A., Wilkinson, C. A., Fisher, C. M., Pickup, E., Rangan, L. K., Scarr, J. M., and Segar, A. M. (1965). *Phys. Letters* **14**, 338.

Hart, E. L., Louttit, R. I., Luers, D., Morris, T. W., Willis, W. J., and Yamamoto, S. S. (1962). *Phys. Rev.* **126**, 747.

Harting, D., Blackall, P., Elsner, B., Helmholtz, A. C., Middelkoop, W. C., Powell, P., Zacharov, B., Zanella, P., Dalpiaz, P., Focacci, M. N., Focardi, S., Giacomelli, G., Monari, L., Beaney, J. A., Donald, R. A., Mason, P., Jones, L. W., and Caldwell, D. O. (1965). *Nuovo Cimento* **38**, 60.

Hasegawa, S. (1961). *Progr. Theoret. Phys.* (*Kyoto*) **26**, 150.

Hayakawa, S. (1963). "Theoretical Physics," p. 485. IAEA, Vienna.

Hayman, W. K. (1958). "Multivalent Functions." Cambridge Univ. Press, London and New York.

Heisenberg, W. (1952). *Z. Physik*, **133**, 65.

Henley, E. M., and Muzinich, I. J. (1964). *Phys. Rev.* **136**, B1783.

Högaasen, H., and Frisk, A. (1966). *Phys. Letters* **22**, 90.

Högaasen, H., and Fischer, W. (1966). *Phys. Letters* **22**, 516.

Höhler, G., and Baacke, J. (1965). *Phys. Letters* **18**, 181.

Höhler, G., Ebel, G., and Giesecke, J. (1964). *Z. Physik.* **180**, 430.

Höhler, G., Baacke, J., Giesecke, J., and Zovko, N. (1966a). *Proc. Roy. Soc.* **A289**, 500.

Höhler, G., Baacke, J., Schlaile, H., and Sonderegger, P. (1966b). *Phys. Letters* **20**, 79.

Hufner, J., and de Shalit, A. (1965). *Phys. Letters* **15**, 52.

Igi, K. (1962). *Phys. Rev. Letters*, **9**, 76.

Igi, K. (1963). *Phys. Rev.* **130**, 820.

International Cooperative Emulsion Flight Collaboration (1963). *Nuovo Cimento Suppl.* **1**, 1039.

Jackson, J. D. (1965). *Rev. Mod. Phys.* **37**, 484.

Jackson, J. D., Donohue, J. T., Gottfried, K., Keyser, R., and Svensson, B. E. Y. (1965). *Phys. Rev.* **139**, B428.

Jin, Y. S., and Martin, A. (1964). *Phys. Rev.* **135**, B1369.

Jones, L. W. (1964). *Phys. Letters* **8**, 287.

Jones, L. W. (1965). *Phys. Rev. Letters* **14**, 186.

Kanavets, V. P., Levintov, I. I., and Morosov, B. V. *Proc. 12th Intern. Conf. High Energy Phys., Dubna, 1964*, **1**, 119. Atomisdat, Moscow, 1966.

Khuri, N. N., and Kinoshita, T. (1965a). *Phys. Rev.* **137**, B720.

Khuri, N. N., and Kinoshita, T. (1965b). *Phys. Rev.* **140**, B707.

Khuri, N. N., and Kinoshita, T. (1965c). "High Energy Physics and Elementary Particles," p. 169. IAEA, Vienna.

Khuri, N. N., and Kinoshita, T. (1965d). *Phys. Rev. Letters* **14**, 84.

Kidd, J., Ratti, S., Sichirollo, A., and Vegni, G. (1963). *Proc. Intern. Conf. Elementary Particle Phys., Sienna* **1**, 348. Società Italiana di Fisica, Bologna.

Kidd, J., Mandelli, L., Pelosi, V., Ratti, S., Tallone, L., Conte, F., and Tomasini, G., (1964). Preprint, Univ. of Milan. Unpublished.

Kinoshita, T. (1964). *Phys. Rev. Letters* **12**, 257.

Kinoshita, T., Loeffel, J. J., and Martin, A. (1963). *Phys. Rev. Letters* **10**, 460.

Kinoshita, T., Loeffel, J. J., and Martin, A. (1964). *Phys. Rev.* **135**, B1464.

Kirillova, L. F., Nikitin, V. A., Nomofilov, A. A., Sviridov, V. A., Strunov, L. N., and Shafranova, M. G. (1963). *Zh. Eksperim. i Teor. Fiz.* **45**, 1261; [(1964). *Soviet Phys. JETP* (*English Transl.*) **18**, 867.]

Kirillova, L. F., Nikitin, V. A., Sviridov, V. A., Strunov, L. N., Shafranova, M. G., Korbel, Z., Rob, L., Zlateva, A., Markov, P. K., Todorov, T., Khristov, L., Chernev, Kh., Dalkhazhav, N., and Tuvdendorzh, D. (1966). *Zh. Eksperim i Teor. Fiz.* **50**, 76; [(1966). *Soviet Phys. JETP* (*English Transl.*) **23**, 52].

Kokkedee, J. J. J. (1966). *Nuovo Cimento* **43**, A919.

Krisch, A. D. (1963). *Phys. Rev. Letters* **11**, 217.

Lai, K. W., Jones, L. W., and Perl, M. L. (1961). *Phys. Rev. Letters* **7**, 125.

Landau, L. D. (1953). *Izv. Akad. Nauk. SSR* **17**, 57.

Larsen, R. R. (1960). *Nuovo Cimento* **18**, 1039.

Lautrup, B., and Olesen, P. (1965). *Phys. Letters* **17**, 62.

Lautrup, B., Moller-Nielsen, P., and Olesen, P. (1965). *Phys. Letters* **19**, 422.

Lehmann, H. (1962). *Nucl. Phys.* **29**, 300.

Levintov, I. I., and Adelson-Velsky, G. M. (1964). *Phys. Letters* **13**, 185.

Lewis, H. W., Oppenheimer, J. R., and Wouthuysen, S. A. (1949). *Phys. Rev.* **73**, 127.

Lindenbaum, S. J. (1965). *Proc. 2nd. Conf. Symmetry Principles at High Energies, Coral Gables, Florida*, p. 287. Freeman, San Francisco and London, 1965.

Lindenbaum, S. J. (1966). *Proc. 12th Intern. Conf. High Energy Phys., Dubna, 1964*, **1**, 188. Atomisdat, Moscow.

Lindenbaum, S. J., and Sternheimer, R. M. (1957). *Phys. Rev.* **105**, 1874.

Lock, W. O. (1960). "High Energy Nuclear Physics." Methnen, London.

Logan, R. K. (1965a). *Phys. Rev. Letters* **14**, 414.

Logan, R. K. (1965b). *Phys. Rev. Letters* **14**, 921.

Logan, R. K., and Sertorio, L. (1966). *Phys. Rev. Letters* **17**, 834.

Logunov, A. A., Nguyen Van Hieu, Todorov, I. T., and Khrustalev, O. A. (1964). *Phys. Letters* **7**, 69.

Logunov, A. A., Nguyen Van Hieu, and Todorov, I. T. (1965). *Ann. Phys.* (*N.Y.*) **31**, 203.

Lohrmann, E., Meyer, H., and Winzeler, H. (1964). *Phys. Letters* **13**, 78.

London, G. W., Rau, R. R., Samios, N. P., Yamamoto, S. S., Goldberg, M., Lichtman, S., Primer, M., and Leitner, J. (1966). *Phys. Rev.* **143**, 1034.

Louttit, R. I., Morris, T. W., Rahm, D. C., Rau, R. R., Thorndike, A. M., Willis, W. J., and Lea, R. M. (1961). *Phys. Rev.* **123**, 1465.

Lovelace, C., (1962). *Nuovo Cimento* **25**, 730.

Luming, M., and Predazzi, E. (1966). *Nuovo Cimento* **41**, A22.

Lynch, G. R. (1961). *Rev. Mod. Phys.* **33**, 395.

Lynch, G. R., Foulks, R. E., Kalbfleisch, G. R., Limentani, S., Shafer, J. B., Stevenson, M. L., and Xuong, N. H. (1963). *Phys. Rev.* **131**, 1276.

Lynch, G. R., Ferro-Luzzi, M., George, R., Goldschmidt-Clermont, Y., Henri, V. P., Jongejans, B., Leith, D. W. G., Muller, F., and Perreau, J. M. (1964). *Phys. Letters* **9**, 359.

Mandelstam, S. (1963). *Nuovo Cimento* **30**, 1113, 1127, 1148.

Mannelli, I., Bigi, A., Carrara, R., Wahlig, M., and Sodickson, L. (1965). *Phys. Rev. Letters* **14**, 408.

Manning, G., Parham, A. G., Jafar, J. D., van der Raay, H. B., Reading, D. H., Ryan, D., Jones, B. D., Malos, J., Wills, H. H., and Lipman, N. H. (1966). *Nuovo Cimento* **41**, A-167.

Marshall, L., and Oliphant, T. (1965). *Phys. Letters* **18**, 83.

Martin, A. (1963a). *Phys. Rev.* **129**, 1432.

Martin, A. (1963b). *Nuovo Cimento* **29**, 993.

Martin, A. (1965a). *Nuovo Cimento* **37**, 671.

Martin, A. (1965b). *Nuovo Cimento* **39**, 704.

Martin, A. (1965c). *Phys. Letters* **15**, 76.

Martin, A. (1965d). "High Energy Physics and Elementary Particles," p. 155. IAEA, Vienna.

Meiman, N. N. (1962). *Zh. Eksperim. i Teor. Fiz.* **43**, 2277; [(1963). *Soviet Phys. JETP* (*English Transl.*) **16**, 1609.]

Melissinos, A. C., Yamanouchi, T., Fazio, G. G., Lindenbaum, S., and Yuan, L. C. L. (1962). *Phys. Rev.* **128**, 2373.

Minami, S. (1964a). *Phys. Rev. Letters* **12**, 200.

Minami, S. (1964b). *Phys. Rev.* **135**, B1263.

Morse, P. M., and Feshbach, H. (1953). "Methods of Theoretical Physics." McGraw-Hill, New York.

Musgrave, B., Petmezas, C., Riddiford, L., Böck, R., Fett, E., French, B. R., Kinson, J. B., Peyrou, C., Szeptycka, M., Badier, J., Bazin, M., Blaskovic, L., Equer, B., Huc, J., Borenstein, S. R., Goldsack, S. J., Miller, D. H., Meyer, J., Revel, D., Tallini, B., and Zylberajch, S. (1965). *Nuovo Cimento* **35**, 735.

Narayan, D. S., and Sarma, L. (1963). *Phys. Letters* **5**, 364.

Nevanlinna, R. (1953). "Eindeutige analytische Funktionen" 2nd ed., Springer, Berlin.

Niu, K. (1958). *Nuovo Cimento* **10**, 994.

Okun, L. B., and Pomeranchuk, I. Ya. (1956). *Zh. Eksperim. i Teor. Fiz.* **30**, 424; [(1956). *Soviet Phys. JETP* (*English Transl.*) **3**, 307].

Olesen, P. (1966). *Nuovo Cimento* **43**, A875.

Omnès, R. (1965). *Phys. Rev.* **137**, B653.

Orear, J. (1964a). *Phys. Rev. Letters* **12**, 112.

Orear, J. (1964b). *Phys. Letters* **13**, 190.

Orear, J., Rubinstein, R., Scarl, D. B., White, D. H., Krisch, A. D., Frisken, W. R., Read, A. L., and Ruderman, H. (1965). *Phys. Rev. Letters* **15**, 305.

Palevsky, H., Moore, J. A., Stearns, R. L., Muether, H. R., Sutter, R. J., Chrien, R. E., Jain, A. P., and Otnes, K. (1962). *Phys. Rev. Letters* **9**, 509.

Paris (Ec. Polyt.)-CERN-Torino-Padova Collaboration (1963). *Nuovo Cimento* **29**, 339.
Perl, M. L., Jones, L. W., and Ting, C. C. (1962). *Phys. Rev. Letters* **9**, 468.
Perl, M. L., Jones, L. W., and Ting, C. C. (1963). *Phys. Rev.* **132**, 1252.
Perl, M. L., Lee, Y. Y., and Marquit, E. (1965). *Phys. Rev.* **138**, B707.
Phillips, R. J. N. (1966). *Nuovo Cimento* **45**, A245.
Phillips, R. J. N., and Rarita, W. (1965a). *Phys. Rev.* **138**, B723.
Phillips, R. J. N., and Rarita, W. (1965b). *Phys. Rev.* **139**, B1336.
Phillips, R. J. N., and Rarita, W. (1965c). *Phys. Rev.* **140**, B200.
Phillips, R. J. N., and Rarita, W. (1965d). *Phys. Rev. Letters* **14**, 502.
Phillips, R. J. N., and Rarita, W. (1965e). Preprint, Univ. of California Radiation Lab. 16185.
Phillips, R. J. N., and Rarita, W. (1965f). *Phys. Rev. Letters* **15**, 807.
Pickup, E., Robinson, D. K., and Salant, E. O. (1962). *Phys. Rev.* **125**, 2091.
Pignotti, A. (1964). *Phys. Rev.* **134**, B630.
Pomeranchuk, I. Ya. (1956). *Zh. Eksperim. i Teor. Fiz.* **30**, 423; [(1956). *Soviet Phys. JETP (English transl.)* **3**, 306].
Pomeranchuk, I. Ya. (1958). *Zh. Eksperim. i Teor. Fiz.* **34**, 725; [(1958) *Soviet Phys. JETP (English transl.)* **7**, 499].
Reay, N. W., Melissinos, A. C., Reed, J. T., Yamanouchi, T., and Yuan, L. C. L. (1966). *Phys. Rev.* **142**, 918.
Regge, T. (1960). *Nuovo Cimento* **18**, 947.
Roper, L. D. (1964). *Phys. Rev. Letters* **12**, 340.
Roy, D. P. (1965). *Nuovo Cimento* **40**, A1212.
Rushbrooke, J. G., Bugg, D. V., Oxley, A. J., Zoll, J. A., Jobes, M., Kinson, J., Riddiford, L., and Tallini, B. (1964). *Nuovo Cimento* **33**, 1509.
Saclay-Orsay-Bari-Bologna Collaboration (1962). *Nuovo Cimento* **25**, 365.
Saclay-Orsay-Bari-Bologna Collaboration (1963). *Nuovo Cimento* **29**, 515.
Saclay-Orsay-Bari-Bologna Collaboration (1964). *Phys. Letters* **13**, 341.
Saclay-Orsay-Bari-Bologna Collaboration (1965a). *Nuovo Cimento* **35**, 1.
Saclay-Orsay-Bari-Bologna Collaboration (1965b). *Nuovo Cimento* **35**, 713.
Saclay-Orsay-Bari-Bologna Collaboration (1965c). *Nuovo Cimento* **37**, 361.
Saclay-Orsay-Bari-Bologna Collaboration (1965d). *Nuovo Cimento* **40**, A273.
Saclay-Orsay-Bari-Bologna Collaboration (1965e). *Phys. Letters* **15**, 69.
Saclay-Orsay-Bari-Bologna Collaboration (1965f). *Phys. Letters* **19**, 65.
Saclay-Orsay-Bari-Bologna Collaboration (1966a). *Nuovo Cimento* **41**, A159.
Saclay-Orsay-Bari-Bologna Collaboration (1966b). *Nuovo Cimento* **42**, A606.
Saclay-Orsay-Bari-Bologna-Firenze Collaboration (1965). *Phys. Letters.* **19**, 68.
Salzman, F., and Salzman, G. (1960a). *Phys. Rev. Letters* **5**, 377.
Salzman, F., and Salzman, G. (1960b). *Phys. Rev.* **120**, 599.
Salzman, F., and Salzman, G. (1961). *Phys. Rev.* **121**, 1541.
Satterblom, P. H., Walker, W. D., and Erwin, A. R. (1964). *Phys. Rev.* **134**, B207.
Selleri, F. (1966). *Nuovo Cimento* **42**, A835.
Schmitz, N. (1964). *Nuovo Cimento* **31**, 255.
Serber, R. (1963). *Phys. Rev. Letters* **10**, 357.
Serber, R. (1964). *Rev. Mod. Phys.* **36**, 649.
Simmons, L. M. (1964). *Phys. Rev. Letters* **12**, 229.
Singh, V. (1963). *Phys. Rev.* **129**, 1889.
Smith, G. A., Courant, H., Fowler, E. C., Kraybill, H., Sandweiss, J., and Taft, H. (1960). *Phys. Rev. Letters* **5**, 571.
Smith, G. A., Courant, H., Fowler, E. C., Kraybill, H., Sandweiss, J., and Taft, H. (1961). *Phys. Rev.* **123**, 2160.

Söding, P. (1964). *Phys. Letters* **8**, 285.
Sommerfeld, A. (1949). "Partial Differential Equations in Physics." Academic Press, New York and London.
Sonderegger, P., Kirz, J., Guisan, O., Falk-Vairant, P., Bruneton, C., Borgeaud, P., Stirling, A. V., Caverzasio, C., Guillaud, J. P., Yvert, M., and Amblard, B. (1966). *Phys. Letters* **20**, 75.
Sopkovich, N. J. (1962). *Nuovo Cimento* **26**, 186.
Steinrisser, F., Hahn, B., and Lindt, W. (1962). *Proc. 11th Intern. Conf. High Energy Phys.*, CERN, Geneva, p. 725.
Sternheimer, R. S., and Lindenbaum, S. J. (1958). *Phys. Rev.* **109**, 1723.
Sternheimer, R. S., and Lindenbaum, S. J. (1961). *Phys. Rev.* **123**, 333.
Stirling, A. V., Sonderegger, P., Kirz, J., Falk-Vairant, P., Guisan, O., Bruneton, C., Borgeaud, P., Yvert, M., Guillaud, J. P., Caverzasio, C., and Amblard, B. (1965). *Phys. Rev. Letters* **14**, 763.
Suwa, S., Yokosawa, A., Booth, N. E., Esterling, R. J., and Hill, R. E. (1965). *Phys. Rev. Letters* **15**, 560.
Svensson, B. E. Y. (1965). *Nuovo Cimento* **39**, 667.
Taylor, A. L., Ashmore, A., Chapman, W. S., Falla, O. F., Range, W. H., Scott, D. B., Astbury, A., Capocci, F., and Walker, T. G. (1965). *Phys. Letters* **14**, 54.
Thomas, R. G. (1960). *Phys. Rev.* **120**, 1015.
Titchmarsh, E. C. (1958). "The Theory of Functions." Oxford Univ. Press, London and New York.
Trefil, J. (1966). *Phys. Rev.* **148**, 1452.
Treiman, S. B., and Yang, C. N. (1962). *Phys. Rev. Letters* **8**, 140.
van Hove, L. (1963a). *Phys. Letters* **5**, 252.
van Hove, L. (1963b). *Phys. Letters* **7**, 76.
van Hove, L. (1963c). *Nuovo Cimento* **28**, 798.
van Hove, L. (1964). *Rev. Mod. Phys.* **36**, 655.
van Hove, L. (1965a). "High Energy Physics and Elementary Particles," p. 179. IAEA, Vienna.
van Hove, L. (1965b). Theoretical problems in strong interactions at high energies, CERN Report, 65–22.
van Hove, L. (1966). *Proc. Intern. Symposium Electron Photon Interactions at High Energy, Hamburg, 1965*, **1**, 1. Deutsche Physikalische Gesellschaft, Hamburg.
Wagner, W. G. (1963). *Phys. Rev. Letters* **10**, 202.
Wang Kang Chang, Wang Tsu Tseng, Ting Ta Tsao, Ivanov, V. G., Katyshaev, Yu. V., Kladnitskaya, E. N., Kulyuskaya, L. A., Nguyen Dinh Tu, Nikitin, A. V., Otwinowski, S., Solovyev, M. I., Sosnowski, R., and Shafranov, M. D. (1960). *Zh. Eksperim. i Teor. Fiz.* **38**, 426; [(1960). *Soviet Phys. JETP (English transl.)* **11**, 313].
Wang Kang Chang, Wang Tsu Tseng, Veksler, V. I., Vrana, I., Ting Ta Tsao, Ivanov, V. G., Kladnitskaya, E. N., Kuznetsov, A. A., Nguyen Dinh Tu, Nikitin, A. V., Solovyev, M. I., and Cheng Ling Yen (1961a). *Zh. Eksperim. i Teor. Phys.* **40**, 464; [(1961) *Soviet Phys. JETP (English transl.)* **13**, 323].
Wang Kang Chang, Wang Tsu Tseng, Viryasov, N. M., Ting Ta Ssao, Kim Hi In, Kladnitskaya, E. N., Kuznetsov, A. A., Mikhul, A., Nguyen Dinh Tu, Nikitin, A. V., and Soloviev, M. I. (1961b). *Zh. Eksperim. i Teor. Fiz.* **40**, 734; [(1961) *Soviet Phys. JETP (English transl.)* **13**, 512].
Wangler, T. P., Erwin, A. R., and Walker, T. D. (1965). *Phys. Rev.* **137**, B414.
Wit, R. (1965a). *Zh. Eksperim. i Teor. Fiz.* **49**, 538 [(1966) *Soviet Phys. JETP (English transl.)* **22**, 375].

Wit, R. (1965b). *Acta Physica Polonica* **28**, 295.

Wit, R. (1965c). *Acta Physica Polonica* **28**, 861.

Wu, T. T., and Yang, C. N. (1965). *Phys. Rev.* **137**, B708.

Yamamoto, S. S., Bertanza, L., Moneti, G. C., Rahm, D. C., and Skillicorn, I. O. (1964). *Phys. Rev.* **134**, B383.

Yamamoto, S. S., Smith, J. R., Rahm, D. C., and Lloyd, J. L. (1965). *Phys. Rev.* **140**, B730.

Yao, T. (1964). *Phys. Rev.* **134**, B454.

PERIPHERAL PROCESSES*

A. C. Hearn and S. D. Drell

I. Introduction

The concept of peripheralism and the range of its applications have been extended considerably in the last few years. In its original form it was a method for extrapolating to pole terms arising from single particle exchange contributions in transition amplitudes. Although these poles are often found close by, they are never within the physical region, and so an accurate procedure for extrapolating from experimental points to the nearest lying pole is required. One hoped to learn from this the coupling parameters or unstable particle cross sections appearing as residues at the poles.

As an extension of this idea it was next suggested that one choose particular processes and very limited kinematic conditions so that some particular, well-defined class of Feynman graphs will have unusually small energy denominators. In the analysis of the corresponding cross sections it is assumed that these graphs, generally with single particle exchange poles near the physical region, dominate all others. In this manner several channels are isolated from among the full wealth of strongly interacting channels and approximate theoretical predictions can be presented for experimental testing. Although this is a rather primitive approximation scheme it is more attractive than a weak coupling perturbation expansion in powers of the strength of the interaction among pions and nucleons and offers the possibility of relating different

* Work supported in part by the U.S. Atomic Energy Commission and in part by the U.S. Air Force through Air Force Office of Scientific Research Contract AF 49(638)-1389.

experiments to each other. In this spirit a number of calculations were performed and the successes of the predicted relations with experiment, though far from quantitative or uniform, were sufficiently compelling to trigger a series of more refined analyses attempting to supply some of the more important ingredients missing in the first approximation. These efforts have developed recently into a major program of detailed analyses of the corrections due to the possibility of absorption into the numerous competing open channels that deplete the amplitude in the channel under study. Many promising results have been achieved in this way, and quantitative fits to spectra, angular distributions, and spin correlations have been achieved for a number of interactions.

With this most recent development the emphasis of peripheralism has switched from the search for approximate relations between various experiments and from the prediction of gross qualitative features to a program of detailed analysis. Perhaps the collisions of strongly coupled particles are too rich with detailed information on the nature of their interactions to be analyzed theoretically in full detail. But we may have here a rather valuable phenomenology for many processes. As we shall see, very little of the original "peripheralism" is still in evidence at this stage. However, along with many successes, serious deficiencies will be found and remain unsolved by theory.

Our review will proceed chronologically and will describe this evolution in the saga of peripheral processes.

II. Early Developments

The forward pion-nucleon dispersion relations play a unique role in strong interaction physics, presenting an exact relation between experimental quantities. Equation (II-1), for example, is an exact relation between $T^-(\omega)$, the difference between the $\pi^- p$ and $\pi^+ p$ forward scattering amplitudes at energy ω, and $\sigma^{\pi^+ p}(\omega') - \sigma^{\pi^- p}(\omega')$, the difference of their total cross sections (Goldberger, 1955):

$$T^-(\omega) = \frac{-4f^2\omega}{\omega^2 - [\mu^2/2M]^2} + \frac{\omega}{2\pi^2} \int_\mu^\infty \frac{d\omega'(\omega'^2 - \mu^2)^{1/2}}{\omega'^2 - \omega^2 - i\varepsilon} \left[\sigma^{\pi^+ p}(\omega') - \sigma^{\pi^- p}(\omega')\right].$$

$$(\text{II-1})$$

They are related in Eq. (II-1) to the pion-nucleon coupling constant f^2 which appears in the residue at the pole in the forward scattering amplitude for single nucleon exchange in the energy or ω channel as illustrated in Fig. 1.[1] By

---

[1] For a fuller discussion of pion-nucleon dispersion relations the reader is referred to the article by J. Hamilton, in Volume I of this book.

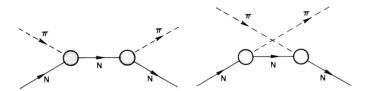

Fig. 1. Nucleon exchange diagrams for pion-nucleon scattering.

extrapolating the scattering amplitude below the threshold for physical scattering, $\omega_t = \mu$, the pion mass, to the pole at $\omega = \mu^2/2M$, a value of $f^2 \approx 0.08$ is found, namely,

$$\lim_{\omega \to \mu^2/2M} \left\{ \frac{\omega^2 - [\mu^2/2M]^2}{-4\omega} \operatorname{Re} T^-(\omega) \right\} = f^2. \tag{II-2}$$

Once this pole was successfully isolated and its residue, or coupling parameter, accurately measured, it became of prime importance to identify other processes also containing this pole term and to attempt to isolate and measure its residue by similar extrapolation procedures. Chew (1958) proposed the study of elastic nucleon-nucleon scattering at high energies and suitably restricted kinematics with just this purpose in mind. In this case there is a pion exchange pole as illustrated in Fig. 2 appearing in the momentum

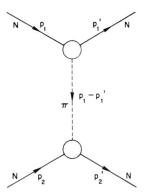

Fig. 2. One-pion exchange contribution to elastic nucleon-nucleon scattering.

transfer channel. It contributes a term to the scattering cross section for unpolarized nucleons of the form

$$\frac{d\sigma}{dt} = \frac{R(t)}{p_{\text{inc}}^2(t - \mu^2)^2} \tag{II-3}$$

where p_{inc}^2 is the laboratory 3-momentum of the incident proton and where $\sqrt{-t}$ is the invariant momentum transfer, i.e., $t = (p_1 - p_1')^2$ in terms of the kinematics shown in Fig. 2[2]; $R(t)$ is a momentum transfer dependent factor free of singularities in the neighborhood of the pole, and can be expanded in power series about $t = \mu^2$ within a circle of radius $3\mu^2$, which extends into the physical region $t \leq 0$. At the pole, $R(t)$ is just the product of f^2 and known kinematical factors arising from isotopic spin considerations and the P-wave coupling of pseudoscalar mesons to nucleons. In particular, if we concentrate on charge exchange neutron-proton scattering, as is convenient in order to avoid interference in the analysis from both Coulomb effects and the forward diffraction peak for elastic channels, the amplitude in Fig. 2 may be written as

$$T = i(\sqrt{2}g)^2 \frac{[\bar{u}(p_2's_2')\gamma_5 u(p_2s_2)][\bar{u}(p_1's_1')\gamma_5 u(p_1s_1)]}{t - \mu^2} F(t). \quad \text{(II-4)}$$

Upon squaring this amplitude, averaging over initial and summing over final spins, the differential cross section for the process may be written as

$$\frac{d\sigma}{dt} = \frac{16\pi M^2 f^4}{\mu^4 p_{\text{inc}}^2} \left| F(t) \right|^2 \frac{t^2}{(t - \mu^2)^2} \quad \text{(II-5)}$$

where

$$f^2 \equiv \frac{(g\mu/2M)^2}{4\pi}$$

and

$$F(0) \simeq F(\mu^2) \equiv 1. \quad \text{(II-6)}$$

The normalized "form factor" $F(t)$ includes all corrections to the pion propagator and vertex functions and becomes unity at the pole as defined. The numerator factor t^2 arises from the P-wave pion-nucleon coupling. We can also write Eq. (II-5) in terms of the center-of-mass momentum p and the scattering angle (backward for exchange scattering) θ through the relation

$$t - \mu^2 = -2|p|^2[1 + \mu^2/2|p|^2 - \cos\theta] \quad \text{(II-7)}$$

and extrapolate to the pole at $\cos\theta = 1 + \mu^2/2|p|^2$ by studying the cross section as a function of angle at fixed center-of-mass momentum. The aim here is to establish that the pion-nucleon coupling constant "measured" by this extrapolation is the same as was found in the forward pion-nucleon amplitude, Eq. (II-2).

[2] For a fuller account of the application of one-pion-exchange graphs in the discussion of the nucleon-nucleon interaction the reader is referred to the article by G. Breit and R. D. Haracz in Volume I of this book.

A very high degree of accuracy has been achieved by these analyses and the pion-nucleon constant as determined by both methods agrees to several per cent (Hamilton and Woolcock, 1963; Chamberlain, 1960; Ashmore et al., 1962).[3] The extrapolation interval for the forward πN-dispersion analysis is $\mu - (\mu^2/2M) \approx 130$ MeV from the physical threshold at $\omega_t = \mu$, where $T(\omega)$ develops an imaginary part at the onset of the unitarity or right-hand cut in the energy, or ω, plane. The extrapolation in nucleon-nucleon scattering may be over a very small interval in $\cos \theta$ if we are working at a large momentum so that $\mu/p \ll 1$. Also, other singularities corresponding to two or more pion exchanges are further removed from the physical region as shown in Fig. 3.

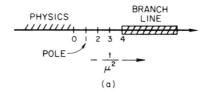

(a)

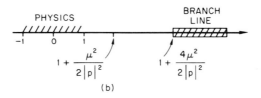

(b)

Fig. 3. Singularities in amplitude for elastic nucleon-nucleon scattering: (a) t picture and (b) θ picture.

The branch point at the onset of additional singularities occurs at $t = 4\mu^2$ or the square of the minimum mass of a two-pion state.

However the extrapolation to the pole in this case has been very difficult to accomplish with high accuracy, the reason for this originating from the P-wave character of the coupling of pions of odd intrinsic parity to nucleons. This means that the pole term Eq. (II-5) to which we are extrapolating vanishes at the edge of the physical region as $t \to 0$, corresponding to the very peripheral collisions with zero momentum transfer and large impact parameters. For

[3] See also the chapter by J. Hamilton in Volume I of this book.

such collisions the velocity of the exchanged pion and hence its P-wave absorption amplitude vanishes. In fact, Eq. (II-5) shows that the pole term goes through a second-order zero at $t = 0$ on its way to the pole. Since its contribution to the observed cross section is negligible it is no wonder that it is very difficult to isolate this term.

The foregoing discussion shows clearly that quantitative meaning can be attached to the pole analysis for one-pion exchange only if small energy denominators are joined by large numerator functions. We therefore turn our attention to processes with reasonably large amplitudes in the peripheral limit. Consider for example, the cross section for

$$\pi + p \to \pi + \pi + p$$

in the vicinity of the pion pole shown in Fig. 4. This study was first proposed

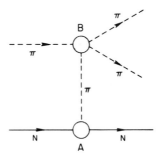

Fig. 4. One-pion-exchange contribution to the process $\pi + N \to \pi + \pi + N$.

by Goebel (1958) and by Chew and Low (1959) as a method for obtaining information about the $\pi\pi$-scattering amplitude which occurs at the vertex B, and which cannot be measured directly. The residue at the pion exchange pole at $t = \mu^2$ in this process has the form

$$R = Cf^2\sigma_{\pi\pi} \tag{II-8}$$

where C is a known kinematical factor. So given the value of f, the pion-nucleon coupling constant determined from the earlier extrapolation, we may determine a value for $\sigma_{\pi\pi}$ by extrapolation to this pole. The value we obtain for $\sigma_{\pi\pi}$ is not, of course, the physical pion-pion cross section as one of the pions is necessarily off the mass-shell in the determination. Presumably, however, it is approximately equal to the physical cross section. This assumption that $\sigma_{\pi\pi}$ does not change appreciably in an energy interval of ~ 140 MeV as the mass of one of the external pion lines is extrapolated to $\leqslant 0$ is similar to that made in Eq. (II-6) in relating the pion-nucleon coupling constants as determined from πN and NN-scattering pole terms. Without this assumption of a smooth behavior and of slow variation over the energy range $\sim \mu = 140$ MeV, no quantitative analyses relating different cross sections of the strongly interacting particles to each other can be achieved.

Our remarks apply with equal validity to many other processes where similar unmeasurable cross sections occur; e.g., extrapolation of $\pi p(\pi) K \bar{K} p$ gives $\sigma_{\pi\pi K K}$, and extrapolation of $K p(\pi) K \pi p$ gives $\sigma_{K\pi K\pi}$, where our notation for a process indicates the exchanged particle in parentheses.

The next extension of the peripheral idea again rests on the importance of the near-lying pole. If this pole is close by, then it is reasonable that the peripheral diagram should dominate in the physical region nearest the pole. This assumption is motivated theoretically by the fact that the energy denominator is very small in this region and the transition amplitude falls off rapidly with increasing momentum transfer. If the exchanged particle is very light, then the effect is obviously even more marked, and so should work best with pion exchange. Experimentally, too, a forward peaking is observed in many processes and can be attributed to large impact parameter collisions such as the peripheral model provides. In this manner we can see that the cross section for $\pi p \rightarrow 2\pi p$ should have a maximum at low momentum transfer if the $\pi\pi$ interaction is not negligibly small. A larger cross section and perhaps simpler experiment now suggests itself for determining unstable particle cross sections as illustrated in Fig. 5, where now only the two high energy pions emerging in

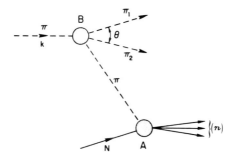

Fig. 5. One-pion-exchange contribution to the process $\pi + N \rightarrow \pi + \pi + (n)$, where (n) denotes an arbitrary final state of two or more particles.

the forward direction within an angle $\theta \sim \mu/k$ of the incident pion of energy k are detected (Salzman and Salzman, 1960, Drell, 1961). The exchanged virtual pion is allowed to plough into the target nucleon and to initiate reactions to any possible final states. In this way the full pion-nucleon cross section is developed at vertex A in place of the small amplitude for absorbing a slow pion, and so the physical value of $\sigma_{\pi\pi}$ may be determined from studying the forward cross section of the production process.

Since the simple peripheral model offers such a straightforward method of calculation it is easy to carry the calculations far into the physical region away from the single particle exchange pole, and compare the results with experiment. It is not surprising that such a simple picture cannot reproduce the experimental data far from the pole, because we can now no longer regard the exchanged particle as quasi-real as we could in the forward region. "Off-mass-shell" corrections arising from the virtual nature of the exchange particle have to be made and other particle exchange graphs considered as well. This realization triggered a whole series of calculations which include form factor corrections to the vertices, but we shall leave the discussion of these until the next section.

Up till now we have discussed extensions of the peripheral idea without subjecting the model to any serious test of its validity. In fact, even if one allows some arbitrary form factor dependence at the vertices, the assumption of single particle exchange in a process makes very simple and unique predictions about the angular distribution of the scattered particles. These predictions are supplementary to any made about momentum and energy distributions and can form the basis for tests of the one-pion-exchange (OPE) model as pointed out by Treiman and Yang (1962) and Goldhaber (1964). For example, in the particular case illustrated in Fig. 4, it is clear that the spin zero meson exchanged cannot communicate information between the vertices A and B about the direction of the momentum transfer but only about its magnitude. From this it follows that there can be no correlation between the production plane of the pions in the rest system of the incident pion and the scattering

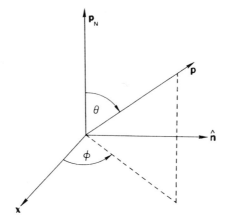

Fig. 6. Coordinate system in the frame **O** of zero total momentum for the pions produced in the reaction $\pi + N \to \pi + \pi + N$. Here, **p** is the momentum of one of the final state pions, $\mathbf{p}_N$ is the momentum of the incident nucleon as seen in **O** and $\hat{\mathbf{n}}$ is perpendicular to the production plane defined by $\mathbf{p}_N$ and **x**.

plane of the nucleons. In other words, in terms of the angles illustrated in Fig. 6, the distribution of the produced pions is independent of the azimuthal angle ϕ and therefore has the form

$$W(\theta, \phi) = \sum a_n \cos^n\theta. \tag{II-9}$$

If, furthermore, the production occurs through a single resonance channel of well-defined spin and parity as in Fig. 7, the decay distribution is limited to the

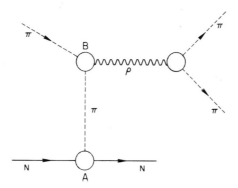

Fig. 7. One-pion-exchange contribution to pion production of a ρ meson.

form

$$W(\theta, \phi) = \sum_{n=1}^{N} a_{2n} \cos^{2n}\theta \tag{II-10}$$

where N is the spin of the resonant state.

In this particular case as well, if we observe the decay distribution in the rest frame of the ρ, there can be no component of spin along the incident pion direction (which, in this frame, is parallel to the momentum direction of the exchanged pion). This requires that the ρ have only longitudinal polarization along the incident pion direction and implies that the decay distribution vanish at $\theta = 90°$ and thus have the form

$$W(\theta, \phi) = \cos^2\theta. \tag{II-11}$$

Similar but more complicated arguments can be made when the exchanged particle has nonzero spin (Stodolsky and Sakurai, 1963; Gottfried and Jackson, 1964b). These will be discussed in Section IV.

So far, the only extension of the simple peripheral model we have considered has been the addition of form factors at the vertices. Another possibility is that some form of interaction between the target and scatterer may occur in addition to the peripheral exchange. In particular, in the high energy region (above 1 GeV) one expects that elastic diffraction scattering will occur in the initial and final states as shown in Fig. 8. Even if this initial and final state

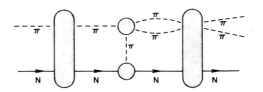

Fig. 8. Initial and final state interaction corrections for the one-pion-exchange contribution to the process $\pi + N \rightarrow \pi + \pi + N$.

scattering does not cause any spin or helicity change in the amplitudes, it is now possible for information on the direction of the momentum transfer to be carried between the target and the scatterer, and so our previous predictions on decay correlations will no longer be valid. We shall show that observed deviations in angular and t distributions from the simple peripheral picture can be attributed either to form factors or to such initial and final state interactions. Changes in the decay distributions, however, can only be explained by rescattering corrections.

Statements can also be made about the energy dependence of the cross section but so far there has been little theoretical progress on this point as will be most apparent in Section V.

III. The Peripheral Model with Form Factors

We now consider in more detail the application of the peripheral mechanism to inelastic processes. The approach we use is to look for particular Feynman graphs which have very small energy denominators in the kinematical region we are considering. We turn again to the reaction

$$\pi + N \rightarrow \pi + \pi + N.$$

In addition to the formation of nucleon isobars in the scattering channel, which contribute calculable amounts over known energy and momentum ranges, there are poles in the matrix elements coming from peripheral exchanges. Of these, the pion is the lightest state and has a pole lying very near to the physical region which is expected to influence the reaction most.

Direct experimental evidence for this assumption is provided by looking at the angular distributions for $\pi^- + p \rightarrow \pi^- + \pi^+ + n$ at 1.59 GeV/c as shown in Fig. 9. We see there a marked forward peaking which suggests the dominance of a long-range interaction mechanism such as single pion exchange.

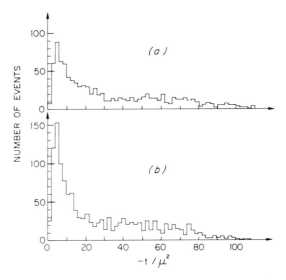

Fig. 9. Distribution of $-t/\mu^2$ for the processes: (a) $\pi^- + p \rightarrow \pi^- + \pi^0 + p$; (b) $\pi^- + p \rightarrow \pi^- + \pi^+ + n$ [taken from SOBB Collaboration (1964a)].

According to the usual Feynman rules, the amplitude for such a diagram has the form

$$T = V_{\mathrm{A}} V_{\mathrm{B}} / (t - \mu^2) \qquad \text{(III-1)}$$

where t as before is the negative squared four-momentum transfer in the production channel and V_{A}, V_{B} are the contributions from the vertices A and B in Fig. 4. These vertices can be expressed generally as form factors depending on t multiplying the spinor factors as computed for the lowest order Feynman graph; V_{A} and V_{B} contain all contributions from diagrams which contribute to the vertex "blobs" of Fig. 4, but do not include initial and final state interactions of the form shown in Fig. 8, which we shall discuss later.

At the πNN vertex, a spectral form can be written for the form factor. We define a form factor $F(t)$ by

$$V_{\pi \mathrm{NN}} = \bar{u}(p_2) \gamma_5 g F(t) u(p_1) \qquad \text{(III-2)}$$

where $\bar{u}$ and u are final and initial Dirac spinors for the nucleons, g is the rationalized πN-coupling constant ($g^2/4\pi = 14.4$) and $F(\mu^2) = 1$. Then $F(t)$ satisfies a dispersion relation of the form

$$F(t) = 1 + \frac{(t - \mu^2)}{\pi} \int_{9\mu^2}^{\infty} \frac{\sigma(t') \, dt'}{(t' - \mu^2)(t' - t)}. \qquad \text{(III-3)}$$

The weight function in the spectral integral has a threshold at $t = 9\mu^2$, the square of the least massive state to which a pion couples, and may assume negative as well as positive values, so no general statements about $F(t)$ can be made; $F(t)$ is a dispersion-theoretic form factor as distinct from a Dyson irreducible vertex function and thus includes corrections to the virtual pion propagator.

There are analogous "form factor" corrections at the four particle $\pi\pi$-scattering vertex which depend upon the distance of the exchanged pion from the mass-shell at $t = \mu^2$. These unknown form factors depend only on the momentum transfer. On the one hand, they must be introduced phenomenologically since accurate calculation is impossible; on the other hand, as they do not depend on the energy of the reaction, the adequacy of an approach which keeps only the class of diagrams that correspond to one-pion exchange can be readily tested. The energy dependence of the cross sections at fixed t is the same as the Born approximation result from lowest order perturbation theory, and the various angular decay tests such as the Treiman-Yang test (1962) can be applied.

This form factor approach has been applied most extensively in a series of papers describing work initiated by Ferrari and Selleri and a review of the fits with references complete up until 1962 is given by Ferrari and Selleri (1962). A more recent discussion with references may be found in Selleri (1964). In expression Eq. (III-1) for the matrix element, the unknown part appears as a product of form factors, $G(t)$ and it is this product which is fitted, using a Clementel-Villi (1956) form:

$$G(t) = A - B\mu^2/(t - C\mu^2) \qquad \text{(III-4)}$$

the constants A, B, and C being found from experiment. By an analysis of the processes

$$p + p \rightarrow p + n + \pi^+$$

$$p + p \rightarrow p + p + \pi^0.$$

Ferrari and Selleri (1963) found the following values for the constants:

$$A = 0.28, \qquad B = 3.42, \qquad C = 5.75 \qquad \text{(III-5)}$$

which gave a quantitative fit to the processes up to about 1 GeV. A significant feature of the analysis was that the *same* product of form factors could also reproduce the cross sections for other one-pion-exchange reactions such as $\pi N \rightarrow \rho N$, $\pi N \rightarrow \rho N^*$, $KN \rightarrow K^*N^*$, $N\bar{N} \rightarrow N^*\bar{N}^*$. In other words, once the product was determined phenomenologically for one such reaction, the theory was determined for a whole class of reactions over an appreciable range of energies.

In spite of this success, there are several shortcomings to the form factor approach. First, on a purely theoretical level, there is the question of trying to relate the parameters Eq. (III-5) to "reasonable" or "physically simple" approximations to the dispersion integrals. For example, can one understand the t dependence of $G(t)$ near $t = 0$, or is this dependence too rapid? Since $G(t)$ represents a product of form factors at the two vertices of Fig. 4 divided by a propagator form factor, there is however no direct way of relating the constant C to the known physical singularities.

Second, as we shall see later, the observed angular correlations of final state particles cannot be reproduced by a simple form factor modification of the single particle exchange amplitude.

In addition we have limited ourselves so far to reactions below 1 or 2 GeV. If we attempt to take the form factor approach to higher energies, even for the simplest case of one-pion exchange, further adjustments to the model are necessary in order to reduce the excessively high predictions of the model for large momentum transfer. Several authors have treated the exchanged particle as a Regge pole (Islam, 1963; Islam and Piñon, 1963; Shaw and Wong, 1963; Gottfried and Jackson, 1964a). This has the required effect of reducing the high energy cross section, but introduces more parameters into a fit which already has a certain amount of arbitrariness. Another approach is that of Amaldi and Selleri (1964), who expressed the product of form factors $G(t)$ as a sum of two terms of the Clementel-Villi type: one to give a rapid decrease at small momentum transfers and the other with a long tail to fit the data at relatively large momentum transfers, *viz*:

$$G(t) = \frac{0.72}{1 - (t - \mu^2)/4.73\mu^2} + \frac{0.28}{1 + [(t - \mu^2)/32\mu^2]^2}. \tag{III-6}$$

Again this seems a rather ad hoc procedure, and so leads one to believe that some other mechanism not yet taken into account may be operating.

Finally, fits with the form factor model are far from satisfactory for processes involving vector exchange. Not only must the value of C in Eq. (III-5) be much smaller (in fact smaller than μ^2) if a Clementel-Villi form factor is used (Daudin *et al.* 1963), but the energy dependence of the reactions cannot be satisfactorily fitted for processes which are dominated by an exchange with spin greater than zero.

For these reasons, various authors have suggested that initial and final state interactions must be considered in order to understand the peripheral mechanism correctly. This approach, which we discuss in the next section, suggests that the form factor model is inadequate for dealing with anything but medium energy phenomena, and that, even there, it may only be one of several alternative ways of parametrizing the true physical situation.

IV. The Peripheral Model with Absorption

A. DERIVATION OF THE MODEL

We have seen in the previous section that in spite of the success of the form factor approach to inelastic peripheral processes at medium energies, the technique needs such serious modification at higher energies that its whole validity must be questioned. The peripheral mechanism was suggested by the obvious dominance of the forward peaking in all reactions we have studied so far. However, a naive calculation with the unmodified model is unable to account for *all* the observed peaking, implying a mechanism more peripheral than we have discussed so far. The forward peaked cross sections suggest a long-range mechanism, but it is well known that the pole approximation has appreciable contribution from the low partial waves; the S wave, in particular, being strong enough in many cases to violate the limit imposed by unitarity. At the same time, at very high energies, the production process under consideration may constitute only a small part of the total cross section. For example, in an experiment involving $2.08 \text{ GeV}/c \, \pi^+$ incident on hydrogen, some of the cross sections measured (James and Kraybill, 1966) were as follows:

$$\pi^+ p \to \pi^+ p \pi^0 \qquad 5.29 \pm 0.13 \text{ mb} \qquad \begin{cases} \to p \rho^+ & 2.07 \pm 0.15 \text{ mb} \\ \to N^* \pi^0 & 0.55 \pm 0.08 \text{ mb} \end{cases}$$

$$\to \pi^+ p \pi^+ \pi^- \qquad 3.40 \pm 0.11 \text{ mb} \qquad \begin{cases} \to N^* \pi^+ \pi^- & 2.30 \pm 0.20 \text{ mb} \\ \to \pi^+ p \rho^0 & 1.20 \pm 0.20 \text{ mb} \end{cases}$$

$$\to \pi^+ p \pi^+ \pi^- \pi^0 \qquad 2.41 \pm 0.09 \text{ mb} \qquad \begin{cases} \to \pi^+ p \omega^0 & 1.66 \pm 0.13 \text{ mb} \\ \to \pi^+ p \eta^0 & 0.15 \pm 0.03 \text{ mb} \end{cases}$$

$$\to \pi^+ \pi^+ \pi^+ \pi^- n \qquad 0.26 \pm 0.03 \text{ mb}$$

Intuitively, one would expect the more complex interactions to be initiated by collisions involving low partial waves, and conversely this would imply that the low partial wave interactions are less likely to contribute to the process under discussion. In other words, the existence of many competing open channels should imply a reduction in the low partial wave interaction amplitudes to any one channel while leaving the higher partial waves essentially unchanged. This would require a reduction of the production cross section and modify the angular distributions, producing as we shall see an enhancement of the forward angle cross section as given by experiment.

The idea that such final state interactions must be included in order to describe the peripheral mechanism correctly is not new. Baker and Blankenbecler (1962) considered the coupling of many open channels by dispersion theory and found strong absorption in the low partial waves. A simpler approach was used by Sopkovich (1962a,b) to calculate angular distributions for $p \bar{p} \to \Lambda \bar{\Lambda}$. He used the Glauber (1959) high energy approximation for the production amplitude, distorting the amplitude by an optical potential to describe the initial and final state scattering. The results of this calculation were, however, dependent on the parameters used to describe the optical potential.

An even simpler model to explain the observed diffraction effect in the same process (Fig. 10) was proposed by Dar *et al.* (1964). This was essentially

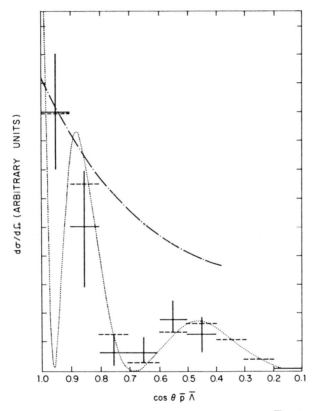

Fig. 10. Comparison of experimental data for the process $\bar{p} + p \rightarrow \bar{\Lambda} + \Lambda$ at 3.3 GeV/c, and the fit of Dar (1964). The theoretical curves were normalized to give correctly the number of events in the first interval of the experimental histogram [taken from Dar (1964)]: (– · –) K exchange; (···) modified K exchange, $R = 1.1 \times 10^{-13}$; (—) experimental results; and (– – –) theoretical curve after integration over experimental bin, $R \sim 1 \times 10^{-13}$ cm.

Fraunhofer diffraction scattering from an illuminated ring. If the ring has radius R, then one can write

$$d\sigma/d\Omega = A[1 + (k_i/k_f) \cos \theta]^2 [J_0(qR)]^2 \qquad \text{(IV-1)}$$

where A is a normalization faction, J_0 is the cylindical Bessel function and $\mathbf{q} = \mathbf{k}_f - \mathbf{k}_i$, the difference between final and initial momenta. The parameters

A and R were adjusted to fit the data. Obviously this is a gross oversimplification of the true physical situation, but it gives a very simple qualitative explanation of a possible mechanism. A more convincing approach along similar lines is to assume that below some fixed angular momentum L all partial wave projections of the single particle exchange matrix element are zero. This forms the basis of a model of Bugg (1963) which was used to fit n-p charge exchange scattering. The same idea is discussed in more generality by Dar and Tobocman (1964), and was used by Dar (1964) to fit a wide variety of processes involving pseudoscalar and vector exchange. These analyses were made using the impact parameter representation of the scattering amplitude rather than partial waves, which is appropriate when one is dealing with high energies and small angles and so a large number of partial waves are contributing. In this case, we can replace the partial wave sum

$$T_{fi} = \sum_{l=0}^{\infty} (l + \tfrac{1}{2})T_l(k)P_l(\cos \theta) \qquad (IV-2)$$

by an integral

$$T_{fi} = \int_0^{\infty} b \, db \, T(k, b)J_0(\Delta b), \qquad (IV-3)$$

where k is the incident 3-momentum in the center of mass, $kb = l + \tfrac{1}{2}$, $\Delta = \sqrt{-t}$ is the magnitude of the invariant 4-momentum transfer, and J_0 is the Bessel function of zeroth order. We have also made use of the small angle approximation

$$P_l(\cos \theta) \simeq J_0[(2l + 1) \sin(\theta/2)] \qquad (IV-4)$$

in deriving Eq. (IV-3).

We see that the integration variable b may be identified with the classical impact parameter, leading to a simple physical interpretation of the representation.

The impact parameter representation of the single particle exchange scattering amplitude is given by

$$A = (M^2 - t)^{-1} = \int_0^{\infty} b \, dbK_0(Mb)J_0(\Delta b) \qquad (IV-5)$$

where K_0 is the zeroth order modified Bessel function of the second kind. If we now assume that the integrand is zero below a fixed radius R, we have

$$A_{\text{modified}} = \int_R^{\infty} b \, dbK_0(Mb)J_0(\Delta b)$$
$$\simeq MR(M^2 - t)^{-1}\{K_1(MR)J_0(\Delta R) - iK_0(MR)J_1(\Delta R)\} \qquad (IV-6)$$

and we can therefore fit experiments with a single phenomenological parameter R.

Values of R found in the fits varied between 0.7 and 1.3 fermis. As we see in Fig. 10, which is a fit to the $p\bar{p} \to \Lambda\bar{\Lambda}$ data of Baltay *et al.* (1962), the model is able to fit convincingly the diffraction peak away from the forward angles, but it also predicts a diffraction minimum at small angles which does not appear in the experimental data. The same fault appeared in the diffraction ring model. Fits to most other processes, however, such as $K^+p(\pi)K^*N^*$ as shown in Fig. 11 do not suffer from this defect.

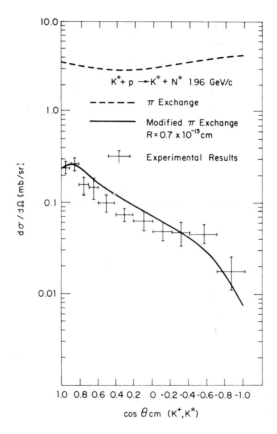

Fig. 11. Comparison of experimental data for the process $K^+p \to K^*N^*$ and the theoretical fit of Dar (1964). [The experimental data were taken from Goldhaber *et al.* (1963).] The calculation of the one-pion-exchange curve is due to Berman as quoted in this reference [taken from Dar (1964)].

The anomalous diffraction minimum in the fit of $p\bar{p} \to \Lambda\bar{\Lambda}$ is a consequence of the sharp cutoff in the matrix elements and can be removed by rounding the edge of the distribution. To do this one must however introduce more parameters into the fit.

A more natural way of introducing absorption into the peripheral model is an extension of the distorted wave approximation of Sopkovich, and was first suggested by Durand and Chiu (1964a,b; 1965a,b) and Gottfried and Jackson (Gottfried and Jackson, 1964c; Jackson, 1965; Jackson *et al.*, 1965). This gives for the elements of the T matrix.

$$T_{fi}^l = \exp(i\delta_f^l)B_{fi}^l \exp(i\delta_i^l) \qquad \text{(IV-7)}$$

where δ_i^l and δ_f^l are the initial and final complex scattering phase shifts, and B_{fi}^l is the partial wave projection of the amplitude for unmodified single particle exchange. The success of this formula in fitting pseudoscalar exchange processes is indisputable, but, as we shall see, the theoretical justification is not so firmly based and the success is not maintained in fitting processes with vector exchange. To understand the derivation of this formula we shall follow closely the potential theoretic derivation of Gottfried and Jackson (1964c) using the impact parameter representation. An alternative derivation of this result as the solution of two-channel coupled partial wave equations is given by Durand and Chiu (1965b).

In the distorted wave Born approximation, the transition amplitude is approximated by the matrix element

$$T_{fi} = \langle \psi_f^{(-)}|V|\psi_i^{(+)}\rangle \qquad \text{(IV-8)}$$

where the interaction potential V causing the transition is considered weak enough to be treated as a perturbation. The wave function of the system in the initial state is $\psi_i^{(+)}$. It represents an incoming wave for a particle propogating through a complex potential $U^{(+)}$. The analogous wave function in the final state, $\psi_f^{(-)}$, represents an outgoing wave emerging from a potential $U^{(-)}$. We work to all orders in $U_{\pm}^{(-)}$, the optical potentials for the incoming and outgoing states, respectively, and to first order in the perturbation V.

As we are working at high energies and with small momentum transfers, it is appropriate to use the Glauber (1959) approximation for the wave functions. This gives for $\psi^{(\pm)}$:

$$\psi_{q\pm}^{(\pm)}(\mathbf{b}, z) \simeq \exp[i q_{\pm} \cdot \mathbf{x}] \exp\left[(-i/v_{\pm}) \int_{\mp\infty}^{z} U^{(\pm)}(\mathbf{b} + \hat{\kappa}z') \, dz'\right] \qquad \text{(IV-9)}$$

where $v_{\pm}$ is the relative velocity of the particles in the given state, q_+ and q_- are the initial and final 3-momenta, respectively, and we have assumed one 3-dimensional degree of freedom z chosen along $\kappa = q_+ + q_-$. The impact parameter vector b is perpendicular to κ and $r = b + \hat{\kappa}z$. In this approximation, the expression for the scattering amplitude is

$$T_{\text{fi}} \simeq \int d^2b \int_{-\infty}^{\infty} dz \, \exp[i\Delta \cdot \mathbf{b}]V(\mathbf{b} + \hat{\kappa}z)$$

$$\times \exp\left\{\frac{-i}{v_-} \int_z^{\infty} U^{(-)}(\mathbf{b} + \hat{\kappa}z')^* \, dz'\right\} \exp\left\{\frac{-i}{v_+} \int_{-\infty}^{z} U^+(\mathbf{b} + \hat{\kappa}z'') \, dz''\right\}. \tag{IV-10}$$

In order to make the equations more tractable, it is necessary to make further assumptions about $U^{(\pm)}$. The simplest is to assume that the elastic interactions are the same in the initial and final channels, i.e., $U^{(+)} = U^{(-)} = U$ and $v_+ = v_- \equiv v$. Equation (IV-10) then becomes

$$T_{\text{fi}} = 2\pi \int_0^{\infty} J_0(\Delta b) \exp[2i\delta(b)]B(b)b \, db \tag{IV-11}$$

where

$$2\delta(b) = -\frac{1}{v} \int_{-\infty}^{\infty} U(\mathbf{b} + \hat{\kappa}z) \, dz \tag{IV-12}$$

is the phase shift of a wave packet traveling through the potential U, at an impact parameter $\mathbf{b}$, and

$$B(b) = \int_{-\infty}^{\infty} V(\mathbf{b} + \hat{\kappa}z) \, dz \tag{IV-13}$$

is the unmodified Born approximation for the amplitude. Another case in which a simple approximation can be found for T_{fi} is when the range of V is much smaller than that of $U^{(+)}$ or $U^{(-)}$. In this case, Eq. (IV-10) reduces to

$$T_{\text{fi}} = 2\pi \int_0^{\infty} b \, db J_0(\Delta b)B(b) \exp\{i[\delta^{(+)}(b) + \delta^{(-)}(b)]\}. \tag{IV-14}$$

For the problems we are considering however, this is hardly a valid assumption, and so the Gottfried-Jackson derivation is based on the assumption that the initial and final elastic scattering amplitudes are equal. A comparison of Eq. (IV-11) with Eq. (IV-3) now gives for the distorted wave Born approximation

$$T(b) = e^{2i\delta(b)}B(b) \tag{IV-15}$$

where we have set $\delta^{(+)} = \delta^{(-)} = \delta$. We now see that the model of Bugg and Dar and Tobocman comes directly from this equation by writing

$$e^{i\delta(b)} = \begin{array}{ll} 0 & \text{for} \quad b < R \\ 1 & \text{for} \quad b > R. \end{array} \tag{IV-16}$$

In order to calculate Eq. (IV-15) in any given case, a further approximation is also made for the scattering phase shift $\delta(b)$. If we assume that at high

energies the elastic scattering cross sections are essentially imaginary, and
that the experimental angular distributions are well fitted by a Gaussian form:

$$T_{el} = i(\sigma_T q/4\pi) \exp[-\tfrac{1}{2}A\Delta^2] \qquad \text{(IV-17)}$$

with σ_T the total cross section, q the center-of-mass momentum, and A a
slowly varying function of energy, then we have for δ:

$$\exp[2i\delta(b)] = 1 - C \exp[-b^2/2A] \qquad \text{(IV-18)}$$

with $C = \sigma_T/4\pi A$. Note that $C \leqslant 1$, since, for imaginary δ,

$$\exp[2i\delta(b)] \geqslant 0. \qquad \text{(IV-19)}$$

Recent measurements (for example, Foley *et al.*, 1965) have shown, however, an appreciable real part (up to 30%) in πp and pp cross sections even
at forward angles, indicating that the above parametrization is at best approximate. In actual calculations, Gottfried and Jackson have also generalized
Eq. (IV-15) to the impact parameter form of Eq. (IV-7):

$$
\begin{aligned}
T(b) &= \exp[i\delta_+(b)]B(b)\exp[i\delta_-(b)] \\
&= \{1 - C_+ \exp[-\gamma_+(x - x_{min})^2]\}^{1/2} \\
&\quad \times B(b)\{1 - C_- \exp[-\gamma_-(x - x_{min})^2]\}^{1/2}
\end{aligned}
\qquad \text{(IV-20)}
$$

where C_+ and C_- are the amounts by which the lowest partial waves are
absorbed in the initial and final states, respectively, $2\gamma_\pm A_\pm q_\pm^2 = 1$ and
$x = qb$; x_{min} is introduced here so that it is possible to achieve full absorption
in the S wave with $C = 1$.

The inclusion of spin in the formalism necessary to predict the correct
form of angular distributions and resonance decay correlations requires only
a straightforward generalization of Eq. (IV-7) using the helicity formalism
of Jacob and Wick (1959), and one writes

$$\langle \lambda'\mu'|T^l|\lambda\mu\rangle = \exp(i\delta_f^l)\langle\lambda'\mu'|B^l|\lambda\mu\rangle \exp(i\delta_i^l) \qquad \text{(IV-21)}$$

where $\lambda\mu$, $\lambda'\mu'$ are the helicities of initial and final particle states, respectively.
In generalizing the spinless equation to this form we have made the additional
assumption that the diffraction scattering in the "blobs" of Fig. 8 does not
change the initial or final state helicities.

B. DECAY CORRELATIONS

In our discussion of the mechanisms responsible for the production of
resonant states, we have so far treated the resonances as stable particles. In
any experiment, however, one usually recognizes these resonances by studying
their decay products, and, as discussed in Section II, the angular distribution

of these decay products contains information on the method of formation of the particle which is additional to that obtained from momentum and energy distributions. We shall consider again the reaction $\pi p(\pi)\rho p$, but our remarks are readily generalized to other processes, and a discussion of the general case may be found in Gottfried and Jackson (1964b).

We begin by writing the amplitude for the decay $\rho \to \pi\pi$ in the rest frame of the ρ. It is possible to show, using general helicity arguments, that this has the form

$$A_m(\theta, \phi) = (3/4\pi)^{1/2} d^1_{m0}(\theta) \exp[i\phi m] \qquad \text{(IV-22)}$$

where $d^1_{m0}\theta)$ is a reduced rotation matrix (Jacob and Wick, 1959) and where we have expressed our polar angles θ, ϕ with respect to p, the momentum of one of the decay pions as shown in Fig. 6; m is the component of the spin of the ρ in an arbitrary direction of quantization.

The probability for decay in the direction (θ, ϕ) of the produced ρ may now be written as a function of A in the form

$$W(\theta, \phi) = \sum_{m,m'} A_m A^*_{m'} \rho_{mm'} \qquad \text{(IV-23)}$$

where $\rho_{mm'}$ is the canonical spin-space density matrix of the ρ. Choosing again the 3-momentum axis of the incident pion as the spin quantization direction we may express $\rho_{mm'}$ in terms of the helicity matrix elements $\langle \mu'\lambda'|T|\lambda\rangle$ of the process $\pi p_\lambda \to \rho_\mu p_{\lambda'}$

$$\rho_{mm'} = N \sum_{\mu\mu'\lambda\lambda'} d^1_{m\mu}(\psi)\langle\mu\lambda'|T|\lambda\rangle^*\langle\mu'\lambda'|T|\lambda\rangle d^1_{m'\mu'}(-\psi). \qquad \text{(IV-24)}$$

In this equation, the angle ψ is defined by

$$\sin \psi = 2m_\rho p \sin \theta\{[t - (m_\rho + \mu)^2][t - (m_\rho - \mu)^2]\}^{1/2}$$

N is chosen to give $\rho_{mm'}$ a unit trace, and m_ρ is the mass of the ρ. In terms of Eqs. (IV-22) and (IV-23) we can now write for $W(\theta, \phi)$:

$$W(\theta, \phi) = (3/4\pi) \sum_{m,m'} \exp[i(m - m')\phi] d^1_{m0}(\theta) d^1_{m'0}(\theta)\rho_{mm'} \qquad \text{(IV-25)}$$

which gives the complete angular dependence of the decay cross section directly in terms of the density matrix elements, or alternatively, in terms of the matrix elements of the production reaction.

In addition to the trace condition, we may further relate the elements of the density matrix by the Hermiticity condition

$$\rho_{mm'} = (\rho_{mm'})^+ \qquad \text{(IV-26)}$$

and by parity conservation, which requires that

$$\rho_{-m,-m'} = (-1)^{m-m'} \rho_{mm'}. \qquad \text{(IV-27)}$$

Thus, for a resonance with $J = 1$, the density matrix has the explicit form

$$\rho_{mm'} = \begin{pmatrix} \rho_{11} & \rho_{10} & \rho_{1,-1} \\ \rho_{10}^* & \rho_{00} & -\rho_{10}^* \\ \rho_{1,-1} & -\rho_{10} & \rho_{11} \end{pmatrix} \tag{IV-28}$$

where all elements are real except ρ_{10}, and

$$\rho_{00} = 1 - 2\rho_{11}. \tag{IV-29}$$

In terms of these elements, the explicit form of the ρ-decay distribution is then

$$W(\theta, \phi) = (3/4\pi)\{\rho_{00} \cos^2\theta$$
$$+ \rho_{11} \sin^2\theta - \rho_{1,-1} \sin^2\theta \cos 2\phi - \sqrt{2} \operatorname{Re} \rho_{10} \sin 2\theta \cos \phi\} \tag{IV-30}$$

where we see that all the density matrix elements except $\operatorname{Im} \rho_{10}$ are known from a measurement of the decay distribution.

Our earlier discussions show that for unmodified pion exchange, with or without form factor corrections, only ρ_{00} is nonzero (and unity in this case), but this is no longer true if appreciable absorption corrections or contributions from other particle exchanges occur. Of course, such allowed exchanges in this case are limited, the next lightest exchange being an ω which contributes only to ρ_{11} and $\rho_{1,-1}$. Present data (for example, Hagopian *et al.*, 1966) indicate significant contributions from both ρ_{10} and $\rho_{1,-1}$ (Fig. 12). The existence of a nonzero ρ_{10} term in particular is strong evidence against any form factor model of this process which allows only one pion and ω exchange without initial and final state absorption.

C. APPLICATIONS

The absorption model has been applied now to a large variety of processes mediated by pseudoscalar and vector exchange. These include the following:

$\pi N \rightarrow \rho N$	(Durand and Chiu, 1965a; Gottfried and Jackson, 1964c; Hagopian *et al.*, 1966; Jackson *et al.*, 1965),
$\pi p \rightarrow \rho N^*(1238)$	(ABBBHLM Collaboration, 1965; Jackson *et al.*, 1965),
$\pi p \rightarrow \omega N^*(1238)$	(ABBBHLM Collaboration, 1965; Svensson, 1965a),
$\pi^- p \rightarrow \pi^0 n$	(Barger and Ebel, 1965; Högaasen and Högaasen, 1965a),
$\pi^+ n \rightarrow \omega p$	(Jackson *et al.*, 1965),
$\pi N \rightarrow N + \text{spin } 2^+$	(Högaasen *et al.*, 1966),
$Kp \rightarrow KN^*$,	
$Kp \rightarrow K^*N^*$,	
$Kp \rightarrow K^*N$,	
$Kp \rightarrow \pi Y^*$,	

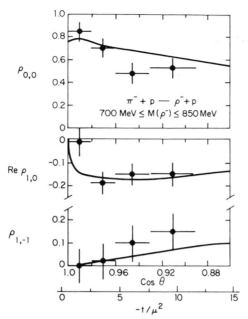

Fig. 12. Spin density matrix elements for the ρ^- in the process $\pi + p \to \rho^- + p$ [taken from Hagopian *et al.* (1966)]. The curves give the theoretical predictions of the absorption model at 2.75 GeV/*c* as quoted in this reference. The *t* scale is given for 2.88 GeV/*c* and for $M_{\pi\pi} = 765$ MeV.

$Kp \to \pi Y^*$, and the analogous reactions with $\overline{K}$	(Jackson *et al.*, 1965),
$pp \to nN^*$	(Alexander *et al.*, 1966),
$np \to pn$ (charge exchange	(Durand and Chiu, 1965a; Ringland and Phillips, 1964),
$N\bar{N} \to Y\,\overline{Y}$	(Durand and Chiu, 1965a; Högaasen and Högaasen, 1965b)
$N\bar{N} \to N^*\bar{N}^*$	(Svensson, 1965b).

The common feature of many of these interactions is the dominance of the forward peak, and in most cases the distributions are confined almost entirely to momentum transfers less than $0.5(\text{GeV}/c)^2$. In the most pronounced case, $\pi p \to \rho p$, the important range of momentum transfers has an average of approximately 0.15 $(\text{GeV}/c)^2$.

Cross sections have also been calculated using a modified OPE model for several processes involving photoproduction of resonant states (Cambridge Bubble Chamber Group, 1965; Locher and Sandhas, 1965). In these cases, one assumes of course that absorption occurs only in the strongly interacting final state as shown in Fig. 13.

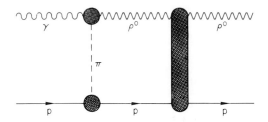

Fig. 13. Final state interaction corrections for the one-pion-exchange contribution to the process $\gamma + p \rightarrow \rho + p$.

A detailed discussion of all these reactions is given in the cited references and we shall therefore restrict ourselves to discussing the fits to a few processes which show general trends of the model.

We begin by considering the process $\pi p \rightarrow \rho p$ which we have assumed previously is mediated by a one-pion-exchange mechanism. This interpretation is confirmed by a study of the ρ-decay distribution which is essentially of the form $\cos^2\theta$. We show in Fig. 14 a comparison of the absorption model

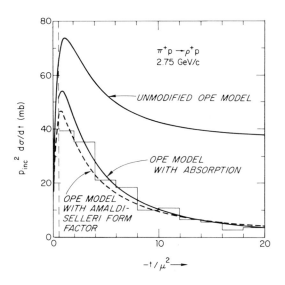

Fig. 14. Comparison of theory and experiment for the process $\pi^+ + p \rightarrow \rho^+ + p$ at 2.75 GeV/c [taken from Jackson (1965)]. The histogram represents the data of SOBB Collaboration (1964b) as quoted in this reference.

fit to $\pi^+ p \to \rho^+ p$ at 2.75 GeV/c with the Amaldi-Selleri form factor fit discussed in the last section. Included in the figure is the unmodified OPE cross section for the reaction, which has the form

$$\frac{d\sigma}{dt} = \frac{\pi}{4m_\rho{}^2 M^2 p_{\text{inc}}^2} \frac{g^2}{4\pi} \frac{g_\rho{}^2}{4\pi} \frac{t[t - (m_\rho + \mu)^2][t - (m_\rho - \mu)^2]}{(t - \mu^2)^2} \qquad \text{(IV-31)}$$

where p_{inc} is the incident momentum of the pion in the laboratory system, and g, g_ρ are the πNN and $\rho\pi\pi$ rationalized, renormalized, coupling constants, respectively. The assumption of "complete absorption" is made in this and all subsequent fits using the absorption model. We see that the unmodified OPE cross section is too large by a factor of 50% at the low momentum peak and predicts too slow a fall-off with increasing momentum transfer. On the other hand, as the absorption model cannot be preferred to the form factor fit to the cross section, it is necessary to make a detailed examination of the ρ-spin density matrix in order to distinguish between them. The form factor fits predict $\rho_{00} = 1$ and all other elements zero, while the absorption model predicts $\rho_{00} \sim 0.7$ with small contributions to the other elements. Presently available data (Fig. 12) are consistent with the latter value.

Fits have been made to the various modes of πN $\to \rho$N up to 8 GeV/c, and in all cases, provided one assumes complete absorption, an effective fit can be made. Variations necessary in the initial state absorption factors are consistent with one's knowledge of the elastic scattering. In particular, the energy dependence of the total cross section is well fitted by the theory as shown in Fig. 15. We note, however, that the variation with energy is already correctly given by unmodified one-pion exchange. On integrating Eq. (IV-31) with respect to t, and ignoring the almost negligible t dependence of the lower limit of integration at the energies we are considering, we see that the total cross section has the form

$$\sigma = c/q_{\text{inc}}^2 \qquad \text{(IV-32)}$$

where c is an energy independent constant. This qualitative prediction of $1/q_{\text{inc}}^2$ dependence in the cross section agrees well with experiment. As the addition of any t-dependent variations in the model can only change the normalization of the cross section, any correctly normalized theory based on one-pion exchange must automatically predict the correct energy dependence of the total cross section. It is not surprising therefore that the absorption model can fit the energy distributions, as the only energy dependence in its modification of one-pion exchange comes from the elastic total cross section σ_T and the width of the diffraction peak in Eq. (IV-17) both of which have a small variation with energy. When the "complete absorption" philosophy is applied, this dependence is not sufficient to produce appreciable deviations in the general energy behavior of the inelastic cross section.

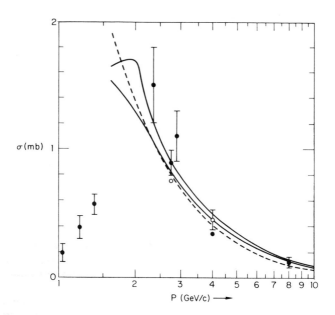

Fig. 15. The total cross section for the processes $\pi^{\pm} + p \to \rho^{\pm} + p$ as a function of incident pion momentum [taken from Jackson *et al.* (1965)]: (●) π^+ and (○) π^-. The upper (lower) solid curve is a fit for $\pi^+(\pi^-)$ assuming only one-pion exchange with absorption corrections, the difference being caused by different absorption effects. The dashed curve is the cross section fit with the Amaldi-Selleri (1964) form factor.

A study of the decay distributions in many other processes also indicates a single pion exchange mechanism, but with sufficient variation from the unmodified model predictions to require either a mechanism like absorption or corrections from higher mass or spin exchange. For example, the process $K^+p \to K^*N^*$ is particularly interesting because one can study the decay distribution of both the K* and N*, and in each case one sees strong evidence for one-pion exchange. The deviations in the density matrix elements from one-pion exchange in each case can be fitted by absorption corrections and do not seem to indicate a need for higher spin exchange. Data for this process are only available at present in the 2–3 GeV/c region, so no test can be made here of the energy dependence of the theory.

The cases we have considered so far provide the easiest test of the various models in fitting the data, as they involve both spin zero exchange and a pole very near the physical region. In order to test the validity of the fits to spin zero processes in general, it would be useful to examine reactions dominated by the exchange of a single spin zero particle of heavier mass, for example, a K meson. Unfortunately, relatively little data are available on such reactions, so we must turn our attention to the fits which have been made to processes which also involve vector exchange. Several reactions have been observed whose decay distributions indicate evidence for both spin zero and spin one exchange, For example, we show in Fig. 16 the angular distributions

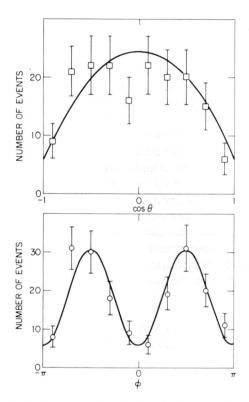

Fig. 16. Angular distributions in cos θ and ϕ for the decay products K^0 and π^+ from the resonance K^* produced in the process $K^+ + p \rightarrow K^* + p$ at 3 GeV/c. The angles are as defined in the text [taken from Jackson (1965)].

at 3 GeV/c for the decay products (K^0 and π^+) from the resonance K^* produced in the reaction $K^+ p \rightarrow K^* p$. The density matrix elements are also shown in Fig. 17. The marked cos 2θ dependence in the decay distributions suggests a dominant vector exchange contribution, and this is confirmed by a detailed study of the density matrix elements. We notice that for cos $\theta < 0.9$, only ρ_{11} (given in terms of ρ_{00} by Eq. (IV-29)) and $\rho_{1,-1}$ are appreciably different from zero, and that the only evidence for one-pion exchange is seen at very forward angles.

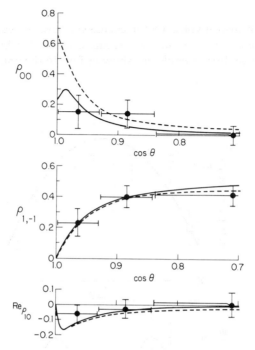

Fig. 17. Theoretical and experimental K* density-matrix elements for the process
K$^+$ + p → K* + p at 3 GeV/c [from Jackson *et al.* (1965)]. The solid and dashed curves
refer to different values for the vector meson coupling constants as described in this reference.

Successful fits to the process at this energy have been made using the
complete absorption model, assuming both π and ρ exchange as shown in
Fig. 18. A fit was also made to data at 5 GeV/c using the same coupling
constants (Fig. 19), but it was found that although the agreement was satisfactory for $\Delta^2 \lesssim 15\mu^2$, the theoretical estimate was much too high at larger
momentum transfers. The failure of the fit to the energy dependence of the
data was indicated by the theoretical total cross section estimate of 0.85 mb
compared with the experimental value of 0.3 mb. The lack of success of this
model in fitting energy distributions is even more marked when one considers
a process where only vector exchange is allowed such as $\pi^- p(\rho)\pi^0 n$ and
$\pi^+ n(\rho)\omega p$. In these cases the model is off by orders of magnitude in fitting
the high energy distributions. This failure again reflects the fact that the
"complete absorption" model is essentially a scheme for t modification of the
one particle exchange amplitude. The cross section as calculated from unmodified ρ exchange gives a distribution which remains constant with energy, and
so absorption model has little hope of predicting the fall-off of the cross
section with increasing energy which is found in the data. A more detailed

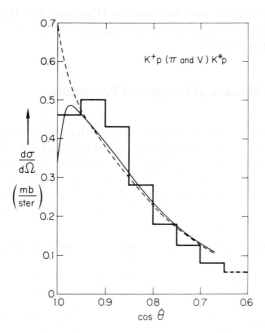

Fig. 18. Comparison of absorption model fit with experiment for the differential cross section of the process in Fig. 17. The solid and dashed curves correspond to those of Fig. 17 [from Jackson *et al.* (1965)].

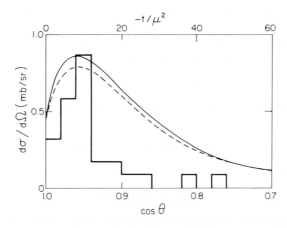

Fig. 19. Absorption model fit to the process $K^+ + p \rightarrow K^* + p$ at 5 GeV/c [taken from Jackson *et al.* (1965)]. The curves are calculated with the same coupling constants as those of Fig. 18.

discussion of this point may be found in Högaasen and Högaasen (1965a). To improve such fits requires further drastic assumptions which we shall discuss in the next section.

V. *K*-Matrix Models of Peripheral Processes

In spite of the relative success of the absorption model in fitting processes involving pseudoscalar exchange, it is obvious that the procedure still involves a certain amount of curve fitting. Although the initial state absorption parameters are given to us by experiment, the "complete absorption" philosophy used to determine the final state parameters is apparently an ad hoc prescription which seems to work. However, the fits to processes involving vector exchange are as unsatisfactory as ever; the energy variation predicted being in gross disagreement with experiment.

The model we discussed in the last section in the form given by Eq. (IV-7) is not the only way of introducing the apparently necessary damping of the low partial waves in the one particle exchange matrix elements, however, and in this section, we shall consider other approaches which have been used recently to fit peripheral processes. We shall see that none of the methods appears to fit the energy behavior of vector exchange processes satisfactorily, but at least we can gain a better idea of why they fail.

In order to understand the derivation of these models we must restrict ourselves to two particle reactions, allowing, of course, a final state resonance to be treated as a single particle. As most of the reactions we have discussed so far fall into this category, this is not too serious a restriction.

A natural framework for describing such reactions is provided by the N/D equations first introduced by Chew and Mandelstam (1960, 1961) in their study of the pion-pion interaction.[4] If we wish to relate a series of two-body reactions using this formalism, we may write, in matrix form

$$T^l = N^l D^{l-1} \tag{V-1}$$

where we define a particular partial wave amplitude $T_{ij}^l(s)$ in terms of the S matrix by

$$T_{ij}^l(s) = (S_{ij}^l(s) - \delta_{ij})/2i\rho_i\rho_j. \tag{V-2}$$

In this equation,

$$\rho_i = (2k_i/W)^{1/2} \tag{V-3}$$

is a phase space factor associated with the ith channel, and k_i, W are the center-of-mass three-momentum and energy in that channel.

---

[4] See the article by J. Hamilton in Volume I of this book.

In Eq. (V-1), D is a real analytic function of energy except for a right-hand cut on the real axis from the first two particle threshold to infinity. Similarly, N is a real analytic function except for poles and a left-hand cut.

In order to have a simple form for the unitarity equation it is necessary to make the further drastic approximation of retaining only two partical intermediate states. The unitarity condition can then be expressed for each partial wave in the form

$$\text{Im } \boldsymbol{T}^l = \boldsymbol{T}^l \boldsymbol{P} \boldsymbol{T}^l \tag{V-4}$$

where the operator P has elements

$$P_{ij} = \delta_{ij}\theta(s - s_i)\rho_i\rho_j. \tag{V-5}$$

We thus have that

$$\text{Im } \boldsymbol{D}^l = -\boldsymbol{P}\boldsymbol{N}^l. \tag{V-6}$$

Knowing the analytic properties of D and its imaginary part we may therefore write a dispersion relation in the form

$$\boldsymbol{D} = \boldsymbol{I} - \frac{s - s_0}{\pi} \int_{s_0}^{\infty} \frac{ds' \boldsymbol{P}\boldsymbol{N}(s')}{(s' - s)(s' - s_0)}. \tag{V-7}$$

In writing Eq. (V-7) we have made one subtraction and normalized D at s_0 to unity. Writing now

$$\boldsymbol{D} = \text{Re } \boldsymbol{D} - i\boldsymbol{P}\boldsymbol{N} \tag{V-8}$$

we see that Eq. (V-1) may be written in the form

$$\boldsymbol{T} = \boldsymbol{N}/(\text{Re } \boldsymbol{D} - i\boldsymbol{P}\boldsymbol{N}) \tag{V-9}$$

or

$$\boldsymbol{T} = \boldsymbol{K}/(\boldsymbol{I} - i\boldsymbol{P}\boldsymbol{K}) \tag{V-10}$$

where

$$\boldsymbol{K} = \boldsymbol{N}/\text{Re } \boldsymbol{D}. \tag{V-11}$$

Equation (V-10) is the (multichannel) K-matrix equation (Heitler, 1944; Dalitz, 1961; Goldberger and Watson, 1964), and it has formed the basis for several models designed to fit peripheral processes. In order to use these equations in any actual calculation, it is necessary to make further simplifying assumptions about the form of N and Re D. The singularities of N provide the exchange forces which drive the interaction, and the strongest contributions to these come from the longest range forces, or the cross-channel poles nearest the physical region. If we also assume that the principal value integral in D may be neglected, we can write for K,

$$K^l = B^l \tag{V-12}$$

where B^l is the contribution from the one particle exchange terms in the lth partial wave. Most calculations using the K-matrix equations employ this approximation for the inelastic elements, although the early calculations of Baker and Blankenbecler (1962) which used the impact parameter form of Eq. (V-10) developed by Blankenbecler and Goldberger (1962) also considered other models for K. We shall discuss the fits made using the K-matrix approach later in this section. A calculation of Ross and Shaw (1964), which considered the effect of absorption on the apparent position and width of the ρ in $\pi N \rightarrow \rho N$ was also equivalent in predictions to the model of Baker and Blankenbecler, although it does not have a well-defined K-matrix structure.

The significance of the approximations equations (V-10) and (V-12) is easiest illustrated by a diagrammatic representation of the one-channel K-matrix equations as shown in Fig. 20. If intermediate state particles a' and

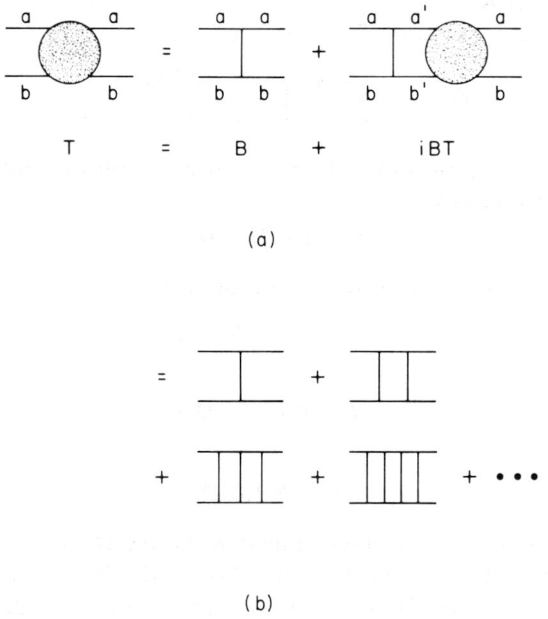

Fig. 20. (a) Diagrammatic representation of one-channel K-matrix equation, Eq. (V-13). (b) Expansion as a series of ladder graphs.

b' are on the mass-shell, which is equivalent to setting Re $D = 1$ in Eq. (V-11), then Fig. 20a represents the one channel equation

$$T = B + iBT \tag{V-13}$$

which may be further expanded as shown in Fig. 20b as a series of ladder graphs.

In order to fit an elastic scattering process such as $\pi p \to \rho p$, however, it is evident that the coupling of at least the two channels πp and ρp must be considered in order to fit the data. It is found, however, that a simple two-channel model is a very poor fit to the data and the reason is not hard to see. Even at energies of the order of 2 GeV we saw in Section IV that the πp and ρp channels represent only a fraction of the total cross section for πp scattering and the coupling of the other channels to the πp channel will have a marked effect on the process under consideration. This fact was, of course, one of the main reasons for introducing the idea of absorption in the first place. In addition, it is not clear that Eq. (V-12) is a valid approximation in the elastic channels which presumably are all strongly absorptive. Nevertheless, to improve the calculation at least requires contributions from more channels. However, even if we restrict ourselves to two particle channels which couple to the πp system, there are a bewildering number to be considered, e.g., πN^* (1238), ρN^*, ωN^*, ωp, πN^* (1512), etc. To include all these in a calculation, assuming that the K-matrix elements are approximated by Born terms, requires a knowledge of all coupling constants involved in the relevant Born amplitude. Most of these are still unknown, so, even at this level, such a calculation becomes necessarily phenomenological; all one can do is show that experiments can be fitted with reasonable values for the many coupling constants involved using, for example, a symmetry scheme such as SU(6) as a guide in determining the relative magnitude of the coupling.

In addition if one wishes to extend the formalism further to include three or more particle channels then the simple form of the unitarity equation, Eq. (V-6), is replaced by a complicated integral equation, and the simplicity of Eq. (V-10) is lost.

On the other hand, it is possible that all but the most important channels each have a small effect on the process considered and moreover are produced in a reasonably incoherent manner, so that their total effect may be estimated by appeal to some form of randomness hypothesis. This idea has been taken furthest by Squires (1964, 1965a,b; Kumar and Squires, 1965) and Trefil (1966), although all K-matrix fits make some effort to include the effect of neglected channels.

The basic assumption in this approximation is that the many unknown coupled channels contribute to the scattering with equal weight but random signs. The simplest approximation is to assume that *all* elements of the K matrix have the same order of magnitude but random signs. The random phase hypothesis then requires that the off-diagonal elements of K^2 be small compared with the diagonal elements, and it is possible to show by standard statistical arguments (Squires, 1965a; Wigner, 1955) that

$$T_{12} = \frac{(1 + e^{-2\gamma})^2}{4} B_{12} \qquad \text{(V-14)}$$

where B_{12} as before is the inelastic one particle exchange amplitude and γ is the imaginary part of the elastic phase shift.

Of course it is physically unreasonable that all elements of K have the same magnitude, and several improvements of this basic idea have been suggested. These assume either that all the unknown terms of the K matrix—that is, those we cannot calculate—have the same weight and random phase, but this weight is different from that of the known (calculable) part, or that the unknown channels which couple directly to those under consideration have a greater weight than the remaining unknown terms coupling with each other. Each of these approximations naturally introduces further arbitrary parameters into the theory.

Fits to a variety of processes using the K-matrix model have now been made. Dietz and Pilkuhn (1965a,b) made an exhaustive study of $K^+p \rightarrow K^{*+}p$, including explicitly the effects of the K^+p, KN^*, K^*N, and K^*N^* channels and allowing for three and multiparticle channels with a simple random phase hypothesis. Although satisfactory fits to the inelastic process were obtained they required an excessively large contribution from three-body channels in the low partial waves, which in fact almost masked the S wave completely. Arnold (1964) considered fits to several processes with reasonable success, although no attempt was made to test the energy dependence to the theory. His fit to $\bar{K}N$ charge exchange at 1.80 GeV/c is shown in Fig. 21. Finally,

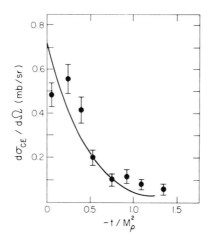

Fig. 21. K-matrix fit to $\bar{K}N$ charge exchange cross section for 1.80 GeV/c beam momentum [taken from Arnold (1964)].

Trefil (1966) carried out a detailed study of forward and backward charge exchange pion-nucleon scattering, and found that although the data at a given energy can be fitted, the energy dependence of the theory is in disagreement with experiment with the two random phase models used to include unknown channels. Thus the K-matrix model in the form we have discussed fails to explain the energy dependence of processes dominated by vector exchange, and requires a stronger damping of the low partial waves than seems given by the theory, just as we found in the absorption model.

The reasons for the similarity in the failure of the two approaches would be more understandable if it were possible to derive the absorption model using an approach based on the N/D equations or dispersion theory rather than potential theory. This has been attempted by several authors (Ball and Frazer, 1965; Griffiths and Saperstein, 1965; Omnes, 1965; Watson, 1965), but requires very stringent restrictions on the form of the scattering amplitudes involved. The only reliable conclusion to be drawn is that the K-matrix and absorption models are consistent when the absorption is weak, but no convincing proof can be found in the more important case of strong absorption. In particular, a two-channel model of a scattering process is clearly inconsistent with the absorption model in the limit of strong absorption. The explicit expression for the inelastic amplitude in a unitarized two-channel model is

$$T^l_{12} = \exp(i\delta_1{}^l)[1/\eta_l^2 - 1]^{1/2} \exp(i\delta_2{}^l)/2\rho_1\rho_2 \qquad (V\text{-}15)$$

where δ_1 and δ_2 are the initial and final complex scattering phase shifts, respectively, and

$$\eta_l = |\exp(2i\delta_1{}^l)| = |\exp(2i\delta_2{}^l)| \qquad (V\text{-}16)$$

is the absorption coefficient.

A comparison with Eq. (IV-7) shows then that the absorption model in this case associates the unmodified amplitude with the term $[(1/\eta_l^2) - 1]^{1/2}/2\rho_1\rho_2$, and this is clearly impossible in the strong absorption limit ($\eta_l \to 0$). We note also that in terms of the elements of the two channel K matrix, T_{12} has the form

$$T^l_{12} = K^l_{12}/\Delta_l = \exp(i\delta_1{}^l)K^l_{12} \exp(i\delta_2{}^l)/\eta_l|\Delta_l| \qquad (V\text{-}17)$$

where

$$\Delta_l = (1 - i\rho_1 K^l_{11})(1 - i\rho_2 K^l_{22}) + \rho_1\rho_2(K^l_{12})^2. \qquad (V\text{-}18)$$

If one now approximates K_{12} by B_{12}, we have equivalence with the absorption model only in the limit of weak absorption ($\eta \to 1$) and high energies ($\Delta \to 1$). There is not, of course, an argument against the absorption model, which is designed to apply in the case of many channels rather than few, but merely points out the inadequacy of trying to study the problem at a two-channel level.

The more easily understandable structure of the K-matrix model, however, allows us to investigate further the reasons for its failure in the cases we have discussed. Presumably similar reasons also apply in the case of the absorption model. Apart from the restriction to two-body processes, which can be relaxed if one is prepared to solve unitarity equations, the most drastic assumption made in deriving the model is that K can be approximated by the Born term, or in other words, that the cuts in N and D can be neglected. Probably a more realistic assumption is that the off-mass-shell behavior of the exchanged particle is important, as we assumed in the form factor model, and thus to approximate K by a Born term with form factors. Presumably one can use much less drastic form factors in this case than were needed by Ferrari and Selleri (1963), as unitarity is automatically built into our equations. Calculations by Bander and Shaw (1965) using the absorption model of $\pi N \to \rho N$ also indicate that these corrections must be small, otherwise the effect of absorption corrections on the density matrix of the ρ is reduced and the decay correlation data can no longer be fitted. However, as discussed in the last section, such t-dependent form factor correction have no effect on the energy dependence of the theory; this can only come from a mechanism which changes the energy dependence of the K matrix. As the momentum transfer collimation of this theory, that is, a suppression of high momentum transfer events, comes from the summation of the set of ladder diagrams in the scattering channel as shown in Fig. 20, it is reasonable to assume that a reduction to the high energy behavior will come similarly from a sum of ladder iterations of the K-matrix element in the crossed (t) channel as shown in Fig. 22. It was shown by

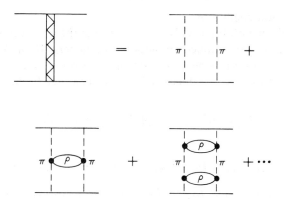

Fig. 22. t-channel ladder approximation for a "Reggeized" ρ-exchange K-matrix element.

Amati *et al.* (1962) that the summation of such graphical series leads naturally to a Regge pole behavior for the elastic scattering amplitudes. The inclusion of " Reggeized " K-matrix elements in the vector exchange model would cause a collimation of the energy distributions required by the data. It is not clear however (Arnold, 1965; Jackson, 1965; Barger and Ebel, 1965) whether a similar application of the absorption model to a Reggeized vector exchange is consistent, as the absorption model may already contain corrections of the form shown in Fig. 22. Presumably, though, a correction of this sort is necessary if the model is to have the correct energy dependence for vector exchange. On the other hand, a calculation in a K-matrix framework avoids this possible ambiguity.

Of course, we have suggested the impossible; a calculation involving form factors, Regge poles, and corrections for unknown channels would involve so many arbitrary parameters as to be almost meaningless. Still, it is apparent from our discussion that all effects may be there, and it may be indeed true that strong interactions are too rich in detail to allow accurate quantitative analysis over a complete spectrum of energies and momentum transfers.

On the other hand, given an understanding of the mechanisms involved we have seen that we can still draw qualitative conclusions from processes which are peripheral in nature and this allows us, for example, to make order-of-magnitude predictions of the size of particle beams at higher energies, as will be discussed in the next section.

VI. Beams

In this concluding section we revert to a much more primitive level of theoretical discussion in order to consider the photoproduction of secondary beams of strongly interacting particles (Drell, 1965). Up to this point we have looked at transition amplitudes for two strongly interacting paticles (stable or unstable) in the initial and final states and analyzed the quantitative successes and shortcomings of the theoretical analyses in fitting magnitudes of cross sections, their energy and momentum transfer dependence, and the observed decay correlations. The applications to photoproduction processes which we now discuss make much less stringent demands on the theory since we are concerned only with approximate predictions of fluxes of high energy pions, K mesons, and antibaryons which can then serve as projectiles in subsequent experiments. We are more interested here in the practical use to which these beams can be put than in casting light upon the detailed theoretical nature of the interactions involved.

We consider first charged pion beam production via one-pion exchange as illustrated in Fig. 23. Under kinematical conditions such that a high energy photon of momentum k produces a high energy pion with energy $\omega_q \sim k \gg \mu$, at a small angle $\theta_q \sim \mu/k$, the impact parameter is large $(\sim 1/\mu = 1.4$ fermis) and an almost real pion is exchanged between vertices (A) and (B)

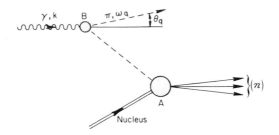

Fig. 23. One-pion-exchange contribution to photoproduction of a charged pion beam.

in Fig. 23. The corresponding contribution (Drell, 1960) to the differential cross section in this very restricted phase space interval is, in the peripheral approximation,

$$d^2\sigma_{\gamma,\pi\pm}(k, \omega_q, \theta_q) = \frac{\alpha}{2\pi} \frac{\sin^2\theta_q}{(1 - \beta_q \cos\theta_q)^2} \frac{d\Omega_q}{4\pi} \frac{\omega_q(k - \omega_q)\,d\omega_q}{k^3} \sigma_{\pi\mp}^{\text{tot}}(k - \omega_q).$$

(VI–1)

The numerator factor $\sin^2\theta_q$ comes from angular momentum conservation since a transversely polarized photon cannot transfer its spin to a pion moving forward; $\sigma_{\pi\mp}^{\text{tot}}$ $(k - \omega_q)$ is the total $\pi^\mp$-proton cross section at a laboratory energy $k - \omega_q$ and is an exact expression of the interaction vertex (B) if we extrapolate to the pion exchange pole at $(k - q)^2 \approx \mu^2$, or $(1 - \beta_q \cos\theta_q) \to 0$. The accuracy of this extrapolation is questionable for nuclear targets with atomic number $A > 1$ in which case the interval of extrapolation from the physical region to the pion exchange pole, $(\sim 2\mu = 300$ MeV), is large compared to the excitation energies of the target instead of being small as we require (Bell, 1964). The accuracy of this approximation for hydrogen targets is however the basic assumption of the peripheral model.

Keeping this reservation in mind we show in Fig. 24 the experimental results for π^- photoproduction from beryllium (Blanpied et al., 1963; Blumenthal et al., 1963). The agreement to within a factor of two near the peak of the theoretical distribution supports the optimism of the peripheral model in its predictions that intense charged pion beams may be produced by high energy electron accelerators. However, the difference between theory and experiment and in particular the failure of the observed angular distribution to drop at the forward angle $\mu/k > \theta_q \to 0$ suggest the importance of the inclusion of other diagrams in addition to the various corrections which have been made to the one-pion-exchange result, Eq. (VI-1), and which are discussed with references by Drell (1965).

A leading candidate to explain this difference is the amplitude for coherent diffraction production of ρ^0 mesons in the forward direction followed by

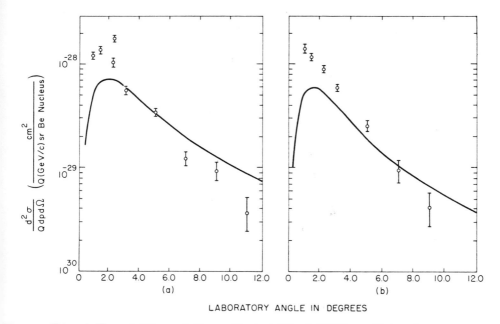

Fig. 24. Comparison of experimental results for π^- photoproduction from beryllium with predictions of the one-pion-exchange calculation [taken from Blumenthal *et al.* (1963)]: (a) $k_{max} = 4.85$ GeV, $p_\pi = 4.0$ GeV/c and (b) $k_{max} = 5.82$ GeV, $p_\pi = 5.0$ GeV/c.

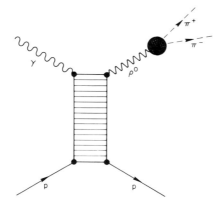

Fig. 25. Coherent diffraction photoproduction of ρ^0 followed by decay into pions.

their decay into a π^+, π^- pair as shown in Fig. 25. A forward diffraction peak in high energy photoproduction of zero strangeness neutral vector mesons is theoretically expected since they have quantum numbers in common with the photon. This peak has also been observed (Crouch, 1964; Lanzerotti, et al., 1965) with a very large cross section, viz.,

$$\left[\frac{d\sigma(k, 0°)}{d\Omega}\right]_{\gamma\rho 0} \simeq A^{1.7}\left[\frac{k^2}{20 \text{ GeV}^2}\right] \text{mb/sr.} \qquad (\text{VI-2})$$

The magnitude of this cross section in hydrogen is in agreement with the predictions of a simple model (Berman and Drell, 1964) and also with dimensional arguments, since

$$\left[\frac{d\sigma(k, 0°)}{d\Omega}\right]_{\gamma\rho 0} \sim \frac{1}{137}\left[\frac{d\sigma(k, 0°)}{d\Omega}\right]_{\pi}$$

where $[[d\sigma(k, 0°)]/d\Omega]_{\pi}$ denotes the forward peak of elastic pion-nucleon scattering. A discussion of the $A^{1.7}$ variation of this result may be found in Drell and Trefil (1966) and Ross and Stodolsky (1966).

The resulting flux of $\pi^{\pm}$ from the ρ^0 decay is readily computed in terms of the observed parameters of the ρ^0-production cross section. It peaks at an angle

$$\theta_{\max} \simeq m_\rho/k[(k - \omega_-)/\omega_-]^{1/2} \qquad (\text{VI-3})$$

where m_ρ is the ρ^0 mass, k the incident photon energy, and ω_- the energy of the pion detected at an angle θ. In the neighborhood of this peak, the cross section may be written, for $k - \omega_- < \omega_-$,

$$\frac{d^2\sigma}{d\omega_- d\Omega} \simeq \left[\left(\frac{d\sigma(k, 0°)}{d\Omega}\right)_{\gamma\rho 0}\right] \frac{3 \exp(-bm_\rho^2/4k^2)}{(\pi b)^{1/2}}$$

$$\times \frac{(\omega_-/k)^{3/2}(1 - \omega_-/k)^{1/2}}{k} \exp\{-b(k/m_\rho)^2(\theta - \theta_{\max})^2\} \qquad (\text{VI-4})$$

where $b \approx 6A^{2/3}$ is a dimensionless parameter fit to the observed width of the ρ^0-diffraction peak.

The resulting pion flux from diffraction production on beryllium targets is computed (Hicks, 1965; Tsai, 1966) to exceed that via the pion exchange, Eq. (VI-I), as shown in Fig. 26 when averaged over the experimental conditions. Since Eq. (VI-4) increases roughly in proportion to $A^{4/3}$ it is reduced relative to the one-pion-exchange result Eq. (VI-I) for hydrogen targets. At the peak angle $\theta_q = \mu/\omega_q$ the one-pion exchange cross section is proportional to k for fixed ratio of pion to photon energy ω_q/k. A similar energy dependence is predicted by Eq. (VI-4) at the peak angle $\theta = \theta_{\max}$ and at sufficiently high energies such that $bm_\rho^2/4k^2 \approx 1.5(m_\rho/k)^2 A^{2/3} < 1$. Their variation with fraction of energy $(1 - \omega_q/k)$ transferred to the observed pion differs, however, and by a study of this dependence together with the angular

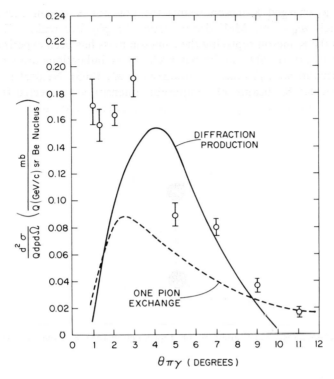

Fig. 26. Comparison of one-pion-exchange and diffraction scattering fit to pion photo-production from beryllium (Hicks, 1965): $p_\pi = 3$ GeV/c and $k_{max} = 3.88$ GeV. [The experimental data were taken from Blumenthal *et al.* (1963).]

and A variation it will be possible to clarify further the relative importance of these two mechanisms for beams.

For pion exchange processes at small angles and high energies, the impact parameter may become as large as $b \sim 1/\mu$. Therefore the magnitude of the cross section at low momentum transfer is little affected by absorption factors of the type discussed in Section IV. At 8 GeV, for example the absorption calculation leads to no reduction in the magnitude of the peak in $\pi p \to \rho p$, in spite of the large collimation produced in the tail. In any case, photo-induced reactions have no initial state absorption factors to reduce the calculated cross sections, and the relevance of absorption factors for multiparticle final states as in Fig. 23 is not theoretically established or observed (Jones, 1965). No such absorption factors appear in the theoretical models of the diffraction production which calculate ratios to observed strong interaction diffraction processes. Therefore these pion beam predictions should be applicable at higher energies than shown in Fig. 24.

Turning to charged K-meson beams the pole for K-meson exchange is approximately $m_K \approx 500$ MeV distant from the physical region. Equation (VI-1) with the K meson replacing the π-meson mass has been experimentally checked only very roughly so far but preliminary indications are similar to what was seen in pion production (Blanpied *et al.*, 1965). Neutral K beams, and in particular K_2 beams, of comparable intensity are expected from the K*-exchange amplitude (Fig. 27) as has been analyzed in detail and with full

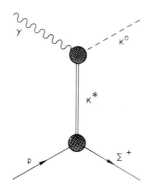

Fig. 27. K*-exchange contribution to photoproduction of a K^0 beam in the process $\gamma + p \to k^0 + \Sigma^+$.

inclusion of final state absorption factors (Drell and Jacob, 1965; Tsai, 1966).

Finally, we make some predictions on the production of antinucleon or antibaryon beams by comparison with the observation of backward peaks in pion-nucleon scattering by Orear *et al.* (1965) and their analysis by Trefil (1966). The basic mechanism in the calculation of

$$\gamma + p \to \bar{p} + \text{(anything)}$$

as in

$$\pi + p \to p + \pi$$

is assumed to be baryon, or baryon resonance exchange, but the details of mechanism differ in each case in two important ways. First, the photo-induced process has no initial state absorption, and all final states are summed over. Thus, the effect of absorptive corrections is expected to be much smaller than in the pion-nucleon case. Second, the product of the electric charge part of the electromagnetic vertex at A in Fig. 28 and the nucleon propagator will not change as the nucleon goes off-mass-shell, whereas form factor effects will influence the pion-nucleon case. However, even if we retain the full final state absorption factors and the form factor reductions which were used

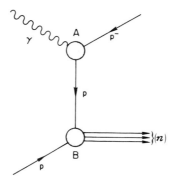

Fig. 28. Nucleon exchange contribution to photoproduction of an antiproton beam.

in Trefil's fit to the backward pion-nucleon scattering we are led to the prediction of an antinucleon or antibaryon beam of $\sim 10^{-30}$ cm^2/sr-GeV at ~ 15 GeV energy. Similar intensities are computed (Berman and Drell, 1966) for antibaryon beams via the diffraction mechanism in Fig. 29, but these numbers

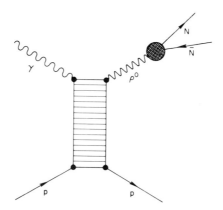

Fig. 29. Coherent diffraction photoproduction of ρ^0 followed by decay into a proton-antiproton pair.

are highly sensitive to the assumed form factors for the virtual ρ-nucleon or ρ-baryon vertices. These numbers should of course be understood as little better than a dimensional guide, but they lead to tremendous antibaryon beam fluxes from accelerators such as the Stanford linear accelerator and are therefore of some practical importance.

ACKNOWLEDGMENTS

The authors would like to thank their many colleagues for helpful discussions during the preparation of this manuscript. Part of the work was done while one of us (A.C.H.) was a member of the Rutherford High Energy Laboratory, Chilton, and the Clarendon Laboratory, Oxford, England, and the hospitality afforded during this period is gratefully acknowledged.

REFERENCES

Aachen-Berlin-Birmingham-Bonn-Hamburg-London (I.C.)-München Collaboration (1965). *Nuovo Cimento* **35**, 659.

Alexander, G., Haber, B., Shapira, A., and Yekutieli, G. (1966). *Phys. Rev.* **144**, 1122.

Amaldi, U., and Selleri, F. (1964). *Nuovo Cimento* **31**, 360.

Amati, D., Fubini, S., and Stanghellini, A. (1962). *Nuovo Cimento* **26**, 896.

Arnold, R. C. (1964). *Phys. Rev.* **136**, B1388.

Arnold, R. C. (1965). *Phys. Rev.* **140**, B1022.

Ashmore, A., Range, W. H., Taylor, R. T., Townes, B. M., Castillejo, L., and Peierls, R. F. (1962). *Nucl. Phys.* **36**, 258.

Baker, M., and Blankenbecler, R. (1962). *Phys. Rev.* **128**, 415.

Ball, J. S., and Frazer, W. R. (1965). *Phys. Rev. Letters* **14**, 746.

Baltay, C., Fowler, E. C., Sandweiss, J., Sanford, J. R., Taft, H. D., Culwick, B. B., Fowler, W. B., Kopp, J. K., Louttit, R. I., Shutt, R. P., Thorndike, A. M., and Webster, M. S. (1962). *Proc. 11th Intern. Conf. High-Energy Phys., Geneva*, (CERN), p. 233.

Bander, M., and Shaw, G. L. (1965). *Phys. Rev.* **139**, B956.

Barger, V., and Ebel, M. (1965). *Phys. Rev.* **138**, B1148.

Bell, J. S. (1964). *Phys. Rev. Letters* **13**, 57.

Berman, S. M., and Drell, S. D. (1964). *Phys. Rev.* **133**, B791.

Berman, S. M., and Drell, S. D. (1966). Unpublished.

Blankenbecler, R., and Goldberger, M. L. (1962). *Phys. Rev.* **126**, 766.

Blanpied, W. A., Greenberg, J. S., Hughes, V. W., Lu, D. C., and Minehart, R. C. (1963). *Phys. Rev. Letters* **11**, 477.

Blanpied, W. A., Greenberg, J. S., Hughes, V. W., Kitching, P., Lu, D. C., and Minehart, R. C. (1965). *Phys. Rev. Letters* **14**, 741.

Blumenthal, R. B., Faissler, W. L., Joseph, P. M., Lanzerotti, L. J., Pipkin, F. M., Stairs, D. G., Ballam, J., DeStaebler, H., Jr., and Odian, A. (1963). *Phys. Rev. Letters* **11**, 496.

Bugg, D. V. (1963). *Phys. Letters* **7**, 365.

Cambridge Bubble Chamber Group (1965). *Proc. Intern. Symp. Electron Photon Interaction High Energies, Hamburg*, **2**, p. 1.

Chamberlain, O. (1960). *Proc. 10th Intern. Conf. High-Energy Phys., Rochester* 655.

Chew, G. F. (1958). *Phys. Rev.* **112**, 1380.

Chew, G. F., and Low, F. E. (1959). *Phys. Rev.* **113**, 1640.

Chew, G. F., and Mandelstam, S. (1960). *Phys. Rev.* **119**, 467.

Chew, G. F., and Mandelstam, S. (1961). *Nuovo Cimento* **19**, 752.

Clementel, E., and Villi, C. (1956). *Nuovo Cimento* **4**, 1207.

Crouch, H. R. (1964). *Phys. Rev. Letters* **13**, 640.

Dalitz, R. H. (1961). *Rev. Mod. Phys.* **33**, 471.

Dar, A. (1964). *Phys. Rev. Letters* **13**, 91.

Dar, A., and Tobocman, W. (1964). *Phys. Rev. Letters* **12**, 511.

Dar, A., Kugler, M., Dothan, Y., and Nussinov, S. (1964). *Phys. Rev. Letters* **12**, 82.

Daudin, A., Jabiol, M. A., Kochowski, C., Lewin, C., Selleri, F., Mongelli, S., Romano, A., and Waloscheck, P. (1963). *Phys. Letters* **7**, 125.
Dietz, K., and Pilkuhn, H. (1965a). *Nuovo Cimento* **37**, 1561.
Dietz, K., and Pilkuhn, H. (1965b). *Nuovo Cimento* **39**, 928.
Drell, S. D. (1960). *Phys. Rev. Letters* **5**, 278.
Drell, S. D. (1961). *Rev. Mod. Phys.* **33**, 458.
Drell, S. D. (1965). *Proc. Intern. Symp. Electron Photon Interactions High Energies, Hamburg*, **1**, p. 17.
Drell, S. D., and Jacob, M. (1965). *Phys, Rev.* **138**, B1312.
Drell, S. D., and Trefil, J. (1966). *Phys. Rev. Letters* **16**, 552. Erratum: *Phys. Rev. Letters* **16**, 832.
Durand, L. III, and Chiu, Y. T. (1964a). *Phys. Rev. Letters* **12**, 399. Erratum: *Phys. Rev. Letters* **13**, 45.
Durand, L. III, and Chiu, Y. T. (1964b). *Lectures Theoret. Phys.* **7b**, 206.
Durand, L. III, and Chiu, Y. T. (1965a). *Phys. Rev.* **137**, B1530.
Durand, L. III, and Chiu, Y. T. (1965b). *Phys. Rev.* **139**, B646.
Ferrari, E., and Selleri, F. (1962). *Nuovo Cimento Suppl.* **24**, 453.
Ferrari, E., and Selleri, F. (1963). *Nuovo Cimento* **27**, 1450. Erratum: *Nuovo Cimento* **28**, 454.
Foley, K. J., Gilmore, R. S., Jones, R. S., Lindenbaum, S. J., Love, W. A., Ozaki, S., Willen, E. H., Yamada, R., and Yuan, L. C. L. (1965). *Phys. Rev. Letters* **14**, 862.
Glauber, R. J. (1959). *Lectures Theoret. Phys.* **1**, 315.
Goebel, C. (1958). *Phys. Rev. Letters* **1**, 337.
Goldberger, M. L. (1955). *Phys. Rev.* **99**, 979.
Goldberger, M. L., and Watson, K. M. (1964). "Collision Theory." Wiley, New York.
Goldhaber, A. S. (1964). *Phys. Rev.* **135**, B508.
Goldhaber, G., Chinowsky, W., Goldhaber, S., Lee, W., and O'Halloran, T. (1963). *Phys. Letters* **6**, 62.
Gottfried, K., and Jackson, J. D. (1964a). *Phys. Letters* **8**, 144.
Gottfried, K., and Jackson, J. D. (1964b). *Nuovo Cimento* **33**, 309.
Gottfried, K., and Jackson, J. D. (1964c). *Nuovo Cimento* **34**, 735.
Griffiths, D., and Saperstein, A. M. (1965). Preprint, Argonne National Laboratory.
Hagopian, V., Selove, W., Alitti, J., Baton, J. P., and Neveu-René, M. (1966). *Phys. Rev.*, **145**, 1128.
Hamilton, J., and Woolcock, W. S. (1963). *Rev. Mod. Phys.* **35**, 737.
Heitler, W. (1944). "The Quantum Theory of Radiation." Oxford Univ. Press, London and New York.
Hicks, N. (1965). Unpublished.
Högaasen, H., and Högaasen, J. (1965a). *Nuovo Cimento* **39**, 941.
Högaasen, H., and Högaasen, J. (1965b). *Nuovo Cimento* **40A**, 560.
Högaasen, H., Högaasen, J., Keyser, R., and Svensson, B. E. Y. (1966). *Nuovo Cimento*, **42A**, 323.
Islam, M. M. (1963). *Nuovo Cimento* **30**, 579.
Islam, M. M., and Piñon, R. (1963). *Nuovo Cimento* **30**, 837.
Jackson, J. D. (1965). *Rev. Mod. Phys.* **37**, 484.
Jackson, J. D., Donohue, J. T., Gottfried, K., Keyser, R., and Svensson, B. E. Y. (1965). *Phys. Rev.* **139**, B428.
Jacob, M., and Wick, G. C. (1959). *Ann. Phys.* (*N.Y.*) **7**, 404.
James, F. E., and Kraybill, H. L. (1966). *Phys. Rev.*, **142**, 896.
Jones, L. W. (1965). *Phys. Rev. Letters* **14**, 186.

Kumar, R. C., and Squires, E. J. (1965). *Nuovo Cimento* **40A**, 756.

Lanzerotti, L. J., Blumenthal, R. B., Ehn, D. C., Faissler, W. L., Joseph, P. M., Pipkin, F. M., Randolph, J. K., Russell, J. S., Stairs, D. G., and Tannenbaum, J. (1965). *Phys. Rev. Letters* **15**, 210.

Locher, M. P., and Sandhas, W. (1965). Preprint, Univ. of Bonn.

Omnes, R. (1965). *Phys. Rev.* **137**, B649.

Orear, J., Rubinstein, R., Scarl, D. B., White, D. H., Krisch, A. D., Frisken, W. R., Read, A. L., and Ruderman, H. (1965). *Phys. Rev. Letters* **15**, 309.

Ringland, G. A., and Phillips, R. J. N. (1964). *Phys. Letters* **12**, 62.

Ross, M. H., and Shaw, G. L. (1964). *Phys. Rev. Letters* **12**, 627.

Ross, M. H., and Stodolsky, L. (1966). Preprint, Brookhaven National Laboratory.

Saclay-Orsay-Bari-Bologna Collaboration (1964a). *Nuovo Cimento* **29**, 515.

Saclay-Orsay-Bari-Bologna Collaboration (1964b). *Intern. Conf. High Energy Phys.*, *Dubna* Abstract VII–42 (unpublished.)

Salzman, F., and Salzman, G. (1960). *Phys. Rev.* **120**, 599.

Selleri, F. (1964). *Lectures Theoret. Phys.* **7b**, 183.

Shaw, G. L., and Wong, D. Y. (1963). *Phys. Rev.* **129**, 1379.

Sopkovich, N. J. (1962a). Dissertation, Carnegie Inst. of Technology, unpublished.

Sopkovich, N. J. (1962b). *Nuovo Cimento* **26**, 186.

Squires, E. J. (1964). *Nuovo Cimento* **34**, 1328.

Squires, E. J. (1965a). *Nuovo Cimento* **39**, 300.

Squires, E. J. (1965b). *Nuovo Cimento*, to be published.

Stodolsky, J., and Sakurai, J. J. (1963). *Phys. Rev. Letters* **11**, 90.

Svensson, B. E. Y. (1965a). *Nuovo Cimento* **37**, 714.

Svensson, B. E. Y. (1965b). *Nuovo Cimento* **39**, 66.

Trefil, J. (1966). *Phys. Rev.*, **148**, 1452.

Treiman, S. B., and Yang, C. N. (1962). *Phys. Rev. Letters* **8**, 140.

Tsai, Y. S. (1966). SLAC Users Handbook, Stanford Linear Accelerator Center, Section D.

Watson, H. D. D. (1965). *Phys. Letters* **17**, 72.

Wigner, E. P. (1955). *Ann. Math.* **62**, 548.

INTERACTIONS AT VERY HIGH ENERGIES

J. M. Kidd

I. Introduction

The cosmic radiation is an important source of astronomical information and has an important role in astrophysical processes. The interactions of the cosmic radiation with the atmosphere are the only source of high energy electromagnetic and nuclear interactions. Both the primary radiation and its propagation in the atmosphere have been studied for several decades, but neither is well understood even today. The study of very high energy interactions is important because a study of the cosmic radiation presupposes a precise knowledge of the properties of very high energy interactions; all information of the initial state of a singly charged particle must come from the interaction. It would be very surprising indeed if the energy dependence of nuclear interactions were so weak that the properties remained unchanged in the eight orders of magnitude of energy available in the cosmic radiation.

It might appear that after three decades, the understanding of this field would be practically complete. For many reasons, however, measurements are difficult at very high energies, the experimental conditions being vastly different from those found at lower energies. In experiments with cosmic rays it is not possible to achieve the detail and subtlety characteristic of those with accelerators. This is primarily due to the low intensity and isotropic flux of the primary particles, the large spread in energy, the lack of observable quantities, and the difficulty of collecting large numbers of events.

The intensity distribution of the primary radiation is given approximately by

$$N(0, E) \, dE = 23500 \, E^{-(\gamma + 1)} \, dE \, (\text{nucl/m}^2 \text{ sr sec}) \qquad \gamma = 1.67, \quad E \lesssim 10^6 \text{ GeV}$$

(I-1)

where E is expressed in GeV, and the notation $N(0, E)$ implies that the intensity is measured at zero depth in the atmosphere. The intensity falls off rapidly with increasing energy. Most of the radiation is protons, but there is a heavier component. The flux of α particles and heavy nuclei amounts to ≈ 5–10% of the total cosmic radiation flux above a given energy per nucleon. In contrast however, the flux of multiply charged particles above a given total energy is approximately equal to the flux of protons and contributions come from the entire charge spectrum at least up to $Z \sim 90$ (Fowler *et al.*, 1967).

At very high energies, there are fewer observable quantities. The velocities of the charged particles are usually relativistic and their momenta too large to measure by magnetic deflection. In this case, it is not even possible to distinguish their masses. This difficulty does not apply to γ rays, because they can be measured with greater accuracy at cosmic ray energies than in bubble chambers at accelerator energies. Although the paths of γ rays are not directly visible as tracks, they convert into electron showers which give a measure of their energy to $\sim 25\%$ for $E > 50$ GeV.

Particles from the forward hemisphere in the center-of-mass system (c.m.s.) are thrown into an extremely small cone in the laboratory system. For example, at 10^6 GeV, the median angle is 1.4×10^{-3} rad, and individual tracks may form angles as small as 10^{-5} rad.

The multiplicity of the interactions is large and in individual cases may vary from one to well over one hundred. Even if the secondary particles could be measured with an accuracy comparable to that in bubble chambers, the mathematical analysis would be formidable, especially if resonant states and final state interactions were included.

These features may be seen in Figs. 1 and 2. In Fig. 1 a very high energy interaction and the ensuing electromagnetic (E.M.) cascade are shown. In Fig. 2 an electromagnetic cascade initiated by a γ ray is shown. Most γ rays are from the decay of neutral π mesons.

Many features of the cosmic radiation and the highest energy interactions

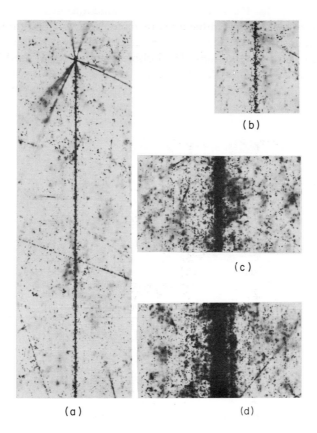

Fig. 1. An example of a nuclear interaction with a multiplicity of over 100 and $E_0 \sim 2$ $\times 10^{14}$ eV. This event was found in an emulsion chamber exposed for 1100 hours at ~ 220 gm/cm² in a Comet airplane: (a) origin (b) 2 mm (c) 2 radiation lengths, and (d) 5 radiation lengths. The development of the electromagnetic cascade may be seen in (b), (c), and (d). This interaction is part of an extensive air shower observed in this chamber (Perkins, 1960).

directly observable must be studied at very high altitudes ($\gtrsim 100{,}000$ ft.) before the primary radiation can interact appreciably with the atmosphere. For example, in order to ensure nucleon primaries, experiments must be made at very high altitudes. This restricts the mass and size of the apparatus. At mountain and airplane altitudes, where experiments have been done, the events are not easily interpretable because of the large background produced for example, by bremsstrahlung and interactions of secondary charged π-meson primaries.

The techniques for the study of nuclear interactions at cosmic ray energies were developed with these difficulties in mind, and will be briefly reviewed. Table I contains the characteristics of the detectors allowing direct observation of very high energy interactions. The bubble chamber is not used because the "latent image" is so short-lived that it is necessary to know when particles will enter the chamber—a condition that cannot be fulfilled by the cosmic

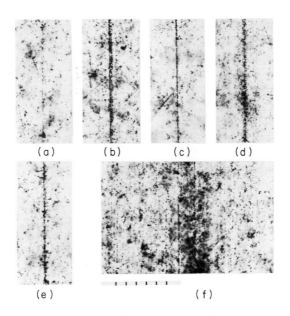

Fig. 2. An example obtained by the Bristol group of an electromagnetic cascade initiated by a photon with energy $\sim 1.5 \times 10^{13}$ eV from the same emulsion chamber: (a) 2 cm, (b) 6 cm, (c) 3 cm, (d) 8 cm, (e) 4 cm, and (f) 8 cm emulsion, 4 cm lead.

radiation. Above energies of $\sim 10^{15}$ eV (extensive air showers), the detectors are arrays usually made of combinations of Geiger-Muller (G.M.), scintillation and Cherenkov counters and absorbers.

Below $\sim 10^{12}$ eV, the best measurements have been done with large installations that can still employ magnetic deflection. The "total absorption calorimeter" (Grigorov et al., 1960a) is essentially two cloud chambers on top of a large number of counters and absorbers (the calorimeter). The first cloud chamber allows the primary particle to be photographed and the second the products of the interaction. All secondaries then pass into the "calorimeter" which gives the total energy (E_0).

TABLE I

DETECTORS FOR DIRECT OBSERVATIONS OF INDIVIDUAL INTERACTIONS

Detector	Maximum altitude	Practical energy upper limit (eV)	Spatial resolution (μ)	Effective angular resolution (rad)	Observable quantities
Pure nuclear emulsion	Balloon ($\sim 100,000$ ft)	$\lesssim 10^{15}$	~ 0.5	$\approx 10^{-4}$	Charge of primary geometrical quantities total energy in E.M. cascades
Emulsion chambers	Balloon	$\lesssim 5 \times 10^{15}$	~ 0.5	$\approx 10^{-5}$	Occasionally charge of primary geometrical quantities energy of individual γ rays
Spark chamber	Mountain ($\sim 20,000$ ft)	$\approx 10^{12}$	~ 400	$\approx 10^{-3}$	Geometrical quantities of charged particles and momentum
Cloud chamber	Mountain	$\approx 10^{12}$	~ 400	$\approx 5 \times 10^{-3}$	Geometrical quantities of charged particles and momentum
Total absorption calorimeter	Mountain	$\approx 10^{12}$	~ 400	$\approx 5 \times 10^{-3}$	Geometrical quantities of charged particles, momentum, and charge and energy of primary

Particles emitted into the forward hemisphere of the c.m.s. appear in the laboratory system as particles of great momenta and at small angles to the direction of the primary. On the other hand, particles emitted into the backward hemisphere of the c.m.s. appear in the forward hemisphere in the laboratory system but with much smaller momenta and moving at larger angles to the primary direction. In nucleon-nucleon interactions there is, on the average, symmetry between the properties of the interactions as seen in the laboratory system and as seen in the "mirror" system relative to which the incident particle is at rest. Therefore, by studying the more easily identified and measured low momentum wide-angle tracks, the average properties of the whole interaction can be deduced. This is a very effective technique, useful up to energies somewhat in excess of 10^{12} eV. If, however, the incident and target particles are different, a systematic lack of symmetry between the laboratory and mirror systems can be expected.

There is also a proposed experiment (Alvarez, 1964) which uses magnetic deflection in this energy region. This would be a balloon-borne apparatus (80,000–100,000 ft) which briefly consists of the following: (a) a Cherenkov counter to select particles with $E_0 > 100$ GeV and "fire" the spark chambers, (b) an associated spark chamber-emulsion arrangement with transverse magnetic field which allows the momentum and direction of the primary to be determined with very good resolution, (c) a two-meter liquid hydrogen target to produce p–p interactions, and (d) an additional spark chamber with transverse magnetic field for the analysis of the products of the interaction. The fields are produced by superconducting magnets because of restrictions of weight. This experiment would study interactions in the range $10^{11} < E_0 \lesssim 10^{12}$ eV.

Above $\sim 10^{12}$ eV, the high resolving power of nuclear emulsion is essential. The detectors may be pure emulsion or composite structures of nuclear emulsion and other materials (lead, tungsten, carbon). This technique is normally used up to $\sim 10^{15}$ eV. Above this energy the intensity is so low that it is difficult to obtain a useful number of events in a direct manner. Composite structures with materials of different Z are used to vary the mean free path of γ rays. For example, after the interaction, a large pathlength of low density, low Z material is desirable in order to allow the secondary particles to separate from each other without a large probability of interacting. When they are sufficiently separated to make analysis possible, a high Z material is desirable to enable the E.M. cascade to develop quickly so that each γ ray forms an easily measurable, tightly bound core of electrons. In a homogeneous detector (pure emulsion), the nature of the primary can be determined when a nuclear interaction occurs in the detector. The total energy in γ rays ($\Sigma E\gamma$) can be measured, but not the energy of the individual γ rays. In a composite detector, the products are allowed to separate and can be measured independently. In favorable cases it is still possible to determine the nature of the primary.

At still higher energies, knowledge is indirect. It is impractical to observe these particles directly. A detector of one square meter at the top of the atmosphere would collect an average of only one cosmic ray of energy 10^{19} eV every $\sim 100,000$ years! The nuclear cascades initiated by the highest energy cosmic rays develop in the atmosphere (a low density, low Z medium) and can be easily detected at sea level or mountain altitudes. A large extensive air shower may have as many as 10^9 particles and lateral dimensions of the order of kilometers. With extensive air shower arrays the lateral distribution and the arrival direction may be observed, and the primary energy and the number of particles may be inferred. Indirect methods have been used to estimate the nature of the primary. Air showers have been observed with an energy approaching 10^{20} eV. They are important for deciding among the possible acceleration mechanisms of the primary cosmic radiation and the primary energy spectrum as well as some features of the interactions.

For these reasons, the study of interactions at very high energy is not advanced to the point at which a well-developed theory may be applied. There are theories which might be applicable, (Feinberg and Chernavskii, 1964, and Kobayashi and Namiki, 1965). It is not even known whether these interactions are central or peripheral, although there is some evidence that they are predominantly peripheral. In the meantime models must be used.

The isobar model of high energy interactions will be examined here as a possible explanation of some observed properties of very high energy interactions and as a basis for the comparison of other explanations and models. First, the characteristics of nucleon-nucleon and nucleon-nucleus collisions will be briefly reviewed at accelerator and cosmic ray energies.

Even at accelerator energies, *pp* interactions are not well understood above about 4 GeV. Above this energy there is no general agreement about which nucleon isobars are excited, although there is clear evidence from selected events that the isobar process plays an important role. Since there is a good deal of work to be done at accelerator energies, it will be some time before definitive answers about the importance of the isobar process will be available at very high energies.

The isobar process very probably occurs at all energies. At low energy, nucleon isobars are produced—sometimes copiously. Then, whenever in a system in which the relative velocities of a nucleon and one of the produced pions is small, it is reasonable that nucleon isobars will be produced. It is of some interest to know how important this process is at cosmic ray energies. Since the present data are incomplete, especially at cosmic ray energies, this chapter will concern itself with a summary of the problem and a discussion of likely solutions.

II. Experimental Situation

A. Low Energy Characteristics

At accelerator energies, most work on *pp* interactions has been done below 4 GeV, primarily in hydrogen bubble chambers. Even at these energies, *pp* interactions are not completely understood. Up to 4 GeV, single and double pion production proceeds largely via the first isobar of the πN system, $M^*_{3/2,3/2}$ (1238). The contribution of higher isobars is less than several per cent. These collisions are peripheral—characterized by low momentum transfer—and are well described by the one-pion-exchange model.

Above 4 GeV, there are many studies of pion and kaon production at various angles, and these remain the only source of information on isobar production until appropriate bubble chamber experiments up to 30 GeV have been analyzed. Most of these experiments were done primarily for the calculation of neutrino spectra and secondary particles were not measured at momenta sufficiently close to that of the primary. Experiments which measure the secondary particles near 0° are most useful in the investigation of the isobar process, since production falls off exponentially with the momentum transfer t and therefore with angle. An experiment has recently been done which measured the momentum spectra of all produced particles at 0 and 100 mrad, at primary proton momenta of 18.8 and 23.1 GeV/c (Dekkers *et al.*, 1965).

The pion spectra are shown at 0° in Fig. 3. The peak in the π^+ spectrum is what would be expected from a large contribution by the pions from isobar decay. The π^- spectrum, on the other hand, is more nearly that predicted from phase-space considerations albeit with a slightly larger tail. In these collisions with a low multiplicity it is apparent that isobars contribute predominantly positive pions. This, and the smaller number of negative pions, implies that the incident nucleon does not usually change its charge when excited.

The experiment by Cocconi *et al.* (1963) first indicated that the excitation of the $M^*_{3/2,3/2}$ (1238) isobar, which dominated below 4 GeV, might decrease rapidly with increasing energy and apparently vanish above ~ 8 GeV. There is other evidence that the $M_{3/2,3/2}$ (1238) isobar is not strongly excited at higher energies, although this is still an open question. There is evidence at 24 GeV, (Hansen, 1965) that this isobar does not vanish in all channels. It appears that the isobars $M_{1/2,3/2}$ (1512) and $M_{1/2,5/2}$ (1588) make the largest contribution at 18.8 and 23.1 GeV/c. The strange isobars Y_0^* (1520) and Y_0^* (1815) seemingly do not contribute significantly.

The nature of the process of exciting isobars is not well understood but it has been suggested (Dekkers *et al.*, 1965) that the probability of changing the orbital angular momentum by one or more units would be reduced if the

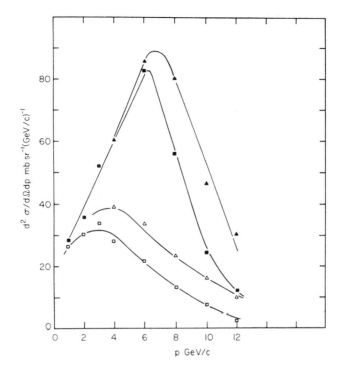

Fig. 3. The momentum spectrum of positive and negative pions at 0 mrad, [from the experiment of Dekkers *et al.* (1965)]: (■) $\pi^+ p_0 = 18.8$ GeV/c, (□) $\pi^- p_0 = 18.8$ GeV/c, (▲) $\pi^+ p_0 = 23.1$ GeV/c, and (△) $\pi^- p_0 = 23.1$ GeV/c.

nucleon did not change direction after the collision (0 mrad). The bulk of the positive pions observed at 0 mrad could then be explained in two ways. Either the isobars which are observed in the detector (0 ± 8 mrad) are produced at small but finite angles or consist solely of the state $M^*_{1/2,1/2}$ (1480) which could proceed without a change in angular momentum.

It is the large momentum pions—the tail of the momentum spectrum— that will be helpful in estimating the importance of nucleon isobars. As will be seen later, the decay pion (or pions) from an isobar moving in the forward direction is expected to have a momentum that can be a significant fraction of the energy of the nucleon isobar. In the experiment by Lundy *et al.* (1965) at 13.4 GeV/c, the momentum of the secondary pions and kaons was measured up to $\sim 0.9\, p_0$, the incident momentum. Figures 4 and 5 show the momentum spectra of positive and negative pions at different angles. It is evident that at this energy the secondary pions are distributed exponentially and have tails extending up to the highest measured momenta. The isobar hypothesis is, however, sufficient to explain this data.

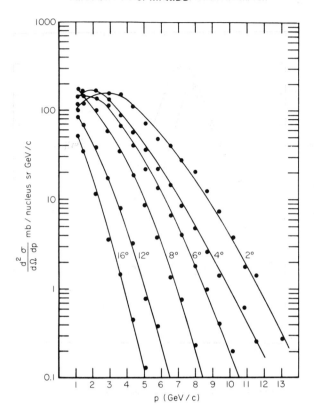

Fig. 4. The momentum spectrum of positive ions from the experiment of Lundy *et al.* (1965).

In summary, the data available at accelerator energies indicate that below 4 GeV, *pp* interactions are peripheral and that pion production proceeds largely by the excitation of one or both nucleons to the first isobar of the πN system. Above 4 GeV the interpretation must be considered tentative and must await an improvement in the experimental situation. The evidence is not striking, but the isobar hypothesis is able to explain the present data. The best evidence for the importance of the isobar process at the moment is the momentum spectrum of pions (Fig. 3) which gives a distribution characteristic of isobar decay.

B. High Energy Characteristics

The description of nuclear interactions above 100 GeV is necessarily different from that at lower energies for the reasons described in the introduction. At very high energy, where the nature of the primary is often unknown and the few observable quantities can only rarely be measured as accurately

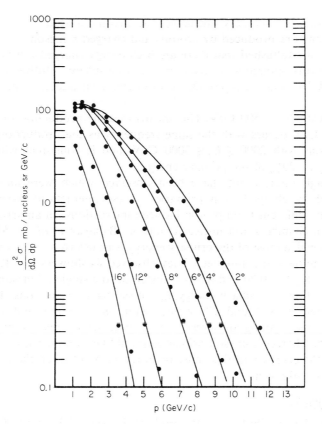

Fig. 5. The momentum spectrum of negative pions from the experiment of Lundy *et al.*
(1965).

as those at accelerator energies, the interactions are necessarily described in
terms of a small number of parameters and their variation with the primary
energy.

Before reviewing the characteristics of interactions at very high energies, it
is worthwhile mentioning the primary radiation and its interaction with the
atmosphere. The primary radiation is mostly protons with $\sim 10\%$ alpha
particles and a few per cent heavier nuclei. The interactions produced by the
primary radiation with the atmosphere change the composition of the radiation with depth in the atmosphere. The energies and intensities of the proton,
alpha, and heavy components change with respect to one another, both
because the interaction length of the heavier components is shorter than that
of the protons and "fragmentation" increases the number of protons and
alpha particles. Additional components are also formed, for example, the
electron, muon, and pion components. While at balloon altitudes, the

composition is essentially unchanged, at airplane altitudes and below, most interactions are produced by protons and charged π mesons.

It is well established that there are high energy charged π mesons capable of producing interactions deep in the atmosphere. Duthie *et al.* (1962) observed that near the top of the atmosphere, the production rate per gm/cm^2 for pions with $E > 500$ GeV is 7% of the production rate of nuclear interactions with $E_0 > 500$ GeV. This means that the production of pions with $E > 500$ GeV occurs with the same frequency as the production of nuclear interactions with $2000 \lesssim E_0 \lesssim 3000$ GeV, and is consistent with one pion receiving 15–20% of the primary energy.

Although rarer, events have been observed which were most probably produced by charged pion primaries. These interactions have characteristics quite different from proton induced interactions. In an arrangement of ionization chambers and nuclear emulsion, Babayan *et al.* (1963a,b) found events in which most of the primary energy is transferred, via a small number of pions, to the soft component. They observed six showers with $K_{\pi^0}E_0 > 2 \times 10^{12}$ eV, $\langle K_{\pi^0} \rangle \sim 0.70$ and $0.5E_0$ transferred to a single π^0 meson where K_{π^0} is the fraction of primary energy E_0 appearing in π^0 mesons. In a similar arrangement they found 279 events with $\langle K_{\pi^0} \rangle = 0.68$ and $\langle K \rangle = 0.81$. These events ("young air showers") occurred with a relative probability of 0.10–0.15. Charged π-meson primaries should be as numerous as γ rays, but at twice the energy and this must be borne in mind when the nature of the primary is unknown.

1. *Multiplicity*

Ideally the distribution of the multiplicity should be made for nucleon-nucleon collisions alone. Unfortunately this is not possible. Attempts have been made to separate nucleon-nucleon collisions by choosing interactions with $N_h = 0$ or $N_h = 0, 1$ (N_h is the number of black and grey tracks). While hydrogen is the most abundant element in emulsion, its cross section represents only about 3% of the total for protons. The observed number of events with $N_h = 0, 1$ is 2–3 times too many and this almost certainly represents glancing collisions on heavier nuclei (Ag, Br). Then, $N_h = 0, 1$ represents a heavily biased sample and can lead to systematic errors in the interpretation of the multiplicity. Another possibility is to consider $N_h < 6$. This sample includes, in addition, most of the collisions with light nuclei (C, N, O), and the fractional contamination by the glancing collision with heavier nuclei is less. This represents, on the average, a sample of lighter nuclei with better statistics. Figures 6 and 7 show two multiplicity distributions: one for $N_h \leqslant 2$ at cosmic ray energies, and the other for $N_h \leqslant 5$. It should be noted that there is a fairly large uncertainty in the mean energy of the last two points in both distributions.

The distribution about the mean value is large. Fowler and Perkins (1964)

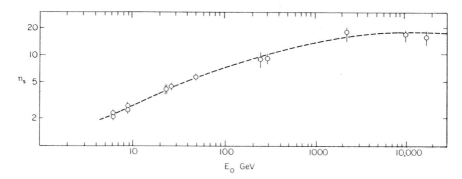

Fig. 6. Mean shower particle multiplicity n_s as a function of the primary energy E_0 from Malhotra (1963a,b). Below $E_0 = 25$ GeV, the data are from accelerator experiments: Bogachev *et al.* (1960) and Beliakov *et al.* (1958) at 9 GeV; Cvijanovich *et al.* (1961); Baudinet-Robinet *et al.* (1962), and Dodd *et al.* (1961) at 25 GeV. At cosmic ray energies: 200–300 GeV, Lohrmann, *et al.* (1961) and Guseva *et al.* (1961). The high energy points are the combined results ($N_h \leqslant 2$) of the Bristol group, the Chicago group, and the ICEF Collaboration (1961).

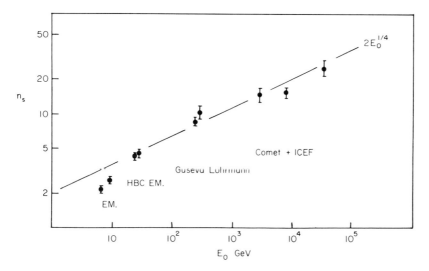

Fig. 7. Mean shower particle multiplicity n_s as a function of the primary energy E_0 from Fowler and Perkins (1964). Below $E_0 = 30$ GeV, the data are the result of accelerator experiments: Berkeley, 6.2 GeV; Dubna, 9 GeV; CERN, 23 and 24 GeV; Lohrmann *et al.* (1961) and Guseva *et al.* (1961), 200–300 GeV. The high energy points ($E_0 > 10^3$ GeV) are the combined results ($N_h \leqslant 5$) of the Bristol Comet stack events, and the ICEF Collaboration. The primary energy in these events was taken as 10 times the energy in the resulting electromagnetic cascade.

estimated that the r.m.s. fluctuations are about half the mean value. Unfortunately, the data do not allow the dependence of the multiplicity on the primary energy to be determined below $\sim 10^{13}$ eV. The data cannot distinguish between a dependence of $aE_0^{1/4}$ or $(\log E_0)^b$, nor, of course, can it exclude a dependence of the form $a + bE_0^{1/2}$. In fact, all that can be said at the moment is that the multiplicity is higher than at machine energies and is rising.

2. *Angular Distributions*

Any knowledge of the energy of the primary particle must come from studying the interaction that it produces. A common method is to assume a "fore" and "aft" symmetry in the c.m.s. and to infer the primary energy from the angular distribution of the secondary particles. This method tends to overestimate the primary energy in individual cases. A composite angular distribution, which includes the angular distributions of the secondary interactions produced by fragments when the primary is a heavy nucleus, tends to decrease the overestimate. The coordinate system $x = \log \tan \theta$ (θ is the angle between the primary and secondary directions in the laboratory system) is normally used. If there is symmetry in the c.m.s. of the interaction, the distribution of $\log \tan \theta$ is symmetric about the value of $\log \tan \theta = \log 1/\gamma_{\text{c.m.s.}}$.

In order to interpret angular distributions, it is necessary to know how

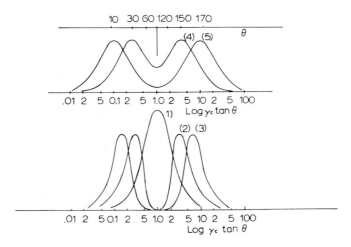

Fig. 8. The different types of calculated angular distributions in the variable $x = \log \tan \theta$ from Powell *et al.* (1959): (1) isotropic, (2) $\cos^n \theta$, $n = 4$, (3) $\cos^n \theta$, $n = 20$, (4) $\gamma = 1.5$, and (5) $\gamma = 4.0$. Distribution (1) corresponds to isotropic emission from a center at rest in the c.m.s., while (2) and (3) correspond to emission proportional to $\cos^4 \theta$ and $\cos^{20} \theta$, respectively. Distributions (4) and (5) are those expected from an isotropic emission of two centers recoiling in opposite directions in the c.m.s. with $\gamma = 1.5$ and 4.0, respectively.

different types of emission appear in this coordinate system. In Fig. 8 distribution (1) corresponds to isotropic emission from a center at rest in the c.m.s., while (2) and (3) correspond to emission proportional to $\cos^4\theta$ and $\cos^{20}\theta$, respectively. Distributions (4) and (5) are those expected from an isotropic emission of two centers recoiling in opposite directions in the c.m.s. with $\gamma = 1.5$ and 4.0, respectively.

An isotropic emission gives a distribution in the log tan θ coordinate system that is nearly Gaussian. This distribution has a standard deviation $\sigma = 0.39$, that may be used as a measure of the anisotropy of the distribution in the c.m.s. Typical experimental distributions are shown in Fig. 9.

Roughly speaking, most angular distributions below $\sim 10^{12}$ eV may be interpreted in terms of an isotropic emission from one centre either at rest or moving slowly in the c.m.s. In particular, Dobrotin (Dobrotin *et al.*, 1961)

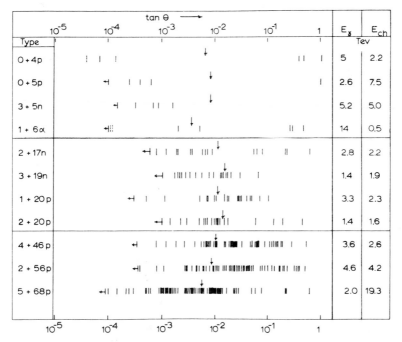

Fig. 9. Angular distribution of shower tracks in a sample of high energy collisions for three groups of multiplicity, from Fowler and Perkins (1964). The value of tan θ for each track is shown by a short vertical line. The two right-hand columns list the energies in units of 10^3 GeV, carried by (a) the γ rays in the associated electron cascade, (b) the charged secondaries from the collision. This estimate is derived from the angular distribution and the exponential model mentioned in the text, for a value of $p_t = 0.5$ GeV/c. The vertical arrow on each event gives the value of θ corresponding to 90° in the c.m.s. based on the assumption of a nucleon-nucleon collision, and total radiated energy $= E_\gamma + E_{ch} = 0.3E_0$. The horizontal arrows on the left-hand tracks indicate that these angles are upper limits.

and others, found asymmetric jets in this energy region, in which the primary energy was not at the mean. They found considerable asymmetries in the c.m.s. corresponding to centers moving slowly either forward or backward. These events were asymmetric either way with equal frequency, and are consistent with isobar production with only one isobar excited, either forward or backward. The angular distribution in the rest system of the moving center was consistent with an isotropic emission.

Above $\sim 10^{12}$ eV, the angular distributions become more complicated. The groups at Krakow and Chicago (Gierula *et al.*, 1961) found in the analysis of 116 jets a " double maximum " structure [a structure similar to distributions (4) and (5), in Fig. 8] in the angular distributions. This was about three standard deviations, from a normal distribution.

These angular distributions have been interpreted in terms of the "two-center" model in which the secondary particles are emitted from two centers ("fireballs") moving in opposite directions in the c.m.s. with different velocities and roughly in the line of collision. They showed that the emission in the rest system of each center was approximately isotropic. This depletion around 90° in the c.m.s. is consistent with isobar production but with both nucleons excited.

At still higher energies the situation is complicated and no simple structure is apparent. Pal and Peters (1964) suggested that baryon-antibaryon isobars might also be produced at these energies, which would serve to complicate the angular distributions. However, if isobar production were dominant and the products from the " fireballs " were produced with a low energy in the c.m.s., it would be expected that these two processes might be separated at very high energy. The situation may, of course, be more complicated. The Japanese and Brazilian emulsion groups (to be published in 1965) in some cases observed the mesons from fireballs and the baryon. They found that the mesons had a transverse momentum of ~ 1.0 GeV/c with respect to the baryon. This would suggest that the fireballs might be emitted with a large net transverse momentum. Then if the mesons were formed asymmetrically in this way, it might be possible to observe this as an azimuthal asymmetry in individual interactions.

There are other possibilities. Recently, Czyzewski and Krzywicki (1963) began with the two well-established facts that the transverse momentum and the inelasticity are both small and calculated a group of " jets " by the Monte Carlo method. They were able to show that the type and magnitude of the deviations from a Gaussian distribution for the group of calculated " jets " were the same as those of the experimental distributions.

3. *Transverse Momentum*

The transverse momentum is a Lorentz invariant quantity, and is easily measured even at high energy; a knowledge of the primary energy is not required. The mean value of the transverse momentum of secondary particles is very nearly constant over a large range of energies at a value equal to a few pion masses. It is plotted in Fig. 10 as a function of the primary energy.

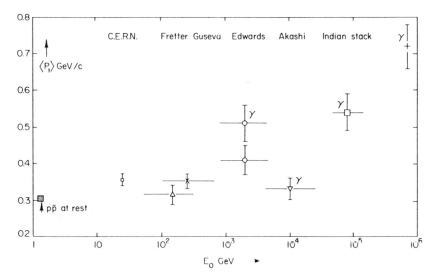

Fig. 10. Mean transverse momentum of pions as a function of $E_0 \cdot \langle p_t \rangle_\pi = 2 \langle p_t \rangle$, has been used where applicable (Fowler and Perkins, 1964).

There is a clear indication of a very slow increase in the transverse momentum over the five orders of magnitude of energy above accelerator energies.

The distribution of the transverse momentum at any energy is well approximated by

$$\frac{dN}{dp_t} \propto p_t \exp\{-p_t / \tfrac{1}{2} \langle p_t \rangle\} \qquad \text{for} \quad p_t > m_\pi c \qquad \text{(II-1)}$$

from accelerator energies to $\gtrsim 10^6$ GeV. This dependence of the distribution of p_t was first suggested by cosmic ray measurements. This form (II-1) for the distribution of the transverse momentum and

$$\frac{dN}{dp_\parallel} \propto \exp\{-p_\parallel / \langle p_\parallel \rangle\} \qquad \text{for} \quad p_\parallel \lesssim \frac{2}{3} \frac{E_0}{c} \qquad \text{(II-2)}$$

for the longitudinal momentum were taken as a trial solution by Cocconi *et al.* (CKP) (1961). The distributions of transverse and longitudinal momenta are then independent and give the joint probability for a pion with energy in the laboratory system E and transverse momentum p_t as

$$P(E, p_t) \, dp_t \, dE \propto p_t \exp\{-p_t / \tfrac{1}{2} \langle p_t \rangle\} \exp\{-E/T\} \qquad \text{(II-3)}$$

where $T \propto E_0^{3/4}$ is the mean pion energy in the laboratory system. This model has been successful wherever checked ($E_0 \gtrsim 10$ GeV). These are probably the correct distributions or are close to the correct ones and if the isobar model is correct, these distributions should be derivable.

Above $\sim 10^3$ GeV, the transverse momentum is only known accurately from measurements of the energy and angle of the γ rays from π^0 meson

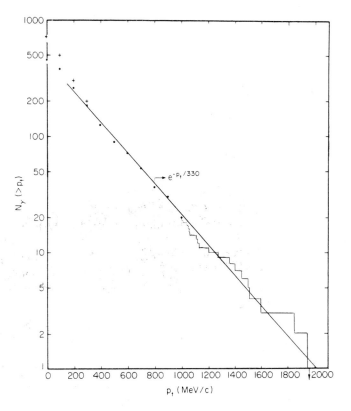

Fig. 11. The integral transverse momentum spectrum of all γ rays emitted within an angle of 10^{-2} rad: ($\cdot$) number of observed γ rays with $E_\gamma \geq 50$ GeV, and ($+$) correction for γ rays with $E_\gamma < 50$ GeV [Bristol-Tata Collaboration, (Malhotra et al., 1965)].

decay. The energy of the γ rays can be measured using the three-dimensional shower theory of Kamata and Nishimura (1958). If the distribution of the π^0 mesons follows Eq. (II-3), the distribution of the γ rays is a simple exponential. Figure 11 shows the integral p_t spectrum of all γ rays within an angle of 10^{-2} rad for a median primary energy of $\sim 2 \times 10^{13}$ eV.

4. *Energy Spectra*

The energy spectra of the secondary components indicate the partition of the primary energy among the different types of created particles. The spectra which can be measured accurately at high energy are those of the electron-photon component. The resulting electron cascades are measured using the shower theory mentioned earlier.

Two types of cascades must be distinguished. The first are those produced by individual γ rays from the decay of π^0 mesons produced in nuclear interactions in the atmosphere above the detector. When these γ rays reach the detector, their components are separated by distances which allow them to be measured separately. The interpretation is easier when individual γ rays are measured near the top of the atmosphere before there is an appreciable probability of their materializing. The second type of cascade is that produced by nuclear interactions in the detector, and the entire energy given to the π^0 component ($K_{\pi^0}E_0 = \Sigma E_\gamma$) is measured. These energy spectra are shown in Figs. 12 to 15. Figures 12, 13, and 14 are integral spectra of individual γ rays at different altitudes (mountain, airplane, and balloon). Figure 15 is an integral spectrum of ΣE_γ.

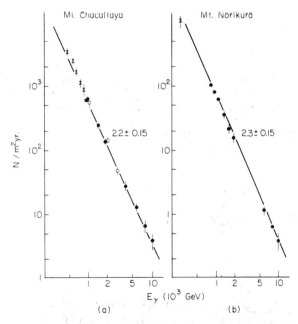

Fig. 12. The integral energy spectrum of individual γ rays at mountain altitudes (emulsion chamber): (a)—(x) general scan, ($\square$) Lattes, 1962, ($\blacksquare$) Lattes, 1963, ($\bigcirc$) Japan and ($\bullet$) Brazil and Japan; (b)—(x) general scan and ($\bullet$) x-ray scan. The power-law indices are indicated (Akashi *et al.*, 1963).

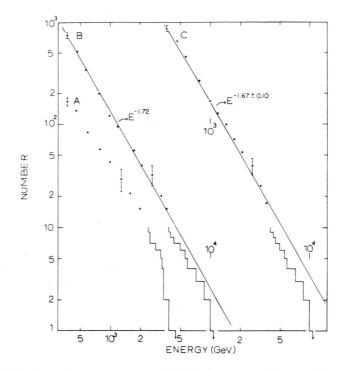

Fig. 13. The integral energy spectrum of individual γ rays at airplane altitudes (emulsion chamber at ~ 220 gm/cm²): A is the spectrum from nuclear interactions in the producing layer, and B that in the overlying atmosphere. The power-law index of the combined spectrum C is 1.67 ± 0.10. The scale of energy has been displaced by a factor of ten for C. The rates of production of γ rays above a given energy per steradian second per gram of material at the top of the atmosphere can be obtained by multiplying the ordinate by 1.32×10^{-10}, 2.3×10^{-11}, and 2.0×10^{-11} for A, B, and C, respectively [Bristol-Tata Collaboration (Malhotra *et al.*, 1965)].

The π^0 component of the inelasticity, K_{π^0}, may be determined from the second type of spectrum and the integral energy spectrum of the primary radiation. For a given value of the intensity N, K_{π^0} is given by

$$\left[P^{\gamma}(K_{\pi^0})\right]^{1/\gamma}\bigg|_{N} = \frac{\langle K_{\pi^0}\rangle E_0}{E_0}\bigg|_{N}. \tag{II-4}$$

The main uncertainty in K_{π^0} is that of the primary spectrum. The best estimate of K_{π^0} is from the Russian work, of Dobrotin *et al.* (1961, 1963) and Dobrotin and Feinberg (1964) mentioned earlier. The current value is $\langle K_{\pi^0}\rangle_{\text{eff}} \simeq 0.14$.

If several π^0 mesons are produced in an interaction and all the γ rays are observed, the two spectra should have the same power-law index, but the ratio of the two fluxes will depend on the partition of the energy among the

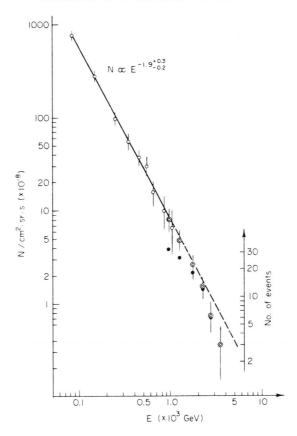

Fig. 14. The integral energy spectrum of individual γ rays at balloon altitudes (pure emulsion stack at $\sim 9\,\mathrm{gm/cm^2}$). The open circles and the doubles circles are the data corrected for detection and other losses. The power law index is $1.9^{+0.3}_{-0.2}$ (Abraham *et al.*, 1963).

π^0 mesons. The two spectra will have the same power-law index only if the cross section is homogeneous, that is, only if the multiplicity is independent of the primary energy or if most of the energy is carried by a fixed number of particles. If the two spectra have different indices, a comparison is difficult because a certain amount of mathematical simplicity is lost and better statistics are needed.

Some evidence now exists that there is a small change in the exponent of the spectrum of individual γ rays. It was generally agreed in the past that this either reflects a change in the primary spectrum between $\approx 2 \times 10^{14}$ and $\approx 2 \times 10^{15}$ eV (Fig. 16), or that it represents a change in the nature of the interactions themselves—either a change in the partition of the energy among the π^0 mesons that carry the bulk of the energy or, of course, a decrease in the inelasticity of the π^0 component.

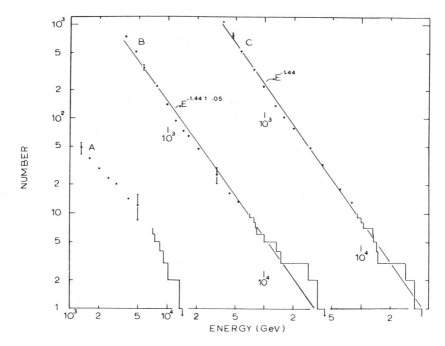

Fig. 15. Integral spectra of the total energy, ΣE_γ, radiated in nuclear interactions occurring in A the producing layer and B the detector; C is the combined spectrum of events originating in both these regions. The scale of energy has been displaced by factors of 10 and 100 for B and C, respectively. The rates of production of events above a given energy per steradian second per gram of producing layer or detector at the top of the atmosphere can be obtained by multiplying the ordinate by 1.36×10^{-10} or 2.5×10^{-11}, respectively [Bristol-Tata Collaboration (Malhotra *et al.*, 1965)].

At balloon altitudes where most of the γ rays from nuclear interactions in the atmosphere enter the detector before materializing, the interpretation of the spectra of individual γ rays is simple, but the collection of large numbers of γ rays is difficult. Deep in the atmosphere the situation is reversed.

In the earlier spectra, the components entering the detector were analyzed (cascade analysis) in order to find the energy of the original γ ray. Not only was the procedure uncertain but also the presence or absence of a single high energy air shower could alter the power index of the high energy part of the γ ray spectrum considerably. More details may be found in Akashi *et al.* (1963) and Hayakawa *et al.* (1964). The γ ray spectra are now made using only the individual γ rays that enter the detector, because if the spectrum of γ rays at production is a power law, the spectrum of individual γ rays, whether accompanied or not, is a power law of the same index.

The earlier spectra showed quite a large change in the power-law index of

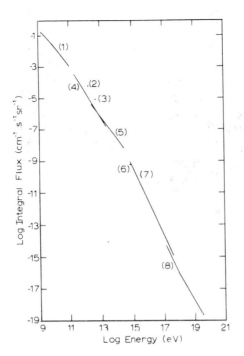

Fig. 16. The integral energy spectrum of the primary cosmic radiation. The references are those in the Bristol-Tata Collaboration (Malhotra *et al.*, 1965).

the γ ray spectrum at $\sim 2 \times 10^{12}$ eV. This was partly due to the cascade analysis and the effect is now considered to be rather small.

With the recent improvement in the knowledge of the primary spectrum, additional γ ray data will certainly give some new information on the properties of nuclear interactions at $\approx 5 \times 10^{14}$ eV, and will be a first step in deciding if the description from lower energies is applicable at these energies as well. Hayakawa *et al.* conclude from the present data that the γ ray spectrum is simply a reflection of the primary spectrum. This means that the properties of nuclear interactions do not change rapidly up to $\sim 5 \times 10^{14}$ eV.

5. *Energy Spectra of Individual Interactions*

There are now some data which indicate the primary energy dependence of the momentum spectrum of the created pions in the c.m.s. Many authors stress that not infrequently a few pions are produced with a large fraction of the primary energy. This behavior does not appear to persist at very high energy.

Dobrotin *et al.* (1963) have observed separate pions with $0.10E_0$ in the energy range 100–400 GeV. The number of charged and neutral pions of this type appears to be 1–2 per interaction. Similar results were obtained by Daniel *et al.* (1963) in emulsion. Baradzei *et al.* (1963) conclude that the most energetic π^0 receives 0.06–0.08 E_0.

The spectra of the momentum in the c.m.s. of γ rays allows the pion energy spectra in the same system to be inferred. They are consistent with an exponential distribution for the momentum of the parent π^0 mesons. In Fig. 17 are the integral spectra of γ rays in two energy groups, where T refers to the mean π^0 energy in GeV. The high energy group ($T = 3.7$) has $E \geqslant 2100$ GeV and the low energy group ($T = 2.0$) has 1300 GeV $\leqslant E < 2100$ GeV. Figure 18 shows the integral spectrum of the fractional energy $f = E_\gamma/\Sigma E_\gamma$ for the same γ rays.

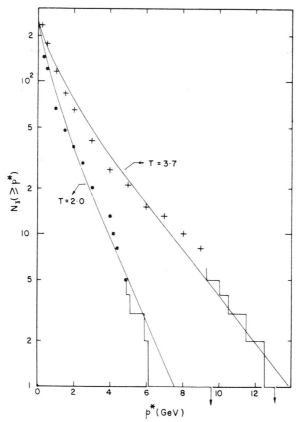

Fig. 17. Integral momentum spectrum in the c.m.s. for γ rays from events in the high energy group (+) and the low energy group (●). The curves correspond to exponential distributions for the momenta of the parent π^0 mesons [Bristol-Tata Collaboration, (Malhotra *et al.*, 1965)].

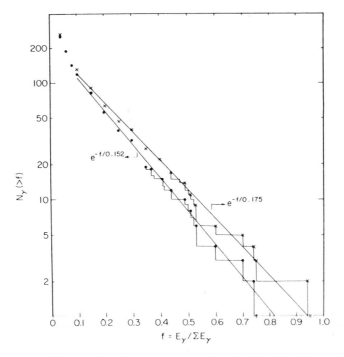

Fig. 18. Integral f spectra for all γ rays carrying a fraction $f \geqslant 0.04$ of the total radiated energy ΣE_γ: ($\times$) $N_\gamma \geq 2$, the combined spectrum for all events in the high and low energy groups, and ($\bullet$) only those events with $N_\gamma \geqslant 4$ [Bristol-Tata Collaboration (Malhotra et al., 1965)].

The distributions do not suggest a dominance of isobars which have a large fraction of the primary energy. If isobars are produced, they do not decay into one meson but several. They do suggest that the fireball products might be exponentially produced. Once again, on energy measurements alone, the isobar process does not appear self-evident. As the best evidence at machine energies comes from the momentum spectra of the charged pions and not from the energy measurements, so also at cosmic ray energies, the most convincing evidence comes from the muon charge ratio—which will be discussed later—and not from energy measurements.

6. Inelasticity

The inelasticity K is defined as the sum of the energies of the created particles divided by the primary energy. The average value is approximately constant and lies in the interval 0.40–0.60. The inelasticity of an individual interaction may be calculated from measured quantities in a variety of ways, but unfortunately it may be very inaccurate. In individual cases K may lie anywhere

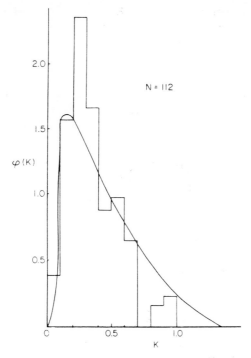

$N = 112$

Fig. 19. The distribution of the inelasticity $K = 1.5\,\Sigma E_\pi{}^{\pm}/E_0$ [from the experiment of Guseva *et al.* (1961)].

between zero and one. The best data, although over a restricted energy range, of the distribution of K is shown in Fig. 19 for nucleon-nucleon collisions at ~ 250 GeV (Guseva *et al.*, 1961).

The attenuation length of the nuclear-active component of the cosmic radiation in the atmosphere is known to be one and a half times as large as the interaction length. These quantities are related by

$$\lambda_{\text{int}}/\Lambda_{\text{att}} = 1 - \langle\eta\rangle^{\gamma} \qquad (\text{II-5})$$

where $K = 1 - \langle\eta\rangle$ and γ is the power-law index of the primary spectrum. An attenuation length much larger than the interaction length means that the interactions are generally quite elastic, that is, the primary particle retains a large part of its energy after the collision. This appears to be a characteristic of very high energy interactions and is one indication that they might be peripheral.

If the energy loss of nucleons in collisions in the atmosphere is, on the average, a constant fraction of their energy (constant inelasticity), then the exponent of the nucleon energy spectrum at sea level should be the same as that of the primary spectrum at a higher energy. Figure 20 shows the proton energy spectrum measured with a magnetic spectrograph at sea level (Brooke *et al.*, 1963). After correction for ionization loss, the exponent is $\gamma + 1 = 2.67$ in agreement with the exponent of the primary spectrum at $\approx 5 \times 10^{13}$ eV. This is a necessary but not sufficient condition for a constant inelasticity.

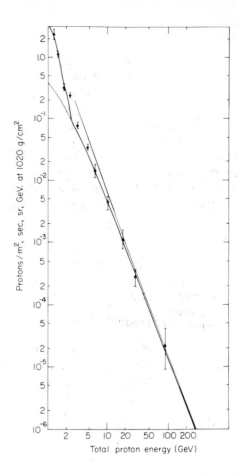

Fig. 20. The energy spectrum of protons at sea level. The solid curve represents $N(x, E) = N(O, E)e - (x/\Lambda)$ with $\Lambda = 123$ gm/cm² and corrected for ionization loss and for the contribution of protons from target nuclei (Brooke *et al.*, 1963).

7. *Composition of Secondary Particles*

The major fraction of the particles produced in a high energy interaction is pions, but the secondary particles cannot be identified directly and their composition must be inferred. The electron-photon cascades produced by γ rays converting within a given distance (~ 1 radiation length) from the interaction may be accurately measured. This gives the number of π^0 mesons produced in the interaction because they are essentially the only source of γ rays. Twice this many charged pions will be produced. For a large number of interactions, this method indicates that pions form $\approx 80\%$ of the produced particles. A similar result is obtained from the ratio of neutral-to-charged secondary interacting particles. This is the ratio of the number of neutral and charged interactions produced in the core of a jet shower. The lifetime of the π^0 meson is so short that particles producing neutral interactions cannot be pions.

For $100 \lesssim E_0 \lesssim 10^4$ GeV, the ratio $K/\pi < 0.2$ is to be compared with $K/\pi \lesssim 0.2$ at accelerator energies. Air shower data indicates that some nucleon-antinucleon pairs are produced and some emulsion data indicates that this fraction might be quite high (Levi Setti, 1963).

From the present data, it can only be concluded that the composition of secondary particles may not change from accelerator energies to $\sim 10^4$ GeV. This would be the kind of behavior expected if high energy physics were a superposition of low energy physics—of decay processes involving only a few GeV of energy. This question awaits a more precise determination of the K/π ratio or of the fraction of heavy particles produced at very high energies.

III. The Isobar Model

The isobar model is an extrapolation of known properties of NN inter-actions at accelerator energies together with some features of the fireball model. It is, in fact, a combination of two separate and independent processes which have different dependences on the primary energy. The mesons produced may be separated into two groups.

In the first group are those mesons produced by the evaporation of a fireball. This is an approximately isotropic emission from a center slowly moving or at rest in the c.m.s. The amount of energy given to the fireball is assumed to be a constant average fraction of the primary energy. The detailed nature of fireballs, their production, velocity in the c.m.s., decay or even their existence is not firmly established as might be gathered from the name "fireball." The difficulty at these energies is that the incoming and target particles, in the c.m.s., are contracted along the direction of motion and collide as very thin disks. The problem of multiple production is then reduced to what happens when an enormous energy is placed in a minute volume for a very short interval of time. This is still unknown and fireballs are primarily a pheno-menological aid to interpreting angular distributions and other features of the collisions process.

The mesons produced by the disintegration of the fireball all move relatively slowly in the c.m.s. of the fireball. They have a mean momentum which is by assumption independent of the primary energy and equal to

$$\langle p_f \rangle = 0.450 \text{ GeV}/c = 4/\pi \langle p_t \rangle. \tag{III-1}$$

The multiplicity of these mesons is assumed to increase in proportion to the energy given to the mass of the fireball.

These assumptions imply that the energy available to the fireball in the c.m.s. divided by the multiplicity must be a constant equal to the average energy of the created particles if the fireballs are slowly moving in the c.m.s. The energy available in the c.m.s. is proportional to $E_0^{1/2}$ and this requires that $n_s' \propto E_0^{1/2}$ as well, where n_s' is the mean number of shower particles from the decay of the fireball.

Thus the following quantities are assumed to be independent of the primary energy: (a) the average fraction of the primary energy available in the c.m.s. for the fireball and (b) the mean momentum of the mesons from the fireball in the c.m.s. One reason for invoking the fireball model is that if the high average multiplicity at high energy were from the decay of isobars, it would require extremely high isobar masses and an inelasticity near unity. This has not been observed, nor would it necessarily produce any high energy pions.

The second group corresponds to the nucleons in the fireball model, and it is assumed that each is an isobar of the πN system. The mesons are emitted as decay products of the isobar. It is assumed that the incident nucleon emerges in some excited state with a high probability and decays by the isotropic emission, in its own rest system, of several pions. It is further assumed that each isobar retains a significant fraction of the c.m.s. energy.

The pions from the decay of the forward isobar may have a significant fraction of the energy of the isobar. The frequency and distribution of the isobars excited are not specified and must be determined from experimental data. The energy of the "fast" pions—those of the second group—will increase if it is assumed that the mass spectrum of the isobars is independent of the primary energy and not too large.

IV. Secondary Spectra

The isobar model, even in its present form, is able to account for the propagation of the cosmic radiation in the atmosphere. There are, however, a number of different models which allow the calculation the secondary spectra. The agreement of all models is equally good and implies that the secondary spectra will not be helpful in deciding among these models until there are better statistics.

The calculation of the secondary spectra with the isobar model depended upon the two processes of particle production (isobar and fireball) not to contribute comparable numbers to the flux of secondary particles above a given energy. Above a few GeV, the mesons from isobar decay could dominate the propagation process even for small values of the probability of isobar excitation, if the "pionization" pions—pions from the decay of fireballs— were always moving slowly in the c.m.s. In this way there was hope that the propagation of the cosmic radiation in the atmosphere could be treated independently of any assumptions about the pionization process. It appears now that fireballs do not always produce low energy mesons in the c.m.s., and that the calculation of the secondary spectra by the isobar model may be more complicated.

V. Charge Composition of Secondary Spectra

The isobar model may also be used to calculate the charge composition of the secondary components of the cosmic radiation. The nuclei of the atmosphere contain equal numbers of protons and neutrons. The cosmic radiation, however, is approximately 87% protons and 13% neutrons, and there is, on the average, a charge excess per collision over the charge symmetric case of incoming and target nuclei of 0.37. The distribution of this charge excess can give some information on the partition of the primary charge and energy among the produced particles.

A. CHARGE RATIO OF MUONS AT SEA LEVEL

The charge ratio of muons at sea level is the strongest single piece of evidence in support of the isobar process at high energy. It has a value of $\mu^+/\mu^- \simeq 1.25$ for $1 \leqslant E \lesssim 100$ GeV. This may be explained by the positive excess of charge of the primary radiation if strange particles and strange decays can be considered unimportant.

If each interaction of the primary radiation were to produce pions as in the pionization process, and fluctuations were ignored, the charge excess, $\delta_\pi = (\pi^+ - \pi^-)/(\pi^+ + \pi^-)$, would be inversely proportional to the multiplicity. With the observed multiplicity, the muon charge ratio would be less than observed—the positive excess would be lost given a large multiplicity. If fluctuations were considered, δ_π would be inversely proportional to $\ln[(n_s + 1)/2]$ and this cannot be excluded (Bowler et al., 1961). If the multiplicity were large and kaons were produced with $K^+/K^- > 1$, the muon charge ratio might be explained in this way. The other possibility is that a small subgroup of pions exists which receives a large part of the charge and energy of the primaries via the supposed isobar.

In the isobar model, the charge persistence is carried by the isobars and can be transferred to the fast pions efficiently. On the other hand, an exponential spectrum of the pionization pions with a multiplicity that can extend to low values, allows fluctuations to occur in which one pion may receive a large fraction of the primary energy. There is a good deal of evidence indicating that a low multiplicity is accompanied by a large c.m.s. energy of the pions and not a small K. The primary spectrum then emphasizes those processes in which a large amount of energy is given to a small number of particles. According to this model, high energy pions would come predominantly from interactions with low multiplicity.

The two models are distinct in that the charge excess in the isobar model is carried away only by the high energy pions whether or not a large number of pions is created in the collision. In the second, this is accomplished by using the large spread in multiplicity among π mesons carrying the same total energy. The fast pions occur in only a fraction of low multiplicity events.

The muon charge ratio has been calculated with the isobar model as a function of the muon energy. This can be done in terms of the primary charge excess and the charge excess of the pions from the decay of isobars—this being the small subgroup of pions. Above a few GeV, muons are produced primarily from pions generated high in the atmosphere. In this case, the muon charge excess would simply be

$$(\mu^+ - \mu^-)/(\mu^+ + \mu^-) = \delta_0 \langle \delta_\pi' \rangle \tag{V-I}$$

where δ_0 is the charge excess of the primary radiation.

In the calculation of the muon charge ratio, the effect of several processes was considered, in particular, the contribution of strange decays of non-strange isobars, primarily the decay- $N^* \rightarrow K + Y$.

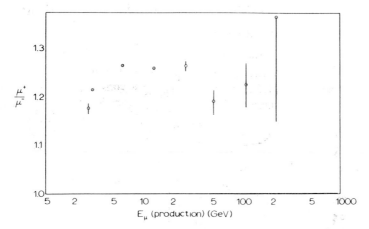

Fig. 21. A summary of all measurements of the muon charge ratio at sea level as a function of the muon energy at production (Ashton *et al.*, 1964).

Figure 21 shows a summary of all measurements of the charge ratio of muons at sea level. The increasing importance of the decay channel in which kaons are produced could account for an increase in the charge ratio above 100 GeV. If K, Y pairs are produced, however, the net effect of the charge excess would depend on the partition of the energy between the K and the Y. This partition would be calculable if the K, Y pairs were produced exclusively by isobars, but if they were produced, for example, in peripheral collisions, the partition would not be easily determined.

There is evidence that long-lived ($\sim 10^{-10}$ sec) strange isobars are not copiously produced at any energy. A frequent production of hyperons would give a muon charge ratio less than unity.

Ashton *et al.* (1964) conclude that until it is established that the charge ratio increases appreciably at high energies, it would seem more likely that a combination of pionization with large fluctuations plus an isobar production cross section of the order of that found at machine energies could account for the experimental results. Little information on the nature of these isobars can be deduced.

VI. Discussion

The isobar model is an extrapolation from low energy to cosmic ray energies. For this extrapolation to be possible, it is necessary to have a very detailed knowledge of pp interactions at accelerator energies. This assumption seems unavoidable because the cosmic radiation is primarily suited to the analysis of individual events and not, for example, to the determination of branching ratios. There is much work still to be done at accelerator energies, but in this section, the present data will be discussed in order to see whence any conclusions about the isobar process are likely to come.

A. MULTIPLICITY

The early form of multiplicity in the isobar model was $n_s = a + bE_0^{1/2}$, where the first term is a contribution from fast pions and the second from pionization pions. This is a consequence of the assumption that the c.m.s. energy of the pionization pions is constant. This restriction is not necessary and is not the case at very high energy where $p_{\parallel} \gg p_t$ is observed. The energy available, and assumed to be transferred to π mesons in the c.m.s., is proportional to $E_0^{1/2}$, and if n_s is proportional to E_0^{β}, the average energy per pion in the c.m.s. is $E_{\pi}^* \propto E_0^{1/2 - \beta}$. This is constant if $\beta = \frac{1}{2}$.

There is evidence from one event at $\sim 10^3$ GeV (Fowler and Perkins, 1964) that E_{π}^* is in the region of 1.0–1.6 GeV depending on the nature of the primary which was unknown. This event had a large multiplicity ($n_t \sim 600$), and the statistics were therefore good. However, these are very low values. In the Bristol-Tata collaboration (Malhotra et al., 1965) the mean energy was close to 3.0 GeV/c. This would mean that up to $\sim 10^5$ GeV, $\beta < \frac{1}{2}$, and nearer $\frac{1}{4}$. The latest data from the same collaboration indicate that $n_{\pi} = 33$ or $n_s \simeq 22$, at $E_0 \sim 2 \times 10^{13}$ eV, in agreement with $\beta = 1/2$. At present, none of the data at any energy favors a multiplicity as strong as $E_0^{1/2}$. In fact, other authors have suggested that the multiplicity saturates, but as explained in Section II,B,1, their selection may include systematic errors in the multiplicity.

The present data could be explained if the effective mass of the fireball as well as its velocity in the c.m.s. were proportional to $\gamma_c^{1/2}$ where γ_c is the Lorentz factor. This would also allow $\langle p_{\parallel}^2 \rangle > \frac{1}{2}\langle p_t^2 \rangle$ which is observed at very high energy.

B. GAMMA-RAY DATA

At very high energy, the γ ray component of nuclear interactions can be measured accurately. At the highest available energy [Fowler and Perkins

(1964) and Bristol-Tata Collaboration (Malhotra *et al.*, 1965), $\sim 2 \times 10^{13}$ eV and one event at $\sim 10^{15}$ eV], the γ ray data indicate that the energy distribution of the π^0 mesons in the c.m.s. is exponential. There is no indication of a separation into two processes. The energy of the π^0 mesons was frequently shared among several γ rays and only rarely did one γ ray have a significant fraction of the total energy appearing in γ radiation. In particular, in the event at $\sim 10^6$ GeV mentioned earlier, the highest energy γ ray carried only 1.5% of the estimated primary energy. No evidence for baryon isobars was seen. Most of the γ rays were of low momentum in the c.m.s. (< 500 MeV/c), although there were others with $p_\parallel \gg p_t$. The values of $p_\parallel$ and p_t in the c.m.s. for individual γ rays are shown in Fig. 22.

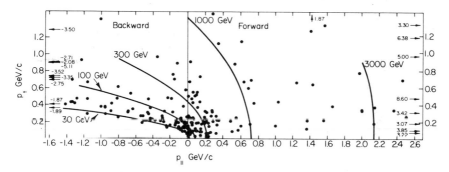

Fig. 22. The values of $p_\parallel$ and p_t in the c.m.s. for individual γ rays in the event at $\sim 10^6$ GeV. The energy threshold for detection of γ rays was ~ 30 GeV. Curves of constant energy in the laboratory system are included (Fowler and Perkins, 1964).

It is expected that γ rays from π^0 mesons arising from the decay of isobars would be seen if they were produced. A charged π meson from isobar decay is expected to carry on the average only $\sim 0.08E_0$. This would mean that the highest energy γ ray would have only 0.04–$0.08E_0$. The more important effect is the size and "blackness" of the event in the emulsion—its probability of detection. If $K_{\pi^0}E_0 = \Sigma E\gamma$ is the energy given to a large number of low energy π^0 mesons, the event will be more difficult to detect than one π^0 meson with the same energy. Not only will the single high energy π^0 meson produce a few more electrons but, more important, the E.M. cascade is in the region of its maximum for a much larger distance in the emulsion. This normally means that it passes through a large number of scanned plates and has a correspondingly high probability of detection. If an isobar π^0 meson were produced such that one γ ray had a large fraction of $K_{\pi^0}E^0$, the event would most likely be observed in the emulsion.

Whatever the cause of the increase in the exponent of the γ ray spectrum, it can be independent of the isobar process; however, if there is a strong isobar process which will tend to augment the number of high energy γ rays the index of the γ-ray spectrum must eventually decrease.

C. Angular Distribution

Some information can be gained from the angular distributions of the charged pions as well. It is clear from kinematics and a constant transverse momentum that, as the primary energy increases, a larger band of the log tan θ plot will be populated. The maximum number of resolvable "centers" is clearly expected to increase with the primary energy. At very high energy, the angular distributions are so complicated that they have not yet been analyzed.

Angular distributions, because of the difficulty of identifying individual particles and measuring their energy, offer little more than guidance and can show only consistency with any hypothesis. Attempts have been made (Kazuno, 1964) to distinguish, in the backward hemisphere, the charged isobar decay pions from the pionization pions. So far this method has not yielded any detailed results.

VII. Conclusions

The conclusions which can be reached at present are limited. They are as follows:

(1) It will be quite some time before the exact dependence of the multiplicity on energy is decided. The present data are in favor of the two parameter fit, aE^n with $n = \frac{1}{4}$. It is not surprising that a three-parameter form can be adjusted to fit as well. This indicates a weak energy dependence of the momentum of the "pionization" pions in the c.m.s. In any case, the exact energy dependence of the multiplicity is not critical in the isobar model.

(2) The separation of the charged pions from the isobar and pionization processes in angular distributions is difficult and, at best, is only a necessary condition for the presence of nucleon isobars. The γ ray data from nuclear interactions in emulsion chambers (Fig. 17) do not show any strong evidence for isobar production. When the γ ray spectrum in the atmosphere is known at higher energy, and when the increase in the index at $2 - 3 \times 10^{12}$ eV is well known, it should give some indication of the strength of the isobar process at very high energy.

(3) The muon charge ratio is a valuable quantity. When it is known above ~ 100 GeV, it is expected that it can distinguish between the two extreme possibilities: (a) pionization with large fluctuations, with or without an isobar production cross section of the order of that at machine energies, and (b) dominant isobar production with or without the channel $N^* \to K + Y$.

(4) The energy spectra of produced particles in the c.m.s. will be very

valuable. When interacting storage rings for protons are available (possibly in the early 1970's), those energy spectra should be known up to energies equivalent to 10^{12} eV in the laboratory system. There is already evidence that the spectrum at all energies is well fitted by an exponential which would mean that the pionization process as well as nucleon isobars produce fast pions. The isobar and pionization processes are not as easily separable as was originally hoped.

In conclusion, it is hoped that the cross section for isobar production and the distribution of produced isobars up to 10^{12} eV will be extracted with the aid of large installations like the "total absorption calorimeter." Above 10^{12} eV, the hope is that the very high energy data, mainly the production spectra of γ rays from individual interactions, can be interpreted with the help of the information gained at lower energy.

ACKNOWLEDGMENTS

The author is indebted to Professor C. F. Powell, F.R.S., for offering him the full facilities of his laboratory. He gratefully acknowledges the suggestions, discussion, and the assistance that he received from Professor P. H. Fowler, F.R.S., and it is a pleasure to acknowledge the suggestions offered by Professor D. H. Perkins, F.R.S. He is grateful to The Royal Society for a maintenance grant which enabled him to write this chapter.

REFERENCES

Abraham, F., Kidd, J., Koshiba, M., Levi Setti, R., Tsao, C. H., and Wolter, W. (1963). *Nuovo Cimento* **28**, 221.

Aizu, K., Fujimoto, Y., Hasegawa, H., and Taketani, M. (1964). *Prog. Theo. Phys., Suppl.* **30**, 2.

Akashi, M., Shimizu, K., Watanabe, B., Ogata, T., Ogita, N., Misaki, M., Mito, I., Oyama, S., Tokunaga, S., Tamura, M., Fujimoto, Y., Hasegawa, S., Nishimura, J., Niu, K., and Yokoi, K. (1961). *Proc. 7th Intern. Conf. Cosmic Rays and Earth Storm, Kyoto*, III, p. 427, the Physical Society of Japan.

Akashi, M., Shimizu, K., Watanabe, B., Nishimura, J., Niu, K., Ogita, N., Tsuneoka, Y., Taira, T., Ogata, T., Misaki, A., Mito, I., Oyama, Y., Tokunaga, S., Nishio, A., Dake, S., Yokoi, K., Fujimoto, Y., Suzuki, T., Lattes, C. M. C., Orsini, C. Q., Pacca, I. G., Cruz, M. T., Okuno, E., and Hasegawa, S. (1963). *Proc. 8th Intern. Conf. Cosmic Rays, Jaipur*, p. 326.

Akashi, M., Watanabe, Z., Misaki, A., Mito, I., Oyama, Y., Tokunaga, G., Ogata, T., Tsuneoka. P., Dake, S., Yokoi, K., Hasegawa, S., Nishimura, J., Nui, K., Taira, T., Nishio, A., Fujimoto, Y., and Ogita, N. (1965). *Prog. Theo. Phys., Suppl.*, **32**, 1.

Alexander, G., Haber, B., Shapiro, A., Yekutieli, G., and Gotsman, E. (1966). *Phys. Rev.* **144**, 1122.

Alvarez, L. (1964). Univ. of California at Berkeley Space Laboratory, Report No. 192.

Amati, D., Fubini, S., and Stanghellini, A. (1961). *Nuovo Cimento* **22**, 569.

Ankenbrandt, C. M., Clyde, A. R., Cork, B., Keefe, D., Kerch, L. T., Layson, W. M., and Wenzel, W. A. (1965). *Nuovo Cimento* **35**, 1052.

Ashton, F., Mackeown, P. K., Pattison, J. B. M., and Wolfendale, A. W. (1964). Final Report Air Force European Office of Atmospheric Research 62–117.

Babayan, Kh. P., Brikker, S. I., Grigorov, N. L., Podgurskaya, A. V., Savelyeva, A. I., and Shestoperov, V. Ya. (1963a). *Proc. 8th Intern. Conf. Cosmic Rays, Jaipur*, p. 51.

Babayan, Kh. P., Grigorov, N. L., Mamidjanian, E. A., Shestoperov, V. Ya., and Tretyakova, Ch. A. (1963b). *Proc. 8th Intern. Conf. Cosmic Rays, Jaipur*, p. 248.

Bacon, T. C., Hopkins, H. W. K., Robinson, D. K., Salant, E. O., Engler, A., Fisk, H. E., Meltzer, C. M., and Westgard, J. (1965). *Phys. Rev.* **139**, B1420.

Baradzei, L. T., Rubstov, V. I., Smorodin, Y. A., Solovtov, M. V., and Tolkachev, B. V. (1961). *Proc. 7th Intern. Conf. Cosmic Rays and Earth Storm, Kyoto*, III, p. 432.

Baradzei, L. T., Rubstov, V. I., Smoradin, Y. A., and Solovtov, M. V. (1963). *Proc. 8th Intern. Conf. Cosmic Rays, Jaipur*, p. 283.

Barkow, A. G., Chamany, B., Haskin, D. M., Jain, P. C., Lohrmann, E., Teucher, M. W., and Schein, M. (1961). *Phys. Rev.* **122**, 617.

Baudinet-Robinet, Y., Morand, M., Tjai-Chu, Castognoli, C., Dascola, G., Mora, S., Barbaru-Galtieri, A., Baroni, G., and Manfredini, A. (1962). *Nucl. Phys.* **32**, 452.

Beliakov, V., Shu-fen, Van, Glagolev, V., Dalkhazhav, Kirillova, L., Markov, P., Lebedev, R., Tolstov, K., Tsyganov, E., Shafranova, M., Jao Tsyng-se, Bannik, B., Bajatjan, G., Gramenitski, I., Danysz, M., Kostanashvili, N., Lyubimov, V., Nomofilov, A., Podgoretski, M., Skshipchak, E., Tuvdendorge, D., Shahulashvili, O., Bogachev, N., Bunyatov, S., Vishki, T., Merekov, Yu., and Sidorov, V. (1958). *Proc. Intern. Conf. High Energy Phys. Geneva*, CERN.

Bogachev, N. P., Bunyatov, S. A., Gramenitski, I. M., Lyubimov, V. B., Merekov, Yu. P., Podgoretski, M. I., Sidorov, Y. M., and Tuvdendorge, D. (1959). *Soviet Phys. JETP (English transl.)* **37**, 1255.

Bogachev, N. P., Bunyatov, S A., Merekov, Yu. P., Sidorov, V. M., and Yarba, U. A. (1960) *Soviet Phys. JETP (English transl.)* **38**, 1346.

Bowler, M. G., Duthie, J. G., Fowler, P. H., Kaddoura, A., Perkins, D. H. (1961). *Proc. 7th Intern Conf. Cosmic Rays and Earth Storm, Kyoto*, III, p. 423.

Brooke, G., Hayman, J. P., Kamiya, Y., Wolfendale, A. W. (1963). *Nature* **198**, 1293.

Chernavskii, D. S., and Feinberg, E. L. (1963). *Proc. 8th Intern. Conf. Cosmic Rays, Jaipur*, p. 395.

Cocconi, G., Koester, and Perkins (1961). "Particle fluxes from proton synchrotrons of energy 10–1000 Bev," Berkeley High Energy Accelerator Report.

Cocconi, G., Lillethun, E., Scaclon, J. P., Stahlbrandt, C. A., Ting, C. C., Walters, J., and Wetherell, A. M. (1963). *Proc. Intern. Conf. Elem. Particles, Sienna*, p. 608.

Cvijanovich G., Dayton, B., Egli, P., Klaiber, B., Koch, W., Nikolic, M., Schneeberger, R., and Winzeler, H. (1961). *Nuovo Cimento* **20**, 1012.

Czyzweski, O., and Kryzywicki, A. (1963). *Proc. Intern. Conf. Elem. Particles, Sienna*, p. 672.

Daniel, R. R., Durgaprasad, N., Malhotra, P. K., and Vijayalakshmi, B. (1963). *Proc. 8th Intern. Conf. Cosmic Rays, Jaipur*, p. 9.

Dekkers, D., Geibel, J. A., Mermod, R., Weber, G., Willitts, T. R., Winter, K., Jordan, B., Vivargent, M., King, N. M., and Wilson, E. J. N. (1965). *Phys. Rev.* **137**, B962.

Dobrotin, N. A., and Feinberg, E. L. (1964). *Proc. Roy. Soc. (London)* **A278**, 391.

Dobrotin, N. A., Guseva, V. V., Zelevinskaya, N. G., Kotelnikov, K. A., Lebedev, A. M., and Slavatinsky, S. A. (1961). *Proc. 7th Intern. Conf. Cosmic Rays and Earth Storm, Kyoto*, III, p. 375.

Dobrotin, N. A., Zelevinskaya, N. G., Kotelnikov, K. A., Maximenko, V. M., Puchkov, V. S., Slavatinsky, S. A., and Fetisov, I. N. (1963). *Proc. 7th Intern. Conf. Cosmic Rays, Jaipur*, p. 79.

Dodd, P., Jobes, M., Kinson, J., Yallini, B., French, B. R., Sherman, H. J., Skillicorn, I. O., Davies, N. T., Derrick, H., and Roddjicic, D. (1961). *Proc. Aix-en-Provence Intern. Conf. on Elem. Particles.*

Duthie, J., Fowler, P. H., Kaddoura, A., Perkins, D. H., and Pinkau, K. (1962). *Nuovo Cimento* **24**, 122.

Eisner, A. M., Hart, E. L., Louttit, R. I., and Morris, T. W. (1965). *Phys. Rev.*, **138**, B670.

Feinberg, E. L., and Chernavskii, D. S. (1964). *Usp. Fiz. Nauk* **82**, 3–81.

Ferrari, E., and Selleri, F. (1962). *Nuovo Cimento* **27**, 1450.

Ferrari, E. (1963). *Nuovo Cimento* **30**, 240.

Fickinger, W. J., Pickup, E., Robinson, D. K., and Salant, E. O. (1962). *Phys. Rev.* **125**, 2082.

Fowler, P. H. (1963). *Proc. 8th Intern. Conf. Cosmic Rays, Jaipur*, V, 182.

Fowler, P. H., and Perkins, D. H. (1964). *Proc. Roy. Soc. (London)* **A278**, 401.

Fowler, P. H., Adams, R. A., Cohen, V. G., and Kidd, J. M. To be published in *Proc. Roy. Soc.*, 1967.

Frautschi, S. (1963). *Nuovo Cimento* **28**, 409.

Gierula, J., and Miesowicz, M. (1963). *Nuovo Cimento* **27**, 149.

Gierula, J., Miesowicz, M., and Zielinski, P. (1960). *Nuovo Cimento* **18**, 102.

Gierula, J., Haskin, D. M., and Lohrmann, E. (1961). *Phys. Rev.* **122**, 626.

Greisen, K. (1960). " Progress Elementary Particle and Cosmic Ray Physics," Vol. 3. North Holland, Amsterdam.

Grigorov, N. L., Guseva, V. V., Dobrotin, N. A., Kotelnikov, K. A., Murzin, V. S., Ryabikov, S. J., and Slavatinsky, S. A. (1960a). *Proc. 6th Intern. Conf. Cosmic Rays, Moscow*, p. 143.

Grigorov, N. L., Kondratiev, N. A., Savelieva, A. I., Sobinyakov, V. A., Podgurskaya, A. V., Shestoperov, V. Ya. (1960b). *Proc. 6th Intern. Conf. Cosmic Rays, Moscow*, p. 130.

Guseva, V. V., Robrotin, N. A., Zelevinskaya, N. G., Kotelnikov, K. A., Lebedev, A. M., and Slavatinsky, S. A. (1961). *Proc. 7th Intern Conf. Cosmic Rays and Earth Storm, Kyoto*, III, p. 375.

Hansen, K. (1965). Private communication.

Hart, E. L., Louttit, R. I., and Morris, T. W. (1962b). *Phys. Rev. Letters* **9**, 133.

Hart, E. L., Louttit, R. I., Luers, D., Morris, T. W., Willis, W. T., and Yamamoto, S. S. (1962a). *Phys. Rev.* **126**, 747.

Hayakawa, S., Nishimura, J., and Yamamoto, Y. (1964). *Prog. Theo. Phys. Suppl.* **32**, 104.

ICEF Collaboration. (1963). *Nuovo Cimento Suppl.* **1**, 1038.

Japanese and Brazilian Emulsion Group (1965). *Proc. 9th Intern. Conf. Cosmic Rays, London*, **2**, 835.

Kamata, K., and Nishimura, J. (1958). *Progr. Theoret. Phys. Suppl.* **6**, 93.

Kazuno, K. (1964). *Nuovo Cimento* **34**, 303.

Kidd, J., Mandelli, L., Pelosi, V., Ratti, S., Sichirollo, A., Tallone, L., Conte, F., and Tomasini, G. (1965). *Phys. Letters* **16**, 75; also to be published in *Nuovo Cimento* (1967).

Koba, Z. (1963). *Fortschr. Physik* **2**, 118.

Kobayashi, T., and Namiki, M. (1965). *Prog. Theo. Phys. Suppl.* **33**, 1.

Koshiba, M. (1961). "Exp. prog. requirements for a 300–1000 Bev accelerator," Brookhaven Natl. Lab., Upton, New York.

Koshiba, M. (1963). *Proc. 8th Intern. Conf. Cosmic Rays, Jaipur*, p. 293.

Lattes, C. M. C., Orsini, C. Q., Pacca, I. G., Da Cruz, M. T., Okuno E., Fujimoto, Y., and Yokoi, K. (1963). *Nuovo Cimento* **28**, 614.

Lattes, C. M. C., Orsini, C. Q., Pacca, I. G., Da Cruz, M. T., Okuno, E., Fujimoto, Y., Hasegawa, S., and Yokoi, K. (1964). *Nuovo Cimento* **33**, 680.

Levi Setti, R. (1963). "Storage rings, accelerators and experimentation at super high energies," Brookhaven Natl. Lab., Upton, New York.

Lock, W. O. (1963). *Proc. 8th Intern. Conf. Cosmic Rays, Jaipur*, p. 105.

Lohrmann, E., and Teucher, M. W. (1958). *Phys. Rev.* **112**, 587.

Lohrmann, E., Teucher, M. W., and Schein, M. (1961) *Phys. Rev.* **122**, 672.

Lundy, R. A., Novey, T. B., Yovanovich, D. D., and Telegdi, V. L. (1965). *Phys. Rev. Letters* **14**, 504.

Malhotra, P. K. (1963a). *Proc. 8th Intern. Conf. Cosmic Rays, Jaipur*, p. 40.

Malhotra, P. K. (1963b). *Nucl. Phys.* **46**, 559.

Malhotra, P. K., Shukla, P. G., Stephens, S. A., Vijayalakshmi, B., Boult, J., Bowler, M. G., Fowler, P. H., Hackforth, H. L., Keereetaveep, J., Mayes, V. M., and Tovey, S. N. (1965). *Nuovo Cimento* **40**, 385, 404.

McDonald, F. B., and Webber, W. R. (1959). *Phys. Rev.* **115**, 194.

Pal, Y. (1963). *Proc. 8th Intern. Conf. Cosmic Rays, Jaipur*, p. 445.

Pal, Y., and Peters, B. (1964). *Mat. Fys. Medd. Kal. Danske Videnskab. Selskab.* **33** No. 15.,

Perkins, D. H. (1960). "Progress Elementary Particle and Cosmic Ray Physics," Vol. V., 256. North Holland Publ., Amsterdam.

Perkins, D. H. (1961). *Proc. Intern. Conf. Theoret. Aspects of High Energy Phenomena, Geneva*, CERN,, p. 99.

Peters, B. (1962). *Proc. Intern. Conf. High Energy Phys., Geneva*, CERN, 623.

Peters, B. (1963). *Proc. 8th Intern. Conf. Cosmic Rays, Jaipur*, p. 423.

Pickup, E., Robinson, D. K., and Salant, E. O. (1962a). *Phys. Rev.* **125**, 2091.

Pickup, E., Robinson, D. K., and Salant, E. O. (1962b). *Phys. Rev. Letters* **8**, 329.

Pinkau, K. (1956). *Nuovo Cimento* **3**, 1258.

Pinkau, K., Duthie, J., Fowler, P. H., Kadoura, A., Perkins, D. H., Wolter, W., and Bowler, M. (1961). *Proc. 7th Intern. Conf. Cosmic Rays and Earth Storm, Kyoto*, III, p. 424.

Powell, C. F., Fowler, P. H., Perkins, D. H. (1959). "The Study of Elementary Particles by the Photographic Method." Pergamon, Oxford.

Subramanian, A. (1963). *Proc. 8th Intern. Conf. Cosmic Rays, Jaipur*, p. 166.

Wolfendale, A. W. (1963). "Cosmic Rays." George Newnes, Ltd., London.

GENERAL REFERENCES

"Encyclopedia of Physics" (S. Flügge, ed.), Vol. XLV. Springer, Berlin (1958).

"Proceedings of Conference on Instrumentation for High Energy Physics, Geneva, CERN, 1962." (1962). North Holland, Amsterdam.

"Proceedings of Ninth International Conference on Cosmic Rays (IUPAP), London, 1965." The Institute of Physics and The Physical Society, London.

NEUTRINO PHYSICS

Leon M. Lederman

I. Introduction

A. HISTORICAL

This survey undertakes to present the current status of a very rapidly developing subject and benefits greatly from the recent *Informal Conference on Neutrino Physics* sponsored by CERN and convened in Geneva in January 1965. Some general references are: Bernstein *et al.* (1963), Ruderman (1965), Schwartz (1965), Feinberg and Lederman (1963), Lee and Wu (1965), and Markov (1963). An extensive bibliography is given by Kuchowicz (1966). We begin with an admittedly subjective account of the developments which preceded the inception of this new field.

In 1957 parity violation was discovered, and weak interaction theory entered a new phase. By the efforts of many, but perhaps most noteworthy by T. D. Lee, C. N. Yang, R. Feynman, and M. Gell-Mann and R. Marshak, we had in a relatively short time two component neutrinos and a reformulation of the universal Fermi interaction in terms of vector and axial vector coupling with a close connection between the weak vector and the electromagnetic interaction. The last experimental obstacle, the branching ratio of $\pi \to e + v$ to $\pi \to \mu + v$ was removed by the observation made in the then new laboratory at CERN in 1958. At about this time physicists increasingly turned their attention to a difficulty with this theory which appeared when one considered weak processes induced at higher momenta. For example, the effective interaction Lagrangian which accounts for muon decay, $\mu^+ \to e^+ + v + v$:

$$L = \frac{G}{\sqrt{2}} \, (J_\alpha^{(\mu)})^+ J_\alpha^{(e)} \tag{I-1}$$

with

$$J_\alpha^{(l)} = \bar{\psi}_l \gamma_\alpha (1 + \gamma_5) \psi_v \tag{I-2}$$

represents the interaction of four fermions at a single space-time point and yields a matrix element with no momentum dependence. The virtue of starting with Eq. (I-1) is that it involves leptons only and avoids considerations of the effects of strongly interacting particles. The interaction [Eq. (I-1)] then predicts a cross section for, say, $v + e \to v + \mu^+$, which increases with the square of the center-of-mass (c.m.) momentum given by the phase-space contribution. A conflict with the unitarity limit of the cross section $(\pi \lambda^2/2)$ is reached at a c.m. energy of 300 GeV. An equivalent way of expressing this is to note that there is a fundamental length

$$(G/hc)^{1/2} \simeq 10^{-16} \text{ cm} \tag{I-3}$$

and that the theory must "break down" for impact parameters

$$l < 10^{-16} \text{ cm.} \tag{I-4}$$

Although this question could possibly be resolved by theoretical elaboration, it stimulated the sharp question: Are there modifications to the theory which would damp the increase in cross section at laboratory energies far below the unitarity limit? This led to two channels of activity: Experimentally, one was led to think about weak interaction experiments at high energy and theoretically, the question of the intermediate boson, the source of the four fermion interaction, was raised as an elegant mechanism for giving this interaction a spatial extent. This would act to postpone the unitarity crisis and, with higher order corrections, give a well-behaved theory. The question of an intermediate vector boson focused attention on the famous $\mu \to e + \gamma$ difficulty and both efforts converged in the high energy neutrino interaction experiments which began in 1961. The compelling arguments were made by T. D. Lee and C. N. Yang in 1959–1960. They pointed out that the weak interactions must exhibit some kind of nonlocality at high energies and that this nonlocality must appear virtually and insure a relatively large amplitude for the reaction $\mu \to e + \gamma$. The experimental fact that $\mu \nrightarrow e + \gamma$ then must represent a selection rule, the only one consistent with all the known facts about muon decay was the two neutrino hypothesis: $\pi^+ \to \mu^+ + \nu_\mu, \pi^+ \to e^+ + \nu_e$, and $\nu_\mu \neq \nu_e$.

The experimental approach was to note that up to the time of these considerations (late 1959) all research on weak interactions (Reines-Cowan excepted) depended on the availability of spontaneous decays of nuclei and of particles. These permitted the study of the couplings at momentum transfers up to ~ 100 MeV/c the rest mass of the muon. In fact, the momentum dependent terms were quite small and had not until then been observed. How could one induce reactions at higher energy? The problem was formidable: A particle at rest comes to terms with its environment and eventually decays; an in-flight reaction must compete with the strong and electromagnetic interactions which are $\sim 10^{12}$ times stronger. The brilliant proposal to use neutrinos as a bombarding particle was made independently by Schwartz (1965) at Columbia University and Pontecorvo (1959) in Dubna in late 1959. In particular, these authors noted that neutrinos alone interact only via weak interactions and that they would easily penetrate a shield thick enough to screen all other particles produced by an accelerator. Pontecorvo's specific suggestion was motivated by the question of $\nu_e = \nu_\mu$. He proposed using stopped μ^+ to generate 35 MeV $\bar{\nu}_\mu$ in order to observe: $\bar{\nu}_\mu + p \to e^+ + n$. However, the relatively low cross section would require a "meson factory" of the kind now still only in the planning stage. Schwartz considered a neutrino beam made from the decay in flight of ~ 1 GeV pions produced at the Brookhaven Alternating Gradient Synchrotron (AGS) and, although pessimistic about the required intensity, sketched a possible arrangement to detect neutrino-nuclear interactions.

More detailed considerations by workers at Columbia University (Lederman *et al.*, 1960); and CERN (Krienan *et al.*, 1960; Bernardini, 1960; Ramm,

1960) indicated that, in fact, the available machines were capable of yielding sufficient intensities to observe the weak interaction of neutrinos at energies of the order of 1 GeV. These estimates were made possible by the calculations of the neutrino reaction cross sections made by Lee and Yang (1960a), Cabibbo and Gatto (1960), and Yamaguchi (1960).

The Columbia-BNL estimates were more pessimistic and so a very large detector, consisting of 10 tons of active mass, was prepared. This proved sufficient and in a 500-hour exposure, some 50 events were observed and reported in June 1962 (Danby *et al.*, 1962).

II. Theoretical Predictions

A. General Assumptions

We will list here the reactions which can " in principle " be observed using neutrino beams and the cross sections calculated using "standard" weak interaction theory (Lee and Wu, 1965; Feinberg and Lederman, 1963). The standard theory is defined by a set of assumptions which follow.

1. *Current-Current Hypothesis*

Each weak transition is described by a matrix element written as a product of two current vectors. The form of the currents involves the wave functions of the particles in the initial and final states. Thus the observations have established the existence, in this phenomenological theory, of the following currents:

(a) Lepton currents:

$$(\mu, v_\mu) \qquad (e, v_e)$$

(b) Hadron currents: (II-1)

$$(n, p) \qquad (\Lambda^0, p) \qquad (\Sigma^+, n) \qquad (\pi^-, \pi^0) \qquad (\Xi^-, \Xi^0) \qquad \text{(etc.)}.$$

Of the hadron currents only (n, p) has been observed at q^2 substantially different from zero. The lepton wave functions always carry the factor $1 + \gamma_5$ making the neutrino always left-handed and the electron almost $(\sim v/c)$ left-handed. The negative muon, because its mass is less often negligible, "tends" to come out left-handed. This $1 + \gamma_5$ factor, applied to baryon currents results in the Vector minus Axial Vector (V-A) theory (Feynman and Gell-Mann, 1958), Marshak and Sudarshan (1958), Gershtein–Zel'dovich (1957).

2. *Conservation of Leptons and of Muon Number*

One usually takes e^-, μ^-, v_e, and v_μ to be leptons ($l = +1$), the corresponding antiparticles have $l = -1$. In addition, we take μ^- and v_μ to have muon number $N_\mu = +1$, μ^+ and $\bar{\nu}_\mu$ have $N_\mu = -1$. Similarly, one defines an electron number N_e. We then postulate the additive law that N_e and N_μ must be separately conserved in all reactions. Thus, for example, the reaction

$$\mu^- \to e^- + \nu_e + \bar{\nu}_\mu \tag{II-2}$$

is rigorously forbidden as is

$$\mu^- + e^+ \to e^- + \mu^+. \tag{II-3}$$

However, an alternative postulate (Feinberg and Weinberg, 1961) is to assume a multiplicative conservation law which would then allow the above reactions.

3. Lepton Current Locality

The lepton pairs (μ, ν_μ), (e, ν_e) are assumed to be emitted or absorbed at the same point of space-time (Lee and Yang, 1960a).

4. Muon-Electron Symmetry

It is assumed that the effective interaction involves both electron-type and muon-type currents:

$$j_\lambda^{(l)} - j_\lambda^{(\mu)}(x) + j_\lambda^{(e)}(x).$$

This says that in all leptonic processes, (μ, ν_μ) and (e, ν_e) are identically coupled and differ only in virtue of the muon-electron mass difference.

5. Universal Fermi Interaction

The total weak interaction has been assumed to consist of all possible combinations of current pairs added with the same or simply related multiplicative constant. New theoretical viewpoints have recently appeared and will be discussed where they are relevant to neutrino physics. This is closely connected with the assumption of conserved vector currents listed below.

6. CPT Invariance

It is assumed that all interactions are invariant under the combined operations of CPT where C is the charge conjugation operator, P is the parity transformation operator and T is the time reversal operator. Under this assumption CP and T invariance are equivalent.

7. CP Invariance

This was generally assumed valid; all terms in the effective interaction were thought to have the same transformation properties under CP. This implies the reality of the structure functions (form factors) which appear in the most general form of the operators contained in the hadron currents due to strong

interactions. (It should be noted that the question of the phases of these struc-
ture functions is also influenced by the validity of the $|\overrightarrow{\Delta I}| = 1$ rule for $\Delta S = 0$
processes. Under the assumption of both CP invariance and $|\overrightarrow{\Delta I}| = 1$, it
follows that some of the maximum number of independent structure functions
vanish.)

8. *Conserved Vector Current Hypothesis* (CVC)

It is assumed that the $\Delta S = 0$ vector terms in the hadron current are proportional to the isotopic spin current $I_\lambda^{(\pm)}$. This implies

$$(\partial J_\lambda^v / \partial x_\lambda) = 0 \qquad \text{for} \quad \Delta S = 0 \quad \text{processes.} \tag{II-4}$$

and predicts unique relations between the matrix elements of the weak vector
current and the electromagnetic current. This was originally taken to account
for the equality of the Fermi β-decay and μ-decay constants (Feynman and
Gell-Mann, 1958). It has been proposed that this simple equality is modified
in the newer SU(3) versions of CVC theory.

9. *Cabibbo Hypothesis*

The weak current of strongly interacting particles (hadron current) is a
member of an SU(3) octet (Cabibbo, 1963). Universality then takes the form:

$$J_\lambda = \cos \theta J_\lambda^{(0)} + \sin \theta J_\lambda^{(1)} \tag{II-5}$$

where $J_\lambda^{(0)}$ and $J_\lambda^{(1)}$ are the $\Delta S = 0$, $\Delta Q = 1$, and $\Delta S = \Delta Q = 1$ members
of an octet of currents. The vector part belongs to the same octet as the electro-
magnetic current (CVC). The parameter θ (Cabibbo angle) expresses the
relative strengths of the $\Delta S = 0$ and $\Delta S = 1$ interactions and is obtained from
a comparison of K_{l3} and π_{l3} decay rates as well as from $K_{\mu 2}$ and $\pi_{\mu 2}$ decay
rates. Both give $\theta \simeq 0.26$.

B. ELASTIC NEUTRINO INTERACTIONS

These are taken to be the following

$$\nu_\mu + n \to p + \mu^- \tag{II-6a}$$

$$\bar{\nu}_\mu + p \to n + \mu^+. \tag{II-6b}$$

These are the most "practical" reactions available, with the target nucleons
being part of some convenient nucleus, notably aluminium or bromine
(Freon). Under SU(3) a more general specification of "elastic" processes
would include all octet-to-octet transitions of the baryons, i.e., $\bar{\nu}_\mu + p \to \Sigma^0 +$
μ^+, etc. (see below). Under the standard theory, the cross sections for Eqs.
(II-6) are functions of the neutrino energy, the four-momentum transfer,
and structure functions which appear in the hadron, $\Delta S = 0$ current: $J_\lambda^V(x) +$

$J_\lambda^A(x)$. Since the effects of strong interactions are not well understood, the matrix elements of these terms in the effective Lagrangian are written first in the most general form consistent with Lorentz, space-inversion, and time reversal invariance. Under the further assumption of the validity of the $|\Delta I| = 1$ selection rule two of the six allowed structure functions for the (n, p) current vanish. This assumption is incorporated in the CVC theory which permits the identification of the two vector form factors with the isotopic electromagnetic form factors obtained from electron-proton and electron-neutron scattering. The resulting cross section (Lee and Yang, 1960a; Lee and Yang, 1962; Lee, 1964) is considerably simplified if the mass of the outgoing lepton is set equal to zero. The error made thereby is only a few per cent. There results:

$$\frac{d^2\sigma}{dq^2} = \frac{1}{4\pi} \left\{ \frac{q^2}{2k_v^2} (g_A^2 - g_V^2) + (g_A \pm g_V)^2 + \left[1 - \frac{q^2}{2mk_v}\right]^2 (g_A \mp g_V)^2 \right.$$

$$\left. + \left[2 - \frac{q^2(m + 2k_v)}{2mk_v^2}\right] [(4m^2 + q^2)f_v^2 - 4mg_V f_v)] \right\} \quad \text{(II-7)}$$

where g_V, g_A, and f_v are real functions of q^2, called, respectively, the vector, axial vector, and weak magnetism form factors. In Eq. (II-7), m is the nucleon mass and k_v the neutrino momentum in the laboratory system. Thus, using CVC

$$g_V(q^2) = G_V [F_Q(q^2) + (\mu_p - \mu_n)F_M(q^2)]$$

$$f_v(q^2) = G_V \frac{(\mu_p - \mu_n)}{2m} F_M(q^2) \quad \text{(II-8)}$$

where F_Q and F_m are the isotopic vector electromagnetic form factors for charge and magnetic moment, normalized to unity at $q^2 = 0$. Setting $m_\mu = 0$ caused the induced pseudoscalar form factor term h_A to vanish where:

$$h_A(q^2) = m_l G_p(q^2) \rightarrow 10m_l G_v \quad \text{at} \quad q^2 = 0 \quad \text{(II-9)}$$

$$g_A(q^2) = -\lambda(q^2)G_v \quad \text{where} \quad \lambda(0) = 1.19 \quad \text{(II-10)}$$

$$G_V = 10^{-5}/m^2 = G. \quad \text{(II-11)}$$

This leaves only $g_A(q^2)$ to be determined if we take $m_l \simeq 0$. It has been noted (Lee and Yang, 1962) that the difference between neutrino and antineutrino cross sections, being proportional to V-A interference, is particularly sensitive to g_A:

$$\frac{d\sigma_{\bar{v}}}{dq^2} - \frac{d\sigma_v}{dq^2} = \frac{q^2}{\pi mk_v} \left[1 - \frac{q^2}{4mk_v}\right] g_V g_A. \quad \text{(II-12)}$$

Of course, in the future domain of neutrino experiments on hydrogen and deuterium, one should use the data to test the CVC hypothesis at the high momentum transfers available. In this case it may be possible to observe the possible presence of an additional factor $(1 + q^2/m_w{}^2)^{-1}$ due to the role of an intermediate boson of mass m_w.

Longitudinal polarization effects have been derived in the general case by Lee and Yang (1962) and also by Adler (1963). The observation of CP violation has stimulated further remarks on elastic neutrino scattering. Polarization effects in the elastic reactions have been discussed by Berman and Veltman (1964) on the basis of Cabibbo's model of T noninvariance (Cabibbo, 1964). Thus, terms of opposite G parity interfere to produce maximum violation in reactions (II-6). Large effects are conceivable.

Fujii and Yamaguchi (1966) have noted that there may also be transverse nucleon polarization, i.e.,

$$\frac{d\sigma}{d\Omega} = A + B \cdot \frac{\vec{\sigma}_p \cdot \vec{k}_v x \vec{p}}{k_v p \sin \phi} \tag{II-13}$$

where ϕ is the recoil proton angle; T invariance requires that B vanish. Explicit expressions are given in this reference.

Nuclear structure effects arise when the neutrino-nucleon collision takes place in a complex nucleus. These will be discussed in Section V,E.

C. Inelastic Neutrino Interactions

1. General

Lee and Yang (1962) and Lee (1964) have discussed the general form of reactions

$$v + Z \rightarrow l^- + \Gamma$$

where Z is the target nucleus and Γ is any arbitrary complex of hadrons.

Let P_v, P_l, P_Γ, and P_1 be the four-momenta of the neutrino, lepton, complex of hadrons Γ and initial nucleus, respectively. Also, m_Γ = effective mass of Γ. Then if the mass of the lepton may be neglected, it is shown that the differential cross section depends only on three functions (A_+, A_-, B) of the two invariants q^2 and $m_\Gamma{}^2$. This is a consequence of the *locality* of leptonic currents.

$$\frac{d^2\sigma}{dk_l \, d\Omega} = \frac{k_l}{2k_v} [(k_v + k_l)^2 - P_\Gamma{}^2] \left\{ \left(\frac{k_v + k_l - |P_\Gamma|}{k_v + k_l + |P_\Gamma|} \right) A_+(q^2, m_\Gamma{}^2) \right.$$

$$\left. + \left(\frac{k_v + k_l + |P_\Gamma|}{k_v + k_l - |P_\Gamma|} \right) A_-(q^2, m_\Gamma{}^2) + B(q^2, m_\Gamma{}^2) \right\} \tag{II-14}$$

and similarly for $\bar{v}$ reactions where the functions $\bar{A}_+$, $\bar{A}_-$, and $\bar{B}$ may be related to the ones above if charged symmetry holds between hadron currents J_λ and $J_\lambda{}^*$:

$$A_\pm = \bar{A}_\pm$$

$$B = \bar{B} \tag{II-15}$$

for $\Delta S = 0$ reactions only. Here, k_v, k_l are the three-momenta of the neutrino and lepton in the lab. system.

2. Single Pion Production $v + N \rightarrow N' + \pi + l^-$

Many authors have discussed this reaction (Bell and Berman, 1962; Cabibbo and daPrado, 1962; Dennery, 1962; Berman and Veltman, 1964; Albright and Liu, 1964a,b, 1965; Salin, 1965). Most of the theoretical considerations involve the dominance of the $N^*(\frac{3}{2}, \frac{3}{2})$ isobar:

$$v + N \rightarrow N^* + l^-. \tag{II-16}$$

Calculations on the basis of dispersion relations, static theory (following the Chew-Low theory of photoproduction) and on the basis of SU(6) (Albright and Liu, 1964a,b, 1965) lead to predictions of the energy dependence $\sigma_{N^*}(k_v)$, the momentum transfer dependence, and $d\sigma_{N^*}/dq^2$ the production ratio of positive to neutral pions. We follow the CERN group (Bartley et al., 1965) in discussing this reaction. Let P_1 and P_2 and P_π be the four-momenta of the initial and final nucleon and pion, respectively. The relevant invariants are

$$t = -(P_1 - P_2)^2$$

$$q^2 = (P_v - P_l)^2$$

$$= 2E_v E_l(1 - P_l \cos \theta) - m_l{}^2 \tag{II-17}$$

$$M^{*2} = -(P_2 + P_\pi)^2.$$

The reaction is closely related to inelastic electron scattering and a Rosenbluth-type cross section is obtained, with the vector part of the nucleonic current being derived from the electromagnetic form factors. The general form of the cross section is then given as

$$\frac{d^2\sigma}{dM^{*2}\,dq^2} = \frac{1}{k_l k_v}\left[q^2 R(q^2, M^{*2}) + (2k_l k_v - \tfrac{1}{2}q^2)S(q^2, M^{*2}) \right.$$

$$\left. + (k_l + k_v)T\left(q^2, M^{*2}\,\frac{q_0}{|\vec{q}|}\right)\right]. \tag{II-18}$$

The main contribution is thought to come from isobar formation

$$M^{*2} \approx M^{*2}(\tfrac{3}{2}, \tfrac{3}{2}).$$

The structure functions R, S, and T are of course contained in the hadron current J_λ and may be evaluated in various ways. In the work of Berman and Veltman (1964) the techniques of Gourdin and Salin (1963)—which were developed for electroproduction of N*—are followed by summing relevant graphs. The axial vector form factor is left as an unknown, parameterized by a parameter m_A in

$$g_A = \frac{1.064}{1 + q^2/m_A^2} - 0.064 \tag{II-19}$$

The reaction then involves form factors related to the transition from nucleon to N* about which very little is known. Some information may be forthcoming from photopion production and electroproduction or muon production.

Predictions have also been made on the basis of SU(6) by Albright and Liu (1964a,b, 1965). The symmetry properties of SU(6) relate N* production to the elastic process since N and N* are members of the same 56 representation.

The relative yield of N* components is given by the $|\Delta \vec{I}| = 1$ rule:

$$\begin{aligned} \bar{v} + n &\to N^{*-} + \mu^+ : 3 \\ \bar{v} + p &\to N^{*0} + \mu^+ : 1. \end{aligned} \tag{II-20}$$

In SU(3) theory, these reactions may be related to the analogous reaction for $\Delta S \neq 0$:

$$\begin{aligned} \bar{v} + n &\to Y_1^{*-} + \mu^+ : 2a \\ \bar{v} + p &\to Y_1^{*0} + \mu^+ : a \end{aligned} \qquad \Delta I = \tfrac{1}{2} \tag{II-21}$$

with a being given by SU(3) uniquely:

$$a = \tfrac{1}{80}.$$

More complicated inelastic reactions may be expected.

3. Hyperon Production

Hyperon production is allowed as a $\Delta S = 1$ process for antineutrinos on nucleons

$$\bar{v} + N \to Y + \mu^+ \tag{II-22}$$

e.g.,

$$\bar{v} + p \to \Lambda + \mu^+ \tag{II-23a}$$

$$\bar{v} + n \to \Sigma^- + \mu^+ \tag{II-23b}$$

$$\bar{v} + p \to \Sigma^0 + \mu^+ \tag{II-23c}$$

$\Delta I = \tfrac{1}{2}$ selection rule relates (II-23c) to (II-23b):

$$d\sigma(\Sigma^0) = \tfrac{1}{2} d\sigma(\Sigma^-). \tag{II-24}$$

The differential cross section has been given by Chilton (1964), Bell and Berman (1962), and Adler (1963). Polarizations have been discussed by Adler and by Egardt (1963). Cabibbo and Chilton (1965). have used the SU(3) model of hadron currents (Sections II–V) to make predictions for reactions (II-23). In the spirit of SU(3) symmetry these are all "elastic" equivalents to Eqs. (II-6). Now, however, all six form factors are present: g_V, f_V are taken from the nucleon electromagnetic form factor, g_A is related, on the one hand, to the $\Delta S = 0$ axial vector form factor and, on the other, to the $q^2 = 0$ results of leptonic hyperon decay. The induced pseudoscalar term is neglected (mass of lepton ≈ 0) and the remaining two are ignored as "second class" citizens.

The form factors used in this analysis are then, for Eq. (II-23a):

$$g_V = -G \sin \theta \sqrt{\tfrac{3}{2}} f(q^2)$$

$$g_A = -1.25G \sin \theta \sqrt{\tfrac{3}{2}(\tfrac{1}{2})} f(q^2) \tag{II-25}$$

$$f_V = -G \sin \theta \sqrt{\tfrac{3}{2}} \mu_p f(q^2)$$

for Eq. (II-23b):

$$g_V - G \sin \theta f(q^2)$$

$$g_A = 1.25G \sin \theta \tfrac{1}{2} f(q^2) \tag{II-26}$$

$$f_V = G \sin \theta (\mu_p + 2\mu_n) f(q^2).$$

The axial form factor has been taken the same as the vector form factor

$$f(q^2) = \left(\frac{1}{1 + q^2/a^2}\right)^n \tag{II-27}$$

where two models $n = 1$ and $n = 2$ are evaluated.

Detailed formulas and numerical results are given by Cabibbo and Chilton (1965). The prediction most relevant for present observation is the relative hyperon to nucleon production rate:

$$\frac{\sigma_\Lambda}{\sigma_N} \approx \frac{1}{13}$$

$$\tag{II-28}$$

$$\frac{\sigma_\Sigma}{\sigma_N} \approx \frac{1}{18}$$

for $a^2 \approx 2M_K*^2$ in the model with $n = 1$.

4. Conservation Tests in Inelastic Reactions

Adler (1964) has proposed some "almost practical" tests of CVC and the Goldberger-Trieman relation by noting some special properties of neutrino reactions near $\theta = 0$ where θ is the angle between the neutrino and the out-going lepton. If the lepton mass can be neglected, the matrix element of the lepton current can contain only one four vector $\langle j_\alpha \rangle \sim q_\alpha$, the momentum transfer; hence, the cross section for the reaction $v + \alpha \rightarrow l^- + \beta$ must be proportional to

$$|\langle \beta| \frac{\partial J_\lambda^V}{\partial x_\lambda} + \frac{\partial J_\lambda^A}{\partial x_\lambda} |\alpha\rangle|^2 \qquad (II-29)$$

where α and β are hadron states; CVC tells us that the first term vanishes. Thus, all V–A interference effects vanish in the forward direction for ine-lastic processes. This may be tested by searching for parity violating effects, e.g., $\vec{\sigma} \cdot \vec{p}$ terms in the general reaction:

$$v + \text{nucleus} \rightarrow \mu(\theta = 0) + \text{pions} + \text{residue}$$

e.g., $\vec{\sigma}_N \cdot \vec{q} \times \vec{p}_\pi$ in the reaction

$$v + \alpha \rightarrow \alpha' + \mu + \pi.$$

The second term in Eq. (II-29) can be related to the pion field via the Gold-berger-Treiman relation (partially conserved axial vector current) which says:

$$\frac{\partial J_\alpha^A}{\partial x_\alpha} = \frac{-i\sqrt{2}\, m_N m_\pi^2 g_A}{g_{\pi N}} \phi_\pi \qquad (II-30)$$

where $g_{\pi N}$ is the pion-nucleon constant ($g_{\pi N}/4\pi = 15$) and ϕ_π is the renormal-ized pion field. The author shows that this implies a strong connection between the reactions

$$\pi^+ + \alpha \rightarrow \beta \qquad \text{and} \qquad v + \alpha \rightarrow \mu(\theta = 0) + \beta. \qquad (II-31)$$

Independent of the nature of the state β (which may have 47 pions, etc.), for a fixed invariant mass M_β^*, the distributions of particles within β will be the same in both reactions. Adler has also investigated the conditions of vali-dity of his relations insofar as events are only near $\theta = 0$ and insofar as $m_\mu \neq 0$.

Bell (1964) has discussed Adler's reaction and noted that large q^2 neutrino events depend upon the target nucleus as A, the number of nucleons. However, for forward leptons, under Adler's assumptions, the neutrino cross section is proportional to the pion cross section and should go as $A^{2/3}$ due to pion absorption. This could be tested by comparing events in light and heavy nuclei near $q^2 = 0$.

Adler (1965) has also proposed tests, in high energy neutrino interactions, of a vector and axial vector current algebra suggested by Gell-Mann (1964). This algebra is the basis of a derivation of the axial vector coupling constant renormalization by Adler and by Weisberger (1965). The tests consist of a predicted relation between forward lepton cross sections and matrix elements of the divergence of the axial-vector current at zero four-momentum transfer, this for both $\Delta S = 0$ and $\Delta S = 1$ hadron currents.

D. PRODUCTION OF INTERMEDIATE BOSONS

The speculation that the observed weak interactions are higher order processes generated by a basic vertex containing a fermion current and an intermediate boson has been considered for a long time; it is even implicit in the original Fermi formulation of β decay as well as in Yukawa's theory of β decay (Yukawa, 1935). Although its existence is still in doubt, much is known about this particle via the interactions it was invented to accommodate (e.g., Ogawa, 1956; Schwinger, 1957; Gell-Mann, 1958; Lee and Yang, 1960b). Thus, its spin is 1(V-A interaction), its magnetic moment and quadrupole moment should be close to "normal" $g = 1$ and $Q = 0$; this from the W-electrodynamic considerations of Lee (1962). It can decay into leptons:

$$W^{\pm} \to l^{\pm} + v_l(\bar{v}_l) \tag{II-32}$$

with a rate:

$$R(l = \mu \quad \text{or} \quad e) = Gm_w{}^3/6\pi\sqrt{2}. \tag{II-33}$$

(This is proportional to the square of the coupling constant of the W to lepton currents.) Putting in the numbers

$$R = 6 \times 10^{17}(m_w/m_p)^3 \text{ sec}^{-1}. \tag{II-34}$$

Many of the consequences of the intermediate boson hypotheses are given by Lee and Yang (1960b). (see also Lee and Wu, 1965). We discuss here the production in high energy neutrino beams.

The intermediate boson can be produced by the interaction it was invented to generate. Thus the coupling to leptons gives, with an assist from the Coulomb field of the target nucleus, the production process

$$v_l + Z \to W^+ + l^- + Z^*$$
$$\bar{v}_l + Z \to W^- + l^+ + Z^*. \tag{II-35}$$

The relevant Feynman graphs are given in Fig. 1. Lee (1964) separates the calculation into three regions depending on the energy of the neutrinos. For very high energy neutrinos ($k_v \gtrsim 10^4$ GeV)

$$\sigma \sim \frac{GZ^2}{6\pi\sqrt{2}} \alpha^2 \left(\ln \frac{2k_v\sqrt{12}}{m_w{}^2 R} \right)^3 \tag{II-36}$$

where R is the nuclear radius.

Crudely,

$$\sigma \sim GZ^2\alpha^2 \sim 10^{-5}m_p^{-2}Z^2\alpha^2 \simeq 10^{-37}Z^2 \text{ cm}^2. \qquad \text{(II-37)}$$

In this case the production is coherent (Z^2 term), the nucleus recoiling as a whole.

In the region near threshold ($k_v \gtrsim m_w$) numerical methods must be used. These have been carried out with various modifications by Lee *et al.* (1961), Bell and Veltman (1963a,b), Überall (1964), von Gehlen (1963), and Wu *et al.* (1963, 1965). Near threshold, the production is incoherent ($\sim Z\alpha^2\sigma_{vp} + N\alpha^2\sigma_{vn}$). The comparison with experiment (see Section V,G) involves considerations of the fact that the target is a bound nucleon.

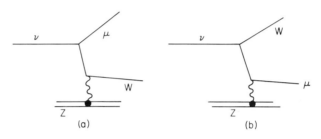

FIG. 1. Feynman diagrams for W production by neutrinos: (a) (b).

Lee *et al.* (1961) have also considered the medium energy region ($k_v \gtrsim m_w^2 R$) and give explicit expressions for the production cross section in this region. The results of the numerical calculations near threshold are compared with experiment in Section V,G. A recent survey of intermediate boson theories has been given by Nakamura (1965). In addition to reviewing the history, a model is presented of a class of theories in which there is a neutral boson carrying a baryon and a lepton number. Thus, in inelastic neutrino interactions one could have, e.g.:

$$v_\mu + n \rightarrow B^0 + \pi^0$$
$$B^0 \rightarrow \mu^- + p. \qquad \text{(II-38)}$$

Further implications of this scheme are given by Nakamura and by Itami *et al.* (1964) who relate the observations of inelastic scattering to the intermediary of the B^0.

E. NEUTRINO-ELECTRON SCATTERING

There has been much weak interaction theoretical and cosmological interest in the elastic reactions

$$v_l(\bar{v}_l) + l^\pm \rightarrow v_l(\bar{v}_l) + l^\pm. \qquad \text{(II-39)}$$

In weak interaction theory, the cross section is given by (Feynman and Gell-Mann, 1958; Bernstein and Lee, 1963; Meyer and Schiff, 1964)

$$\sigma(v_e) = \frac{4G^2}{\pi}\left(\frac{1}{m_e + 2k_v}\right)m_e k_v^2 \tag{II-40}$$

$$\sigma(\bar{v}_e) = \frac{4G^2}{\pi}\frac{m_e k_v^2(m_e^2 + 2m_e k_v + \frac{4}{3}k_v^2)}{(m_e + 2k_v)^3}. \tag{II-41}$$

These interactions are not damped by strong interaction form factors and therefore are of special interest at very high energies.

Neutrinos can also be scattered by electrons via electromagnetic interaction if the neutrino is assumed to have a charge radius. The electromagnetic structure of the neutrino arises via the virtual weak coupling to charged particles and has been calculated by a number of authors (Bernstein and Lee, 1963; Meyer and Schiff, 1964; Chang and Bludman, 1964; Lee and Sirlin, 1964). This gives rise to a $v_e - e$ scattering cross section

$$\frac{d\sigma}{d\Omega} = \frac{\alpha^2\langle r^2\rangle_v^2 k_v^2}{18}\frac{\cos^2 \theta/2}{[1 + (2k_v/m)\sin^2 \theta/2]^3}. \tag{II-42}$$

This is smaller than the Eq. (II-40) by a factor of α^2.

Lee and Sirlin (1964) have calculated the interference between the weak $v - e$ and the electromagnetic $v - e$ scattering and have included radiative corrections up to soft photon emission. The interference term is only down by α from Eq. (II-40) and offers the possibility of an experimental determination of $\langle r^2\rangle_v$.

An upper limit to the charge radius of the electron neutrino comes from the Reines-Cowan experiment and from astrophysical considerations as to the maximum tolerable conversion of electromagnetic to neutrino energy (Bernstein et al., 1963; Ruderman, 1960). This is

$$\langle r^2\rangle_{v_e} \lesssim 2 \times 10^{-29} \text{ cm}^2.$$

The astrophysical implications of Eq. (II-39) in the "crossed" version: $e^+ + e^- \rightarrow v + \bar{v}$, in some stages of stellar evolution have been discussed by several authors (Bernstein et al., 1963; Ruderman, 1965; Pontecorvo, 1959; Chiu and Morrison, 1960; Chiu, 1961; Adams et al., 1963; Stothers and Chiu, 1962). In some processes, a photon (Chiu and Morrison, 1960, Chiu, 1961) or a plasmon (Adams et al., 1963) can decay into a neutrino pair by means of this reaction and by virtue of an effective mass when propagating in a dense electron gas of stellar interiors. The resulting energy loss rate has been invoked to account for the relative abundance of elements in stars and to account for the statistical distribution of star populations in the evolutionary cycle.

III. Experimental Matters

A. Introduction

The bulk of this chapter will be devoted to a description of high energy neutrino experiments. For completeness, the question of the "static" properties of neutrinos should be mentioned. Such matters as the charge, mass, moment, etc., of ν_e and ν_μ are reviewed by Feinberg and Lederman (1963); Bernstein *et al.* (1963), Ruderman (1965), and Schwartz (1965). The results are summarized in Table I.

TABLE I

SUMMARY OF THE KNOWN LIMITS FOR THE ELECTROMAGNETIC INTERSECTIONS OF NEUTRINOS

Property	ν_e	ν_μ
Charge	$< 4 \times 10^{-16}$ from charge conservation	$< 10^{-13}e$ from astrophysics if $m_{\nu_\mu} < 1$ keV
	$< 10^{-13}e$ from astrophysics	$< 3 \times 10^{-5}$ from charge conservation
	$< 3 \times 10^{-10}$ from electron-neutrino scattering	$< 3 \times 10^{-5}$ from pion production by neutrinos
Magnetic moment (in Bohr magnetons)	$< 10^{-10}$ from astrophysics	$< 10^{-10}$ from astrophysics, if $m_{\nu_\mu} < 1$ keV
	$< 1.4 \times 10^{-9}$ from neutrino-electron scattering	$< 10^{-8}$ from pion production by neutrinos
Charge radius (in cm)	$< 4 \times 10^{-15}$ from electron-neutrino scattering	$< 10^{-15}$ from pion production by neutrinos
	$< 4 \times 10^{-14}$ from astrophysics	$< 4 \times 10^{-14}$ from astrophysics if $m_{\nu_\mu} < 1$ keV

B. Production of Neutrino Beams

The primary source of high energy neutrinos is the decay of accelerator produced pions and kaons. Since the decay mean free paths are of the order of hundreds of meters, a drift space must be provided to permit some fraction of the pion-kaon flux to decay. The resulting neutrino intensity on a distant detector then depends on the charged particle angular distribution and the momentum distribution. A relevant design factor is the laboratory angle between neutrino and parent particle. This and the dimensions of the detector and shielding wall determine the benefits of focusing devices. Here we will review the beam arrangements which have been used. In Section VI, we discuss proposed improvements.

1. 1961 BNL *Experiment*

An internal target was used at the leading edge of a 3-meter straight section. The configuration of downstream magnets and the requirements of shielding dictated a production angle of 8°. Furthermore, the machine energy used was 15 GeV in order to reduce the number of muons penetrating the then available shield. No focusing was used. The drift space was 21 meters long and the shield 13 meters thick. The resulting neutrino flux was estimated at $1500/cm^2$ per 10^{11} protons *circulating* in the machine.

2. *Improvements at* CERN and BNL

A substantial improvement was made in the subsequent CERN and Brookhaven National Laboratory (BNL) arrangements by extracting the proton beam from the accelerators permitting the use of secondary particles at more forward angles. This improvement is due to the very strong forward peaking of pions and kaons, especially at higher energy. The production of pions by protons from 20 to 30 GeV is reasonably well represented by equations of the form:

$$\frac{d^2\sigma}{dp\,d\Omega} = A p^2(p_0 - p) \exp[-(p - a)(b + c\theta^n)] \qquad \text{(III-1)}$$

where p_0 is the incident proton momentum, p, θ the pion momentum and angle, and A, a, b, c, n are parameters given in Table II.

TABLE II

PARAMETERS FOR PION PRODUCTION SPECTRA

		A	a	b	c	n
π^+	(20)	3.0	2	0.37	5.2	1
	(30)	2.6	2	0.25	5.2	1
π^-	(20)	2.16	2	0.45	4.8	1.5
	(30)	1.75	2	0.42	1.1	1.5

It is seen that the fall-off with angle for, say, 5 GeV/c π^+ is $\sim e^{-15.6\theta}$.

The kaon contribution is obtained from K to π ratios observed at the accelerators [see Eqs. (III-8) and (III-9)].

The neutrino energy in the laboratory system is given by

$$E_\nu = \frac{m_M{}^2 - m_\mu{}^2}{2(E_M - P_M \cos\theta)} \qquad \text{(lab.)} \qquad \text{(III-2)}$$

where m_M is the mass of the pion (kaon), E_M, P_M, the energy and momentum of the decaying particle, and θ the decay angle. From this we see that the maximum neutrino energy for $P_M/E_M \approx 1$ is

Pions: $(E_\nu)_{max} = (1 - (m_\mu/m_\pi)^2) \quad E_\pi = 0.424E_\pi$ (III-3)

Kaons: $(E_\nu)_{max} = (1 - (m_\mu/m_K)^2) \quad E_k \simeq E_k.$ (III-4)

The angular divergence of neutrinos is given by the angular half-width, i.e., the angle within which half of the neutrinos are to be found:

$$\theta_{1/2} = 1/\gamma \qquad\qquad \text{(III-5)}$$

i.e., for a 5-GeV pion (kaon), $\theta_{1/2} = 28$ mrad (50 mrad). This illustrates the limitation in neutrino beams and the problems presented in the focusing of neutrino parents. Pions give on the average only one-fourth of their energy to neutrinos whereas kaons transfer approximately one-half; however, the divergence of the kaons is worse, the intensity going as $(1/\gamma)^2$.

Placement of shielding, length of beam, and other geometric considerations can vary greatly, depending on the energy and focusing devices employed (Schwartz, 1965; Lederman et al., 1960; Giesh et al., 1963a,b; van der Meer, 1966; Lederman, 1964; Ramm, 1966; Novey, 1966). For a wide-angle source, decay space equal to shielding thickness is optimum. Detailed considerations on the design philosophy based on the CERN horn can be found in Giesch et al. (1963a,b) and van der Meer (1966). A description of the BNL plasma lens (Forsythe et al., 1965) is given below. More radical proposals can be found in the reports of Palmer (1966) (magnetic fingers); Samios and Palmer (1964), and Asner and Iselin (1964). These will be referred to again (Section VI,B).

C. BNL Determination of Neutrino Flux

One of the most important aspects of neutrino experiments is the determination of the neutrino spectrum striking the detector. This knownedge is prerequisite to determining the cross sections for elastic and inelastic neutrino-induced events and to set a lower limit on the mass of the intermediate boson. In the BNL arrangement, the problem was treated with much respect.

The primary particles from the AGS at Brookhaven National Laboratory are 30 GeV/c protons at $0°$. These interact with a 1.5 cm diam by 30 cm Be target to produce the secondary particles (pions and kaons) which subsequently decay into neutrinos and their associated charged leptons. Thus, neutrinos are not only neutral but are tertiary products. Therefore, it is necessary to acquire a detailed knowledge of the spectra of the secondary particles in order to calculate the neutrino spectra. Due to the fast spill of the primary beam (i.e., $\approx 10^{11}$ protons on target in 2 μsec), unique problems arose in monitoring the total proton intensity. These problems were solved by radiochemical analysis of a 2.58 year half-life, induced in an Al foil placed in front of the target. The results were consistent with the known circulating beam intensity and the approximate extraction efficiency.

The philosophy of neutrino flux determination here is that a knowledge of the differential muon flux $d^2 N_\mu / d\Omega_\mu \, dp_\mu$ leads directly to the parent pion flux from which the pion neutrino yield may be calculated. The important K–ν contribution is obtained from the well-measured K to π ratios obtained in beam surveys.

Some knowledge of the spectra of the secondary particles exists in the form of beam survey data from BNL and CERN (Baker *et al.*, 1961; Dekkers *et al.*, 1964). However, due to inadequacies, in these data, emulsions and a solid state detector were used to study the distribution of the muons from the secondary particles (π^+, π^-, K$^+$, K$^-$). The pions are the main source of the muons, while the kaons contribute a small ($\approx 10\%$) "constant" background. A Monte Carlo calculation of the muon distribution was performed using analytic formulas representing pion production suggested by the beam survey data. The subsequent comparison of this calculation with the emulsion data obtained with a thin (3 in. Be) target provided checks and improvements for the analytic formulas. Using these improved formulas and beam survey data for kaon to pion ratios, analytic formulas for kaon production were obtained which are especially important for the knowledge of the high energy region of neutrino spectra.

The first step was to represent the known survey data by analytic formulas which are functions of incident proton momentum P_0, secondary pion momentum p, and angle θ. A suitable function was given in Eq. (III-1).

The results for the fit to the BNL 30-GeV/c data are given in Table II. An excellent fit with $n = 1$ (same as 20 GeV/c fit) was obtained for π^+ but not for the π^- data. Hence, it was necessary to use a different distribution for representing the π^- data. The 20-GeV/c data showed that a value of $n \simeq 1.5$ gave the best fit for π^-'s. There is no reason to believe that this will remain true at 30 GeV/c. Hence a study of the muon spectra was made in order to supplement the beam survey data.

1. Muon Spectra

Two methods of measurement of the muon spectra were used. The first was to employ a set of 1 in. by 3 in. by 100 μ nuclear emulsions and the second was to use a solid state detector. These were inserted into probe holes in the steel shielding after the drift space (see Fig. 2). The probe holes correspond to minimum muon momenta of 4.6, 5.3, 6.0, 6.75, 7.5, 8.25, 9.7, and 11.2 GeV/c and angles of 0 to about 5°. Beryllium targets of 3 and 12 in. were exposed to the proton beam. A count of minimum ionizing tracks, by the emulsion group at Stevens Institute of Technology, in a

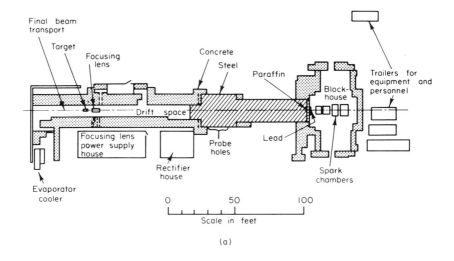

(a)

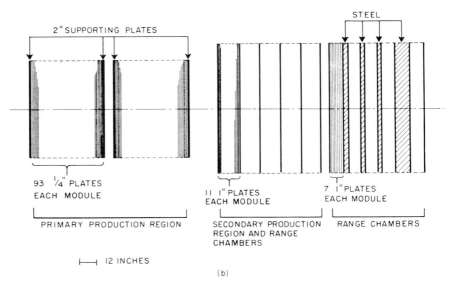

(b)

Fig. 2. BNL Phase II experimental arrangement: (a) over-all layout and (b) spark chamber detector scheme.

particular emulsion divided by the number of protons incident on the target provides an absolute number of muons per proton per square centimeter at a given angle with momenta greater than a given amount. The number of protons incident on the target for a particular exposure of the emulsions was monitored by placing a 4-mil-thick foil of polyethylene (CH_2) in front of the target (i.e., C^{12} $(p, pn)C^{11}$) which was subsequently analyzed for the β^+ decay of C^{11} by radiochemical methods.

The muon spectrum was now calculated using a Monte Carlo program which generates pions according to the distributions which were determined by the above methods. The pion is followed from its point of creation in the target, taking simple absorptive effects in the target into account, to the point along its path at which it decays. All decay kinematics are included. The particle is always assumed to decay. In order to take the decay probability of the pion into account the muon resulting from its decay is multiplied by the probability that it did in reality decay. This method of conditional probability is used in order to avoid a bias against high energy muons. The parameters of the pion production distribution were adjusted until the curves calculated by this program agreed with the 3-in. (thin) target emulsion results. The analytic forms for the pion production spectra thus obtained are

$$\pi^+ : \frac{d^2\sigma}{dp \, d\Omega} = 2.6p^2(30 - p) \exp\left[-(p - 2.0)(0.25 + 5.2\theta)\right] \qquad \text{(III-6)}$$

$$\pi^- : \frac{d^2\sigma}{dp \, d\Omega} = 1.75p^2(30 - p) \exp\left[-(p - 2.0)(0.42 + 1.1\theta^{1.5})\right]. \quad \text{(III-7)}$$

The uncertainties of the parameters in Table II are on the order of 10–20%. The agreement seen here establishes confidence in the method which is now applied to the thick target actually used in the run.

A study of the thick target results indicated that the experimental points exceed the calculated points by approximately 50%. This is quite reasonable in view of thick target effects such as the multiple interactions of the protons, interactions of high energy pions with the target nucleons to produce additional pions, and the inadequacy of the simple absorptive model for the pions used in the Monte Carlo program. These effects do not greatly alter the shape of the subsequent spectra and were taken into account by increasing the normalization of the pion production spectra.

The analytic form for the production formula for kaons was learned by studying the K to π ratios from the beam survey data. These data were fitted by least squares to obtain the following results for 30 GeV/c incident proton momentum:

$$K^+/\pi^+ = (0.085 \pm 0.014) \exp\{[(0.010 \pm 0.012)p + (4.91 \pm 1.9)\theta]\} \qquad \text{(III-8)}$$

$$K^-/\pi^- = (0.099 \pm 0.020) \exp\{[-(0.073 \pm 0.016)p + (0.30 \pm 0.55)\theta]\}. \quad \text{(III-9)}$$

Here we note that K^+/π^+ is consistent with no momentum dependence, while K^-/π^- is consistent with no angular dependence. The formulas (III-8) and (III-9) combined with Eqs. (III-6) and (III-7), respectively, yield the analytic formulas representing kaon production.

The Monte Carlo program for muons (or neutrinos) from kaons is the same as that for pions except for obvious kinematical modifications.

With these production distributions for pions and kaons and with the necessary kinematical modifications to the Monte Carlo program, the neutrino (antineutrino) fluxes at the detector were calculated. The results of these calculations are shown in Fig. 3.

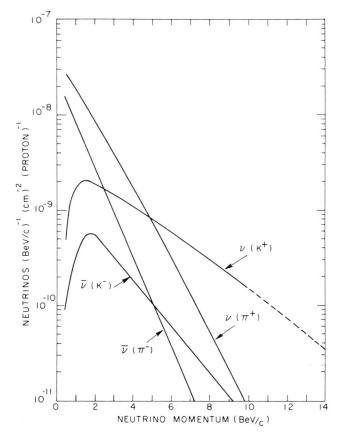

Fig. 3. BNL calculated neutrino flux without focusing, 12 in. Be target.

2. Uncertainties in Neutrino Spectra

The uncertainties in the neutrino fluxes come mainly from four independent sources. These will now be mentioned in order of decreasing importance.

(1) Thick target effects. These effects were discussed above. In addition, to the uncertainty in normalization, the loss of high energy pion interacting to produce low energy pions influences the shape of the subsequent neutrino

spectrum. The magnitude of these effects are hard to estimate, but can probably be assumed to be less than 50% and probably much less for the intermediate energy region of the neutrino spectrum.

(2) The formulas representing production spectra are based on secondary momenta greater than 4 GeV/c. There is no reason to believe the formulas extrapolate to lower momenta. Neutrino flux for neutrino energies below 1 GeV/c are therefore subject to considerable uncertainty.

(3) The cross sections used in the radiochemical analysis of proton exposure are known to only about 10%.

(4) The parameter uncertainties of approximately 10–20% result in comparable errors in the neutrino spectrum but are overshadowed by effects 1 and 2.

The neutrino fluxes are therefore known to no better than 50% over the neutrino energy region of 1 to 10 GeV.

D. CERN NEUTRINO FLUX

The CERN problem was made more difficult by the need to follow pions and kaons through the focusing horn parts of which constituted the target (Giesch et al., 1963a,b; van der Meer, 1966). Thick target effects were more serious in their long copper target. Also, no elaborate preparations were made for studying the muons. The essential elements in the CERN determination is to use the CERN measurements of π and K production at 0 and 100 mrad made in Pb and Be and to find a reasonable "fit" to these angles and a reasonable interpolation to the Cu target used in the horn. Trajectories were traced through the horn taking absorption into account (but not reemission). Consequently, the results below 1 GeV/c are not expected to be too reliable. In order to clarify this, an identical target was inserted into the bubble chamber and an estimate of the production spectra was obtained from bombardment with 25 GeV protons. Some problems arose in the identification of secondary particles, but in general the results were consistent with typical calculated spectra such as is presented in Fig. 4 (Orkin-Lecourtois, 1964, 1965). Additional verifications are discussed below (Section V,E).

E. THE CERN ARRANGEMENT

This description is based on the compact summary given by Bernardini (1964) at the Dubna conference in 1964. A short pulse extraction (designed and put into operation by Kuiper, Plass, and collaborators) had practically 100% efficiency. It ejected into an external copper target (a rod 25 cm long and 4 mm in diameter) an average of 5×10^{11} protons per pulse. The particles emitted (mostly pions) were focused towards the detectors by a device originally designed by van der Meer. The energy of the extracted proton beam incident on the target was 24.9 GeV. The decay path was 25 meters and the iron

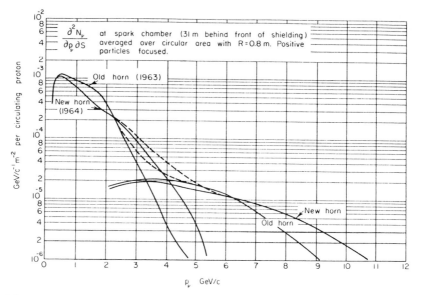

Fig. 4. CERN neutrino flux incident upon the spark chamber with van der Meer horn focusing.

shielding was also 25 meters, corresponding to the range of a 28-GeV μ meson. The "magnetic horn" of van der Meer and collaborators is similar to a conical mirror. It generates a considerable enhancement of the total fluxes, particularly in the energy region above 4 GeV. Furthermore, it allows one to have at wish (apart from contaminations) beams of μ neutrinos or μ anti-neutrinos. The "horn" has been used for focusing positive and negative particles. The corresponding spectra, evaluated by van der Meer and co-workers by an elaborate but straightforward combination of orbit calculations and kinematical rules, are plotted in Fig. 4.

The two curves refer, respectively, to an old and a new improved version of the horn. There are several sources of error in them, the most important of which lies in the uncertainty of angles and momenta about the π and K production. The part of the spectrum above 4 GeV is particularly uncertain. Furthermore, the calculated spectrum concerns only the μ neutrino originating from primary mesons produced in the target and decaying in the tunnel. Secondary sources from interaction in the walls of the horn, in the shielding, etc., were neglected. They may contribute appreciably below 0.5 GeV.

One of the detectors placed in the CERN μ-neutrino beam was a large heavy liquid bubble chamber[1] placed in the more favorable position, i.e.,

[1] The main characteristics of the bubble chamber are the following: Liquid CF_3 BR density: 1.5 gm/cm³; radiation length X_0: 11.5 cm; interaction length λ_0: 68 cm; total volume: 500 $l \simeq 0.75$ ton; Field: 27 kG.

immediately after the iron shield[2]; the other was a multiton spark chamber (see Fig. 5).

The identification of the tracks was made following the standard procedures based on curvature, ionization, δ-ray counting, etc.

In this manner, most protons can be clearly distinguished from π's and μ's. Of course, π's and μ's cannot be separated. The distinction between them was then made on the basis of the observable interactions. The residual contamination of π's which has been taken as μ's cannot exceed 5% of all the events.

Neutral pions have been identified from kinematics when both γ's materialized inside the bubble chamber. The few single γ's found are compatible with π^0 decays when the detection efficiency of the chamber is taken into account. The neutron background for events above 300 MeV is negligible.

In conclusion, the errors in the bubble chamber due to the misinterpretation of the nature of tracks are thought to be no larger than those due to statistics. The other detector was a multiton spark chamber.[3]

The multiton spark chamber had two versions: the 1963 version and the 1964 version, not very different in principle. It consists of three sections. Going downstream with the incident μ neutrinos, the first section is made by relatively thin plates and can be considered a "high resolution production chamber." The second is a magnet with interleaved spark chambers, which indicates the sign of the crossing particles; the third is a thick layer "range" chamber. The 1963 edition, shown in Fig. 5, was a general-purpose instrument. The "production region" was made by a front part in aluminum and brass to increase the efficiency in detecting showers. One of the purposes was to confirm the Brookhaven result.

The magnet was a Helmholtz coil, quite limited in aperture and field strength.

The 1964 edition was mainly designed for the search of the intermediate boson. The high resolution region was made by 5 tons of aluminum plates ~ 7 mm thick, followed by a set of thin brass plates equivalent to 8 radiation lengths. But the main difference was the replacement of the Helmholtz coil by a set of 25 large magnetized iron plates with 12 interposed spark chamber units. The over-all assembly is shown in Fig. 6.

The magnetized iron plates with their field of $\simeq 17$ kG allow the identification of the sign of all particles born inside and having a range of ≥ 200

[2] The persons who contributed to this work were: M. Block, H. Burmeister, D. Cundy, B. Eiben, C. Franzinetti, J. Keren, R. Møllerud, G. Myatt, M. Nikolic, A. Orki-Lecourtois, M. Paty, D. Perkins, C. Ramm, K. Schultze, H. Sletten, K. Soop, R. Stump, W. Venus, and H. Yoshiki.

[3] The list of persons who contributed to the spark chamber experiment is as follows: H. Bienlein, A. Böhm, G. von Dardel, H. Faissner, F. Ferrero, J. M. Gaillard, H. J. Gerber, B. Hahn, V. Kaftanov, F. Kreinen, C. Manfredotti, M. Reinharz, R. A. Salmeron, P. G. Seiler, A. Staude, J. J. Steiner, J. Stein, and G. Bernardini.

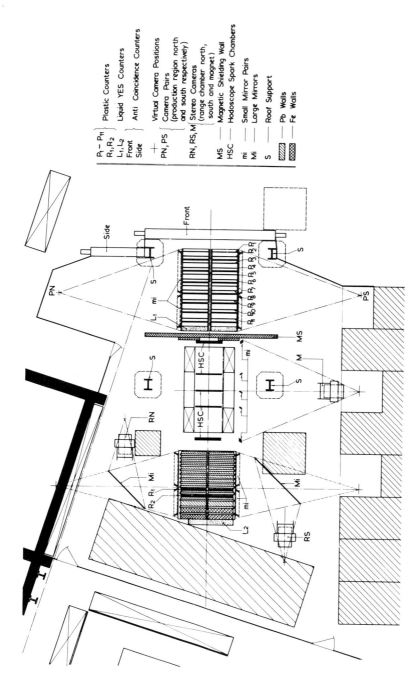

Fig. 5. CERN 1963 arrangement. The CERN heavy liquid bubble chamber is located in front of the spark chamber complex. P_1–P_n and R_1, R_2, plastic counters; L_1, L_2, liquid YES counters; front side, anticoincidence counters; +, virtual camera positions; PN, PS, camera pairs (production region north and south, respectively); RN, RS, M, stereo cameras (range chamber north), south, and magnet); MS, magnetic shielding wall; HSC, hodoscope spark chambers; mi, small mirror pairs; Mi, large mirrors, and S roof support.

gm/cm². It also allows the estimation of the momenta of all crossing particles with momenta ranged between 1.5 and 30 GeV/c, with a 25% accuracy.

The 1500-gm/cm² range chamber was the last part of the apparatus downstream. In most cases, the sign of the escaping particles was identified by means of two slabs of 15 cm thick magnetized iron which were at the end.

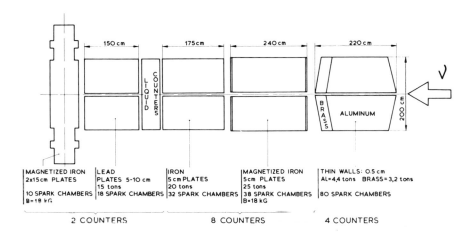

Fig. 6. CERN 1964 spark chambers; neutrino experiment February–May 1964. Spark Chamber dimensions; 1.60 meters in height, 1.00 meter in depth, 3.5 cm thick, photography 18° stereo.

In the high resolution sections of the spark chambers, a good discrimination is possible only between electron and photon showers and other tracks. The many calibrations show that this discrimination is unambiguous for electrons and photons above 300 MeV.

For a "single-line" track, the distinction between a noninteracting or μ-like particle and all others lies in the possibility of identifying single scattering or "stars" along the track. Then its reliability and accuracy depend on the length of each track and on the goodness and completeness of the calibrations. Other procedures related to multiple scattering, ranges, etc., are also applied whenever it is possible.

In the analysis of the events, a conservation law for μ leptons was always assumed as a working hypothesis. A conservation law for μ leptons, similar to that valid for the e neutrino (as has been demonstrated by the absence of double-β decay), may be considered to be normal. However, as $v_\mu \neq v_e$, it has to be shown that this assumption is consistent with the results.

This means that if only positive parents (π's and K's) are focused by the "horn," the μ neutrinos of the beam induce reactions where *only negative*

μ's are produced. This can be seen immediately when one considers, for instance, the reaction chain which starts with the parent π^+ and the target nucleon N_1 and ends with the v_μ interaction

$$\pi + N_1 \to v_\mu + \mu^+ + N_1 \to \mu^+ + \mu_2 + N^* \to N_2 + \mu + \mu_2 + \text{hadrons}.$$

Because there are no leptons initially, μ_2 must be negative at the end.

The "magnetic horn" allowed an almost clean beam of μ neutrinos. There is a $\bar{v}_\mu$ contamination because particles emitted at angles $\leqslant 1.5°$ remain inside the inner core of the horn and do not suffer deflection; but due to the favorable π^+/π^- ratio and the limited solid angle, this contamination is estimated to be 6% for the 1963 horn version and $\sim 3\%$ in the 1964 horn version.

F. BNL ARRANGEMENT

The new high energy neutrino arrangement is based on an external proton beam at the AGS. This arrangement is shown in Fig. 2. Neutrinos are generated by the decay in flight of pions and kaons produced in a 1.5 cm diam by 30 cm Be target by 30 GeV/c protons near zero degrees. No focusing device was employed. The 22-meter flight path was followed by a 27-meter iron shield which permitted about one muon per five pulses to pass into the detector. This was an aluminum spark chamber composed of 184 plates, each 6 ft by 6 ft by $\frac{1}{4}$ in. and weighing a total of 12 tons. The "production chamber" was followed by a "range chamber" consisting of 90 plates, each 8 ft by

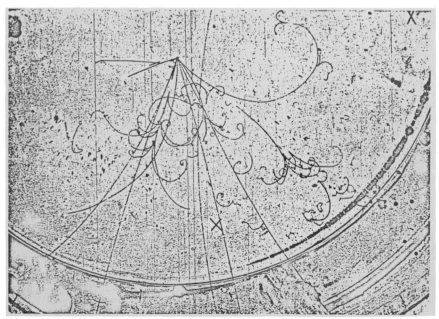

Fig. 7. CERN HLBC neutrino-induced inelastic reaction.

8 ft by 1 in. thick, with interspersed steel plates designed to measure the range of muons up to about 2 GeV (see Fig. 2).

The chambers were triggered after every pulse in order to avoid bias due to counting efficiency. The spark chambers were designed to integrate over the 2.5-μsec spill and maintain multitrack efficiency for this duration. In this mode of operation, the clearing field was pulsed off (to < 1 V) just before the sensitive time. In addition, it was found necessary to purify continuously the Ne-He gas mixture by circulation through a liquid N_2-cooled charcoal trap.

Figures 7, 8, 9, 10, and 11 show typical neutrino events in the heavy liquid bubble chamber (HLBC), in the CERN spark chamber, and in the BNL spark chamber.

Fig. 8. CERN HLBC neutrino-induced electron event.

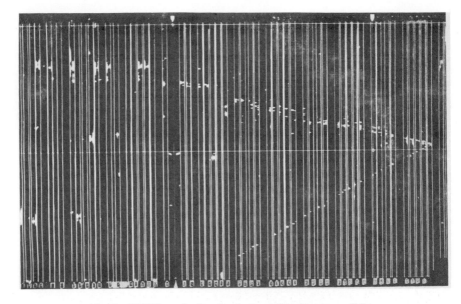

Fig. 9. CERN spark chamber intermediate boson candidate.

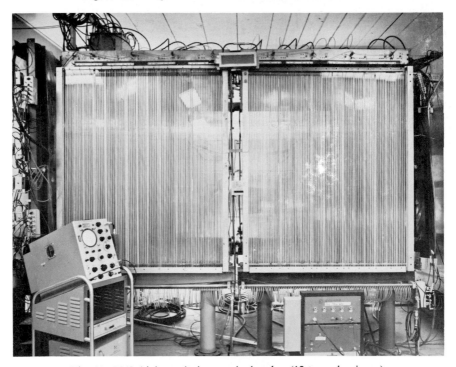

Fig. 10. BNL high resolution spark chamber (12 tons aluminum).

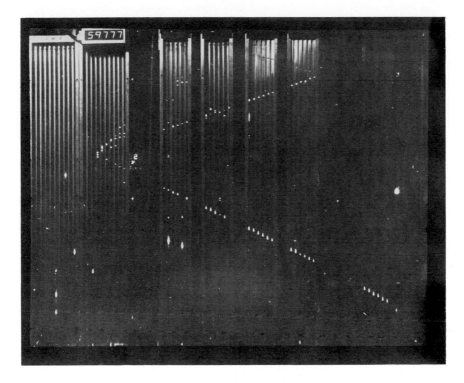

Fig. 11. BNL spark chamber intermediate boson candidate.

An achromatic large aperture focusing device was constructed at BNL (Forsythe *et al.*, 1965). This was an axial current discharge timed to coincide with the extracted beam and to provide an azimuthal magnet field for cylindrically symmetric focusing. It operated for 20 hours giving a gain of 3 for v_μ from π^+ and K^+. Engineering difficulties caused it to be abandoned for the BNL run. The large current required (5×10^5 amp) and the short duration (3μsec) result in a pinch effect which acts to convert capacitor bank energy to heating the gas. The resulting efficiency was only 50%, the calculated gain having been ~ 7. It is not known if some means can be found to avoid the large energy loss.

G. Argonne National Laboratory Arrangement

A third facility for neutrino physics has been established at the 12.5-GeV/c ZGS accelerator but has, at this writing, not yet been placed in operation. It also provides a large spark chamber detector constructed from very thin plate modules so that the interaction material, now independent of the spark chamber, may be varied. The long machine "spill" forced several elaborations in the design of the focusing horn and in the very complete anticoincidence shield entirely surrounding the detector Novey, (1966).

IV. Cosmic Ray Neutrinos

A. INTRODUCTION

We consider in this section calculations and attempts to observe the flux of high energy neutrinos from the decay of pions and kaons generated in the atmosphere by cosmic ray primaries. The objectives of this research are several: (a) Cosmic rays give rise to a distribution of neutrino energies considerably higher than is now available at accelerators. Even crude measurements of their interaction properties would be interesting. (b) Neutrino sources from outside the atmosphere may conceivably be present with sufficient intensity to be observed. The first objective is concerned with the extrapolation of the weak interaction coupling to very high energies; the second concerns questions of cosmology and has been discussed by several authorities and given the name, "neutrino astronomy." Earlier discussions of cosmic ray neutrino flux have been given by Greisen (1961), Zatsepin and Kuzmin (1961), Markov and Zheleznykh (1961), and others.

B. COSMIC RAY NEUTRINO FLUX

There have been several calculations of the neutrino flux based on the observations of the muon spectrum at sea level (Greisen, 1961; Zatsepin and Kuzmin, 1961; Markov and Zheleznykh, 1961; Cowsik et al., 1966; Osborne, 1965; Lee et al., 1963; Keuffel, 1965; Menon, 1965). The main assumptions are as follows: Cosmic ray primaries (protons) incident upon the atmosphere generate pions and kaons according to some assumed spectrum. The primary nucleons, pions, and kaons are attenuated with a characteristic length of 120 gm/cm^2. These decay according to well-known lifetimes and branching ratios. The resulting muon spectrum is compared with observation—this is used to adjust the production spectrum before calculating the final neutrino flux. The major uncertainties arise from the fact that the muon spectrum is uncertain above 100 GeV and K/π ratio is not known at all for $E_{primary} > 30$ GeV and is not very sensitive to the muon spectrum. The recent calculations take a K/π ratio of 0.20. A power law fit to the spectrum of $v_\mu + \bar{v}_\mu$ is given by Cowsik et al., (1966), as

$$n(k_v) = 0.058k_v^{-2.89}(cm^2 \text{ sec sr GeV})^{-1}.$$

The K/π ratio uncertainty is not too serious at $E < 100$ GeV but may be very large at higher energies.

C. Expected Interaction Rates

There have also been several estimates of the rates of muons produced in the earth (as a target) by this neutrino flux (Lee *et al.*, 1963; Keuffel, 1965). Here one must make various assumptions as to the behavior of $\sigma(k_v)$, as to the mass of the intermediate boson (if it exists), and as to the fraction of neutrino energy which is transferred to the muon which is to be detected. The results must then be compared with the minimum background, muons which penetrate to the detector from the atmosphere.

A typical example of the *expected* rates is given by Table III presented by Keuffel (1965) from the report of Menon (1965). This table assumes a constant

TABLE III

Rates of Cosmic Ray Neutrino-Induced Muons

Process		Cross section (cm²)	Fraction of k_v retained by muon	Neutrino event rate per cm² sec sr[b]
(a)	Elastic $\sigma_{el} = 0.75 \times 10^{-38}$ per $n-p$ pair		1.0	0.065×10^{-12}
(b)	Inelastic (i) $\sigma_{inel} = 0.45 \times 10^{-38}k_v(1\text{--}10 \text{ GeV})$		$\frac{1}{0}$	0.17×10^{-12}
	$0.45 \times 10^{-37}(10 \text{ GeV up})$		1	
	(ii) $\sigma_{inel} = 0.45 \times 10^{-38}k_v$ (all k_v)		$\frac{1}{2}$	0.29×10^{-12}
(c)	Boson production cross sections of Wu *et al.* (1963)	(i) 0.15		0.13×10^{-12}
	$M_w = 2.5$ up to 20 GeV joined to von Gehlen	(ii) 0.55		0.46×10^{-12}
	asymptotic expression at 100 GeV[a]			
(d)	Summary of predictions		$(0.24 - 0.81) \times 10^{-12}$	
(e)	Experimental results			
	KGF[c]			$\sim 0.85 \times 10^{-12}$
	Case-Wits[d]			0.4×10^{-12}

[a] These are two extreme limits of the combined fraction of k_v given both to the associated muon and the muon from W- decay (branching ratio $W \to \mu + v \,/\, W \to$ all $= 0.4$.)

[b] Since the events are produced in the rock surrounding the apparatus, the expected rate depends on the area and angular acceptance of the apparatus as well as on the assumptions as to energy dependence.

[c] Menon, M. G. K., Naranan, S., Narasimham, V. S., Hirotani, K., Ho, N., Miyake, S., Craig, R., Creed, D. R., Osborne, J. L., Wolfendale, A. W. (1966). Report to the 13th International Conference on High Energy Physics, Berkeley (1966).

[d] See also Reines (1966), and Reines *et al.*, (1965).

elastic neutrino cross section of 0.7×10^{-38} cm² and an inelastic cross section which transfers half the energy to the muon. It assumes a cross section increasing with E_v up to a cutoff energy of 10 GeV (thence constant) or no cutoff at all. These rates assume a neutrino (incident isotropically) interaction in the rock surrounding the apparatus and a muon which survives the subsequent energy loss in the rock in order to cross the equipment.

D. EXPERIMENTAL RESULTS

Three experiments have recently reported some results. An Indian, Japanese, U.K. collaboration has established a detector deep underground (7000 m.w.e. in the Kolar Gold Mines (KGF) in South India.[4] The detector subtends 48 m² sr and consists of two vertical walls of scintillator separated by 2 Pb walls (2.5 cm thick) and having arrays of neon flash tubes which can delineate tracks when triggered (see Fig. 12).

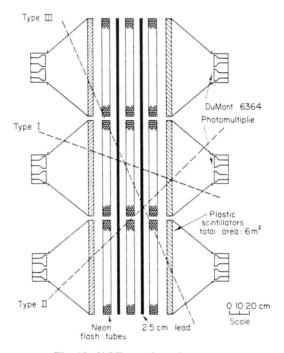

Fig. 12. KGF neutrino telescope.

Another arrangement at a similar depth is a U.S.-South African collaboration (Reines, 1965, 1966) (8400 m.w.e.) and consists of a 37 m² sr array of liquid scintillators so designed as to favor large azimuth muons. Pulse height is used to discriminate against backgrounds.

Both arrangements depend on a very large difference between vertical and horizontal components of the "back-ground" cosmic ray muons which is

[4] See *Proceedings of the Cosmic Ray Conference* held in London in 1965; Keuffel, 1965; Achar *et al.*, 1965a,b, 1966.

extrapolated from measurements at much higher depths in the earth. Both experiments have reported events.

The KGF collaboration (Keuffel, 1965) has reported 15 events of interest (*Proceedings of the Cosmic Ray Conference*; Achar *et al.*, 1965a,b), in that their neon discharge hodoscope identified two incoming tracks permitting the identification of an origin and hence the sense of the initiating track (slightly upward). Both tracks are consistent with muons or pions and represent at least 1 GeV of energy, allowing for the energy loss in the rock. This one event would seem to be most certainly of neutrino origin. An additional event is almost horizontal and consists of a single track. Backgrounds of atmospheric muons are seen in this visual technique in the form of soft wide-angle radiation accompanying vertical tracks. The authors believe that about three additional events are real and this corresponds to a rate of 0.85×10^{-12} events/cm^{-2} sr^{-1} sec^{-1}. Of course, there is no direct measure of n for great depths and low energy muons and therefore a reliable estimate of the background (when the energy detected is $\ll 1$ GeV) must rely on a fairly complicated calculation. If the above distribution of atmospheric muons is assumed, then most of the observed events are not atmospheric muon-induced because of the peaking toward 90° from the zenith angle. The observed rate would seem to require an k_ν^2 behavior (Table III) up to at least 50 GeV, or an anomalous neutrino flux or an enhancement of the cross section due to an intermediate boson. However, the statistical validity at this time corresponds to four sure events.

The Case-Wits collaboration at 8400 m.w.e. has reported seven large zenith angle events, i.e., events which cross the two vertical arrays of scintillator. Since there is no absorber, the energy deposited in the detector is typically 50 MeV. The understanding of background in somewhat more severe in this case since the experiment is sensitive to low energy radiation. The seven events correspond to a rate $\sim 0.4 \times 10^{-12}$ cm^{-2} sr^{-1} sec^{-1}. Within the uncertainties this is consistent with the KGF results and with conventional theory as indicated in the table. The vertical intensity at this depth is about 20 times the signal rate, considerably smaller than the KGF rate, presumably due to the greater depth.

A novel approach is being made by the Utah group (Keuffel, 1965). From Keuffel's report:

" The detector will be of area comparable to the Case-Wits set up, but very much thicker ($10 \times 10 \times 6$ m^3). It will resemble in some respects a multiplate spark chamber such as those used in the Brookhaven or CERN experiments, but scaled up by a factor of 200 in mass. The parallel-plate spark gaps are replaced by trays of cylindrical spark counters of novel design, and the trigger function is provided by water-filled Cherenkov counters.

" The cylindrical spark counters resemble giant Geiger tubes 15 cm in diameter by 10 m long. With a filling of 50 cm argon and 25 cm ethylene, the discharge is a sharply-localized corona spike, which may be located by a simple sonic technique to an accuracy of $\pm$ 3 mm. Four Cherenkov counters will trigger an array of 500 spark counters and determine the sense of travel of upward-going muons produced by neutrinos. A counter consists of a water-filled concrete tank $6 \times 10 \times 1$ m^3 painted black inside. Each 6×10 m^2 surface is covered by an array of 113 light-collector elements. By recording separately the pulses from each face, the sense of travel of the muon may be determined.

"The detector will be located in a nearby mine at a depth of about 1500 m.w.e. The expected flux of background muons through the aperture of the instrument is still about 10^6 yr^{-1}. However, since the sense of travel of a high-energy muon secondary from a neutrino interaction can be unambiguously determined (in the most favorable case by four independent Cherenkov measurements and three time-of-flight measurements) the upward-going muons should furnish a background-free signal despite the relatively shallow depth. Also, neutrinos interacting within the detector volume will probably be easy to identify, even for downward-going neutrinos . . . . The angular resolution of the instrument itself will be about 10^{-6} sr, which will be important for possible neutrino astronomy."

Finally, Cowan (1965) has been observing the apparent production of ~ 100 MeV muons directly by neutral radiation near the surface of the earth. The interpretation of these data is rather tentative and better left for some future review.

E. NEUTRINO ASTRONOMY

Bahcall (1965) and Bahcall and Frauschi (1964) have discussed some general problems of neutrino astronomy including the relevance of underground measurements to the possibilities of "resonances" in the v_μ-nucleon system and in the v_e-nucleon system. These authors have also discussed the possibility of detecting neutrinos from strong radio sources outside the galaxy. They conclude that the only hope of detecting such weak sources would be the (lucky) existence of the resonance in the $\bar{v}_e - \bar{e}$ system proposed by Glashow (1960):

$$\bar{v}_e + e^- \rightarrow W^- \rightarrow \bar{v}_\mu + \mu^-.$$

The collimation relative to the radio source should be very good for a neutrino energy $\sim 10^4$ GeV which is required to effectively produce a $\sim$ 10-GeV W particle. It is reasonably certain that cosmic sources of neutrinos are very weak compared to the flux generated in the atmosphere. This is because where-ever there are charged pions, there should be π^0's, hence γ rays. These have been sought with somewhat simpler arrangements with no success. Discussions of neutrino astronomy are given by Pontecorvo (1963), Pontecorvo and Smorodinskii (1962), and Weinberg (1962a,b).

V. Experimental Results from Accelerators

A. TWO NEUTRINOS

One of the most important questions posed for neutrino physics was the question of the distinguishability of v_μ and v_e where, e.g.,

$$e + p \rightarrow v_e + n \qquad (\text{V-1})$$

and

$$\mu + p \rightarrow v_\mu + n. \qquad (\text{V-2})$$

Since neutrino beams are naturally overwhelmingly v_μ, the experimental problem was to distinguish electrons from muons in the inverse of reactions above. The original spark chambers (Danby et al., 1962) did this easily since electrons would produce showers in about 4 in. of aluminum. Calibrations of spark chambers were made by sending in beams of electrons of known energy and noting the typical spark multiplication and straggling typical of an electromagnetic cascade. The original results established that v_μ and v_e were different beyond any statistical question, there being some 29 muon events and 6 ambiguous events only a small fraction of which could possibly represent electron events (Goulianos, 1966).

A necessary assumption to the conclusion is that the inverse reaction cross sections are not very different. A difference could arise from the induced pseudoscalar term which depends on the lepton mass. This could, at high q^2, conceivably raise the muon production cross section by some factor which could confuse an experiment of limited statistics. Alternatively, the relative electron yield could be reduced if μ-e universality were to break down at high q^2. However, a minimal electron yield (if $v_\mu = v_e$) can be estimated from the CVC theory, using only the vector contribution (Danby et al., 1963). This is quite large and effectively eliminates this possibility. Thus the 29 events of the Columbia-BNL experiment established that

$$v_\mu \neq v_e.$$

There remained the further question of the possibility of some kind of mixing; e.g., are the neutrinos in Eqs. (V-1) and (V-2) rigorously orthogonal? The CERN experiment[5] was able to limit the maximum contribution of v_μ to reaction (V-1), i.e., electron production to a small value. It was limited by

[5] The CERN results are presented in the following publications and conferences: Bartley and Franzinetti, 1965; Bernardini et al., 1964, 1966; Beinlein et al., 1964, Block et al., 1964; Paty, 1965; *International Conference on Elementary Particles* held in Sienna in 1963; *International Conference on Fundamental Aspects of Week Interactions* held at BNL in 1963; *International Conference on High Energy Physics* held in Dubna in 1964.

the background, which is the uncertainty in the v_e contamination of the neutrino flux. In a focused π^+, K^+ beam, v_e's are generated principally by:

$$(1) \qquad K^+ \rightarrow e^+ + v_e + \pi^0$$

$$(2) \qquad K_2^0 \rightarrow e^+ + v_e + \pi^-$$

$$(3) \qquad \pi^+ \rightarrow e^+ + v_e \qquad\qquad\qquad (V\text{-}3)$$

$$(4) \qquad \mu^+ \rightarrow e^+ + \bar{v}_\mu + v_e.$$

Reactions (1) and (2) contribute about 10% of the K-neutrino yield which is $\sim$ 10–20%, hence the v_e's are of the order of 1%. The CERN estimate is $v_e/v_\mu \sim 0.4\%$. The remaining reactions give considerably smaller contributions. An additional source of background are muonic events with accompanying π^0's. In this case, the π^0 shower could simulate an electron. Consequently, one must restrict the class of events to single-lepton events. The experimental results from the CERN bubble chamber are as follows: 57 events with 1 μ^-, 0 events with 1 e^- for $E_{\text{lepton}} > 1$ GeV. This data would seem to indicate that the v_μ and v_e carry independent quantum numbers with a mixing of less than a few per cent. This result is confirmed in the CERN and Columbia spark chambers.

An immediate by-product problem now appears. The v_e interactions can be compared with v_μ interactions to test " μ-e " universality in a unique way. Very few events are available and the energy spectra of v_e (K-source dominates) are different from v_μ. Still within these limitations, v_e seems to have about the same cross sections, i.e., agrees as well with the theory. The CERN experiment is based upon 30 " elastic " events and the Columbia study (Burns, 1966; Burns et al., 1965a, 1966) concerns some 10 such events.

An interesting corollary heading to this section would be: Why only two neutrinos? Of course there could be higher mass leptons coupled to their own neutrinos. The present experiments would only be sensitive to these via electromagnetic production of the charged lepton and this is certainly negligible, ordinarily.

Recently, the Columbia group conducted a search for short-lived neutrino sources. These could, for example, be heavy leptons which decay relatively promptly into lighter leptons, including neutrinos. The background of neutrinos from pions and kaons can be reduced by a factor of several hundred. This is accomplished by transporting the proton beam, in vacuum, up to the shielding wall where it is totally absorbed by a tungsten block. Since less than 3×10^{-4} of the pions and kaons can then decay (i.e., those that give $E_v > 1$ GeV), a production rate of a short-lived neutrino source which is $\sim 0.1\%$ would give about three times the " background " of normal v_μ. This is probably much too large to be very significant if the production mechanism is

$$p + \text{nucleus} \to \pi^0$$

$$\pi^0 \to \gamma + \gamma$$

$$\gamma \to \lambda^+ + \lambda^- \tag{V-4}$$

$$\lambda^+ \to \bar{v}_\lambda + \mu^+(e) + \bar{v}_\mu(\bar{v}_e).$$

An alternative production mechanism could be

$$p + \text{nucleus} \to B \quad \text{(massive boson state)} \quad B \to \lambda + v_\lambda \quad \text{, etc.} \quad \text{(V-5)}$$

However, it is conceivable that such particles could be produced strongly in the 30-GeV proton beam if $m_\lambda \leqslant 3$ GeV (Burns, 1966; Burns *et al.*, 1965a, 1966; see also Lamb *et al.*, 1965).

No anomalous yields were found. The production of v_λ sources then is $\lesssim 0.1\%$ of the production of v_μ sources.

In this respect a novel approach has been made by a London-Brussels-CERN collaboration (Burhop *et al.*, 1965). This group uses a stack of nuclear emulsion pellicles as a target in which to observe neutrino interactions. The emerging tracks are recorded in the spark chambers and serve to locate the vertex of the event. The very high spatial resolution (Fig. 13) could in principle serve to identify heavy lepton secondaries with lifetimes between 10^{-11} and 10^{-15} sec.

B. "NEUTRINO FLIP" HYPOTHESIS

The present neutrino beams contain a significant fraction of neutrinos from K mesons. Since these have a strangeness quantum number, it is interesting to imagine that some quality of this parental property could be inherited by the neutrino. One possibility, suggested by Feinberg *et al.* (1961) and having the great virtue of easy verification, is that the strange particle-derived neutrinos flip their e-μ quantum number, i.e.,

$$\pi^+ \to \mu^+ + v_\mu \quad \text{and} \quad \pi^+ \to \mu^+ + v_e \tag{V-6}$$

but

$$K^+ \to \mu^+ + v_e \tag{V-7}$$

and

$$K^+ \to e^+ + v_\mu. \tag{V-8}$$

The data already discussed above are sufficient also to rule this possibility out, since ~ 10–20% of the high energy neutrino are K products. It is also conceivable that the neutrino from K carries strangeness (von Dardel and Ghani,

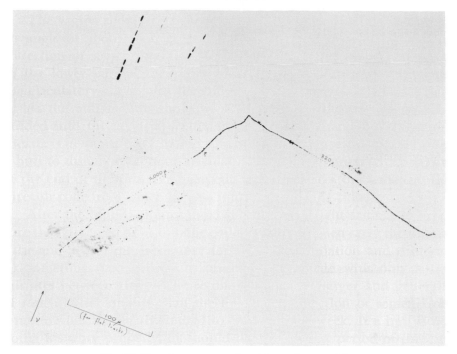

Fig. 13. Neutrino event produced in nuclear emulsion.

1962) and would hence produce only strange particles and leptons. However, very few tracks in the CERN bubble chamber are in fact identified as strange particles.

C. Conservation of Leptons

It is conventional to define the lepton numbers as in the accompanying tabulation from Section II,A,2:

	μ^+	μ^-	ν_μ	$\bar{\nu}_\mu$	e^+	e^-	ν_e	$\bar{\nu}_e$
N_μ	-1	$+1$	$+1$	-1	0	0	0	0
N_e	0	0	0	0	-1	$+1$	$+1$	-1

Conservation of lepton number now is a matter of N_μ and N_e being separately conserved. The experimental question is then

$$\pi^+ \rightarrow \mu^+ + \nu_\mu. \tag{V-9}$$

Then:

$$\nu_\mu + N \rightarrow \mu^- + \Gamma \tag{V-10}$$

is allowed but

$$\nu_\mu + N \rightarrow \mu^+ + \Gamma \tag{V-11}$$

are forbidden.

The search for μ^+ in the ν-beam output of the CERN horn is limited by the $\bar{\nu}$ contamination produced by decaying π^-. Nevertheless, due to smaller cross section and naturally less intense $\bar{\nu}$ flux, a reasonable sensitivity is achieved by the CERN bubble chamber:

$$\mu^+ \text{ events}/\mu^- \text{ events} \lesssim 1.5 \pm 0.3\% \text{ of all elastic events.}$$

The CERN spark chamber improves on the number because of the higher event rate and because of its better discrimination against pions for a selected sample of events reaching the second magnet at the end of the spark chamber arrangement (see Bernardini, 1964). The final observed result

$$\mu^+/\mu^- = 1.45 \pm 0.19\%$$

must be compared with the number expected from the flux of $\bar{\nu}$ calculated by van der Meer of $1.52^{+1.5\%}_{-0.6\%}$. The subtraction yields the relative intensity of lepton violating interaction as being less than 0.4% (95% confidence level).

D. NEUTRAL CURRENTS

The subject of neutral currents is discussed for example, by Bludman (1958), Zel'dovich (1959), Jouvet (1965), and Lee (1966). Neutral leptonic currents are not observed in the weak decays of unstable particles although no reason for suppression is known for, say

$$K^0 \not\rightarrow \mu^+ + \mu^-, \mu \not\rightarrow e^+ + e^- + e^+, \text{ etc.} \qquad \text{(V-12)}$$

It is interesting to study this question with neutrino-induced reactions both because of the higher q^2 and because new channels are available. Thus, one looks for events of the type, e.g.,

$$\nu + p \rightarrow \nu + p + n\pi. \qquad \text{(V-13)}$$

An electromagnetic contribution to this cross section comes from the charge form factor of the neutrino (Bernstein et al., 1963; Ruderman, 1960; Schwartz, 1960). The first neutrino experiment had some sensitivity to this if $n\pi$ includes e.g., a π^0, since unaccompanied single showers are quite rare. The newer data both at CERN and BNL indicate that reaction (V-13) occurs with a rate of the order of or less than 10–20% of the total neutrino cross section. The CERN results are based upon the absence of high energy recoil protons, assuming the same q^2 dependence as in Eq. (V-10). Their limit is $\sim 15\%$. The BNL result (Burns, 1966; Burns et al., 1966) follows from the lack of isolated π^0 showers. Neutron backgrounds limit the sensitivity forcing a high energy cutoff on the recoiling hadrons.

E. Elastic Scattering

The observation of neutrino interactions in complex nuclei (Freon = F_3Br and aluminum) leads to very serious difficulties when one wants to make quantitative comparisons with the theory at hand for the reaction

$$\nu_\mu + n \to p + \mu^- \qquad (V\text{-}14)$$

$$\bar{\nu}_\mu + p \to n + \mu^+. \qquad (V\text{-}15)$$

The following effects must be considered before confronting Eq. (II-7) with an observed $d\sigma/dq$:

(1) The struck nucleon is in motion (Fermi motion).
(2) Not all recoil momenta are acceptable (Pauli principle).
(3) The neutrino momentum is unknown.
(4) The recoiling nucleon has an excellent chance of rescattering.
(5) Pions produced in inelastic processes can be reabsorbed.
(6) Pions and additional nucleons can be produced by recoiling nucleons.

To deal with these effects, Monte Carlo optical model calculations and closure theorems[6] have been invoked. The problem is reminiscent of the theoretical attack on muon capture in nuclei although much more difficult here since the momentum transfer is much larger than m_μ.

For such problems as (5) and (6), these calculations are really only estimates. The experimenter must refine his sample to reduce the contamination of disguised inelastic events and he thereby invariably discards true elastic events in what may be a highly biased (in q^2) manner.

The culmination of these considerations in the CERN bubble chamber sample was presented at the *Argonne Conference* on Weak Interactions (Cundy, 1965; see also Paty, 1965, and Franzinetti, 1965) and is now outlined.

Assume a neutrino of momentum $\boldsymbol{p}_\nu$ gives rise to a muon of momentum $\boldsymbol{p}_\mu$ and a recoil object of mass M^* and momentum $\boldsymbol{p}_R$. Then,

$$\boldsymbol{p}_\nu = \boldsymbol{p}_\mu + \boldsymbol{p}_R \qquad (V\text{-}16)$$

$$m + k_\nu = E_\mu + M^{*2} + p_R{}^2 \qquad (V\text{-}17)$$

where M^* is the effective mass of the recoiling system. For elastic scattering $M^* =$ nucleon mass m. In general, one has

$$E_\nu = \frac{M^{*2} - m^2 + 2mk_\nu - m_\mu{}^2}{2(m - E_\mu + p_\mu \cos \theta)} \qquad (V\text{-}18)$$

$$q^2 = \frac{(M^{*2} - m^2 + 2mE_\mu)(E_\mu - p_\mu \cos \theta) - mm_\mu{}^2}{m - E_\mu + p_\mu \cos \theta}. \qquad (V\text{-}19)$$

[6] See Bludman, 1958; Zel'dovich, 1959; Jouvet, 1965; Lee, 1966; Løvseth, 1963; Berman, 1961; Goulard and Primakoff, 1964; Byers and Ravenhall, 1965.

In the case of Fermi motion of initial momentum p_F

$$k_\nu = \frac{M^{*2} - m^2 - m_\mu^2 + 2mE_\mu - 2p_\mu \cdot p_F + p_F^2}{2[m - E_\mu + p_\mu \cos \theta - (p_F \cdot p_\nu/p_\nu)]} \tag{V-20}$$

$$q^2 =$$

$$\frac{[M^{*2} - m^2 + 2mE_\mu - 2p_\mu \cdot p_F + P_F^2][(E_\mu - p_\mu \cos \theta) - m_\mu^2(m - p_F \cdot k_\nu/k_\nu)]}{m - E_\mu + p_\mu \cos \theta - p_F \cdot p_\nu/p_\nu}. \tag{V-21}$$

Of course, k_ν and q^2 are all one wants to know about an event. The "knowns" in all of this are very few: θ, the angle the muon makes with the ν direction, p_μ, E_μ, and some estimate of $|p_F|$. It is safe to assume the muon emerges from the nucleus without interaction. The CERN analysis is based upon the ability of the bubble chamber to distinguish, in part, pion, kaons, and protons and to thereby define a "visible energy," E_{vis} as the total energy generated by the neutrino collision. Then, $k_\nu \sim E_{vis}$ + residue due to neutrons or stuff reabsorbed in the recoil nucleus. Neglecting the latter gives an estimate of the neutrino energy. Using this, a test is made to determine whether the calculated q^2 exceeds the maximum allowed. In a fiducial volume, 48 out of some 500 events fail this test and are attributed to entering neutrons. The spark chamber suffers much less from this background providing they place a minimum value on the length (hence p_μ) of the muon observed, since incoming neutrons do not produce leptons.

The remaining events are subdivided into "pionic," "nonpionic," and "perhaps pionic." The latter arises from the difficulty of distinguishing protons and pions, a situation clearly worse for the spark chamber. In fact, in the bubble chamber, δ rays serve to identify the tracks in favorable cases and these indicate that most of the ambiguous cases are probably protons. Including these in the nonpionic class, there remains the problem of sorting out the final state events (elastic) from those in which a pion (or N^*) was produced. A study of low q^2 events ($k_\nu \approx E_\mu$) indicates that most of the multiproton events have M^* [Eq. (V-20)] too large for elastic scattering. Consequently, a cut is made in the M^* distribution, events with $M^* > 1.2$ GeV are excluded as probably inelastic (47 events are eliminated from a total of ~ 220 nonpionic events). It is not clear how many elastic events involving large Fermi contribution, measuring error, etc., are thereby eliminated *and what bias in q^2 is thereby introduced*.

Among the remaining events 15 have a visible energy E_{vis} which lies outside the maximum excursion of E_ν as calculated from elastic kinematics. Table IV summarizes the selection of elastic events in the CERN HLBC. The most serious worry is the loss of high q^2 elastic events which appear as multiproton

TABLE IV

SELECTION OF ELASTIC EVENTS

Number of events	Total nonpionic	0 or 1 proton	Multi proton	Rejected by M^* and E_{vis} tests		Number of elastic events		Number of inelastic events	
				0 or 1 proton	Multi proton	0 or 1 p	multi-p	0 or 1 p	multi-p
$E_{vis} < 1$ GeV	103	77	26	12	8	65	~ 1	12	25
$E_{vis} \geqslant 1$ GeV	119	73	46	20	22	53	~ 4	20	42

events due to subsequent interaction. This is estimated by Monte Carlo nuclear cascade calculations (to be ~ 5 events), but since the remaining sample consists of 53 events the danger of strong bias is clear.

The distribution in q^2 is presented in Fig. 14. Before comparing with theory [Eq. (II-7)] the effect of the exclusion principle must be included. The CERN workers use a Fermi gas model and obtain a reduction in the free nucleon cross section by 48%, 16%, 3%, 0 in the q^2 intervals: 0 to 0.1, 0.1 to 0.2, 0.2 to 0.3, and 0.3 to 0.4 $(GeV/c)^2$.

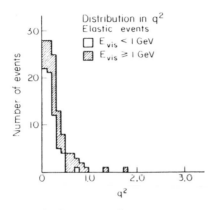

Fig. 14. Elastic events vs four momentum transfer.

The theory is presented with the data in Fig. 15 in a manner which is independent of the uncertainty in neutrino flux but depends on the assignment of $E_{vis} = k_v$ to each neutrino event. Then, with g_A parameterized by

$$g_A = \frac{1}{[1 + (q^2/M_A^2)]^2}$$ (V-22)

one calculates

$$\frac{dN}{dq^2} = \sum_{k_v} \frac{N(E_{vis})}{\sigma(k_v)} \times \frac{d\sigma(k_v, q^2)}{dq^2} .$$ (V-23)

A maximum likelihood analysis yields

$$M_A = 0.9^{+0.2}_{-0.1} \; (GeV/c^2).$$ (V-24)

If the neutrino flux $\phi(k_v)$ as calculated by van der Meer is considered good to $\pm 30\%$, and one calculates

$$\frac{dN}{dq^2} = \sum \frac{d\sigma}{dq^2} \, \phi(k_v)$$ (V-25)

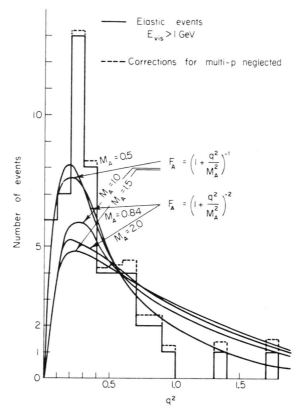

Fig. 15. dN/dq^2 compared with theory for $E_{\text{vis}} > 1$ GeV.

the CERN HLBC results give

$$M_A = 0.78 \begin{array}{c} +0.16 \\ -0.20 \end{array} (\text{GeV}/c^2). \tag{V-26}$$

Figure 16 shows the behavior of the elastic cross section with energy $\sigma(k_\nu)$ and Fig. 17 presents a comparison of the van der Meer flux estimate and the data assuming the theory with $M_A \sim 0.8$.

The spark chamber suffers from the fact that p_μ is known only for a limited and biased sample since leptons produced at large angle leave the chamber before stopping. In small compensation, the aluminum nucleus is smaller than Freon and nuclear corrections are smaller. About 100 events are selected on the basis of analogous criteria concerning the recoil energy (Hyman, 1966; Burns et al., 1966*). Since only the muon angle is known reliably, only this can be compiled. The primary sensitivity here comes from a reliable knowledge of the neutrino flux ($\pm 30\%$) and its use to predict the angular distribution of

* See also Burns (1966).

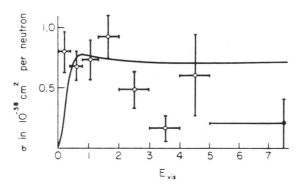

Fig. 16. Cross section for elastic neutrino reactions as a function of E_{vis}. The solid curve is the theoretical cross section calculated with $F = (1 + (Q^2/M_A^2))^{-2}$, $M_A = 0.8$ GeV/c^2, including Pauli principle and Fermi motion.

muons. The Columbia-BNL group used the theory of Goulard and Primakoff (1964) to unfold the complex nuclear effects. However, even their very thin (1.6 gm/cm^2) plates conceal much about the interaction since, to be clearly identified as a track, a particle should penetrate 2 or more plates. The crucial problem here again is the contamination of the elastic sample by inelastic events followed by pion reabsorption. Preliminary indications of these data give somewhat higher values for M_A than one obtained by the CERN workers: $1 \lesssim M_A \lesssim 3$ GeV/c^2.

An angular distribution of muons obtained in the CERN (see footnote 3, page 327) spark chamber is presented in Fig. 18. Comparison with the theory of Løvseth (1963) gives better agreement with equality of vector and axial form factors. Here again, pion absorption is a dominant background.

F. INELASTIC SCATTERING

We have seen that only single pion production:

$$\nu_l + N \rightarrow N + \pi + l^- \qquad (V\text{-}27)$$

is amenable to theoretical treatment. The experimental situation is beset by interference from secondary nuclear effects and by the difficulty of distinguishing pions from fast protons. The latter effect is especially serious in the spark chambers.

A careful analysis of the CERN bubble chamber data has been made (see footnote 2, page 327). The first problem is the selection of single pion events. Protons and positive pions can be separated by ionization criteria up to ~ 0.7 GeV/c. Beyond this, δ rays can give some statistical information. Negative tracks are either π^- or μ^- and sometimes the assignment is ambiguous,

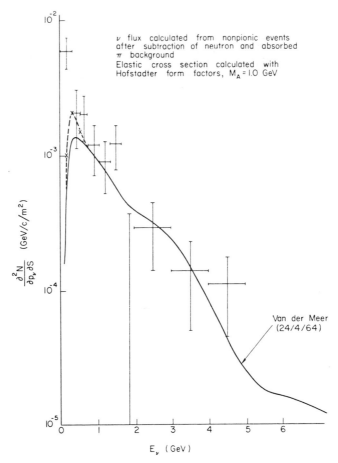

Fig. 17. Neutrino flux as calculated from the elastic events, assuming theory with $M_A = 1.0$ GeV. Comparison is with the van der Meer flux calculation.

but *two* negative tracks must include a pion. Neutral pions are identified by shower production (80% efficiency); there is a small background due to single γ's accompanying radiative "elastic" events.

The ability to measure momenta enables the bubble chamber to define a rough value of M^* for each event, where

$$M^{*2} = -(p_m + p_\pi)^2$$

$$= \text{effective mass of pion-nucleon system}$$

$$= -4k_\nu k_l \sin^2(\theta/2) + m^2 + 2m(k_\nu - k_l) \tag{V-28}$$

$$m = \text{mass of nucleon.}$$

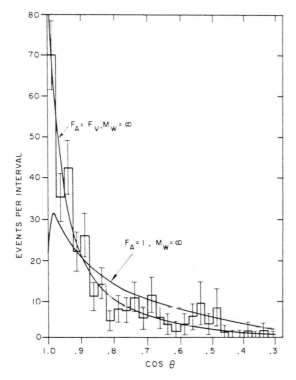

Fig. 18. CERN spark chamber muon angular distribution for events selected as "elastic"; 271 events measured (corrected number 315). Theoretical curves from Løvseth. These are early data presented at the Sienna conference in 1963.

The only unknown is k_v and this is underestimated from the total visible energy in the interaction.

The observed M^{*2} distribution is shown in Fig. 19. The peaking about $M^{*2} = 1.1$ $(GeV/c)^2$ is seen to fall between the elastic rate $M^* = M$ and $M^{*2} = 1.5$ $(GeV/c)^2$ for $(\frac{3}{2} - \frac{3}{2}$ resonance).

The secondary interactions in heavy nuclei are quite serious. Estimates of nuclear pion reabsorption (Byers and Ravenhall, 1965) are as large as 50% and can even be larger. Corrections require a knowledge of the pion spectrum.

The CERN workers, analyzing a total of 550 events in a restricted range of M^*, estimate 124 elastic events, 215 one-pion events, and 211 other events, including background, unmeasurable events, and other inelastic events.

Of the one-pion events 192 are within $M^{*2} \leqslant 2.2$ $(GeV/c)^2$, a criterion designed to supress double pion production. The resulting data are compared with theory of single pion production both as to $\sigma(kv)$ (Fig. 20) and as to $d\sigma/dq^2$ (Fig. 21).

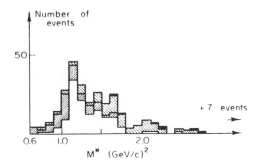

Fig. 19. Distribution in M^* of the inelastic events observed in HLBC.

It should be emphasized that both k_ν and q are only estimated for each event. In both comparisons, the Berman-Veltmann calculation is used to establish the axial vector form factor treated as the only free parameter. The best fit to both distributions uses a form factor of the form given by Eq. (V-22) and obtains a value $M_A \simeq 900$ MeV$/c^2$.

This is rather surprising from one theoretical point of view (Woo, 1963). The three-pion intermediate state had been expected to have an effective mass much higher than this. The result however seems to be in agreement with the elastic results and with the SU(6) considerations of Albright (1965) and others.

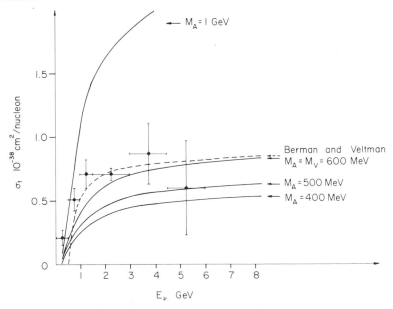

Fig. 20. Inelastic cross section vs neutrino energy.

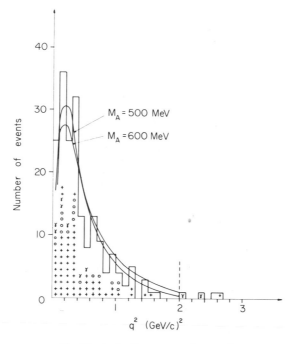

Fig. 21. Inelastic cross section vs q^2.

The final pion-nucleon state in the one-pion events can be in a $T = \frac{1}{2}$ or $T = \frac{3}{2}$ state and the relative numbers of π^+, π^0, and π^- give some indication of whether the N* resonance dominates, if so, we would expect $\pi^+/\pi^0/\pi^-$ to be in the famous ratio $9:2:1$. The observation gives

$$N(\pi^+)/N(\pi^0) = 2.3 \pm 0.9 \qquad \text{(V-29)}$$

whereas the neutron excess effect predicts, for N* formation a ratio:

$$N(\pi^+)/N(\pi^0) = 4.2. \qquad \text{(V-30)}$$

The difference could be due to pion interactions in the nucleus. These go in the right direction, but it could also be due to $T = \frac{1}{2}$ state components.

Finally, the CERN group (Bartley and Franzinetti, 1965) has attempted to apply Adler's PCAC test, selecting 48 out of 319 inelastic events from the HLBC. These events have $\cos \theta > 0.975$. They conclude that, although the data are insufficient to provide a test of the PCAC hypothesis, there is no disagreement.

The total cross section for neutrino interactions as a function of E_{vis} is given in Fig. 22. Although the conclusion depends on the poorest known part of the CERN neutrino flux, there seems to be no evidence for any flattening of the $\sigma_{\text{tot}} \sim E_{\text{lab}}$ behavior.

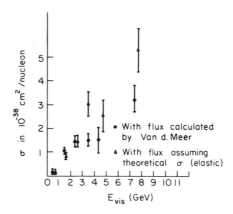

Fig. 22. Behavior of inelastic cross section with neutrino energy (via E_{vis}).

G. Search for Intermediate Boson

The reactions already discussed (Section V,G) coupled with prompt decay of the intermediate boson give the following processes

$$v + Z \rightarrow Z' + W^+ + \mu^-$$

$$\mu^+ + v$$
$$e^+ + v \qquad\qquad (V\text{-}31)$$
$$\pi^+ + \pi^0, \ldots, \text{etc. (nonleptonic decay)}.$$

The significant signature of such an event is the appearance of two leptons at a vertex. Backgrounds of real e, μ, or $\mu\mu$ events are known to be small. (Czyz and Walecka, 1964; Ericson and Glashow; 1964).

The neutrino experiments at CERN (Beinlein et al., 1964; Bernardini et al., 1964) and at BNL (Burns et al., 1965b) had as one of their primary objectives the detection of this reaction. Since the production theory is reliable, failure to observe W's is interpreted in terms of a lower limit on the mass, m_w. The results of both groups (really 3, as the CERN experiment had independent spark chamber and bubble chamber data) are presented in Tables V and VI. Thus, the neutrino experiments conclude that (Bernardini et al., 1966)

$$m_W \geqslant (1.7 + 0.5B) \text{ GeV} \qquad\qquad (V.32)$$

where B is the branching ratio into leptons.

The bubble chamber proved capable of searching for pionic decay modes and thus ruling out the possibility that the boson had small mass but decayed prominently into pions. The thin aluminum plate spark chambers provided a large number of events and good sensitivity to the $\mu - e$ signature of W production and decay. Paramount to reliable results is an understanding of

TABLE V

EXPECTED NUMBER OF EVENTS AND NUMBERS OF OBSERVED CANDIDATES FOR
NONLEPTONIC DECAY OF ELASTICALLY PRODUCED W'S ($B = 0$) FOR DIFFERENT
MASSES M_w AND DIFFERENT ENERGY RANGES[a]
(CERN Bubble Chamber)

M_w(GeV/c^2)	Expected number of events				Observed No.
E_v(GeV)	1.5	1.7	1.9	2.1	of candidates
> 4	13.8	7	3	1.3	5
> 5	11.2	6.2	2.9	1.3	4
> 6	8.6	5.4	2.7	1.3	1
> 7	5.9	4	2.3	1.1	0

[a] Conclusion (Bernardini *et al.*, 1966): $M_w > 1.7$ GeV/c^2 ($B = 0$) 99%
confidence.

TABLE VI

SPARK CHAMBER PREDICTIONS FOR VARIOUS W MASSES
ZERO EVENTS OBSERVED ($B = 0.5$)[a]

m_w (in GeV)	Expected No. of W mesons (Columbia, BNL)[b]	CERN[c]
1.5	9	9(12)
1.8	4	5.4(4.2)
2.0	2	2.7(2.1)
2.2	1	1.4(1.0)

[a] Conclusion: (CERN) (Bernardini *et al.*, 1966) $M_w \geqslant 2.1$
GeV/c^2 99% confidence and (BNL) (Burns *et al.*, 1965b)
$M_w \geqslant 1.8$ GeV/c^2 99% confidence.
[b] $\mu - e$ signature.
[c] $\mu - \mu$ signature, the cutoff on "μ^+" > 80 cm Fe, on
"μ^-" > 30 cm Fe. The numbers in parentheses refer to
alternative criteria, both ranges > 60 cm Fe.

the neutrino flux which we have already discussed. It seems clear that the large
degradation in energy (30 GeV protons → 1 GeV neutrinos) from the primary
beam to the neutrino spectrum makes it difficult to explore higher masses.
Figure 23 shows the W-production cross section for various m_W (Wu *et al.*,
1963, 1965). It is seen that for $m_W = 2$ GeV, neutrinos of at least 6 GeV are
needed. Only a small fraction of the neutrino flux is above 6 GeV. Another
important assumption in these results involves the W-decay branching ratio.

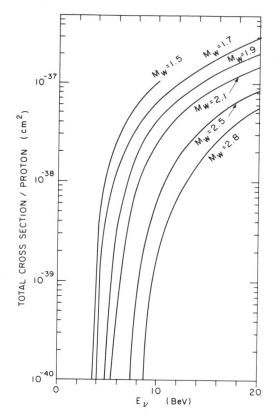

Fig. 23. Excitation curve for boson production vs neutrino energy; W production in Aluminum for $K = 0$.

There have been several calculations although these are all of doubtful reliability due to the possible appearance of resonance enhancements and of form factor suppressions for the nonleptonic part (Namias and Wolfenstein, 1965; Carhart and Dooher, 1966) especially as the W mass increases. It is probably fair to say that our best present knowledge indicates that B, the fraction of W decays into lepton, probably, remains significantly high as the mass of the W increases, in spite of the increased number of channels.

Recently, a group at Columbia-BNL (Burns *et al.*, 1965a, see also Lamb *et al.*, 1965) has used the 20 and 30 GeV proton beam to produce W's searching for decay muons at large angles, generated by the large Q of the reaction. They conclude that $\sigma_W B (20, 30 \text{ GeV } p + p \rightarrow W + \text{anything}) \leqslant 4 \times 10^{-34} \text{ cm}^2$ (for $2.5 \text{ GeV} \lesssim M_W \leqslant 6 \text{ GeV}$).

Unlike neutrino production, the theory here is much less reliable due to the large number of available channels and the large momentum transfer involved.

The experiment is sensitive up to ~ 6 GeV for m_W. If it could someday be reliably shown that this cross-section limit is unreasonably small, one could *then* conclude that $m_W > 6$ GeV. However, it seems more likely that cross sections for production of such massive states involving strongly interacting particles are in fact quite small.

H. ANTINEUTRINO RESULTS

A discussion of antineutrino results is given by Cundy (1965), Paty (1965), and Franzinetti (1965). A short run at CERN with the HLBC was obtained in 1964 with the focusing horn set for π^- particles. About 60 events were obtained of which 26 were in a fiduciary volume satisfying the criteria $E_{vis} > 7.5$ GeV. The total cross section was

$$\sigma \lesssim 3.6 \times 10^{-40} \text{ cm}^2$$

and is consistent with the prediction [Eq. (II-7)] when averaged over the $\bar{\nu}$ spectrum. All events were consistent with an outgoing positive lepton. Using the theory of Cabibbo and Chilton (1965) 4–5 hyperons should have been produced. None was observed. However, since reabsorption in the Freon nucleus and over-all efficiency are effects which are difficult to estimate, the discrepancy is not viewed as compelling.

I. SUMMARY

The present (1965) phase of neutrino physics is based upon the observation of some few thousand events produced by 1–10 GeV neutrinos in complex nuclei. The results of the very large effort would seem to be summarized as follows:

(1) There are two neutrinos.

(2) At momentum transfers ~ 1 GeV/c, "standard" weak interaction theory as outlined in Section II is confirmed. Most dramatically, the prediction that the weak cross section would increase from $k_\nu \sim 0$ by some five orders of magnitude has been confirmed to $\sim 30\%$.

(3) The total cross section is still increasing at $k_\nu \sim 10$ GeV and the increase is consistent with being linear.

(4) It seems likely that the axial weak form factor behaves about like the vector form factor as a function of q^2.

(5) If an intermediate boson exists, its mass is $\geqslant 2$ GeV.

VI. Experimental Outlook

A. FIVE YEARS HENCE

Present neutrino fluxes are based upon zero degree yield of pions and kaons from about 7×10^{11} protons per 3 sec with a magnetic focusing gain of about

4–5. The decay path has been about 25 meters. Anticipated improvements over the next five years consist of the following:

(1) *Machine intensity.* It seems certain that the repetition rate of the CERN Proton Synchrotron and the BNL AGS will be raised by a factor of 2.

(2) The intensity of the protons accelerated has been increasing steadily. At this writing the AGS is up to 1.5×10^{12} protons per pulse (ppp). Without drastic modifications it seems clear that $3–4 \times 10^{12}$ can be achieved. New injectors which have been proposed would bring this number up to $\sim 2 \times 10^{13}$.

(3) New focusing arrangements have been proposed, by Palmer (1966) at BNL and by Asner and Iselin (1964) at CERN. These would increase the gain due to the present horn by a factor of 2–3.

(4) Flight paths can be increased in such as way as to increase the yield of high energy neutrinos.

Thus, an over-all increase of as much as a factor of 100 and at least a factor of 25 can be expected. This would not be too useful if there were not a corresponding improvement in detector techniques. At present, both the heavy liquid bubble chamber and the high resolution spark chamber suffer from the complex nucleus effect. It seems to this writer almost impossible to separate elastic and inelastic events in a wholly bias free manner. If any selection criteria results in even 10% of the events being ambiguous, it does not pay to collect much more than a few hundred events, before the statistical uncertainties become small compared to the systematic ones. Of course, high intensity can be used in a semiquantitative way to survey the energy dependence of the cross section, to improve the sensitivity to neutral currents, etc.

However, the crucial question would seem to be: How much intensity is required to make hydrogen and deuterium exposures possible?

The present bubble chambers contain about 0.07 ton of hydrogen in the sensitive volume. However, we can probably look forward with some confidence to the new generation of ~ 5 meter chambers, containing about 1 ton of H_2. This would bring the event rate up to about 300 elastic events per day (250 in H_2, 500 in D_2) and, due to $\bar{\nu}$, about 15 hyperon events. Several thousand events of the type $\nu + d \rightarrow p + \mu^- + p$ even with deuterium wave function problems, should yield very good information *both* on the CVC hypothesis and on the axial vector form factor.

There is the possibility of doing neutrino experiments with a hydrogen-deuterium target surrounded by spark chambers. The great difficulty here is the lack of information on strongly interacting particles which would be reabsorbed by the target. The lack of knowledge of the neutrino energy does not help either. This technique clearly does not compete with the bubble chamber but might be used in the interim if solutions can be devised for the aforementioned problems.

Large propane chambers have also been proposed and will probably be used before HBC's are practicable. These have the advantage of containing considerable amounts of hydrogen as well as carbon—a much smaller nucleus than Freon. The advantage over the HLBC is very large once the event rate problem is overcome. The cleanliness of interpretation will be much improved. However, one recalls that propane chambers were always of very limited use when their primary function was as a "poor man's" hydrogen chamber.

B. $T > 10$ Years

At some time, probably not much before 10 years, the next generation of accelerators will appear. The transition will be smoothed somewhat by the higher intensity of the present synchrotrons and by the 70-GeV accelerator at Serpukhov in the USSR. The new energies may be in the range of 200–500 GeV, and the significance for neutrino physics will be very large. The most obvious effect will be the much higher energy of neutrino beams, mean energies being $\gtrsim 20$ GeV rather than $\simeq 2$ GeV at present. An example of the kind of things one can do when the concepts of a future neutrino facility match the accelerator in imagination, size (and cost) is given by a 200-GeV design study carried out by Peterson and O'Keefe (1966) at the Lawrence Radiation Laboratory. Their considerations, in outline, are as follows (see Fig. 24).

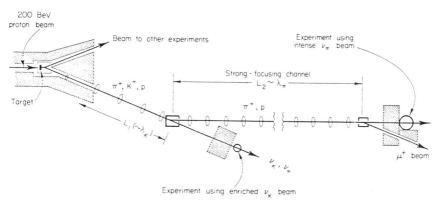

Fig. 24. Arrangement of a possible 200 BeV neutrino facility.

Focusing can be carried out by conventional quadrupoles since the required apertures at 200 GeV are quite small. (The rms production angle of pions ~ 30 mrad for 20 GeV pions.) Capitalizing on the copious production of moderate energy pions (~ 20 GeV), these authors have sought to select the charge of the pions and kaons, momentum analyze to $\pm 10\%$, and stretch the decay path to about a mean free path keeping the pions and kaons together with a quadrupole transport system.

A beam of 200 GeV protons strikes a target at the entrance of a 7-meter-long, 25-kG bending magnet. Mesons of 20 GeV/c mean momentum are bent 0.29 rad and drift another 7 meters before entering a 12 in. aperture lens in a heavy shield wall. High energy protons and mesons are stopped by shielding placed close to the bending magnet. The mean decay lengths for 20 GeV/c kaons and pions are 150 meters and 1100 meters, respectively. Within 150 meters the mesons are bent again parallel to the original proton beam; this serves to cancel chromatic effects due to the first bending and also provides an enriched " K-neutrino" beam passing through the shielding S_1 into the smaller of two bubble chamber detectors D_1. The remaining beam (mainly pions) is then transported over a long distance (or the order of 1000 meters) Pion decays produce a "pi-neutrino" beam passing through shielding S_2 into a large bubble chamber detector D_2. The residual charged particles (mainly protons and muons) in the focused beam are then deflected just before S_2. A relatively pure muon beam can be created by absorbing the pions and protons, and can be used in another experiment.

The disadvantages of such an arrangement are the large number of lenses required, the considerable space involved in the experimental area, and the precise alignment of elements required. However, these requirements are comparable with the dimensions and tolerances of the accelerator. A major advantage seems to be that it is possible to obtain either a well-defined neutrino energy, or a high neutrino intensity integrated over the total spectrum, by relatively simple changes in geometry. The layout also lends itself to multiple use for charged particle beams. The same flight path may be used for mass separators in a side branch beam.

The authors estimate an event rate in the 5-meter hydrogen bubble chamber of ~ 2000 pi-neutrino events per day per 3×10^{13} ppp. The high intensity can be used in another way to sharpen the energy spectrum of neutrinos. The simplest method seems to be to deflect the source of neutrinos away from the detector and at a long distance in order to collect only the very forward produced neutrinos. The combination of focusing and long drift space can result in a neutrino beam, monochromatic to $\pm 10\%$ with a loss in rate of about a factor of 20.

In the region of very high neutrino energy (~ 100 GeV), the yield of events is far lower of course. However, even a very small number of events would be very interesting from the point of view of observing any damping of the total neutrino interaction cross section.

C. Conclusions

The study of weak interactions at high energy seem to require neutrino beams. When strongly interacting particles are involved in large momentum transfers, new states are produced. It would seem that a hope of investigating space in the extremely small domain is just via weak interactions at high energies. Thus, in spite of the great difficulties now apparent in exploiting this new field, it must be done. Ultimately the most fruitful processes will not involve nucleons at all, e.g., $e^+ + e^- \rightarrow v + \bar{v}$. Neutrinos have yet to play the role which Rutherford designed for his α particles but, with the projections described here, there is still hope that the analogous explorations may take place.

REFERENCES

Achar, C. V., Menon, M. G. K., Narasimham, V. S., Ramana Murthy, P. V., Sreekantan, B. V., Hinotani, K., Miyake, S., Creed, D. R., Osborne, J. L., Pattison, J. B. M., and Wolfendale, A. W. (1965a). Proceedings of the Cosmic Ray Conference, London (1965).

Achar, C. V., Menon, M. G. K., Narasimham, V. S., Ramana Murthy, P. V., Sreekantan, B. V., Hinotani, K., Miyake, S., Creed, D. R., Osborne, J. L., Pattison, J. B. M., and Wolfendale, A. W. (1965b). *Phys. Rev. Letters* **18**, 196.

Adams, J. B., Ruderman, M. A., and Woo, C. H., (1963). *Phys. Rev.* **129**, 1383.

Adler, S. (1963). *Nuovo Cimento* **30**, 1020.

Adler, S. (1964). *Phys. Rev.* **135**, B963.

Adler, S. (1965). *Phys. Rev.* **140**, B736 (1965).

Albright, C. H., and Liu, L. S. (1964a) *Phys. Rev. Letters* **13**, 673.

Albright, C. H., and Liu, L. S. (1964b). *Phys. Rev. Letters* **14**, 324.

Albright, C. H., and Liu, L. S. (1965). *Phys. Rev.* **140**, B748.

Asner and Iselin, (1964). CERN, NP.

Bahcall, J. N. (1965). *Science* **147**, 115.

Bahcall, J. N., and Frauschi, S. (1964). *Phys. Rev.* **135B**, 788.

Baker, W., Cool, R., Jenkins, E., Kycia, T., Lindenbaum, S., Love, W., Lüers, D., Niederer, J., Read, A., Russell, J., Ozaki, S., and Yuan, L. (1961). *Phys. Rev. Letters* **7**, 101.

Bartley, J., and Franzinetti, C. (1965). CERN NPA/Int. 65–14.

Bartley, J., Franzinetti, C., Paty, M., and Salin, P. (1965). CERN. NPA/Int. 65–11.

Beinlein, J. K., *et al.* (1964). *Phys. Letters* **13**, 80.

Bell, J. S. (1964). *Phys. Rev. Letters* **13**, 57.

Bell, J., and Berman, S. (1962). *Nuovo Cimento* **25**, 404.

Bell, J. S., and Veltman, M. (1963a). *Phys. Letters* **5**, 94.

Bell, J. S., and Veltman, M. (1963b). *Phys. Letters* **5**, 151.

Berman, S. (1961). CERN, unpublished.

Berman, S., and Veltman, M. (1964). *Phys. Letters* **12**, 275.

Berman, S., and Veltman, M. (1964). CERN 9276/Th 455.

Bernardini, G. (1960). *Proc. Intern. Conf. High Energy Phys.*, *Rochester*, p. 581, Wiley (Interscience), New York.

Bernardini, G. (1964). *Intern. Conf. Elem. Particle Phys.*, *Dubna*. Nat. Bur. Stand., Dept. of Comm., Washington, D.C.

Bernardini, G., *et al.* (1964). *Phys. Letters* **13**, 86.

Bernardini, G., *et al.* (1966). *Nuovo Cimento* **38**, 608.

Bernstein, J., and Lee, T. D. (1963). *Phys. Rev. Letters* **11**, 512.

Bernstein, J., Ruderman, M., and Feinberg, G. (1963). *Phys. Rev.* **132**, 1227.

Block, M. M., *et al.* (1964). *Phys. Letters* **12**, 281.

Bludman, S. A. (1958). *Nuovo Cimento* **9**, 433.

Burhop, E. H. S., Busza, W., Davis, D. H., Duff, B. G., Garbutt, D. A., Heymann, F. F., Potter, K. M., Wickens, J. H., Bricman, C., Lemonne, J., Sacton, J., Schorochoff, G., Roberts, M. A., and Toner, W. T. (1965). *Nuovo Cimento* **39**, 1037.

Burns, R. (1966). Ph.D. thesis, Columbia Univ., NEVIS# 148.

Burns, R., Danby, G., Hyman, E., Lederman, L. M., Lee, W., Rettberg, J., and Sunderland, J. (1965a). *Phys. Rev. Letters* **15**, 830.

Burns, R., Danby, G., Goulianos, D., Hyman, E., Lederman, L. M., Lee, W., Mistry, N., Rettberg, J., Schwartz, M., and Sunderland, J. (1965b). *Phys. Rev. Letters* **15**, 42.

Burns, R., Danby, G., Hyman, E., Lederman, L. M., Lee, W., Rettberg, J., and Sunderland, J. (1966). Informal Conf. Neut. Phys., Geneva, CERN-65-32.

Byers, N., and Ravenhall, D. (1965). Private communication.

Cabibbo, N. (1963). *Phys. Rev. Letters* **12**, 531.

Cabibbo, N. (1964). *Phys. Letters* **12**, 137.

Cabibbo, N., and Chilton, F. (1965). *Phys. Rev.* **137**, B1628; also M. Block, *Phys. Rev. Letters* **12**, 262 (1964).

Cabibbo, N., and Da Prato, G. (1962). *Nuovo Cimento* **25**, 611.

Cabibbo, N., and Gatto, R. (1960). *Nuovo Cimento* **15**, 304.

Carhart, R., and Dooher, J. (1966). *Phys. Rev.* **142**, 1214.

Chang, W. K., and Bludman, S. A. (1964). *Phys. Rev.* **136**, B1787.

Chilton, F. (1964). *Nuovo Cimento* **31**, 447.

Chiu, H. Y. (1961). *Phys. Rev.* **123**, 1040.

Chiu, H. Y., and Morrison, P. (1960). *Phys. Rev. Letters* **5**, 573.

Cowan, C. L., (1965). *Proc. Cosmic Ray Conf., London* (to be published).

Cowsik, R., Pal, Y., and Tandon, I. (1966). *Proc. 8th Intern. Conf. Cosmic Rays, Jaipur, India* (1963), to be published.

Cundy, R. (1965). *Intern. Conf. Weak Interactions, Argonne.* Argonne Nat. Lab. ANL-7130 p. 257.

Czyz, W., Walecka, J. D., (1964). *Phys. Letters* **8**, 77.

Danby, G., Gaillard J.-M., Goulianos, K., Lederman, L. M., Mistry, N., Schwartz, M., and Steinberger, J. (1962). *Phys. Rev. Letters* **9**, 36.

Danby, G., *et al.* (1963). *Phys. Rev. Letters* **10**, 260.

Dekkers, D., *et al.* (1964). NPA/Int. CERN, *Phys. Rev.* **137**, B962 (1965).

Dennery, P. (1962). *Phys. Rev.* **127**, 664.

Egardt, L. (1963) *Nuovo Cimento* **29**, 954.

Ericson, T., and Glashow, S. L. (1964). *Phys. Rev.* **113**, B130.

Feinberg, G., and Lederman, L. M. (1963). *Ann. Rev. Nucl. Sci.* **13**, 431.

Feinberg, G., and Weinberg, S. (1961). *Phys. Rev. Letters* **6**, 381.

Feinberg, G., Gursey, F., and Pais, A. (1961). *Phys. Rev. Letters* **7**, 208.

Feynman, R., and Gell-Mann, M. (1958). *Phys. Rev.* **109**, 193.

Forsythe, E., Lederman, L., and Sunderland, J. (1965). *Trans. Nucl. Sci.*, **NS-12**, 872.

Franzinetti, C. (1965). CERN NPA 66-13.

Fujii, T., and Yamaguchi, Y. (1966). INS-Report 73, to be published.

Gell-Mann, M. (1958). *Proc. Conf. Nuclear Structure Stanford.*, Stanford University Press, Stanford, California.

Gell-Mann, M. (1964). *Physics* **1**, 63.

Gershtein, S., and Zel'dovitch, Ya. B., *Soviet Physics JETP* **2**, 576 (1957).

Giesch, M., van der Meer, S., Pluym, G., and Vahlbruch, K. (1963). *Intern. Conf. Elem. Particle Physics, Sienna.*, p. 536, Societa Italiana di Fisica, Bologna.

Giesch, M., van der Meer, S., Pluym, G., and Vahlbruch, K. (1963b). *Nucl. Instr. Methods*, **20**, 58.

Glashow, S. L. (1960). *Phys. Rev.* **118**, 316.

Goulard, B., and Primakoff, H. (1964). *Phys. Rev.* **135**, B1139.

Goulianos, K. (1966). Ph.D. Thesis, Columbia Univ., NEVIS# 113.

Gourdin, M., and Salin, P. (1963). *Nuovo Cimento* **27**, 193, 309.

Greisen, K. (1961). *Proc. Intern. Conf. Instrumentation, Berkeley*, 1960, p. 209, Wiley (Interscience), New York.

Hyman, E. (1966). Ph.D. Thesis, Columbia Univ., to be published.

Iida, K. (1963). *Nuovo Cimento* **27**, 1439.

Itami, K., Mugibayashi, N., Nakamura, S., and Tanikawa, Y., (1964). *Progr. Theoret. Phys.* **32**, 301.

Jouvet, B. (1965). *Compt. Rend.* **260**, 449.

Keuffel, J. (1965). *Proc. Intern. Conf. Weak Interactions, Argonne*, p. 393. Argonne Nat. Lab., Illinois ANL-7130.

Krienan, P., Salmeron, R. A., and Steinberger, J. (1960). PS/Int. CERN unpublished.

Kuchowicz, B. (1966). The Bibliography of the Neutrino, Nuclear Energy Information Center, Warsaw.

Lamb, R., Lundy, R., Novey, T., Yovanovitch, D., Good, M., Hartung, R., Peters, M., and Subramanian, A. (1965). *Phys. Rev. Letters* **15**, 800.

Lederman, L. M. (1964). Enrico Fermi School, Varenna, Italy. Academic Press, New York and London (1966), p. 176.

Lederman, L. M., Schwartz, M., and Gaillard, J.-M. (1960). *Proc. Intern. Conf. Instrumentation, Berkeley*, p. 201. Wiley (Interscience), New York.

Lee, T. D. (1962). *Phys. Rev.* **128**, 899.

Lee, T. D. (1964). Enrico Fermi School, Varenna, Italy. Academic Press, New York and London (1966), p. 311.

Lee, T. D. (1965). *Phys. Rev.* **140**, B959.

Lee, T. D. (1966). *Informal Conf. Neutrino Phys., Geneva*, 1965, CERN, 65-32.

Lee, T. D., and Sirlin, A. (1964). *Rev. Mod. Phys.* **36**, 666.

Lee, T. D., and Wu, C. S. (1965). *Ann. Rev. Nucl. Sci.* **15**, 381.

Lee, T. D., and Yang, C. N. (1960a). *Phys. Rev. Letters* **4**, 307.

Lee, T. D., and Yang, C. N. (1960b). *Phys. Rev.* **119**, 1410.

Lee, T. D., and Yang, C. N. (1962). *Phys. Rev.* **126**, 2239.

Lee, T. D., Markstein, P., and Yang, C. N. (1961). *Phys. Rev. Letters* **1**, 429.

Lee, T. D., Robinson, Schwartz, M., and Cool, (1963). *Phys. Rev.* **132**, 1297.

Løvseth, J. (1963). *Phys. Letters* **5**, 199.

Markov, M. A. (1963). "The neutrino," Joint Institute for Nuclear Research, Dubna.

Markov, M. A. and Zheleznykh, I. M. (1961). *Nucl. Phys.* **27**, 385.

Marshak, R., and Sudarshan, E. C. G. (1958). *Phys. Rev.* **109**, 1860.

Menon, M. G. K. (1965). *Proc. Cosmic Ray Conf., London*. (to be published).

Meyer, P., and Schiff, D. (1964). *Phys. Letters* **8**, 217.

Nakamura, S. (1965). *Intern. Symposium on Elem. Particles, Kyoto*. Science Council of Japan.

Nahmias, V., and Wolfenstein, L. (1965). *Nuovo Cimento* **36**, 542.

Novey, T. B. (1966). *Informal Conf. Neutrino Phys., Geneva, 1965*, CERN, 65-32.

Ogawa, S. (1956). *Progr. Theoret. Phys.* **15**, 480.

Orkin-Lecourtois, A. (1964). TC/Com. CERN.

Orkin-Lecourtois, A. (1965). Private communication.

Osborne, J. L. (1965). *Informal Conf. Neutrino Phys., Geneva, 1965*, CERN, 65-32.

Palmer, R. (1966). *Informal Conf. Neutrino Phys., Geneva, 1965*, CERN, 65-32.

Paty, M. (1965). CERN. NP-65-12, Geneva.

Peterson, V., and O'Keefe, D. (1966). *Informal Conf. Neutrino Phys. Geneva, 1965*, CERN, 65–32.

Pontecorvo, B. (1959). *Zh. Eksperim. i Teor. Fiz.* **36**, 1615; (1959). *Soviet Phys. JETP* (*English transl.*) **9**, 1148.

Pontecorvo, B. (1959). *Zh. Eksperim. i Teor. Fiz.* **37**, 1751; (1960). *Soviet Phys. JETP* (*English transl.*) **10**, 1236.

Pontecorvo, B. (1963). *Soviet Phys. JETP* **79**, 1.

Pontecorvo, B., and Smorodinskii, Ya. (1962). *Soviet Phys. JETP* **14**, 173.

Ramm, C. A. (1966). *Informal Conf. Neutrino Phys., Geneva, 1965*, CERN, 65–32.

Ramm, C. A. (1960). *Proc. Intern. Conf. Instrumentation, Berkeley*, p. 203. Interscience, N.Y.

Reines, F. (1966). *Informal Conf. Neutrino Phys., Geneva, 1965*, CERN, 65–32.

Reines, F., Crouch, M., Jenkins, T., Kropp, W., Gurr, H., Smith, G., Sellschop, J., and Myer, B., 1965). *Phys. Rev. Letters* **15**, 429.

Ruderman, M. (1965). *Rept. Progr. Phys.* **28**, 411.

Salin, Ph. (1965). *Nuovo Cimento*, in press.

Samios, N., and Palmer, R. (1664). BNL Report.

Schwartz, M. (1960). *Rept. Progr. Phys.* **28**, 61 (1965).

Schwartz, M. (1965). *Phys. Rev. Letters*, **4**, 306.

Schwinger, J. (1957). *Ann. Phys.* **2**, 407.

Stothers, R., and Chiu, H. Y. (1962). *Astrophys. J.* **135**, 963.

Überall, H. (1964). *Phys. Rev.* **133**, B444.

van der Meer, S., (1966). *Informal Conf. Neutrino Phys; Geneva, 1965*, CERN, 65–32.

von Dardel, G., and Ghani, A. (1962). CERN 62–10, Geneva.

von Gehlen, G. (1963). *Nuovo Cimento* **30**, 859.

Weinberg, S. (1962a). *Nuovo Cimento* **25**, 15.

Weinberg, S. (1962b). *Phys. Rev.* **128**, 1457.

Weisberger, W. I. (1965). *Phys. Rev. Letters* **14**, 1047.

Woo, C. (1963). *Phys. Rev. Letters* **11**, 385, 567.

Wu, A., Yang, Fuchel, and Heller, (1963). *Phys. Rev. Letters* **12**, 57.

Wu, A. (1965). Private communication.

Yamaguchi, Y. (1960). *Progr. Theoret. Phys.* (*Kyoto*) **23**, 1117.

Yukawa, H. (1935). *Proc. Phys.-Math. Soc. Japan* **17**, 48.

Zatsepin, G. T., and Kuzmin, V. A. (1961). *Zh. Eksperim. i Teor. Fiz.* **41**, 1818; (1962). *Soviet Phys. JETP* (*English transl.*) **14**, 1294.

Zel'dovich, Ya. B. (1959). *Soviet Phys. JETP* **9**, 1389.

HYPERNUCLEAR PHYSICS

D. H. Davis and J. Sacton

I. Introduction

Since the Λ hyperon is the lightest system having baryon number one and strangeness number minus one it is unable, when at rest, to take part in any transformation reactions in the presence of nucleons. It is able, therefore, since the Λ–N interaction is attractive, to become bound to an aggregate of nucleons to form a hypernucleus (or hyperfragment) which may remain stable until the bound Λ hyperon decays. The first examples of hypernuclei were found in emulsion plates exposed to the cosmic radiation by balloon flights, but now they are almost exclusively studied in emulsion stacks and bubble chambers exposed to separated K^--meson beams.

Because of the short lifetime of the Λ hyperon the accumulation of Λ-nucleon scattering events is very slow and so most of our present knowledge of the Λ–N interaction comes from a study of the properties of hypernuclei, in particular the binding energy of the Λ hyperon to the core, B_Λ, the decay branching ratios and the angular distributions of the decay products.

II. The Detection and Analysis of Hypernuclei

Hypernuclei have short mean lifetimes and are rarely produced with large kinetic energies (see Section III). Thus the distance separating their production and decay vertices is necessarily very small. The result is that the majority of hyperfragment studies have been carried out using nuclear emulsions as detectors since they possess a very high spatial resolution (better than 1 μm), although much valuable information concerning the decay properties of the lightest hypernuclei has been obtained using a helium bubble chamber. For bubble chambers containing heavier elements the direct observation of a hyperfragment is rare but estimates have been made of the trapping probabilities of Λ hyperons in heavy and light nuclei following K^--meson capture in a propane-Freon mixture.

The Λ hyperon bound in a hyperfragment may decay as if it were free by either of the modes

$$\Lambda \to p + \pi^- \qquad\qquad \text{(II-1)}$$

$$\Lambda \to n + \pi^0. \qquad\qquad \text{(II-2)}$$

While the nucleon from the decay is frequently involved in final state interactions, the possibility of absorption of the π meson is small, especially for the case of light hypernuclei, so such decays are usually characterized by the emission of a π meson and are termed "mesonic." In a hyperfragment the Λ hyperon may also interact with a nucleon via one of the weak interaction processes

$$\Lambda + p \to n + p \qquad\qquad \text{(II-3)}$$

$$\Lambda + n \to n + n. \qquad\qquad \text{(II-4)}$$

These interactions which do not conserve strangeness are sometimes referred to as stimulated Λ-hyperon decays and give rise to nonmesonic decays of hypernuclei. Because of the increasing suppression of the π-mesonic decay rate with increase in mass number due to the effect of the Pauli exclusion principle, and to a much lesser extent to π-meson reabsorption effects, nonmesonic decay is the dominant process except for the lightest hypernuclei.

In nuclear emulsion, the π^--mesonic decay of a hypernucleus presents a characteristic configuration and is easily identified. However, among the sample of nonmesonic decays there may well be a contamination of events produced by the captures of slow negative particles and, for the case of very short connecting tracks, the interactions in flight of secondary particles. When the length of the connecting track is long the information which may be obtained from a study of the track itself is sufficient to eliminate most of this contamination. On the other hand, when the length of the connecting track is so short that this discrimination is not possible it has been shown that the contamination is negligible in the sample of hypernuclei produced by K^--meson interactions (Sacton, 1961). However, this is not so for the interactions of fast π mesons where it has been estimated that the contamination in the sample of so-called short-range hypernuclei may be as high as 40% (Silverstein, 1958). In the helium bubble chamber studies the selection of a sample of hypernuclei rests almost solely on the analysis of the production kinematics, thus enabling determinations of decay branching ratios to be made which are free from observational bias.

In nuclear emulsions the method of identification of a hypernucleus is the kinematic analysis of its decay process. This analysis has, to date, been usually confined to π^--mesonic decays since they are relatively free of contamination and the π^- meson is easily identified among the decay products. Also for these events, the Q values of the decays are small so that there can be no great disruption of the core—in fact, the majority of π^--mesonic decays do not involve the emission of a neutron. The analysis consists of establishing a detailed momentum and energy balance at the decay vertex by presuming the identities[1] of all charged decay products, whose ranges and angles of emission are measured. These data are fed into a computer which is instructed to analyze the event for all feasible permutations of the particle identities. Only events for which there exists a single assignment of identities of decay particles leading to a momentum imbalance compatible with zero within the experimental errors are considered uniquely identified. For events which satisfy no such decay scheme the emission of neutrons or of particles of range so short as to be unobserved in the emulsion is taken into account. The pitfalls to be avoided in this somewhat blind approach have been fully discussed elsewhere (Ammar, 1963; Levi Setti, 1963). In particular the emission from the decay of a nucleus in a particle-stable excited state, the decay of which remains unobserved in the emulsion, will give rise to systematic overestimates of the B_Λ values and possibly even to the misclassification of an event.

The production reaction may be studied in order to remove an ambiguity

[1] The particles emitted in the π^--mesonic decay of a hypernucleus, with the exception of the π meson itself, generally have ranges in emulsion so short that their identities cannot be determined from the appearance of their tracks.

in the classification of an event presented by the analysis of its decay. In the case of K^--meson and Σ^--hyperon captures at rest where it is known that the great majority of the π^--mesonically decaying hypernuclei of atomic number greater than two originate from the light emulsion nuclei, carbon, nitrogen, and oxygen (see Section III), an ambiguity may sometimes be removed merely by consideration of charge or baryon conservation. Moreover the complete analysis of the production reaction when used in conjunction with the analysis of the decay has proved a powerful method for the identification of the heavier hypernuclei (see, e.g., Schlein and Slater, 1961) and has even been applied to the identification of nonmesonic decays (Holland, 1964).

Finally, some attempt may be made at determining the charge and even possibly the mass either of the hyperfragment itself or one or other of its decay products from observations of the ionization and scattering of, and the δ-ray frequency along, their tracks. Such measurements, which should only be made upon sufficiently long and flat tracks should be treated with some reserve since they are strongly sensitive to local variations in the formation of the track image.

In the helium bubble chamber the K^--meson absorption reactions which lead to hyperfragment production are particularly simple and so it is possible in many cases to identify hyperfragments solely by a study of the production vertex.

III. The Production of Hypernuclei

The rates of production of observable hyperfragments[2] from the interactions with emulsion nuclei of various particles at a number of incident momenta are given in Table I.

The most notable feature of Table I is the much larger frequencies of production of hyperfragments by K^--meson and Σ^--hyperon interactions than by those of protons and π mesons, as are to be expected. For this reason studies of the production processes of hyperfragments have been almost entirely restricted to the interactions of K^- mesons. Further, since the absorption of particles in flight is expected to take place anywhere within the nuclear volume, whereas the captures at rest of negative particles occur from Bohr orbits and are therefore preferentially peripheral, the production of hyperfragments by the interactions of K^- mesons in flight and at rest will be considered separately.

[2] It has been shown, for example, that for the captures of K^- mesons at rest in emulsion the majority of the hyperfragments have insufficient range (< 0.5 μm) to be detected (Davis et al., 1961).

TABLE I

HYPERFRAGMENT PRODUCTION RATES

Incident particle	Incident momentum (MeV/c)	Observed frequency (%)	References
K⁻ mesons	At rest	6.5 ± 0.2	Lemonne et al. (1964b)
K⁻ mesons	50–300	11.6 ± 0.6	Henrotin et al. (1965)
K⁻ mesons	500	10.0 ± 1.0	Lemonne et al. (1963)
K⁻ mesons	800	5.8 ± 0.2	Jones et al. (1961, 1962); Ahmed and Shaukat (1963)
K⁻ mesons	1150	3.5 ± 0.3	Rinaudo (1963)
K⁻ mesons	1300	4.2 ± 0.2	Fletcher et al. (1963)
K⁻ mesons	1500	4.0 ± 0.1	Fletcher et al. (1963); Baumann et al. (1963); Cuevas et al. (1963a)
K⁻ mesons	2300	2.1 ± 0.2	Prem and Steinberg (1963)
K⁻ mesons	3000	2.9 ± 0.1	Lemonne et al. (1964a–c); Baumann et al. (1964)
K⁻ mesons	5000	2.2 ± 0.1	Lemonne et al. (1966)
Σ⁻ hyperons	At rest	$2.7^{+0.5}_{-0.4}$	Andersen et al. (1963)
π⁻ mesons	3000	0.090 ± 0.012	Schneps et al. (1957); Fry et al. (1956)
π⁻ mesons	4500	0.18 ± 0.01	Silverstein (1958); Deka (1959); Slater (1958); Limentani et al. (1958); Lokanathan et al. (1960)
π⁻ mesons	17000	0.30 ± 0.05	Baumann (1964)
Protons	3000	0.096 ± 0.01	Schneps et al. (1957); Blau (1956); Fry et al. (1955)
Protons	6000	0.07	Schneps et al. (1957); Fry et al. (1956)
Protons	25000	0.30 ± 0.05	Baumann (1964)
Cosmic rays		0.50	Schneps et al. (1957), Fry et al. (1955, 1956)

The range distributions of hyperfragments produced by the interactions in flight of K⁻ mesons of momenta from 50 MeV/c to 5 GeV/c (Henrotin et al., 1965; Lemonne et al., 1963, 1964a, 1966; Jones et al., 1961, 1962; Ahmed and Shaukat, 1963; Rinaudo, 1963; Fletcher et al., 1963; Baumann et al., 1963, 1964; Cuevas et al., 1963a; Prem and Steinberg, 1963) all show a very large grouping of events at very short ranges, less than 10 μm. In fact the only significant effect on the range distributions of increasing the incident momentum from 50 MeV/c to 5 GeV/c is to shift the position of the peak at short ranges slightly to the right. As an illustration of this point, range distributions of hyperfragments produced by the interactions of K⁻ mesons of 50–200 MeV/c, 1.5 GeV/c, and 5 GeV/c momentum are given in Fig. 1. It was first noticed by Jones et al. (1961, 1962), during a study of hyperfragments

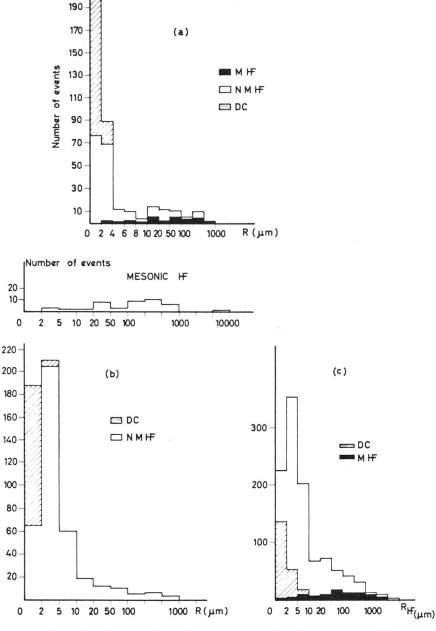

Fig. 1. Range distributions of hyperfragments produced by the interactions of K⁻ mesons of momenta (a) 50–200 MeV/c (Henrotin *et al.*, 1965), (b) 1.5 GeV/c (Fletcher *et al.*, 1963), and (c) 5 GeV/c (Lemonne *et al.*, 1966). (MHF = mesonic hyperfragment; NMHF = hyperfragment decaying without π-meson emission; DC = double centered event in which the hyperfragment track is too short to be seen directly but its presence is deduced because the prongs of the capture star appear to diverge from two close centers.

produced by 800 MeV/c K⁻ mesons, that the majority of the hyperfragments of short range ($\leqslant 5$ μm) originated from interactions in the heavy nuclei of the emulsion, silver and bromine. Moreover, these short-range hyperfragments were seen to decay almost exclusively by nonmesonic modes implying that they were rather heavy (see Section VI). The puzzle presented by the apparently frequent emission of highly charged hyperfragments of very low kinetic energies, well below the Coulomb barrier limit, from heavy nuclei was resolved by postulating that the hyperfragments of short range were not, as had been assumed before, emitted light hyperfragments but were in fact the recoiling residual nuclei (spallation products) into which Λ hyperons had become trapped. In the "recoil model" of Jones *et al.* (1961, 1962) it is assumed that the interactions of K⁻ mesons of high energy are similar to other high energy nuclear interactions; namely, first there is a nuclear cascade during which fast particles are emitted. During this stage it is possible that an energetic light hyperfragment may be emitted although the infrequency of observation of fast hyperfragments suggests that this stage of the interaction does not contribute significantly to the number of hyperfragments. However, often a Λ hyperon remains behind in the highly excited nucleus and it may be emitted either free or bound in a light hyperfragment during the ensuing evaporation stage. A comparison of the emission spectra of light hyperfragments and ordinary fragments suggests that the emission of light hyperfragments may be well explained from evaporation theory (Cüer, 1963; Gajewski *et al.*, 1965). If the Λ hyperon is not emitted in the evaporation stage it must perforce remain trapped in the heavy residual nucleus (spallation product) thus forming a heavy "spallation hyperfragment." As a result of both the cascade and evaporation stages of the interaction this final recoil often receives a sufficient momentum ($\gtrsim 500$ MeV/c) to yield a visible track in the emulsion enabling the primary and decay disintegrations to be resolved.

The suggestion that these hyperfragments of short range are heavy (as spallation products of silver and bromine they would be expected to have mass numbers in the range 40 to 100) is strongly supported by the very large nonmesonic to π^--mesonic decay ratio, $Q^- \sim 150$ (Lagnaux *et al.*, 1964), observed for them. Additional evidence in favor of this suggestion is: the lack of secondary particles of short range coming from their nonmesonic decays (see Fig. 2) implying the existence of a Coulomb barrier effect appropriate to a heavy emulsion nucleus; the very low visible energy releases in their π^--mesonic decays indicating that their binding energies are much higher than those of light hyperfragments, $A \leqslant 16$ (see Section IX); the hyperfragments of short range are projected preferentially in the forward direction with respect to the incident K⁻ meson to about the same extent as are ordinary spallation products observed in radiochemistry studies at comparable incident momenta.

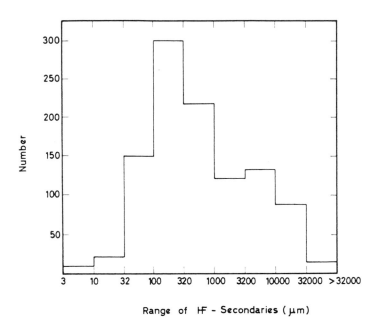

Fig. 2. Range distribution of secondary particles coming from the nonmesonic decays of heavy spallation hyperfragments (Davis, 1963).

It has been shown by means of Monte Carlo calculations that both cascade and evaporation processes contribute significantly to the momentum imparted to the recoiling spallation hyperfragments (Kenyon, 1963; Key *et al.*, 1964; Lemonne, 1965; Renard *et al.*, 1965). In addition, it was estimated that even for incident K^--meson momenta up to 3.5 GeV/c many of these spallation hyperfragments will receive insufficient momenta to allow them to record observable tracks in the emulsion (Key *et al.*, 1964). This fact has been effectively demonstrated by Bosgra and Hoogland (1964) who, by making careful spatial extrapolations of all tracks back to stars produced by the interactions of 800 MeV/c K^- mesons, have detected the presence of hyperfragments of ranges as small as 0.25 μm which are not observed during the course of conventional scanning.

The recoil model has been shown to be equally applicable to the process of production of hyperfragments by the interactions of K^- mesons in the momentum range 50 MeV/c to 5 GeV/c and also explains very well the results obtained from a study of the interactions of 4.5 GeV/c π^- mesons (Zakrzewski *et al.*, 1963). The shift to the right of the peak in the hyperfragment range distribution on increase of the incident K^--meson momentum is easily explained since not only is more momentum imparted to the struck nucleus but also since more energy becomes available for evaporation processes, the residual nuclei will be on the average lighter and hence travel greater distances before coming to rest. At the highest incident energies it is to be expected that the fission process will play some part in the production of hyperfragments but as yet there is no good evidence of a contribution from such a mechanism (Lemonne *et al.*, 1965).

For K⁻-meson captures at rest the situation is different in that there is no incident momentum and the energy available in the evaporation stage is smaller. Also, the capture process is orbital resulting in mainly peripheral capture and in a larger proportion of captures on the light emulsion nuclei than is the case for interactions in flight, 40% as opposed to 25%. The production by the captures at rest of K⁻ mesons and Σ⁻ hyperons of light hyperfragments which decay π⁻ mesonically has been studied by Abeledo *et al.* (1961). From an analysis of the primary star characteristics, in particular the emission of particles of short range and the observation of Auger electron tracks, Abeledo *et al.* (1961) concluded that the light hyperfragments came predominantly from captures on the light emulsion nuclei, carbon, nitrogen, and oxygen. On the basis of the emisson of particles of short range ("under-Barrier particles") alone they estimated that at least 57% of hydrogen, 73% of helium, 84% of lithium, and 94% of heavier hyperfragments decaying π⁻ mesonically originated from light nuclei. They similarly observed that at least 75% of Li^8 fragments came from light nuclei. The momentum spectra for hyperfragments of different atomic numbers are shown in Fig. 3 and are seen to be similar, and striking similarities were also noticed between the momentum spectra of helium nuclei and hyperfragments shown in Fig. 4 and lithium fragments (Li^8) and hyperfragments, Fig. 5. A further feature of the results was that there was a marked tendency for the line of flight of a hyperfragment to be opposite that of a π meson or a fast proton ($E \geqslant 52$ MeV) produced in association with it, the backward-to-forward ratio being 1.8 ± 0.4 for hyperfragments associated with a π meson and 8 ± 4 for those with a proton (Sacton, 1961; Abeledo *et al.*, 1961). A similar angular correlation was found to exist between the directions of Li^8 fragments and π mesons and protons.

In order to explain the above observations Abedelo *et al.* (1961) put forward two models of hyperfragment production, the "trapped Λ hyperon" and the "prompt hyperfragment" models.

In the trapped Λ-hyperon model, a model very similar to the reccil model of Jones *et al.* (1961, 1962), it is suggested that a Λ hyperon, created either directly or by the subsequent internal conversion of a Σ hyperon or even by the decay within the capturing nucleus of a Y_1^* resonance, may become trapped in the struck nucleus. As a result of the nuclear de-excitation process, the trapped Λ hyperon may be emitted free or bound in a hyperfragment. This model accounts very well for the observed preponderance of the emission of

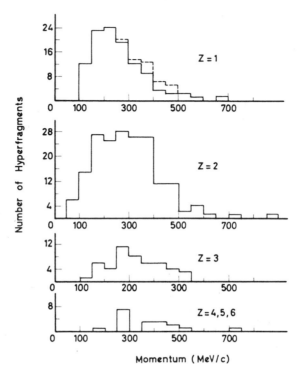

Fig. 3. Momentum distributions for hyperfragments of different atomic numbers produced in K⁻-meson absorption at rest (Abeledo *et al.*, 1961): (—) observed and (- - -) corrected.

light hyperfragments (and also Li^8 fragments) from light nuclei since while the excitation energy available, $\leqslant 100$ MeV, is sufficient to bring about the complete disruption of a light nucleus, rarely will a multiply charged hyperfragment receive enough energy to surmount the Coulomb barrier presented by a heavy one. On the basis of this model the observed similarities in the momentum distributions of fragments and hyperfragments are to be expected while the observed angular correlations are explained as a result of the evaporation of the hyperfragments occurring isotropically from moving nuclei. For captures in silver and bromine, the initial trapping of a Λ hyperon may lead to the evaporation of a very light hyperfragment (there is evidence that a substantial fraction of hydrogen hyperfragments come from heavy nuclei) (Lemonne *et al.*, 1964b; Abeledo *et al.*, 1961), but in general the Λ hyperon will remain behind in the heavy residual spallation product forming a heavy hyperfragment. Abeledo *et al.* (1961) stated that in no case would the decay of such a hyperfragment be distinguished from the primary disintegration, but now more recent work (Lemonne *et al.*, 1964b; Evans *et al.*, 1965) has shown that about one-half of the observed hyperfragments produced

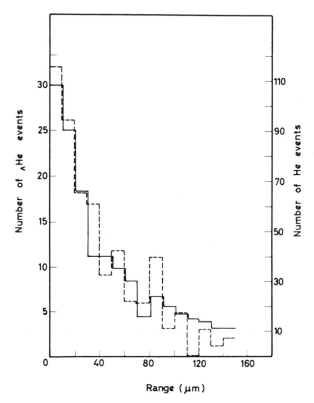

Fig. 4. Momentum distributions of helium nuclei and hypernuclei produced in K^--meson absorptions at rest (Abeledo *et al.*, 1961): (—) inferred He and (---)$_\Lambda$He.

by K^--meson captures at rest are in fact these heavy spallation products of silver and bromine, whose ranges extend up to about 3 μm. This is most easily demonstrated by the high value of Q^- (the nonmesonic to π^--mesonic decay ratio) observed for them, *viz.*, 55, and by the striking similarities observed between the hyperfragments of short range ($R \lesssim 3\mu$m) produced by stopping K^- mesons and those known to be heavy, produced by the inter-actions of K^- mesons in flight. Table II presents the results of such a com-parison.

The range distribution of hyperfragments produced by the interactions of K^- mesons at rest with emulsion nuclei is given in Fig. 6. The large accumula-tion of events at very small ranges strongly suggests that in many cases the range of the hyperfragment will be too short for it to be observed. In fact, from a study of the frequency of emission of Λ, and hence, also Σ^0, hyperons from K^--meson captures in emulsion nuclei, Davis *et al.* (1961) estimated that in $30 \pm 7\%$ of the cases a strange particle was not identified among the interaction

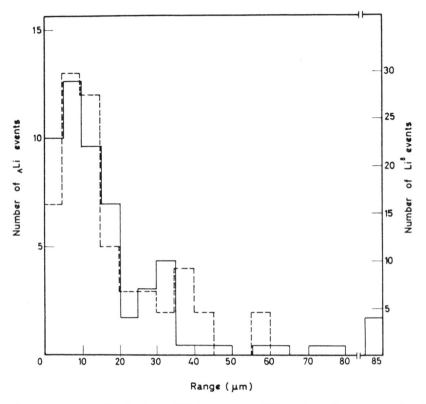

Fig. 5. Momentum distributions of Li^8 fragments and lithium hyperfragments produced in K$^-$-meson absorptions at rest (Abeledo *et al.*, 1961): (—) Li^8 and (---) $_\Lambda$Li.

products and such events had to be ascribed to the formation of crypto-fragments, hyperfragments decaying so close to the parent disintegration as to be not directly observable. From a similar study of Λ-hyperon emission following K$^-$-meson captures at rest in a propane-Freon bubble chamber, Knight *et al.* (1963) concluded that $51 \pm 14\%$ of captures in bromine and $18.5 \pm 3.5\%$ in carbon and fluorine led to hyperfragment formation. Lemonne *et al.* (1964b), by combining their results with those of Davis *et al.* (1961) and by using the result that K$^-$-meson captures at rest in emulsion occur in the light and heavy nuclei in the proportion 2 to 3 (Csejthey-Barth and Sacton, 1962) found that $58 \pm 15\%$ of captures in silver and bromine and $8 \pm 2\%$ in carbon, nitrogen, and oxygen lead to hyperfragment formation, results in very good agreement with those of Knight *et al.* (1963). Lemonne *et al.* (1964b) also noted a marked dependence on the nature of the target nucleus of the emission frequency of charged π mesons from K$^-$-meson captures from which hyperfragments are seen to come. When the struck nucleus was light

TABLE II

COMPARISON OF THE CHARACTERISTICS OF THE DECAY OF SHORT-RANGE HYPERFRAGMENTS

	K$^-$ meson momentum (MeV/c) and reference				
	At rest[a]	50–500[b]	800[c]	1300[d]	1500[e]
Percentage of mesonic hyperfragments	1.8 ± 0.5	0	$0.3 \begin{smallmatrix} +0.4 \\ -0.3 \end{smallmatrix}$	0.9 ± 0.4	0.8 ± 0.5
Percentage of non-mesonic stars with a short prong $(3 < R \leqslant 30\ \mu m)$ (%)	4.9 ± 1.5	5	5 ± 3	9 ± 2	8 ± 2
Percentage of non-mesonic decay stars with a recoil $(R \leqslant 3\ \mu m)$ (%)	36.4 ± 4.0	45	53 ± 7	43 ± 3	43 ± 4

[a] Lemonne et al. (1964b).
[b] Henrotin et al. (1965); Lemonne et al. (1963).
[c] Jones et al. (1961, 1962).
[d] Fletcher et al. (1963).
[e] Fletcher et al. (1963).

the frequency of observation of charged π mesons was $55 \pm 3\%$, when heavy $22 \pm 2\%$. The low value of the frequency of emission of π mesons from heavy nuclei suggests a strong π-meson absorption in apparent contradiction with the surmise that the K$^-$-meson capture takes place predominantly in the periphery of the nucleus and that the absorption probability of charged π mesons is small. However, in order that a heavy spallation hyperfragment be seen it must acquire a momentum in excess of about 500 MeV/c and such a momentum may be most often provided either by a direct multinucleon interaction or by the subsequent reabsorption of a created π meson. It may well be that the frequency of π mesons which accompany heavy hyperfragments which are not seen is considerably greater. A further deduction which has been made from these results is that, on taking into account the emission of π^0 mesons and also a small π-meson reabsorption, the K$^-$-meson multi-nucleon capture mechanism is not responsible for the production of a large number of hyperfragments in light nuclei.

In the second model of hyperfragment production put forward by Abeledo et al. (1961), the "prompt hyperfragment model," it is suggested that the K$^-$ meson or Σ^- hyperon interacts with a large cluster of nucleons to form a hyperfragment directly. While this model may well be cited for particular interactions, notably the production of $_\Lambda H^4$ and $_\Lambda He^4$ hyperfragments in the

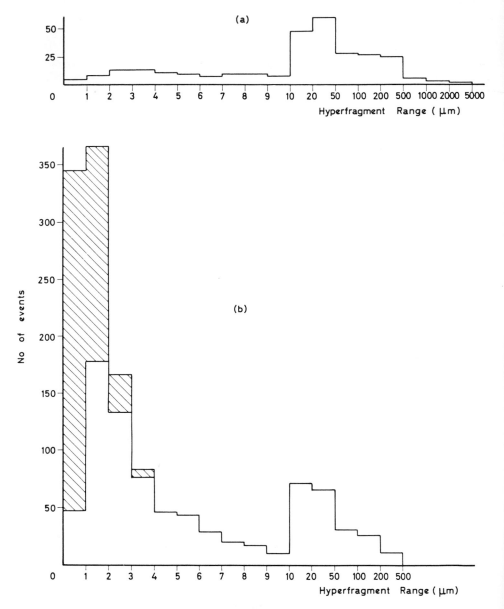

Fig. 6. Range distribution of hyperfragments produced by the interactions of K⁻ mesons at rest (a) mesonic hyperfragments and (b) nonmesonic hyperfragments (Lemonne *et al.*, 1964b).

helium bubble chamber, some features of the observations are not well reconciled to this model. In particular, the similarities of the momentum spectra of fragments and hyperfragments of the same charge go unexplained and the observed angular correlations between the directions of the hyperfragments and π mesons and protons are not as marked as would have been expected on the basis of this model. A final objection to this model is that it implies that the interaction of a K^- meson with a large cluster of nucleons should be a frequent process.

Studies of hyperfragments produced by the captures at rest of Σ^- hyperons have yielded results very similar to those obtained from studies of stopping K^- mesons (Andersen *et al.*, 1963; Sacton *et al.*, 1962; Frodesen *et al.*, 1965a); namely, light hyperfragments preferentially originate from captures on light nuclei whereas the trapping of a Λ hyperon following capture on a heavy nucleus usually leads to the formation of a heavy hyperfragment, whose decay is only rarely distinguished from the primary disintegration. A surprising feature of the results is that although the energy spectra of Λ hyperons produced in K^--meson and Σ^--hyperon captures are similar, the trapping probabilities for Λ hyperons following Σ^--hyperon capture are much smaller in both heavy and light emulsion nuclei than is the case for K^--meson capture. Possible reasons for this are that Σ hyperons may undergo capture on the periphery of the nucleus with a higher orbital angular momentum allowing the Λ hyperons a better chance to be emitted and also that many Λ hyperons formed in K^- interactions arise from the secondary interactions of Σ hyperons and as a result are created deeper within the nucleus with a greater chance of becoming bound.

IV. The Binding Energies of Light Hypernuclei

A. EXPERIMENTAL DATA

The binding energy B_Λ of a Λ hyperon in a hypernucleus is defined by the relation

$$(M_{\text{core}} + M_\Lambda)c^2 - B_\Lambda = M_{HF}c^2 \qquad \text{(IV-1)}$$

where M_{core}, M_Λ, and M_{HF} are the masses of the nuclear core, the Λ hyperon and the hypernucleus, respectively. The mass of the hypernucleus is determined from a study of the decay reaction and it is given by the relation

$$M_{HF}c^2 = \sum_{i=1}^{n} M_i c^2 + Q \qquad \text{(IV-2)}$$

where M_i is the mass of the ith decay product and Q is the total kinetic energy released in the decay.

By combining Eqs. (IV-1) and (IV-2) one obtains

$$B_\Lambda = Q_0 - Q \qquad \text{(IV-3)}$$

where Q_0 is equal to

$$\left(M_{core} + M_\Lambda - \sum_{i=1}^{n} M_i\right)c^2.$$

For the reasons already stated, in general, only π^--mesonic decays have been used for the determination of binding energies. The errors on the determination of B_Λ for a particular event have been discussed extensively by different authors (Slater, 1958; Inman, 1957; Levi Setti et al., 1958; Prem, 1965; Prakash et al., 1961; Raymund, 1964). The error on Q_0 is systematic and amounts to about 0.15 MeV, being dominated by the uncertainty in the mass of the Λ hyperon, since the mass of the π^- meson and those of most of the light nuclei are known to better than 0.02 MeV. The masses used here are those given by Rosenfeld et al. (1965) for the elementary particles and by Everling et al. (1960) for the nuclei. The error in Q is due to

(1) The experimental errors on the measurements of the ranges and angles of emission of the decay products. Under good experimental conditions these contribute only a few tenths of a MeV.

(2) The error due to range straggling which has been estimated by Barkas et al. (1955). This effect may be neglected for protons and heavier nuclei but gives rise to an uncertainty of about 2% in the determination of the kinetic energy of a π meson from its range.

(3) The uncertainty in the range-energy relation. For singly charged particles use is made of the range-energy relation of Barkas (1958) and Barkas et al. (1958) which yields a systematic uncertainty of about 1% in an energy determination. The uncertainty in a B_Λ value arising from this effect is offset to some extent by the fact that the mass of the Λ hyperon is subject to the same systematic error.

(4) The error in the determination of the density of the emulsion. Stacks are calibrated by measuring the ranges of a sample of mono-energetic particles, preferably protons from Σ^+-hyperon decays at rest, or if these are not available in sufficient number, then muons from π^+-meson decays at rest. The stopping power of the emulsion can be determined to much better than 1%, yielding an uncertainty of less than 0.1 MeV in Q.

The appropriate combination of these errors leads to an over-all uncertainty in B_Λ which is usually less than 1 MeV for a particular mesonic decay involving only the emission of charged particles. When a neutron is emitted, the error on B_Λ is larger, of the order of a few MeV.

Table III summarizes the experimental data on the binding energies of the uniquely identified hypernuclei. For the hypernuclei of mass number $A \leqslant 5$, this table is based on the results published by the Chicago-Northwestern Collaboration (Schlein and Slater, 1961; Ammar *et al.*, 1960a, 1961, 1963a; Crayton *et al.*, 1962a) and on more recent data obtained by Raymund (1964) and the K^- European Collaboration (Mayeur *et al.*, 1966a). For heavier species, all published data, for which detailed measurements were available, have been used (Levi Setti, 1965; Baumann, 1965). Homogeneous and severe selection criteria have been applied to these statistics so that only the events for which the identification can be considered as uniquely established were accepted. For example, all decay modes involving a neutron were excluded from this table as were also all π^--recoil decays for which the identification was not confirmed either by a consideration of the production reaction

TABLE III

BINDING ENERGIES OF UNIQUELY IDENTIFIED HYPERNUCLEI

Hypernucleus	Decay mode[a]	No. of events	$B_\Lambda \pm \Delta_\Lambda{}^{b}$ (MeV)
$_\Lambda H^3$	$\pi^- + He^3$	24	0.06 ± 0.15
	$\pi^- + H^1 + H^2$	5	0.59 ± 0.35
	Total	29	0.14 ± 0.14
$_\Lambda H^4$	$\pi^- + He^4$	184	2.23 ± 0.08
	$\pi^- + H^1 + H^3$	24	1.77 ± 0.14
	$\pi^- + H^2 + H^2$	4	2.15 ± 0.32
	Total without (π^- He^4) (see text)	28	1.83 ± 0.12
$_\Lambda He^4$	$\pi^- + H^1 + He^3$	62	2.16 ± 0.07
	$\pi^- + H^1 + H^1 + H^2$	1	1.86 ± 0.45
	Total	63	2.15 ± 0.07
$_\Lambda He^5$	$\pi^- + H^1 + He^4$	322	3.05 ± 0.03
	$\pi^- + H^2 + He^3$	1	2.88 ± 0.50
	Total	323	3.05 ± 0.03
$_\Lambda He^6$	$\pi^- + H^2 + He^4$	4	4.09 ± 0.27
$_\Lambda He^7$	$\pi^- + Li^7$	4	5.06 ± 0.38
	$\pi^- H^1 + He^6$	3	4.14 ± 0.71
	$\pi^- + H^3 + He^4$	4	3.49 ± 0.51
$_\Lambda Li^7$	$\pi^- + Be^7$	11	5.52 ± 0.20
	$\pi^- + H^1 + Li^6$	2	5.65 ± 0.43
	$\pi^- + He^3 + He^4$	20	5.56 ± 0.18
	$\pi^- + H^1 + H^2 + He^4$	16	5.22 ± 0.14
	Total	49	5.39 ± 0.11
$_\Lambda Be^7$	$\pi^- + H^1 + H^1 + H^1 + He^4$	5	5.65 ± 0.44
$_\Lambda He^8$	$\pi^- + Li^8$	1	$(7.4 \pm 0.8)-B_n{}^{c}$

TABLE III—*Continued*

Hypernucleus	Decay mode[a]	No. of events	$B_\Lambda \pm \Delta B_\Lambda$[b] (MeV)
$_\Lambda Li^8$	$\pi^- + He^4 + He^4$	81	6.60 ± 0.12
	$\pi^- + H^1 + H^3 + He^4$	6	6.75 ± 0.35ù
	Total	87	6.62 ± 0.11
$_\Lambda Be^8$	$\pi^- + B^8$	4	6.47 ± 0.29
	$\pi^- + H^1 + Be^7$	1	6.74 ± 0.50
	$\pi^- + H^1 + He^3 + He^4$	4	6.56 ± 0.25
	Total	9	6.55 ± 0.18
$_\Lambda Li^9$	$\pi^- + Be^9$	5	8.36 ± 0.43
	$\pi^- + H^1 + Li^8$	4	8.27 ± 0.25
	$\pi^- + H^3 + Li^6$	1	8.09 ± 0.47
	Total	10	8.25 ± 0.20
$_\Lambda Be^9$	$\pi^- + H^1 + He^4 + He^4$	9	6.31 ± 0.20
$_\Lambda Be^{10}$	$\pi^- + He^4 + Li^6$	1	8.36 ± 0.60
$_\Lambda B^{10}$	$\pi^- + H^1 + H^1 + He^4 + He^4$	2	8.86 ± 0.50
$_\Lambda B^{11}$	$\pi^- + H^1 + H^1 + Be^9$	1	9.98 ± 0.37
	$\pi^- + He^3 + He^4 + He^4$	1	9.93 ± 0.30
	$\pi^- + H^1 + H^2 + He^4 + He^4$	3	10.21 ± 0.23
	Total	5	10.08 ± 0.16
$_\Lambda B^{12}$	$\pi^- + He^4 + He^4 + He^4$	19	10.84 ± 0.16

[a] For acceptance criteria of the events, see text.

[b] (1) For an individual event, the error quoted on B_Λ is the experimental error.

    (2) For small samples ($1 < n \leqslant 30$) the quoted error is the larger of the two estimates of error obtained from (a) dividing the individual experimental error by $\sqrt{n}$, and (b) the use of Student's Distribution, the error defining the interval in which the true mean value is expected to be with a 67% confidence level.

    (3) For large samples ($n > 30$) the error is $[(\overline{X^2} - \bar{x}^2)/(n-1)]^{1/2}$. Possible systematic errors have not been included.

[c] B_n is the binding energy of the last neutron in He^7.

or by the decay configuration of the recoil (Mayeur *et al.*, 1966a). Also since the range-momentum curves for various isotopes become indistinguishable at low values of momentum it was necessary to apply strict cutoffs to the ranges of the recoiling nuclei in π^--proton-recoil decays (see Fig. 7).

The distributions of the individual values of the binding energies of different hypernuclei are given in Figs. 8 to 14. Each species will now be discussed in turn.

1. *A = 2*

No experimental evidence has been found for bound states of the two particle systems Λ–p and Λ–n. This is to be expected from the estimates of the

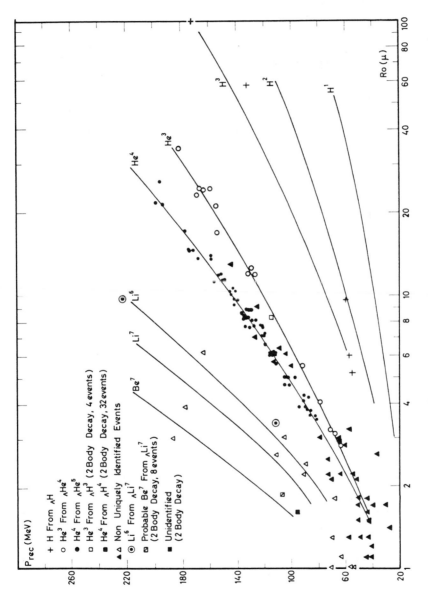

Fig. 7. Range-momentum curves for light nuclei (Ammar, 1963).

strength of the Λ-nucleon potential obtained from the analysis of the heavier nuclei (see Section IV,B).

2. $A = 3$

The lightest of the known hypernuclei is $_\Lambda H^3$. Its binding energy is found to be 0.14 ± 0.14 MeV. The only π^--mesonic decay modes of this hypernucleus which do not involve neutrons are $(\pi^- He^3)$ and $(\pi^- H^1 H^2)$. The first decay mode is relatively free from identification biases but the latter one can be confused with $_\Lambda H^4 \rightarrow \pi^- + H^1 + H^3$ for small values of momentum transferred to the core nucleus. For this reason a cutoff at 10 μm has been imposed

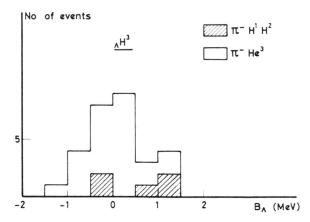

Fig. 8. Distribution of the B_Λ values of the hypernucleus $_\Lambda H^3$.

on the range of the H^2 recoil. The failure to observe the hypernuclei $_\Lambda He^3$ and $_\Lambda n^3$, which could be readily identified from their decay modes $(\pi^- H^1 H^1 H^1)$ and $(\pi^- H^3)$, respectively, leads to the attribution of isotopic spin zero to $_\Lambda H^3$.

3. $A = 4$

The only observed hypernuclei of mass 4, $_\Lambda H^4$ and $_\Lambda He^4$, are members of an isotopic spin doublet and charge symmetry for the Λ–N force would predict their B_Λ values to be equal once the contributions from the distortions of the core nuclei have been taken into account. The result of an analysis by Raymund (1964) indicated that the B_Λ value of $_\Lambda He^4$ was greater than that of $_\Lambda H^4$, the difference $\Delta B_\Lambda = B_\Lambda (_\Lambda He^4) - B_\Lambda (_\Lambda H^4)$ being 0.30 ± 0.14 MeV. On the other hand, the mean binding energies obtained from Table III for $_\Lambda H^4$ and $_\Lambda He^4$ by consideration of all decay modes are 2.11 ± 0.07 MeV and 2.15 ± 0.07 MeV, respectively, giving a value of ΔB_Λ compatible with zero. However, the B_Λ value of $_\Lambda H^4$ obtained from the decay mode $(\pi^- He^4)$ is greater than that obtained from the other events, the difference being

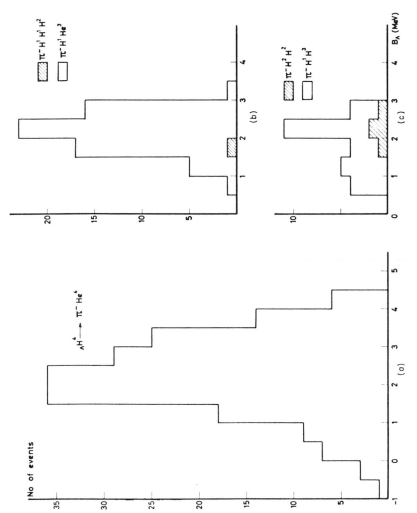

Fig. 9. Distribution of the B_Λ values of the mass 4 hypernuclei: $\pi^- + H^1 + H^3$.

$+0.40 \pm 0.15$ MeV. The possibility that this discrepancy is due to a systematic underestimate of the range of the π^- meson from the $(\pi^-$ He^4) decay mode when it traverses many pellicles, as suggested by Raymund (1964), has been investigated for the greater part of the statistics (131 events) but no variation of B_Λ with the dip angle of the π meson was found. A further possibility which could give rise to a systematic effect is that the range-energy relation may be in error, the energy of the π meson from the $(\pi^-$ He^4) decay mode being about 53 MeV whereas for the other decay modes the energy of the π^- meson is contained in the range 25–35 MeV. Evidence in support of this suggestion is furnished by a recent determination of the mass of the Λ hyperon by Schmidt (1965) from events observed in a hydrogen bubble chamber. By using momentum measurements made upon the tracks and not the range-energy relation he obtained a value for the mass of the Λ hyperon, $M_\Lambda = 1115.61 \pm 0.07$ MeV, to be compared with a compilation of results from emulsion experiments, all relying on the range-energy relation, of $M_\Lambda = 1115.42 \pm 0.10$ MeV. Both this discrepancy and that between the B_Λ values obtained from the different decay modes of $_\Lambda$H^4 could be removed by assuming that there is an error in the range-energy relation, resulting in an underestimate of the energy of a π meson from its range of about 1 or 2%.

Since there is some doubt as to the correctness of the range-energy relation, it is better to compare the B_Λ values of $_\Lambda$H^4 and $_\Lambda$He^4 using events for which the energy releases are very similar, that is, leaving out of consideration the $(\pi^-$ He^4) decay mode of $_\Lambda$H^4. If this be done, ΔB_Λ is found to be $+0.32 \pm 0.14$ MeV, the acceptance criteria for the range of the recoil in π^--proton-recoil decays being 6 μm for $_\Lambda$H^4 and 10 μm for $_\Lambda$He^4. With these severe acceptance criteria it is estimated that the contamination of $_\Lambda$H^3 events in the sample of $_\Lambda$H^4 and $_\Lambda$He^5 among the $_\Lambda$He^4 events is negligible, and so the finding of a positive value of ΔB_Λ cannot be attributed to such a cause.

As pointed out by Dalitz and Downs (1958b), a deviation from charge symmetry for the Λ–N forces could be produced by the existence of a $\Lambda\Lambda\pi^0$ coupling. In fact, the exchange of a π^0 meson contributes a long-range term to the Λ–N interaction which has opposite signs for the Λ–p and Λ–n systems. The effect of this charge-dependent potential has been estimated recently by Dalitz and von Hippel (1964a). They found the difference in B_Λ values of $_\Lambda$He^4 and $_\Lambda$H^4, ΔB_Λ, generated by this potential to be $+0.21 \pm 0.05$ MeV. Other contributions to ΔB_Λ, have also been considered by these authors. The effect of the $\Sigma^- - \Sigma^+$ hyperon mass difference in the two π-meson exchange potential was found to contribute at most of the order of 0.1 MeV. The contributions to ΔB_Λ from nuclear structure effects, such as nuclear core distortion and a difference between the core radii, although small were found to be negative, hence a truly positive value of ΔB_Λ would indicate a breaking of charge symmetry in the Λ–N interaction. It is thus of great interest to substantiate or disprove the present result for the binding energy difference ΔB_Λ by obtaining a large sample of well-identified events.

4. $A = 5$

The most abundantly produced hypernucleus is $_\Lambda\text{He}^5$, resulting from the binding of a Λ hyperon to an α particle. Its binding energy B_Λ calculated from 326 examples of the decay mode (π^- H^1 He^4) in which the range of the He^4 nucleus was required to be greater than 6 μm, is 3.05 ± 0.03 MeV. The distribution of the individual values of B_Λ for $_\Lambda\text{He}^5$ given in Fig. 10 is seen to be Gaussian with a half-width at half height of 0.5 MeV, compatible with the spread expected from the range straggling of π mesons, and thus giving confidence in the method of analysis. As is to be expected from the large binding energy of the nuclear core, the vast majority of the π^--mesonic decays of $_\Lambda\text{He}^5$ hypernuclei, all but one, proceed via the mode (π^- H^1 He^4). No other hypernuclei of mass 5 have been reported although the questions of particle-stable states of $_\Lambda n^5$ and $_\Lambda\text{H}^5$ have been discussed by Dalitz and Levi Setti (1963).

5. $A = 6$

No conclusive evidence for the existence of particle-stable mass 6 hypernuclei has been presented since for all the reported events alternative interpretations in terms of other, well-known, hypernuclei could not be excluded.* Many theoretical speculations have been made concerning the stability of $_\Lambda\text{He}^6$ and these have been summarized recently by Willain (1965). The conclusion of this summary is that $_\Lambda\text{He}^6$ is just not stable against the decay $_\Lambda\text{He}^6 \rightarrow {}_\Lambda\text{He}^5 + n$. However, the finding from the results of Λ–p scattering experiments that the triplet Λ–N interaction is more attractive than had been estimated from the analysis of light hypernuclei leaves the stability of $_\Lambda\text{He}^6$ once more in question (Dalitz, 1965a). In any event, the additional Coulomb repulsion present in the hypernucleus $_\Lambda\text{Li}^6$ renders it extremely unlikely to be particle-stable. It has been pointed out by Dalitz and Levi Setti (1963) that the mass 6 hypernuclei should appear, if not particle-stable, as sharp P-wave resonances in the n–$_\Lambda\text{He}^5$ and p–$_\Lambda\text{He}^5$ systems. This resonance level of $_\Lambda\text{Li}^6$ has been sought by the study of the Q-value distribution of the p–$_\Lambda\text{He}^5$ system by Raymund (1965) but without success.

There is no evidence of the existence of $_\Lambda\text{H}^6$.

* *Note Added in Proof.* The existence of a particle-stable state of $_\Lambda\text{He}^6$ has recently been established by the observation of four examples of the decay ($\pi^-\text{H}^2\text{He}^4$) (Gajewski et al., 1966). The value of B_Λ was found to be 4.09 ± 0.27 MeV. This result indicates that $_\Lambda\text{He}^6$ is only just stable to neutron emission, the binding energy of the last neutron being $+0.08^{+0.27}_{-0.08}$ MeV (taking B_Λ ($_\Lambda\text{He}^5$) to be 3.05 ± 0.03 MeV).

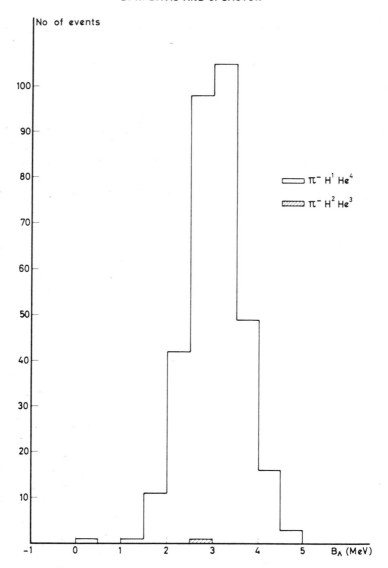

Fig. 10. Distribution of the B_Λ values of the hypernucleus $_\Lambda He^5$.

6. $A = 7$

The isospin singlet $_\Lambda Li^7$ is well established and the distributions of B_Λ values obtained from different decay modes are presented in Fig. 11.

On the basis of charge symmetry one should expect the B_Λ values of $_\Lambda Be^7$ and $_\Lambda He^7$ to be equal, except, that is, for the small changes brought about by the distortions of the core nuclei, since they are two members of an isospin

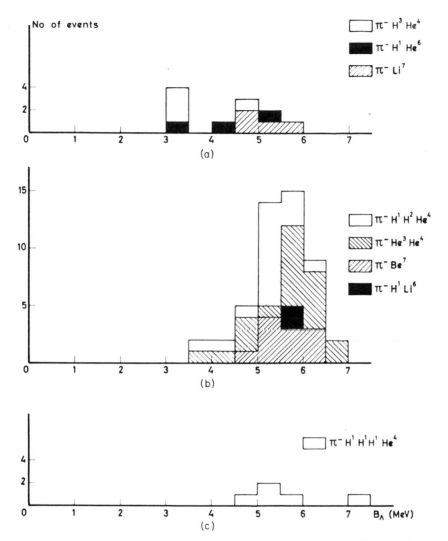

Fig. 11. Distribution of the B_Λ values of the mass 7 hypernuclei: (a) $_\Lambda He^7$, (b) $_\Lambda Li^7$, and (c) $_\Lambda Be^7$.

triplet. However, whereas the five reported examples of $_\Lambda Be^7$ give a mean value of B_Λ equal to (5.65 ± 0.44) MeV,[3] when calculated using the latest mass value of Be^6 (Blair *et al.*, 1964), the B_Λ values of the 11 $_\Lambda He^7$ events are widely distributed between 3 and 6 MeV, (see Fig. 11), the mean value of B_Λ of $_\Lambda He^7$ being (4.30 ± 0.30) MeV.

[3] If one event with an unusually high value of B_Λ, (7.15 ± 0.60) MeV, is left out of consideration this mean value becomes (5.27 ± 0.30) MeV.

A solution to the puzzle presented by the discrepancy of the B_Λ values of $_\Lambda Be^7$ and $_\Lambda He^7$ (in fact, the B_Λ value of $_\Lambda Be^7$ must exceed 4.9 MeV in order that it should be stable against the decay $_\Lambda Be^7 \rightarrow _\Lambda He^5 + H^1 + H^1$) was put forward by Pniewski and Danysz (1962). They suggested that the observed decays of $_\Lambda He^7$ could be from either the ground state or a long-living isomeric state formed by the attachment of a Λ hyperon to the 1.7-MeV isomeric state of He^6. Since the events are always analyzed as if the hypernucleus decayed from its ground state, this situation would lead to a splitting of the B_Λ values into two groups separated by the excitation energy of the isomeric state. While the experimental data are still rather meager, two groupings may be seen in the distribution of the individual B_Λ values of $_\Lambda He^7$ in Fig. 11, four events being located between 3 and 3.5 MeV, the remaining seven events having B_Λ values in the region of 5 MeV. It may also be seen that three of the four events in the first group decay via the mode ($\pi^- H^3 He^4$) while only one such decay is observed in the latter sample. The fact that the B_Λ distribution for $_\Lambda He^7$ may be resolved into two groups separated by about 1.7 MeV together with the expectation that the isomeric state of $_\Lambda He^7$ will decay preferentially with a fragmentation of its core lends strong support to the suggestion of Pniewski and Danysz (1962).

The $E2$ transition probability from the 1.7-MeV 2^+ excited state of He^6 to its ground state in the presence of a Λ hyperon has been calculated by Elton (1962), Rayet (1964), and Law (1965); they found that the lifetime for γ transition is comparable with that expected for the Λ hyperon bound in $_\Lambda He^7$.

The value of B_Λ of $_\Lambda He^7$ obtained from the seven events is 4.86 ± 0.26. With this result the difference between the B_Λ values of $_\Lambda Be^7$ and $_\Lambda He^7$ essentially disappears, becoming (0.41 ± 0.40) MeV. The comparison of the binding energies of the mass 7 hypernuclei in the $I = 0$ and $I = 1$ isospin states leads to the result

$$B_\Lambda (_\Lambda Li^7)_{I=0} - B_\Lambda (_\Lambda He^7 \text{ or } _\Lambda Be^7)_{I=1} = +(0.35 \pm 0.23) \text{ MeV} \quad \text{(IV-4)}$$

7. $A = 8$

The B_Λ values of the mirror hypernuclei $_\Lambda Li^8$ and $_\Lambda Be^8$ are seen to be in agreement as expected from the requirements of charge symmetry (see Fig. 12). The existence of a particle-stable $_\Lambda He^8$ hypernucleus has been discussed by Dalitz and Levi Setti (1963) and an event has been reported (Lemonne et al., 1964c), which is most likely interpreted as an example of $_\Lambda He^8$ decaying by the mode ($\pi^- Li^8$) (see Section XI).

8. $A = 9$

A large difference, about 2 MeV, is observed between the binding energies of $_\Lambda Li^9$ (a member of an isospin triplet) and $_\Lambda Be^9$ (an isospin singlet state)

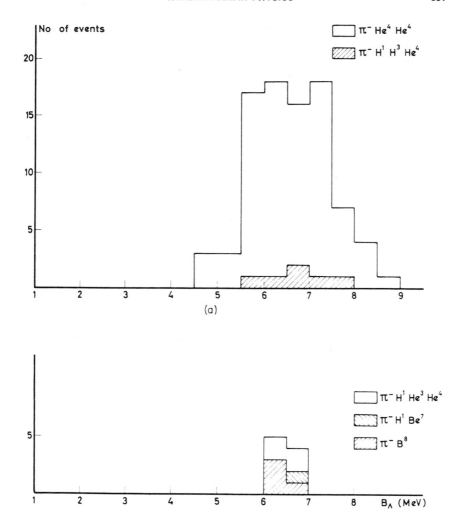

Fig. 12. Distribution of the B_Λ values of the mass 8 hypernuclei: (a) $_\Lambda Li^8$ and (b) $_\Lambda Be^8$.

(see Fig. 13). Dalitz (1963b) has pointed out that this difference would require an important spin dependence of the ΛN interaction which is not really consistent with theoretical estimates (see Section IV,B).

The other members of the isospin triplet to which $_\Lambda Li^9$ belongs are $_\Lambda B^9$ and the first $I = 1$ excited state of $_\Lambda Be^9$. No example of $_\Lambda B^9$ has been reported although the decay modes (π^- H^1 B^8) and (π^- C^9) should be readily recognized. The excited state of $_\Lambda Be^9$ should be unstable to the decays $_\Lambda Be^9 \rightarrow Be^8 + \Lambda^0$ and $_\Lambda Be^{9*} \rightarrow _\Lambda He^5 + He^4$ but searches for well-defined states of

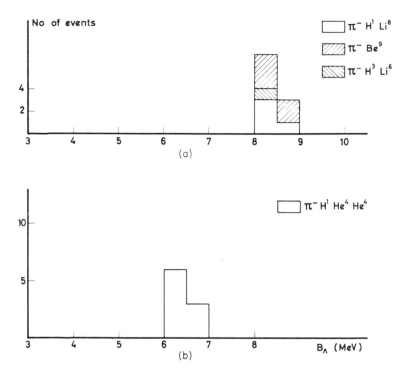

Fig. 13. Distribution of the B_Λ values of the mass 9 hypernuclei: (a) $_\Lambda Li^9$ and (b) $_\Lambda Be^9$.

$_\Lambda Be^9$ among the invariant mass distribution of the ($_\Lambda He^5 + He^4$) system have so far proved unsuccessful (Raymund, 1965; Frodesen et al., 1965b).

The existence of the hypernucleus $_\Lambda He^9$ has been conjectured (Dalitz and Levi Setti, 1963) but not established.

9. $A \geqslant 10$

As can be seen from Table III the number of well-identified events with mass numbers in this region is very few. The information to be obtained on B_Λ values from decays of the type π^- recoil should be treated with some reserve, because even when the identity of the hypernucleus is established from a study of the production reaction, the recoil may still be emitted in a low-lying excited state giving rise to a systematic overestimate of the binding energy (see Fig. 14).

B. THEORY

The major contributions to the Λ-nucleon interaction are expected to arise from the exchange of virtual π and K mesons between the Λ hyperon and the nucleons, as illustrated by the diagrams of Fig. 15 since the exchange of a

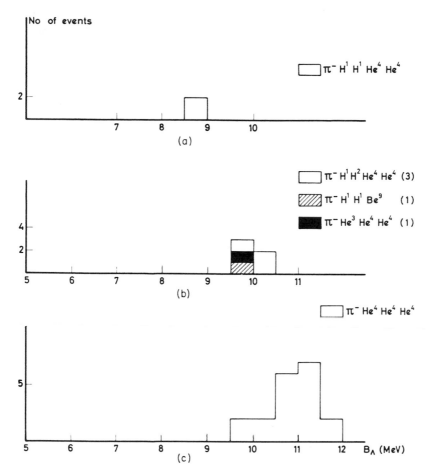

Fig. 14. Distribution of the B_Λ values of the hypernuclei of mass number $A \geqslant 10$: (a) $_\Lambda B^{10}$, (b) $_\Lambda B^{11}$, and (c) $_\Lambda B^{12}$.

single π meson is forbidden by isospin conservation. The transfer of two π mesons gives rise to a direct interaction of range $\hbar/(2m_\pi c) \sim 0.65$ Fermi between the Λ hyperon and the nucleon while the exchange of a single K meson contributes an exchange term (transfer of strangeness) of range $\hbar/(m_k c) \sim 0.4$ Fermi. Both of these ranges are considerably smaller than in the case of the nucleon-nucleon interaction where the exchange of a single π meson is allowed, leading to a force of range $\hbar/(m_\pi c) \sim 1.3$ Fermis. More complicated processes, involving the exchange of two or more K mesons, with or without additional π mesons, will not be considered as they will contribute only at very short range $\hbar/(2m_K c) \lesssim 0.2$ Fermi.

Most of the calculations which have been made for light hypernuclei are based on a charge-independent but spin-dependent two-body interaction between the Λ hyperon and a nucleon. It is assumed that the Λ–N interactions are almost entirely S-wave interactions. That the Λ-nucleon interaction is spin-dependent is demonstrated by the fact that the B_Λ values for hypernuclei with the same A value but belonging to different isospin multiplets are some-times different. This is, for example, the case for $_\Lambda Li^9$ and $_\Lambda Be^9$ where this

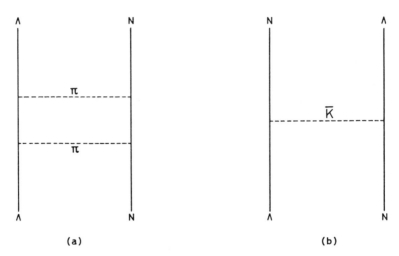

(a)   (b)

Fig. 15. Diagrams important in the Λ–N interaction: (a) two π-meson exchange and (b) one K-meson exchange.

difference is of about 2 MeV, the lower value corresponding to the hyper-nucleus whose core has zero spin (see Section IV,A).

For the ith nucleon in a given hypernucleus, the Λ–N potential may be written as

$$V = \frac{3 + \bar{\sigma}_\Lambda \cdot \bar{\sigma}_i}{4} V_t + \frac{1 - \bar{\sigma}_\Lambda \cdot \bar{\sigma}_i}{4} V_s \qquad (IV\text{-}5)$$

V_t and V_s denote the triplet and singlet interaction, respectively; the coeffi-cients of V_t and V_s are the spin projection operators for the states of total spin 1 and 0.

For a hypernucleus of spin J and mass number A, the expectation value of the Λ-nucleus potential is of the form

$$\bar{V} = \left\langle J \left| \sum_{i=1}^{A-1} \left\{ \frac{3V_t + V_s}{4} - \frac{V_s - V_t}{4} \bar{\sigma}_\Lambda \cdot \bar{\sigma}_\Lambda \right\} \right| J \right\rangle. \qquad (IV\text{-}6)$$

In the case of $j-j$ coupling of the nucleons in the core, this expression has been evaluated by Lawson and Rotenberg (1960) and Iwao (1960)

$$\bar{V} = (A - 1)\frac{3V_t + V_s}{4} - \alpha(j, l)\{J(J + 1) - J_c(J_c + 1) - \tfrac{3}{4}\} \times \frac{V_s - V_t}{4} \quad \text{(IV-7)}$$

where J_c is the spin of the core; $\alpha(j, l) = 2$ or $\tfrac{2}{3}$ for s-shell or $p_{3/2}$-shell hypernuclei, respectively.

For $L-S$ coupling

$$\bar{V} = (A - 1)\frac{3V_t + V_s}{4} - \langle J|\bar{\sigma}_\Lambda \cdot \bar{S}|J\rangle \frac{V_s - V_t}{2} \quad \text{(IV-8)}$$

where $\bar{S}$ is the total spin, $\tfrac{1}{2}\sum_i \bar{\sigma}_i$ (Dalitz 1965b).

1. Hypernuclei of the 1s Shell

The hypernuclei whose nucleons belong to the $1s$ shell are $_\Lambda\mathrm{H}^3$, $_\Lambda\mathrm{H}^4$, $_\Lambda\mathrm{He}^4$, and $_\Lambda\mathrm{He}^5$. Appropriate theoretical treatments have been used for each of these hypernuclei in order to take adequately into account both the variation in the B_Λ values and the characteristics of the core nuclei (e.g., masses and sizes).

a. $_\Lambda\mathrm{H}^3$. The three particle system consisting of a Λ hyperon and two nucleons can exist in states of isospin $I = 0$ or $I = 1$. The $I = 0$ state results from the coupling of a Λ hyperon with a neutron and a proton whose total isospin is zero and whose total spin S is 1. The ground state of this $I = 0$ hypertriton state will have spin $J = \tfrac{1}{2}$ or $\tfrac{3}{2}$ depending upon whether the singlet Λ-nucleus interaction is more attractive than the triplet one or vice versa. According to Eq. (IV-7) the volume integral U_2 of the total Λ-nucleon interaction in this state is then

$$U_2 = \tfrac{3}{2}\bar{V}_s + \tfrac{1}{2}\bar{V}_t \qquad \text{if} \quad \bar{V}_s > \bar{V}_t \qquad \text{(IV-9a)}$$

and

$$U_2 = 2\bar{V}_t \qquad \text{if} \quad \bar{V}_t > \bar{V}_s \qquad \text{(IV-9b)}$$

The members of the $T = 1$ hypernuclear triplet ($_\Lambda\mathrm{He}^3$, $_\Lambda\mathrm{H}^3$, and $_\Lambda n^3$) consist of a Λ hyperon together with two nucleons of total isospin $I = 1$ and of total spin $S = 0$. The volume integral U_2' of the total interaction in these states is

$$U_2' = \tfrac{3}{2}\bar{V}_t + \tfrac{1}{2}\bar{V}_s \qquad \text{(IV-9c)}$$

The hypertriton is known to be a $I = 0$, $J = \tfrac{1}{2}$ singlet state (see Section V). The low value of its total binding energy 2.41 MeV[4] means that this system

---

[4] The total binding energy of the hypertriton is given by the Λ-deuteron separation energy $(0.14 \pm 0.14$ MeV$)$ and the binding energy of the deuteron, i.e., 2.266 MeV.

has a very open structure. On the other hand, the Λ–N forces are of short ranges. The wave function of this n–p–Λ system must thus be flexible enough to describe adequately the region of correlations in position between the Λ hyperon and the nucleons and to have a suitable asymptotic form in order not to overestimate the total binding energy. This system is sufficiently simple to allow accurate variational calculations. The basic analysis has been performed by Dalitz and Downs (1958a,b) who discussed in some detail the features desirable in the trial function. A variational calculation of the strength of the Λ-nucleon interaction required to account for the observed binding energy of the hypertriton was made by these authors (Downs and Dalitz, 1959) using a rather flexible six-parameter trial function with a space part of the form

$$\Psi(\Lambda np) = g(r_{np}) f(r_{n\Lambda}) f(r_{p\Lambda}) \tag{IV-10}$$

where r_{np} denotes the neutron-proton separation and $r_{n\Lambda}$ and $r_{p\Lambda}$ the Λ-neutron and Λ-proton separations. The functions $f(r)$ and $g(r)$ are of the form

$$f(r) = \exp(-a_1 r) + x \exp(-a_2 r) \tag{IV-11a}$$

and

$$g(r) = \exp(-b_1 r) + y \exp(-b_2 r) \tag{IV-11b}$$

$a_1, a_2, b_1, b_2, x,$ and y being the parameters to be determined.

Upper bounds of the strength of the Λ-nucleon potential were obtained for Gaussian and Yukawa shape potentials of intrinsic ranges corresponding to the exchange of either two π mesons (1.48 Fermis) or one K meson (0.84 Fermi). The results are illustrated in Table IV giving measures of this strength

TABLE IV

MEASUREMENTS OF THE STRENGTH OF THE Λ-NUCLEON INTERACTION IN THE HYPERTRITON
(POTENTIAL WITHOUT HARD CORE)[a]

B_Λ (MeV)	s	Yukawa		Gaussian	
		a_0 (Fermi)	r_0 (Fermi)	U_2 (MeV Fermi³)	U_2 (MeV Fermi³)
		(a) K-meson exchange (0.84 Fermi)			
0	0.636	−1.03	1.45	407	405
0.25	0.659	−1.13	1.40	422	420
		(b) 2π-meson exchange (1.48 Fermis)			
0	0.550	−1.30	3.05	621	615
0.25	0.595	−1.55	2.75	672	667

[a] Data from Downs and Dalitz (1959).

in terms of the volume integral U_2 of the total Λ-nucleon interaction in the hypertriton and of the corresponding scattering length a_0 for Λ-nucleon scattering at zero energy, the effective range r_0 and the effective well-depth parameter s of the Λ-nucleon potential.

Similar calculations were made for the $I = 1$ hypernuclear triplet $_\Lambda\text{He}^3$, $_\Lambda\text{H}^3$, and $_\Lambda n^3$ and have led to the conclusion that these states are not bound (Downs and Dalitz, 1959). This is not unreasonable since the total binding energy of the $I = 0$ hypertriton is already small and both the N–N interaction and the mean Λ–N interaction are weaker in the $I = 1$ system than is the corresponding interaction in the $I = 0$ system [see Eqs. (IV-9)].

Variational calculations of the strength of the average Λ-nucleon interaction potential in the hypertriton have also been made using central two-body potentials with hard cores for both the Λ–N and the N–N interactions [Downs et al., 1963; Muller (quoted by Dalitz, 1963b); Smith and Downs, 1964; Dietrich et al., 1964; Gutsch, 1963 (quoted by Dalitz, 1963b); Herndon et al., 1964, 1965]. In particular, Smith and Downs (1964) used a ten-para-meter trial function of the form given by Eq. (IV-10)

with $f(r) = 0$, $\qquad\qquad\qquad\qquad\qquad$ for $\quad r < d$

$$= \{\exp[-\alpha(r-d)] - \exp[-\beta(r-d)]$$
$$+ x\{\exp[-\mu(r-d)] \tag{IV-12a}$$
$$- \exp[-v(r-d)]\} \qquad \text{for} \quad r > d$$

$g(r) = 0 \qquad\qquad\qquad\qquad\qquad$ for $\quad r < d$

$$= \{\exp[-\gamma(r-d)] - \exp[-\delta(r-d)]$$
$$+ y\{\exp[-\varepsilon(r-d)] \tag{IV-12b}$$
$$- \exp[-\eta(r-d)]\} \qquad \text{for} \quad r > d$$

where d, the hard-core radius, was chosen equal to 0.2, 0.4, and 0.6 Fermis. Outside the hard-core radius, the Λ-nucleon potential was taken of the exponential form

$$V_{\Lambda\text{N}}(r) = \bar{U} \exp\left[\frac{-3.54(r-d)}{b_0}\right] \tag{IV-13}$$

where b_0, the intrinsic range of the attractive well translated to the origin is equal to $b - 2d$, b being the intrinsic range of the potential, chosen as 1.5 Fermis. In Table V results of these calculations for $B_\Lambda = 0.2$ MeV are com-pared with those obtained by Downs et al. (1963) using a less flexible four parameter trial function of the form given by Eq. (IV-10) with f and g of the form (IV-12) with $x = y = 0$. It is seen that the well depths calculated

TABLE V

THE Λ-NUCLEON INTERACTION IN THE HYPERTRITON
(POTENTIAL WITH HARD CORE)

d (Fermi)	U_0 (MeV)	s	a (Fermi)	r_0 (Fermi)
		(a) Ten-parameter trial function[a]		
0.2	402	0.701	−1.75	2.31
0.4	1144	0.810	−1.82	2.24
0.6	7123	0.925	−2.11	2.10
		(b) Four-parameter trial function		
0.2	426	0.744	−2.20	2.13
0.4	1202	0.851	−2.56	2.01
0.6	7352	0.955	−4.09	1.80

[a] Data from Smith and Downs (1964).　　　　[b] Data from Downs et al. (1963).

with the ten-parameter trial function are only about 3 to 6% less than those obtained with the four-parameter function so that their value can be considered to be close to the true value. The low energy scattering parameters obtained with the ten-parameter function are not very sensitive to the value of the hard-core radius. For fixed intrinsic ranges, these parameters are rather insensitive to the shape of the potential. This is illustrated by the comparison of the results of Tables IVb and Va. Also, Dietrich et al. (1964) obtained a scattering length $a_0 = -2.6$ Fermis and an effective range $r_0 = 1.9$ Fermis for a square-well potential with a hard-core radius $d = 0.2$ Fermi.

The effect of the tensor part of the neutron-proton interaction in $_\Lambda H^3$ has been studied by Barsella and Rosati (1961) and Rosati (1965). The correction found for the volume integral of the Λ-nucleon interaction is of the order of 3 or 4% (Rosati, 1965).

b. $_\Lambda He^5$. The α core of $_\Lambda He^5$ has a spin-saturated structure with high total binding energy so that distortion effects due to the presence of the weakly bound Λ hyperon are not expected to be serious. Its nucleon density distribution $\rho(r/R)$ is known from electron scattering experiments to have a Gaussian form with r.m.s. radius $R = 1.44 \pm 0.07$ Fermi. The spin of the α core being zero, $_\Lambda He^5$ will have spin $\frac{1}{2}$ as does the Λ hyperon. The volume integral U_4 of the total Λ-nucleon potential in $_\Lambda He^5$ is seen from Eq. (IV-7) to be

$$U_4 = 3\overline{V}_t + \overline{V}_s. \tag{IV-14}$$

Assuming a Gaussian shape for both V_t and V_s, Dalitz and Downs (1958b) have estimated U_4 appropriate to the observed binding energy of $_\Lambda He^5$ by solving the Schrödinger equation for the motion of the Λ hyperon relative to the α core. For intrinsic ranges corresponding to the exchange of two π mesons or one K meson they obtained for U_4 the values 925 ± 45 MeV Fermi^3 and 715 ± 25 MeV Fermi^3, respectively. Taking into account a uniform radial compression of the α core due to the presence of the Λ hyperon the values of U_4 are found to be reduced by 1.5% for the case of π-meson exchange and by 3% for K-meson exchange (Dalitz and Downs, 1958b).

   c. $_\Lambda H^4 - _\Lambda He^4$. In a similar way, Dalitz and Downs (1958b) have studied the doublet $_\Lambda H^4 - _\Lambda He^4$. Depending upon whether the spins of the Λ hyperon and the unpaired nucleon are coupled parallel or antiparallel, the spin of the doublet will be $J = 0$ or $J = I$. According to Eq. (IV-7) the volume integral U_3 of the total Λ-nucleon interaction is

$$U_3 = \tfrac{3}{2}\bar{V}_s + \tfrac{3}{2}\bar{V}_t \qquad \text{if} \quad \bar{V}_s > \bar{V}_t \qquad \text{(IV-15a)}$$

and

$$U_3 = \tfrac{1}{2}\bar{V}_s + \tfrac{5}{2}\bar{V}_t \qquad \text{if} \quad \bar{V}_t > \bar{V}_s. \qquad \text{(IV-15b)}$$

It is probable that the cores H^3 and He^3 will be distorted appreciably by the presence of the Λ hyperon. In their calculation, Dalitz and Downs (1958b) represented the He^3 nucleus by a wave function of the form $\exp[-\tfrac{1}{2}\alpha(r_{12}^2 + r_{23}^2 + r_{31}^2)]$, α being adjusted in order to give the corresponding r.m.s. radius of the nucleon distribution as derived from electron scattering experiments. The strength U_3 of the total Λ-nucleon interaction appropriate to a binding energy of 2.25 ± 0.10 MeV was obtained in the same way as in the case of $_\Lambda He^5$. For Gaussian-shaped potentials with intrinsic ranges corresponding to the exchange of two π mesons or one K meson and after allowance for a uniform radial core compression U_3 was found to be 1010 ± 100 MeV Fermi^3 and 780 ± 100 MeV Fermi^3.[5] The errors on these values come almost entirely from the uncertainties in the values of the core radii.

   Estimates of $\bar{V}_s$ and $\bar{V}_t$ obtained from the values of U_2 and U_4 calculated by Dalitz and Downs (1958b) are given in Table VI. The spin dependence of the Λ-nucleon interaction is clearly illustrated. An internal check on these values could be obtained since they could be used to predict values for U_3 to be compared with the ones determined from the study of the $_\Lambda H^4 - _\Lambda He^4$ doublet. However, this comparison is made hazardous by the fact that the values of U_3 obtained from this study are overestimated and affected by large errors. In the case of two π-meson exchange, one obtains from the values given in Table VI, $U_3 = 845 \pm 35$ MeV Fermi^3 and 800 ± 30 MeV Fermi^3 for

_____

[5] The reduction of U_3 due to the effect of the radial compression was found to be of the order of 5 and 10% in the case of K- and π-meson exchanges, respectively; larger reductions are expected from modes of distortion which are other than radial.

TABLE VI

<small>ESTIMATES OF THE Λ-NUCLEON INTERACTION STRENGTH IN THE SINGLET
AND TRIPLET CONFIGURATIONS[a]</small>

	Two-pion exchange	K-meson exchange
$\bar{V}_s > \bar{V}_t$	$\bar{V}_s = 385 \pm 20$ MeV Fermi³	$\bar{V}_s = 225 \pm 10$ MeV Fermi³
	$\bar{V}_t = 180 \pm 20$ MeV Fermi³	$\bar{V}_t = 165 \pm 15$ MeV Fermi³
$\bar{V}_t < \bar{V}_s$	$\bar{V}_s = -75 \pm 55$ Mev Fermi³	$\bar{V}_s = 85 \pm 30$ MeV Fermi³
	$\bar{V}_t = 335 \pm 15$ MeV Fermi³	$\bar{V}_t = 210 \pm 5$ MeV Fermi³

[a] If $\bar{V}_s < \bar{V}_t$, $\bar{V}_t = \frac{3}{8} U_4 - \frac{1}{4} U_2$ and $\bar{V}_s = \frac{3}{4} U_2 - \frac{1}{8} U_4$; If $\bar{V}_t > \bar{V}_s$, $\bar{V}_t = \frac{1}{2} U_2$ and $\bar{V}_s = U_4 - \frac{3}{2} U_2$. The values of U_2 used in this table are those given in Table IV, lines 2 and 4. The errors reflect the uncertainties in B_Λ for $_\Lambda H^3$ and $_\Lambda He^5$ and in the core radius of $_\Lambda He^5$.

$\bar{V}_s > \bar{V}_t$ and $\bar{V}_t > \bar{V}_s$, respectively, to be compared with the value 1010 ± 100 MeV Fermi³ given above. Similarly, for K-meson exchange the disagreement between the different estimates of U_3 is smaller for $V_s > V_t$. That the singlet interaction should be stronger is however substantiated by the experimental determinations of the spins of $_\Lambda H^3$ ($J = \frac{1}{2}$) and $_\Lambda H^4$ ($J = 0$) (see Section V).

The hypernuclei $_\Lambda H^3$, $_\Lambda H^4$, and $_\Lambda He^5$ have been discussed also by Dietrich et al. (1964), Beck and Gutsch (1965), and Herndon et al. (1964, 1965) using central two-body potentials with hard cores. Dietrich et al. (1964) and Beck and Gutsch (1965) made use of an independent-pair approximation (Mang and Wild, 1959) in order to take into account all two-body correlations and to allow for distortion of the core nucleus. The interactions were described by potentials with square-well shapes outside of a hard core of radius 0.2 Fermi (Dietrich et al., 1964). For both the force ranges considered (2π-meson and K-meson exchange) it is concluded from the discussion of $_\Lambda H^4$ and $_\Lambda He^5$ that the case $\bar{V}_s > \bar{V}_t$ is slightly favored. In that case the ratio $\bar{V}_t/\bar{V}_s$ was found to be 0.53 and 0.65 for 2π-meson and K-meson exchange, respectively. The corresponding values obtained by Dalitz and Downs (1958b) are 0.47 and 0.73 (see Table VI). Using a central two-body Λ-nucleon potential with a hard core of radius 0.4 Fermi and an attractive well of exponential shape with a range corresponding to the exchange of two π mesons, Herndon et al. (1965) also concluded that the singlet interaction is dominant. The ratio of the triplet to the singlet strength was found to be 0.78, showing that this ratio increases with the radius of the hard core.

The values of the low energy scattering parameters of the Λ-nucleon potentials obtained by Dalitz and Downs (1958b), Dietrich et al. (1964), Herndon et al. (1965), and Beck and Gutsch (1965) are listed in Table VII. It has been argued (Herndon et al., 1965; Dalitz, 1963b) that the method of

TABLE VII

Low energy Scattering Parameters of the Λ-Nucleon Potentials

Potential		Gaussian Shape without hard core[a]	Square-well hard core $d = 0.2$ Fermi[b]	Exponential-well hard core $d = 0.4$ Fermi[c]	Harmonic-oscillators hard core $d = 0.4$ Fermi[d]
Scattering length (Fermi)	Singlet	$-\left(2.25 \begin{smallmatrix} +0.80 \\ -0.54 \end{smallmatrix}\right)$	$-\left(4.6 \begin{smallmatrix} +3.8 \\ -1.7 \end{smallmatrix}\right)$	$-\left(2.89 \begin{smallmatrix} +0.59 \\ -0.41 \end{smallmatrix}\right)$	-3.3 ± 0.7
Effective range (Fermi)		1.97 ± 0.14	1.7 ± 0.1	1.94 ± 0.08	1.83 ± 0.07
Scattering length (Fermi)	Triplet	-0.51 ± 0.09	-0.53 ± 0.11	-0.71 ± 0.06	-0.64 ± 0.9
Effective range (Fermi)		3.62 ± 0.35	3.88 ± 0.65	3.75 ± 0.22	3.7 ± 0.2

[a] Data from Dalitz and Downs (1958b).
[b] Data from Dietrich et al. (1964).
[c] Data from Herndon et al. (1965).
[d] Data from Beck and Gursch (1965).

calculation used by Dietrich *et al.* (1964) would not be accurate for small binding energies, as it does not give a correct account of the asymptotic region. As a result, the average well-depth obtained in their calculation might have a somewhat too large value.

From the estimates of the well-depth parameter s, all smaller than unity, made in these different analyses it is concluded that, in the absence of three-body interactions, the two-body Λ–N system is not expected to be bound even for Λ–N potentials with hard-core radii as large as 0.6 Fermi.

The possibility of a $J = 1$ particle stable excited state of the doublet $_\Lambda H^4$–$_\Lambda He^4$ has been discussed by different authors (Dalitz and Downs, 1958b; Dalitz, 1962, 1963b; Dietrich *et al.*, 1964; Herndon *et al.*, 1965, Beck and Gutsch, 1965). The question whether this state exists is of importance because of its bearing on the determination of the K-meson parity through the selection rules for the reaction $K^- + He^4 \rightarrow {}_\Lambda He^4 + \pi^-$ or $_\Lambda H^4 + \pi^0$ (see Section V). The volume integral appropriate to the interaction between a Λ hyperon and H^3 or He^3 in the $J = 1$ state is

$$U'_3 = U_3 - (\overline{V}_s - \overline{V}_t). \qquad (IV\text{-}16)$$

A bound state with $J = 1$ will exist only if U'_3 exceeds a certain critical value corresponding, according to Dalitz and Downs (1958b), to U_3 for $B_\Lambda ({}_\Lambda H^4) = 0$. It is obvious from Eq. (IV-16) that the greater the spin dependence of the potential, the less likely is the existence of a $J = 1$ bound state .The calculations made with potentials without hard core do indicate the existence of such a state with $B_\Lambda \sim 1.3$ MeV (Dalitz and Downs, 1958b). The possible existence of a $J = 1$ state with $B_\Lambda{}^* \sim 0.3$ MeV is indicated by the results of Herndon *et al.* (1965) using hard-core potentials with exponential shapes outside of the hard core. On the other hand, Dietrich *et al.* (1964), using a less realistic square-well shape outside of the hard core, concluded that no such state exists. This conclusion is also reached by Beck and Gutsch (1965).

It has been noted by different authors that the spin dependence of the two-body potentials deduced from the above studies could depend upon the assumption that the effect of three-body interactions is negligible in the binding of hypernuclei. Such interactions arise in the lowest order through the exchange of one π meson with each of a pair of nucleons. Two of the graphs contributing to this Λ–N–N three-body potential are given in Fig. 16. The range of the interaction between the Λ hyperon and each nucleon in this two π-meson exchange three-body potential is about twice the range of the two π-meson exchange two-body interaction. On the other hand, the probability for the three particles to be sufficiently close together in light hypernuclei that the three-body interaction can be effective is expected to be small. Different authors have studied the role of a three-body force in the binding of hypernuclei (Spitzer, 1958; Weitzner, 1958; Bach, 1959; Dalitz, 1959; Bodmer and

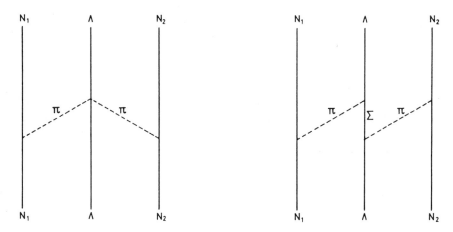

Fig. 16. Two of the graphs contributing to the Λ–N–N three-body potential.

Sampanthar, 1962; Abou-Hadid, 1963; Chalk and Downs, 1963). The most comprehensive study is due to Bodmer and Sampanthar (1962) who considered a potential of the form

$$V_3 (1, 2, \Lambda) = \omega \, (\sigma_1 \cdot \sigma_2) \, (\bar{\tau}_1 \cdot \bar{\tau}_2) \, W \, (\bar{r}_1, \bar{r}_2, \bar{r}_\Lambda) \qquad (\text{IV-17})$$

where 1, 2, and Λ denote the coordinates of the two nucleons and of the Λ hyperon; $\bar{\tau}_i$ and $\bar{\sigma}_i$ are the isospin and spin operators of the two nucleons; ω measures the strength of the interaction, and W, the shape factor, has been taken of exponential or Yukawa form. The contribution of this potential to the binding energy of $_\Lambda H^3$ has been estimated by a perturbation technique and found to be small. For $_\Lambda He^5$ where the spatial correlations among pairs of nucleons are stronger than for $_\Lambda H^3$, the effect of the three-body forces is increased. At the present time, however, the study of $_\Lambda H^3$ and $_\Lambda He^5$ does not seem sufficient to make a quantitative estimate of the relative role of the two- and three-body forces in the binding of light hypernuclei. Bodmer and Sampanthar (1962) also concluded that the system consisting of a Λ hyperon and a nucleon cannot be bound unless there should exist very strongly attractive three-body forces.

The importance in the binding energy of the hypertriton of a three-body noncentral potential of the form

$$V \, (\bar{r}_1 \, \bar{r}_2) = (\bar{\tau}_1 \cdot \bar{\tau}_2) \, (\bar{\sigma}_1 \cdot \bar{r}_1) \, (\bar{\sigma}_2 \cdot \bar{r}_2) \, f \, (\bar{r}_1 \, \bar{r}_2) \qquad (\text{IV-18})$$

where $\bar{r}_1$ and $\bar{r}_2$ are the Λ-nucleon separation vectors, has been studied by Chalk and Downs (1963) on the basis of a perturbation theory.[6] The unperturbed wave functions were the hard-core wave functions used by Downs

---

[6] The derivation of this potential is discussed in detail by Chalk and Downs (1963).

et al. (1963) in the analysis of the binding energy of $_\Lambda H^3$ in terms of two-body potentials. The ratio of the volume integral of the three-body potential to the volume integral of the total two-body Λ-nucleon interaction was found to be less than 5%.

The analysis of the recent Λ–p scattering experiments of Sacton. Sechi-Zorn *et al.* (1964; quoted by Dalitz, 1965c) and Alexander *et al.* (1966) shows that the mean Λ–p interaction is significantly stronger than that which has been estimated from the measurements of the binding energies of light hypernuclei. The best fit values of the Λ–p scattering lengths and effective ranges quoted by Alexander *et al.* (1966) are

$$a_s = -2.46 \text{ Fermis} \qquad r_s = 3.87 \text{ Fermis}$$
$$a_t = -2.07 \text{ Fermis} \qquad r_t = 4.50 \text{ Fermis}$$

and were obtained using the expression

$$\sigma_{\Lambda p} = \frac{\pi}{k^2 + [(-1/a_s) + (r_s k^2/2)]^2} + \frac{3\pi}{k^2 + [(-1/a_t) + (r_t k^2/2)]^2}. \qquad \text{(IV-19)}$$

Although these values of the scattering parameters are strongly correlated and subject to considerable uncertainties, they disagree with those obtained from hypernuclear studies and presented in Table VII. As pointed out by Bodmer (1966) the simplest possible cause of this discrepancy is that the strength of the triplet ΛN interaction, which is determined almost solely from the B_Λ value of $_\Lambda He^5$, has been underestimated. Three possible reasons for such an underestimate have been given by Dalitz (1965c). They are a strong tensor interaction in the ΛN system, significant three-body ΛNN interactions, and the partial suppression of some intermediate ΣN states (Bodmer, 1966). In particular the 2π-meson exchange mechanism illustrated in Fig. 15a is forbidden for $_\Lambda He^5$ unless the intermediate He^4 is elevated to a state of isospin unity. A rough estimate of the change in a_t brought about by the inclusion of this effect has been made by Bodmer (1966) by increasing the threshold energy for the ΣN channel in the calculations of de Swart and Iddings (1962) by the necessary excitation energy of He^4, and it seems possible that this change may be large enough to eliminate this discrepancy.

2. *Hypernuclei of the p Shell*

The remaining hypernuclei identified up to now have cores belonging to the $p_{3/2}$ shell. First discussions of these hypernuclei were made by Dalitz and Downs (1958b), Lawson and Rotenberg (1960), and Iwao (1960), using two-body Λ–N forces and shell model wave functions with the assumption of either j–j or L–S coupling for the core nuclei. These discussions assumed the Λ-wave function to be the same for all the hypernuclei and the expectation value of the Λ–N interaction between the Λ hyperon and a $p_{3/2}$ nucleon to be constant throughout the $p_{3/2}$ shell. Also the center-of-mass effects were considered to be unimportant. Starting from Eq. (IV-6) giving the expectation value of the Λ-nucleus potential, Lawson and Rotenberg (1960), and also Iwao (1960), obtained the following expression for the binding energies of hypernuclei with nuclear cores belonging to the p shell

$$B_\Lambda = C + N_p \langle \overline{V} \rangle + \alpha_N \langle \Delta \rangle \qquad \text{(IV-20)}$$

where the constant C is the sum of the kinetic energy of the Λ hyperon and the interaction energy between the Λ hyperon and the s-shell nucleons; N_p represents the number of p-shell nucleons, and α_N is a coefficient depending on the spin J of the hypernuclear state and on the structure of the nuclear core; $\langle \overline{V} \rangle$ and $\langle \Delta \rangle$ are the expectation values of $\overline{V} = (3V_t) + (V_s)/4$ and $\Delta = \overline{V}_s - \overline{V}_t$ respectively, between the Λ-hyperon wave function and the wave function of a p-shell nucleon.

For j–j coupling, α_N is given (Lawson and Rotenberg, 1960) by

$$\alpha_N = -\tfrac{1}{4}\left[1 - \frac{l(l+1) - \tfrac{3}{4}}{j(j+1)}\right][J(J+1) - J_C(J_C+1) - \tfrac{3}{4}] \qquad \text{(IV-21)}$$

where J_C is the spin of the nuclear core. For $p_{3/2}$ hypernuclei, $l = 1$ and $j = \tfrac{3}{2}$ so that α_N reduces to

$$\alpha_N = -\tfrac{1}{6}[J(J+1) - J_C(J_C+1) - \tfrac{3}{4}]. \qquad \text{(IV-22)}$$

In the case of L–S coupling, one has (Lawson and Rotenberg, 1960)

$$B_\Lambda = C + N_p\langle \overline{V} \rangle(J_C, J_C') - \tfrac{1}{2}\langle \Delta \rangle(-1)^{(J_C + J_C')}$$

$$\times (2J_C + 1)(2J_C' + 1)^{1/2} \sum_{S = S_C - 1/2}^{S_C + 1/2} (2S + 1)[S(S+1) - S_C(S_C+1) - \tfrac{3}{4}]$$

$$\times W(S_C S J_C J; \tfrac{1}{2} L)W(S_C S J_C' J; \tfrac{1}{2} L) \qquad \text{(IV-23)}$$

where L is the total orbital angular momentum of the nucleons; S_C is the total spin of the core, $S_C = \sum_i s_i$; S, which is the result of combining the nuclear spin and the Λ-hyperon spin, is equal to $S_C \pm \tfrac{1}{2}$ and $W(abcd; ef)$ is the Racah coefficient giving the amplitude of the spin state S.

Assuming j–j coupling for the nuclear cores, Dalitz (1963b) determined empirical values for $\overline{V}$ and Δ by comparing expression (IV-20) with the observed B_Λ values of the different hypernuclei. His results regarding the parameter Δ were found to be in disagreement with those obtained from the analysis of the s-shell hypernuclei. He pointed out that this might reflect the failure of the extreme assumption of j–j coupling for p-shell hypernuclei or might be due to the neglected contribution of the three-body ΛNN forces. A three-body force of the form given by Eq. (IV-17) was found by Conte and Iwao (1964) to contribute significantly to the binding energy of p-shell hypernuclei, under the assumption of j–j coupling of the nuclear cores. On the other hand, Dalitz and Soper (quoted by Dalitz, 1963b), using intermediate coupling wave functions for the nuclear cores and including the admixture of excited nuclear states where they are of significance, have estimated from different hypernuclei the spin-dependent term Δ and noted an increase of Δ as N_p increases through the p shell, roughly in proportion to N_p.

A comprehensive study of the p-shell hypernuclei has recently been made by Bodmer and Murphy (1965). These authors considered both central two- and three-body spin-dependent interactions with Yukawa shape functions. The two-body interaction was taken without hard core and the three-body force was assumed to be of the form given by Eq. (IV-17). Their considerations are based on a two-body model consisting of the Λ hyperon and the nuclear core for which intermediate coupled wave functions and different density distributions are assumed. The possibility of core distortion was taken into account whenever it was likely to be important. In particular, a special treatment was applied to the hypernucleus $_\Lambda Be^9$ for which the isolated Be^8 core is unbound: $_\Lambda Be^9$ was considered to be a three-body system consisting of two α particles and a Λ hyperon as was done first by Wilhelmsson and Zielinski (1958) and more quantitatively by Suh (1958). A detailed study of this three-body model has been made by Bodmer and Ali (1964) using phenomenological, static, s-state α–α potentials for which they calculated the corresponding α–α phase shifts which were compared with the experimental data. Their results have been used extensively in the general discussion of the p-shell hypernuclei by Bodmer and Murphy (1965).

Considering first that only two-body forces are effective in binding the hypernuclei, these authors found that the values of the spin-averaged volume integral of the Λ–N interaction that can be calculated from $_\Lambda He^5$, $_\Lambda Be^9$, and $_\Lambda C^{13}$,[7] all spinless core nuclei, agree well with each other, although the cores have different structure. These values are given in Table VIII for ordinary Yukawa interactions of intrinsic ranges corresponding to the exchange of two π mesons and one K meson, respectively. From this result one cannot necessarily conclude that the three-body forces may be neglected. However, the inclusion of a central three-body force of the form given by Eq. (IV-17) was found not to modify strongly the values obtained for U both from $_\Lambda He^5$ and $_\Lambda C^{13}$. In particular, for $_\Lambda C^{13}$, the ratio of the three-body to the total potential energy is 0 ± 0.15 and is independent of the range assumed for the two-body force (exchange of two π mesons or one K meson). On the other

[7] For $_\Lambda C^{13}$, Bodmer and Murphy (1965) have taken a value of $B_\Lambda = 10.90 \pm 0.30$ MeV given by Ismail et al. (1963) on the basis of three examples of the decay $_\Lambda C^{13} \rightarrow \pi^- + N^{13}$. As pointed out in Section IV,A, the values of B_Λ obtained from π-r events should be taken with some reserve.

TABLE VIII

<small>Spin-Averaged Volume Integral of the Interaction Calculated from $_{\Lambda}He^5$, $_{\Lambda}Be^9$, and $_{\Lambda}C^{13a}$</small>

	Two π-meson exchange	One K-meson exchange
$U = \bar{V}_s + 3\bar{V}_t = U_4 = \frac{1}{2} U_8 = \frac{1}{3} U_{12}$ (MeV Fermi³)		
$_{\Lambda}He^5$	1038 ± 30	786 ± 25
$_{\Lambda}Be^9$	1026 ± 60^b	793 ± 50^b
$_{\Lambda}C^{13}$	990 ± 60^c	815 ± 50^c

[a] Data from Bodmer and Murphy (1965).
[b] Data from Bodmer and Ali (1964).
[c] The nucleon density distribution in C^{12} is taken to be of the form

$$\rho(r) = \frac{A-1}{3\pi^{3/2}a^3}\left(1 + \frac{Z-2}{3}\frac{r^2}{a^2}\right)\exp(-r^2/a^2)$$

with $a = 1.64 \pm 0.05$ Fermi as given by the electron-scattering experiments.

hand, since most of the error on the different values of U is due to uncertainties in the nuclear core sizes, it is not possible to give realistic upper limits on the strength of the three-body forces. It is found, however, that the three-body force is most probably attractive or repulsive provided the range assumed for the two-body force corresponds to the exchange of 2 π mesons or one K meson, respectively. This range cannot be fixed from the present data: It is seen from Table VIII that the values of U obtained from $_{\Lambda}He^5$, $_{\Lambda}Be^9$, and $_{\Lambda}C^{12}$ are consistent with each other for both ranges considered. From their study of $_{\Lambda}C^{13}$, Bodmer and Murphy (1965) also concluded that for soft two-body forces the binding energies of the p-shell hypernuclei do not enable one to say anything definite about the contribution of the interactions in relative Λ–N angular momentum states with $l > 1$.

Two other $p_{3/2}$-shell hypernuclei with spinless cores for which B_{Λ} is fairly well known have not been discussed yet, i.e., $_{\Lambda}He^7$ and $_{\Lambda}Be^7$. In fact, the $T = 1$ (He^6 and Be^6) nuclei as well as the $T = 0$ (Li^6) nucleus appear somewhat exceptional in that the p nucleons are quite weakly bound, with a rather extended density distribution while, on the other hand, the s nucleons are very tightly bound and more compressed. In view of this it is expected that very little, if any, information about the Λ–N interaction will be deduced from studies of the mass 7 hypernuclei by using a simple two-body treatment which neglects correlations between the Λ hyperon and the nucleons. However, assuming that the mean value of U deduced from $_\Lambda He^5$, $_\Lambda Be^9$, and $_\Lambda C^{13}$ also holds for $_\Lambda He^7$ and $_\Lambda Be^7$, then the study of these hypernuclei can throw light on the structure of their cores. In this way, Bodmer and Murphy (1965) have established that the experimental binding energy values for these hypernuclei imply that the Λ hyperon effectively sees an s-shell nucleon distribution which is very similar to that of an α particle. This result is confirmed by the analysis of $_\Lambda Li^7$, resulting from the binding of a Λ hyperon to a Li^6 core with spin $J_C = 1$. This may be regarded as evidence that the structure of the $A = 6$ nuclei consists of an α particle plus two nucleons.[8] It is then reasonable to expect a strong correlation between the Λ hyperon and the α particle and consequently a relatively slight distortion of the core nucleus as a whole as indicated by the calculations of Bodmer and Murphy (1965). The spin-dependent interaction energy which could, in principle, be deduced from a comparison of $_\Lambda He^7$ and $_\Lambda Be^7$ with spinless cores, on the one hand, and $_\Lambda Li^7$, on the other, appears to be completely masked by uncertainties in the core sizes and in the rearrangement energies, i.e., the difference between the total energy of the core appropriate to its configuration in the hypernucleus and the energy of the isolated core nucleus in its ground state. This remark is valid for all p-shell hypernuclei. Indeed, Bodmer and Murphy (1965) have tried to obtain information on the spin-dependent term $\Delta = \overline{V}_s - \overline{V}_t$ by studying the pairs $_\Lambda Be^9$–$_\Lambda Li^8$, $_\Lambda Be^8$–$_\Lambda Li^9$, and $_\Lambda C^{13}$–$_\Lambda B^{12}$ for which the differences in binding energies are experimentally known. Assuming no differences in the size and rearrangement energies of the members of each of these pairs, they obtained values for Δ considerably larger than those obtained from the study of s-shell hypernuclei. However, from their calculations it appears that with some more flexibility in the choice of the parameters of the cores it is easy to obtain values of Δ which are consistent with those of the s-shell analysis.

V. Hypernuclear Spins

Spin determinations of various hypernuclei provide the most direct information concerning the spin dependence of the Λ–N force. To date spin assignments have been made for $_\Lambda H^3$, $_\Lambda H^4$ (and hence, from charge symmetry, $_\Lambda He^4$) and $_\Lambda Li^8$.

A direct determination of the spin of $_\Lambda H^4$ could be made from a study of the sequence of reactions

$$K^- + He^4 \rightarrow {}_\Lambda H^4 + \pi^0 \tag{V-1}$$

$$_\Lambda H^4 \rightarrow He^4 + \pi^- \tag{V-2}$$

[8] It must be noted that in this model the density distribution of the s-shell nucleons in the free $A = 6$ nuclei will be spread out by the recoil motion of the α particle, relative to the center of mass of the whole nucleus, due to the presence of the two p nucleons.

occurring after stopping K^- mesons in a helium bubble chamber. If it is assumed that the K^- meson is captured from an S orbit, following the arguments of Day and Snow (1959), then it is expected that, since all the particles involved in the reactions are spinless, with the possible exception of $_\Lambda H^4$, the angular distribution of the decay products of the hypernucleus with respect to its line of flight should be isotropic for $J(_\Lambda H^4) = 0$ and proportional to $\cos^2 \theta$ for $J(_\Lambda H^4) = 1$. Figure 17 gives the $\cos \theta$ distribution for 96 events

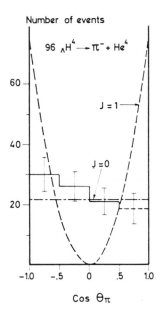

Fig. 17. Angular distribution of the π^- meson from the decay $_\Lambda H^4 \rightarrow He^4 + \pi^-$, for hypernuclei produced in the reaction $K^- + He^4 \rightarrow {_\Lambda H^4} + \pi^0$ (Block *et al.*, 1963a).

observed in a helium bubble chamber (Block *et al.*, 1963a), the result being clearly consistent with isotropy and at variance with a $\cos^2\theta$ distribution. This result alone would seem to establish the spin of $_\Lambda H^4$ as zero except that, unlike the situation existing for hydrogen, there is no reason to expect a K^--mesonic helium atom to be a particularly small neutral object and therefore the Day and Snow argument (1959) concerning K^--meson capture from an S orbit in helium is open to serious question. In fact, the observations of Burleson *et al.* (1965) on K^--mesonic X rays from helium indicate that K^--meson capture takes place predominantly from the $2P$ orbit.

Another, more indirect, spin determination of $_\Lambda H^4$ has been made. This stems from the impulse model calculations of Dalitz and Liu (1959) which relate the branching ratio R_4, defined as

$$R_4 = \frac{{}_\Lambda H^4 \rightarrow He^4 + \pi^-}{\text{all } \pi^-\text{-mesonic decays of } {}_\Lambda H^4} \tag{V-3}$$

both to the two possible spin assignments to ${}_\Lambda H^4$, namely, 0 and 1, and to the S- and P-wave amplitudes in the decay of the free Λ hyperon. Their results for R_4 are

$$\text{For } J({}_\Lambda H^4) = 0: \quad R_4 = \frac{1.41 s^2}{1.84 s^2 + 0.35 p^2} \tag{V-4}$$

$$\text{For } J({}_\Lambda H^4) = 1: \quad R_4 = \frac{0.76 p^2}{0.43 s^2 + 1.12 p^2}. \tag{V-5}$$

The general form of these results is easily understood since, if $J({}_\Lambda H^4) = 0$, all of the particles involved in the decay ${}_\Lambda H^4 \rightarrow He^4 + \pi^-$ are spinless and therefore in order to conserve orbital angular momentum the π meson must be emitted in an S wave. The two-body decay is thus forbidden for P-wave Λ-hyperon decay and allowed, and also energetically favored, for S-wave decay, i.e., R_4 will be directly related to the magnitude of s^2. On the other hand, if $J({}_\Lambda H^4) = 1$, the reverse situation holds, the two-body decay being forbidden to S-wave decay but enhanced for the P-wave case. The ratio R_4 has been determined from a study of the π^--mesonic decays of ${}_\Lambda H^4$ in both emulsions (Ammar et al., 1961) and the helium bubble chamber (Block et al., 1963a), the result being $R_4 = 0.68 \pm 0.05$. The ratio $p^2/(p^2 + s^2)$ for the free Λ-hyperon decay has been measured by Beall et al. (1961) and Cronin and Overseth (1963) as 0.12 ± 0.03, and this result, together with the experimental determination of R_4 and the predicted variation of R_4 with the $p^2/p^2 + s^2)$ ratio for the two ${}_\Lambda H^4$ spin possibilities, is presented graphically in Fig. 18. It is at once obvious that the only spin assignment compatible with the observations is $J({}_\Lambda H^4) = 0$. From considerations of charge symmetry spin zero may also be assigned to the hypernucleus ${}_\Lambda He^4$.

For ${}_\Lambda H^3$, the spin of the core nucleus is 1 and hence one may expect $J({}_\Lambda H^3) = \frac{1}{2}$ corresponding to the Λ hyperon bound to the core in the antiparallel spin configuration or $J({}_\Lambda H^3) = \frac{3}{2}$, the parallel case. Dalitz and Liu (1959) have made similar impulse approximations for ${}_\Lambda H^3$ decay and predict the ratio R_3

$$R_3 = \frac{{}_\Lambda H^3 \rightarrow \pi^- + He^3}{\text{all } \pi^-\text{-mesonic decays of } {}_\Lambda H^3} \tag{V-6}$$

again in terms of the S- and P-wave amplitudes in Λ-hyperon decay

For $J(_\Lambda H^3) = \frac{1}{2}$: $R_3 = \dfrac{0.71s^2 + 0.10p^2}{1.35s^2 + 0.915p^2}$ (V-7)

For $J(_\Lambda H^3) = \frac{3}{2}$: $R_3 = \dfrac{0.403p^2}{0.915s^2 + 1.14p^2}$ (V-8)

The measured value of R_3 is 0.39 ± 0.07 (Ammar et al., 1962; Block et al., 1963a), and this is shown graphically in Fig. 19 together with the predictions for spin $\frac{1}{2}$ and $\frac{3}{2}$. From this figure it is clear that $J(_\Lambda H^3) = \frac{1}{2}$.

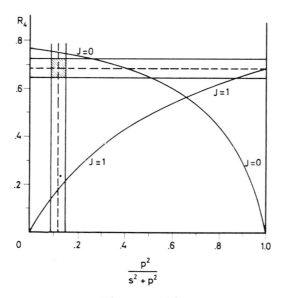

Fig. 18. The ratio $R_4 = \dfrac{_\Lambda H^4 \to \pi^- + He^4}{\text{all } \pi^-\text{-mesonic decays of } _\Lambda H^4}$, as a function of $p^2/(p^2 + s^2)$ (Block et al., 1963a). The curves illustrate the results of the calculations of Dalitz and Liu (1959) for $J(_\Lambda H^4) = 0$ and 1.

The possibilities of spin assignment to $_\Lambda Li^8$ are more complex since, although the core nucleus Li^7 has spin $\frac{3}{2}$ leading to expected possible values of $J(_\Lambda Li^8) = 1$ or 2, there is also a low-lying excited state of Li^7 at 0.475 MeV with $J = \frac{1}{2}$. The Λ hyperon bound to this excited state may give rise to a hypernuclear state with spin zero or one. An attempt has been made to elicit the spin of $_\Lambda Li^8$ from a study of the decay process

$$_\Lambda Li^8 \to \pi^- + He^4 + He^4.$$

It was suggested by Crayton et al. (1962a) that this decay process often proceeded through an intermediate state involving first formation, then the subsequent decay of the 2.9-MeV 2^+ first excited level of Be^8. This indication was substantiated by Davis *et al.* (1963) who found that this $_\Lambda Li^8$ decay went dominantly via the 2.9-MeV level, although the decay was also seen to proceed through the Be^8 ground state and a level (or levels) at about 17 MeV. An ideogram of the relative energies in their center-of-mass system of the two

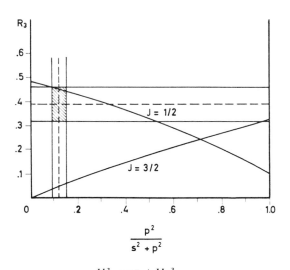

Fig. 19. The ratio $R_3 = \dfrac{_\Lambda H^3 \to \pi^- + He^3}{\text{all } \pi^-\text{-mesonic decays of } _\Lambda H^3}$, as a function of $p^2/(p^2 + s^2)$ (Block *et al.*, 1963a). The curves illustrate the results of the calculations made by Dalitz and Liu (1959) for $J(_\Lambda H^3) = \tfrac{1}{2}$ and $\tfrac{3}{2}$.

He^4 nuclei involved in the decay of $_\Lambda Li^8$ is shown in Fig. 20. The transitions to the Be^8 ground state, 2.9 MeV level and ~ 17 MeV level (or levels) are in the ratio 11:66:6 there being little evidence from Fig. 20 of any transitions not involving discrete states of Be^8. It has also been estimated, despite the experimental difficulties of uniquely identifying $_\Lambda Li^8$ decays by the mode

$$_\Lambda Li^8 \to \pi^- + H^1 + Li^7$$

that this decay mode is much less important than those involving Be^8 states; in fact, the ratio [Chicago-Northwestern Collaboration quoted by Dalitz (1963a)]

$$\frac{_\Lambda Li^8 \to \pi^- + Be^8(\text{in the ground state or first excited state only})}{\text{all } \pi^-\text{-mesonic decays of } _\Lambda Li^8} \geqslant 60\%. \quad \text{(V-9)}$$

The S-wave Λ-hyperon decay, which is dominant, violates parity and therefore

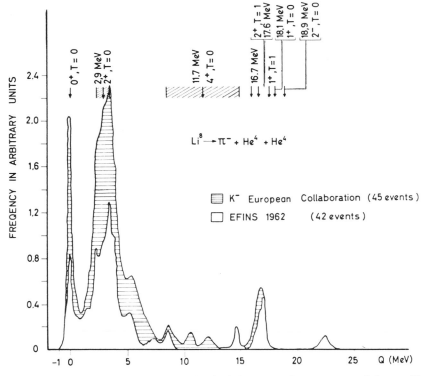

Fig. 20. Ideogram of the relative energies in their center-of-mass system of the two He⁴ nuclei involved in the decay of the hypernucleus $_\Lambda\text{Li}^8$ [combined results from Davis *et al.* (1963) and K⁻ European Collaboration (quoted by Sacton, 1965a)].

transitions from the odd-parity state $_\Lambda\text{Li}^8$ to Be^8 states of even parity as observed, require the emission of the π^- meson with odd orbital angular momentum, almost entirely $l_\pi = 1$. On the other hand, for P-wave decay l_π has to be even, zero or two. Dalitz (1963a) has made estimates of the transition rates and angular distributions of the decay particles to be expected in the sequence of reactions

$$_\Lambda\text{Li}^8 \rightarrow \text{Be}^{8*} + \pi^-$$
$$\hookrightarrow \text{He}^4 + \text{He}^4$$

for the possible spin values of $_\Lambda\text{Li}^8$ (namely, 0, 1, and 2) using intermediate coupling nuclear wave functions. His findings may be summarized as follows.

For $J(_\Lambda\text{Li}^8) = 2$, the decay to the Be^8 ground state, 0^+, is forbidden[9] for

---

[9] The early failure to observe $_\Lambda\text{Li}^8$ decays to the ground state of Be^8, rendered inconspicuous because in general the two short He⁴ tracks are juxtaposed, gave an indication that $J(_\Lambda\text{Li}^8) = 2$.

S-wave Λ-hyperon decay since l_π has to be unity, and the calculated transition to the 2.9-MeV 2^+ level is very small, a factor of about 4.5 less than the transition rate to the 17 MeV, $I = 1, 2^+$ level. Both the transition to the ground state and that to the first excited state of Be^8 are allowed by the P-wave decay of the Λ hyperon, but since other π^--mesonic decay modes of $_\Lambda Li^8$, in particular $(\pi^- H^1 Li^7)$, $(\pi^- H^1 H^3 He^4)$, are allowed by the dominant S-wave interaction, it is difficult to reconcile the high value of the ratio (V–9) with $J(_\Lambda Li^8) = 2$. The possibility that, even for $J(_\Lambda Li^8) = 2$, the transition rate to the 2.9-MeV level of Be^8 may be large for the S-wave interaction has been considered by Dalitz (1963a), possibly arising from a strong spin-orbit component in the Λ–N potential which would upset the expected nuclear coupling scheme. In this case, the angular distribution of the decay of the Be^8 with respect to the π^--meson direction is expected to be of the form of $\sin^2\theta$.

For $J(_\Lambda Li^8) = 1$, both the decays to the first excited state and ground state of Be^8 are allowed by the S-wave Λ-hyperon decay, the ratio between the transitions is estimated to lie within the range 2.7 to 6.4. The expected angular distribution of the Be^8 decay is of the form $1 + 3 \cos^2\theta$.

For $J(_\Lambda Li^8) = 0$ transitions to any Be^8 state with even spin or parity are forbidden for the S-wave Λ-hyperon decay interaction. The transitions to the first two levels of Be^8 are allowed by the P-wave interaction, but as for the case of $J(_\Lambda Li^8) = 2$, it is hard to equate the high value of the ratio (V-9) with this explanation.

The experimental angular distribution of the decay of the 2.9-MeV 2^+ level of Be^8 with respect to the π^--meson direction is given in Fig. 21 together with the predicted distributions, $P(\theta) \sim \sin^2\theta$ corresponding to $J(_\Lambda Li^8) = 2$ and $P(\theta) \sim (1 + 3 \cos^2\theta)$ for $J(_\Lambda Li^8) = 1$.

The observed angular distribution, the dominant transition to the first excited level of Be^8, and the presence of transitions to the Be^8 ground state are all readily explained only for $J(_\Lambda Li^8) = 1$.

The values obtained for the spins of $_\Lambda H^3$, $_\Lambda H^4$, and $_\Lambda Li^8$ demonstrate conclusively that the singlet Λ–N interaction is stronger than the triplet, the opposite situation to the N–N case, and suggest the spin of a hypernucleus is equal to the spin of the core minus one-half $(J = J_c - \frac{1}{2})$. This is not however expected to be a general rule, probably it is broken in the case of the $_\Lambda C^{14}$, $_\Lambda N^{14}$ doublet (Dalitz, 1963b).

The measurement of the spin of $_\Lambda H^4$ to be zero is of prime importance in the determination of the relative K–Λ parity. The observation of the K^--meson capture reactions on helium [reactions (V-1) and (V-2)] require, for spin-zero hypernuclei, that the K^--meson parity must be odd with respect to that of the Λ hyperon (even parity by convention). This must be so irrespective of which orbital state the K^- meson is in when captured. The only possible

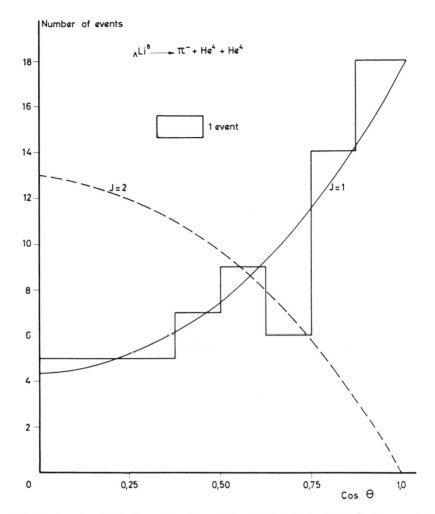

Fig. 21. Angular distribution of the decay of the 2.9-MeV 2^+ level of Be^8 with respect to the π^--meson direction in the decay of the Li^8 hypernucleus [combined results from Davis *et al.* (1963) and K^- European Collaboration (quoted by Sacton, 1965a)]. The curves illustrate the predictions of Dalitz (1963a) for $J(_\Lambda Li^8) = 1$ and 2.

refutation of this argument has been put forward by Dalitz and Downs (1958b), this is that a low-lying excited state of $_\Lambda H^4$ (also $_\Lambda He^4$) with spin one may always be produced in the capture reaction and this subsequently decays rapidly by γ emission to the ground state with spin zero. If this were the case then the K–Λ parity would be even. Many authors have considered the possible existence of such an excited state and various estimates of the binding energy of the Λ hyperon to the core have been made and these range from negative values to 1.5 MeV (see Section IV,B). The difference in the B_Λ values for the ground and possible excited states of $_\Lambda H^4$ and $_\Lambda He^4$, of the order of 2 MeV, is too small to be detected by a study of the production kinematics in a helium bubble chamber and hence direct evidence for an excited state must come from the detection of the γ ray, preferably in coincidence with the mono-energetic π^- meson from the production reaction (V-1). An argument against the intervention of an excited state of $_\Lambda He^4$ is as follows: The ratio

$$R = \frac{(_\Lambda He^4 + \pi^-)}{(_\Lambda He^4 + \pi^-) + (\Lambda^0 + He^3 + \pi^-)} \qquad \text{(V-10)}$$

should be proportional to $(B_\Lambda)^{1/2}$. Dalitz and Downs (1958b) calculated R to be 22% using an impulse model and Block (1963), assuming the intervention of a Y_1^*, found $R = 14\%$ for the formation of the ground state $_\Lambda He^4$, and both found $R \leqslant 5\%$ for an excited $_\Lambda He^4$. The experimentally observed value of R, $20 \pm 2\%$ strongly suggests that the reactions (V-1) and (V-2) do not proceed via excited states and therefore that the K–Λ parity is odd.

The determination of the spin of $_\Lambda He^4$ as zero also permits a determination of the relative amplitudes s_0 and p_0 of the S- and P-wave components in the neutral decay of the Λ hyperon ($\Lambda \to n + \pi^0$). The ratio R_0 defined as

$$R_0 = \frac{\text{all } \pi^0\text{-mesonic decays of } _\Lambda He^4}{\text{all } \pi^-\text{-mesonic decays of } _\Lambda He^4} \qquad \text{(V-11)}$$

will depend on the ratio $p_0^2/(p_0^2 + s_0^2)$ since the two-body decay mode, $_\Lambda He^4 \to \pi^0 + He^4$, is enhanced for S-wave decay and forbidden for P-wave Λ decay, exactly as is the case for the two-body decay of $_\Lambda H^4$. The predicted value of R_0 found by Dalitz and Liu (1959) from an impulse model calculation is

$$R_0 = \frac{1.96 s_0^2 + 0.35 p_0^2}{0.40 s^2 + 0.32 p^2}. \qquad \text{(V-12)}$$

On substituting the known value for $p^2/(p^2 + s^2)$, namely, 0.12 ± 0.03, and also putting $p^2 + s^2 = 2(p_0^2 + s_0^2)$ since the charged-to-neutral decay rates for the Λ hyperon are known to be in the ratio 2 to 1 the prediction for R_0 becomes

$$R_0 = 2.51 - 2.06(p_0^2/p_0^2 + s_0^2). \qquad \text{(V-13)}$$

The experimental determination of R_0, found after applying observation corrections to the $_\Lambda He^4$ decays in the helium bubble chamber, is 2.49 ± 0.34 (Block *et al.*, 1963a). The equation of this result to the prediction of Dalitz and Liu (1959) gives $p_0^2/(p_0^2 + s_0^2) = 0.01 \, {}^{+\,0.17}_{-\,0.01}$ in agreement with the $\Delta I = \frac{1}{2}$ rule, which requires this ratio to be equal to $p^2/(p^2 + s^2)$, i.e., 0.12 ± 0.03.

VI. Nonmesonic Decays

A. THEORETICAL ASPECTS

Early in the study of the hypernuclei it was found that the frequency of π^--mesonic decays decreased rapidly with increase in the mass of the core. As shown by Fowler (1956) this effect cannot be accounted for by simply assuming π^--meson reabsorption. It was suggested by Cheston and Primakoff (1953) that in nuclear matter the Λ-hyperon decay could be stimulated by the presence of the neighboring nucleons, the decay proceeding then through an intermediate step involving the emission and reabsorption of a virtual pion:

$$\Lambda + p \rightarrow (\pi^- + p) + p \rightarrow p + n \qquad \text{(VI-1)}$$

$$\Lambda + p \rightarrow (\pi^0 + n) + p \rightarrow n + p \qquad \text{(VI-2)}$$

$$\Lambda + n \rightarrow (\pi^0 + n) + n \rightarrow n + n. \qquad \text{(VI-3)}$$

Ruderman and Karplus (1949) estimated the ratio Q^- of the rates of nonmesonic to π^--mesonic decay considering it as an internal conversion coefficient whose value is characteristic of the angular momentum of the pion wave effective in the decay. Although there are uncertainties in their predictions (Dalitz, 1958) they were sufficiently accurate to establish in 1957 from the existing experimental data that the spin of the Λ hyperon was $\frac{1}{2}$ and that the P-wave channel was not dominant in the decay of the Λ hyperon. Both these conclusions have since been confirmed by direct measurements on the decay of free Λ hyperons.

Later on, it was suggested by Treiman (1958) that the Λ-hyperon decay could also proceed through a direct Fermi coupling of the (V–A) type involving four strongly interacting fermions $(\overline{\Lambda}p)$ $(\overline{p}n)$. The $\Delta I = \frac{1}{2}$ rule requires also an interaction of the form $(\overline{\Lambda}n)$ $(\overline{n}n)$, although there exists no direct evidence for a neutral weak interaction current (Dalitz, 1963b). Since the four fermions involved in the interaction are strongly interacting particles, distortion from the (V–A) form may be expected to arise from meson exchange. The Λ–N $\rightarrow$ N–N interaction can thus be considered as a sum of different processes: (a) a direct four-fermion weak interaction and (b) correction terms involving the exchange of different mesonic systems $(\pi, \eta, \rho \ldots)$ between the strangeness-conserving and the strangeness-nonconserving currents, an example of which being given by the Karplus-Ruderman term.

Some important properties of the Λ–N $\rightarrow$ N–N interaction, like its spin and charge dependences, can be studied with the aid of a phenomenological description of the interaction. For light hypernuclei, the form of the nonrelativistic[10] matrix elements for Λ–p and Λ–n captures has been given by Block

[10] The final nucleon momentum in Λ—N $\rightarrow$ NN is ~ 400 MeV/c.

and Dalitz (1963) assuming that the Λ–N interaction occurs in a S state. The transitions allowed from singlet ($^1S_0$) and triplet ($^3S_1$) Λ–N states as well as the corresponding matrix elements are given in Table IX. Expressions for the total nonmesonic decay rates have been given in terms of these matrix elements under the simplifying assumption that the Λ hyperon de-excitation

TABLE IX

NONRELATIVISTIC MATRIX ELEMENTS FOR THE PROCESS $\Lambda N \rightarrow NN$ FROM
$^1S_0$ AND $^3S_1$ ΛN STATES

Allowed transitions	Matrix element[a]
$^1S_0 \rightarrow {}^1S_0$ $\qquad I=1$	$aS_{\Lambda N}^\sigma$
$\rightarrow {}^3P_0$	$\dfrac{b}{2M}(\sigma_\Lambda - \sigma_N)\cdot qS_{\Lambda N}^\sigma$
$^3S_1 \rightarrow {}^3S_1$	$cT_{\Lambda N}^\sigma$
$\rightarrow {}^3D_1 \qquad I=0$	$\dfrac{3d}{\sqrt{2M^2}}(\sigma_\Lambda \cdot q\sigma_N \cdot q - \tfrac{1}{3}\sigma_\Lambda \cdot \sigma_N q^2)$
$\rightarrow {}^1P_1$	$\dfrac{e\sqrt{3}}{2M}(\sigma_\Lambda - \sigma_N)\cdot qT_{\Lambda N}^\sigma$
$\rightarrow {}^3P_1 \qquad I=1$	$\dfrac{f\sqrt{6}}{4M}(\sigma_\Lambda + \sigma_N)\cdot q$

[a] $S_{\Lambda N}^\sigma = (1 - \sigma_\Lambda \cdot \sigma_N)/4$ and $T_{\Lambda N}^\sigma = (3 + \sigma_\Lambda \cdot \sigma_N)/4$ are the spin projection operators in singlet and triplet state; M is the mass of the nucleon and q the relative momentum of the outgoing nucleons. The coefficients a, b, $\cdots$, denote the transition amplitudes. For Λ–n stimulation, terms of the form c, d, and e are absent, as they lead to final states which are forbidden for the n–n system.

by different nucleons is incoherent (Block and Dalitz, 1963). This amounts to neglecting interference effects from the surrounding nucleons as well as final state interactions for the two fast outgoing nucleons.

For a given hypernucleus $_\Lambda Z^A$, the total nonmesonic decay rate Γ_{nm} is given by

$$\Gamma_{nm} = \rho_A \bar{R}(_\Lambda Z^A) \qquad (VI\text{-}4)$$

where ρ_A is the mean nucleon density at the Λ-hyperon position and $\bar{R}$ is the spin and charge average of the elementary decay rates R_{NS} for the nonmesonic de-excitation of a Λ–N system with total spin S for unit density of nucleons N at the Λ-hyperon position. In terms of the matrix elements given in Table IX, these elementary decay rates are

$$R_{p0} = |a_p|^2 + |b_p|^2(q/M)^2 \tag{VI-5}$$

$$R_{p1} = |c_p|^2 + |d_p|^2(q/M)^4 + |f_p|^2(q/M)^2 + |e_p|^2(q/M)^2 \tag{VI-6}$$

$$R_{n0} = |a_n|^2 + |b_n|^2(q/M)^2 \tag{VI-7}$$

$$R_{n1} = |f_n|^2(q/M)^2. \tag{VI-8}$$

If the $\Delta I = \frac{1}{2}$ rule holds, then $a_n = 2a_p$, $b_n = 2b_p$, and $f_n = 2f_p$.

In the case of $_\Lambda\mathrm{He}^4$ and $_\Lambda\mathrm{H}^4$, the comparison of the total nonmesonic decay rates calculated by Block and Dalitz (1963) with the experimental data (see Section VI,B) indicates that, assuming the $\Delta I = \frac{1}{2}$ rule, the $\Lambda\text{-N} \to \text{N-N}$ transitions take place preferentially to $I = 1$ final states and that the dominant transition is $^3S_1(\Lambda\text{-N}) \to {}^3P_1(\text{N-N})$. These results cannot be interpreted in terms of a simple combination of a V–A interaction and Ruderman-Karplus terms. If the $\Lambda\text{N} \to \text{NN}$ interaction obeys the $\Delta I = \frac{1}{2}$ rule, and if the present ideas about the current-current ntaure of the weak interaction are valid, it must be concluded that important higher order mesonic corrections exist.

Using the matrix elements given in Table IX, Rayet (1965) recently calculated the reaction rates for the two body nonmesonic decays

$$_\Lambda\mathrm{H}^4 \to \mathrm{H}^3 + n \tag{VI-9}$$

$$_\Lambda\mathrm{He}^4 \to \mathrm{He}^3 + n \tag{VI-10}$$

$$_\Lambda\mathrm{He}^4 \to \mathrm{H}^3 + \mathrm{H}^1. \tag{VI-11}$$

Taking into account only the dominant $^3S_1(\Lambda\text{-N}) \to {}^3P_1(\text{N-N})$ transition, reaction (VI-9) is found to contribute 3% and both reactions (VI-10) and (VI-11) 1.5% to the total nonmesonic decay rates of $_\Lambda\mathrm{H}^4$ and $_\Lambda\mathrm{He}^4$, respectively.

The study of the processes

$$_\Lambda\mathrm{He}^5 \to \mathrm{H}^3 + \mathrm{H}^1 + n \tag{VI-12}$$

$$_\Lambda\mathrm{He}^5 \to \mathrm{He}^3 + n + n \tag{VI-13}$$

has been made by Thurnauer (1962), using somewhat different matrix elements, for both zero and finite ranges in the Λ–N weak interaction. He found, as expected, that reaction (VI-12) is dominated by proton stimulation while reaction (VI-13) is determined largely by neutron stimulation.

B. Experimental Results

1. Nonmesonic to π^--Mesonic Decay Ratio Q^-

In the helium bubble chamber, Block et al. (1965a) have determined the nonmesonic to π^--mesonic decay ratio Q^- for $_\Lambda\mathrm{He}^4$ and $_\Lambda\mathrm{He}^4$. From the observation of 42 nonmesonic and 73 π^--mesonic decays of $_\Lambda\text{He}^4$ and after correcting for geometrical losses and other biases they obtained $Q^-_{_\Lambda\text{He}^4} = 0.52 \pm 0.10$.

Since the $_\Lambda\text{H}^4$ are produced in the reaction $K^- + \text{He}^4 \rightarrow {_\Lambda\text{H}^4} + \pi^0$, the only examples of this hypernucleus which are detected in the bubble chamber with a high efficiency are those decaying π^--mesonically (120 events). However, from considerations of charge independence at the production vertex one knows that the total number of $_\Lambda\text{H}^4$ produced should be one-half the number of $_\Lambda\text{He}^4$. Moreover, assuming the $\Delta I = \frac{1}{2}$ rule holds for the decay of these hypernuclei, Dalitz and Liu (1959) have shown that the ratios R_0 of the numbers of π^0- to π^--mesonic decays for $_\Lambda\text{H}^4$ and $_\Lambda\text{He}^4$ are related by

$$R_0({_\Lambda\text{H}^4}) \times R_0({_\Lambda\text{He}^4}) = \tfrac{1}{4} \qquad\qquad \text{(VI-14)}$$

where $R_0({_\Lambda\text{He}^4})$ is found experimentally to be equal to 2.49 ± 0.34 (Block et al., 1963a). Combining these numbers, Block et al. (1963a) obtained $Q^-_{_\Lambda\text{H}^4} = 0.26 \pm 0.13$.

In emulsion it is not possible to identify uniquely the charge and mass of the hypernuclei decaying nonmesonically except in some particular cases (two-body or three-body decays involving at most one neutron). As a result, the information concerning Q^- which can be obtained from this technique must be analyzed with caution. For helium hypernuclei (essentially a mixture of $_\Lambda\text{He}^4$ and $_\Lambda\text{He}^5$), combining the results of different experiments (Silverstein, 1958; Schlein, 1959; Sacton, 1960; Gorgé et al., 1960; Bhowmik et al., 1962) gives $Q^-_{_\Lambda\text{He}} \sim 1.4$ (Sacton, 1963). Using the value $Q^-_{_\Lambda\text{He}^4}$ given by Block et al. (1963a) and taking into account that only about 15% of the π^--mesonic decays of $_\Lambda\text{He}$ observed in the emulsion are due to $_\Lambda\text{He}^4$ decay lead to the value $Q^-_{_\Lambda\text{He}^5} \sim 1.8$

For hypernuclei of charge greater than 2, the only reliable results are those obtained in emulsion by Holland (1964). The analysis was restricted to hyperfragments of range between 3.3 and 20 μm, produced in K^--meson absorptions at rest. These range cutoffs ensure a selection of a clean sample of hypernuclei produced in the light elements of the emulsion (CNO) (Lemonne et al., 1964b). By considerations of the production reaction, such as charge and baryonic number conservation, the events were separated into two classes containing hypernuclei of charge Z equal to 3 or 4 and Z greater than 4, respectively. The value of the nonmesonic to π^--mesonic decay ratio for the events in these two classes was found to be 2.4 ± 0.7 and 5.3 ± 1.5, respectively. These values are lower than those obtained previously by other authors (Abeledo et al., 1961; Sacton, 1963). As pointed out by Lemonne et al. (1964b) this discrepancy is due to the better selection of the events made by Holland (1964) especially regarding the elimination of heavy spallation hyperfragments which are known to contribute essentially at short ranges (<3 μm). A small admixture of this type of events for which the nonmesonic to π^--mesonic decay ratio is of the order of 150 (Lagnaux et al., 1964) will affect drastically the results concerning the light hypernuclei (Zakrzewski et al., 1963).

2. The Stimulated Decay

Several attempts have been made to study experimentally the nucleon stimulation model of the decay of the bound Λ hyperon. The method, first proposed by Baldo-Ceolin et al. (1958), is based on the study of the momentum spectrum of the charged particles emitted from nonmesonically decaying hypernuclei. It is assumed that one nucleon stimulation is the dominant process. In light hypernuclei, it is expected that the nucleons resulting from the process $\Lambda + N \rightarrow N + N$ will not lose too much energy by collisions inside the nucleus so that the proton present in the reaction $\Lambda + p \rightarrow p + n$ will be emitted with a momentum larger than a certain limit that can be determined experimentally or estimated by a Monte Carlo calculation (Lokanathan et al., 1961). It is thus possible to estimate the relative contribution of the neutron and proton stimulation processes by determining the number of events containing such a fast proton. It has been shown by different authors that this cutoff lies around 250 MeV/c. In emulsion, the difficulty of identifying uniquely the nonmesonically decaying hypernuclei makes it impossible to study the stimulation ratio for a given hypernucleus. All the results obtained by this technique thus relate to a mixture of hypernuclei of different charge and mass numbers. The physical interpretation of these results is rather hazardous as has been pointed out in a critical review paper by Zakrzewski and St. Lorant (1962).

The method proposed by Baldo-Ceolin et al. (1958) has been used by Block et al. (1963a) to obtain an estimate of the proton-to-neutron stimulation ratio for the $_\Lambda\mathrm{He}^4$ hypernucleus in the helium bubble chamber. On the assumption that all the decay stars containing a proton of momentum greater than 250 MeV/c are due to proton stimulation reactions, they found $\Lambda p/\Lambda n = 2.2 \pm 0.8$.

3. Discussion

The bubble chamber results concerning $_\Lambda\mathrm{He}^4$ and $_\Lambda\mathrm{H}^4$ are summarized in Table X. These data, combined with the theoretical estimates for the π^--mesonic decay rates given by Dalitz and Rajasekharan (1962), lead for $_\Lambda\mathrm{He}^4$ and $_\Lambda\mathrm{H}^4$ to the nonmesonic decay rates $\Gamma_{nm}(_\Lambda\mathrm{He}^4) = (0.14 \pm 0.03)\Gamma_\Lambda$ and $\Gamma_{nm}(_\Lambda\mathrm{H}^4) = (0.29 \pm 0.14)\Gamma_\Lambda$ where Γ_Λ denotes the decay rate for the free Λ hyperon, corresponding to the lifetime $(2.61 \pm 0.02)10^{-10}$ sec.

TABLE X

Nonmesonic to π^--Mesonic Decay Ratio and
Proton-to-Neutron Stimulation Ratio for
the Hypernuclei $_\Lambda He^4$ and $_\Lambda H^4$

	Q^-	$\Lambda p/\Lambda n$
$_\Lambda He^4$	0.52 ± 0.10	2.2 ± 0.8
$_\Lambda H^4$	0.26 ± 0.13	—

^{a} Data from Block *et al.* (1963a).

On the other hand, the nonmesonic rates of $_\Lambda He^4$ and $_\Lambda H^4$ of spin zero are (Block and Dalitz, 1963)

$$\Gamma_{nm}(_\Lambda He^4) = \rho_4 \times (3R_{pi} + R_{p0} + 2R_{n0})/6 \qquad \text{(VI-15)}$$

$$\Gamma_{nm}(_\Lambda H^4) = \rho_4 \times (3R_{n1} + R_{n0} + 2R_{p0})/6 \qquad \text{(VI-16)}$$

where the nucleon density ρ_4 has the value 0.019 Fermi^3.

Assuming the $\Delta I = \frac{1}{2}$ rule to be valid for these decays and using the experimental data, Block and Dalitz (1963) found for the different R_{NS}

$$R_{n0} = (6.6 \pm 2.1)\Gamma_\Lambda \text{ Fermi}^3 \qquad \text{(VI-17)}$$

$$R_{p0} = \tfrac{1}{2}R_{n0} = (3.3 \pm 1.1)\Gamma_\Lambda \text{ Fermi}^3 \qquad \text{(VI-18)}$$

$$R_{p1} = (8.6 \pm 3.0)\Gamma_\Lambda \text{ Fermi}^3 \qquad \text{(VI-19)}$$

$$R_{n1} = (17.2 \pm 6.0)\Gamma_\Lambda \text{ Fermi}^3. \qquad \text{(VI-20)}$$

From these values and from the expressions of the R_{NS} in terms of the matrix elements given in the previous section, they calculated that the Λ–N $\rightarrow$ N–N transitions take place dominantly to $I = 1$ final states and that the dominant transition is $^3S_1(\Lambda$–N$) \rightarrow {}^3P_1(N$–N$)$.

Although, the experimental data concerning the partial nonmesonic decay rates of $_\Lambda He^4$ and $_\Lambda H^4$ hypernuclei remain up to now very preliminary, it seems that the observation of two-body decays is rather infrequent.[11] This result is in agreement with the predictions of Rayet (1965).

Using the values of the R_{NS} obtained from the analysis of the $_\Lambda H^4$ and $_\Lambda He^4$ hypernuclei, it is possible to make some predictions about the decay of

---

[11] One example each of the reactions $_\Lambda H^4 \rightarrow H^3 + n$ and $_\Lambda He^4 \rightarrow H^2 + H^2$ has been reported by the Helium Bubble Chamber Collaboration (1960), and three examples of the decay $_\Lambda He^4 \rightarrow He^3 + n$ have been observed in emulsion (K^- European Collaboration, 1965b).

$_\Lambda$He^5 (Block and Dalitz, 1963). For this hypernucleus, the total nonmesonic decay rate is given by

$$\Gamma_{nm}(_\Lambda He^5) = \rho_5 \times (3R_{p1} + R_{p0} + 3R_{n1} + R_{n0})/8 \qquad (VI-21)$$

with $\rho_5 = 0.038$ Fermi^3. Taking into account the value of the π^--mesonic decay rate estimated by Dalitz and Rajasekharan (1962), one obtains $Q^-(_\Lambda He^5) = 1.7$, in fair agreement with the emulsion data, and a stimulation ratio $(\Lambda p/\Lambda n)_{_\Lambda He^5} = 0.5$. This last ratio has not yet been measured experimentally. However, in the decay of heavy spallation hypernuclei, for which the nuclear properties of the cores are similar to those of the α particle, it is estimated that neutron stimulation is the dominant process (Lagnaux et al., 1964).

From the data available for $_\Lambda$He^5, Dalitz (1963b) has estimated $Q^-(_\Lambda Li^7) = 2.7$, $Q^-(_\Lambda Be^9) = 6.2$, and $Q^-(_\Lambda C^{13}) = 11.3$; these results are in reasonable agreement with those of Holland (1964).

VII. Other Decay Modes

Beside their nonmesonic and π^- mesonic decay modes, hypernuclei are expected to decay by π^0 meson or lepton emission as does the free Λ^0 hyperon. The π^+-mesonic decays of hypernuclei have also been observed. These decays can, for example, result from either a charge exchange reaction of the π^0 meson from the $\Lambda^0 \rightarrow n + \pi^0$ decay or the transformation of the bound Λ^0 hyperon into a virtual Σ^+-hyperon state which subsequently undergoes $\Sigma^+ \rightarrow n + \pi^+$ decay.

A. π^0-Mesonic Decays

By analogy with the π^--mesonic decays, the π^0-mesonic decay modes are expected to be predominantly of the type $\pi^0 - n - R$ or $\pi^0 - R$. As a result, they will often appear in the emulsion as "hooks" occurring at the end of the hyperfragment track (Ammar, 1959). The detection and identification of such one-prong stars as hyperfragment decays in the presence of an overwhelming background of other phenomena leading to the same configuration (essentially Coulomb and nuclear scatterings) is extremely difficult and hazardous. However, a few examples of the π^0-mesonic decays of light hypernuclei have been identified in emulsion by the observation near the decay vertex of an electron-positron pair. On the other hand, in the helium bubble chamber, where the hypernuclei are identified from the kinematics of the production reactions, some interesting results have been obtained regarding the total π^0-mesonic decay rate of $_\Lambda$He^4 and these results have enabled a determination of the $p_0^2/(p_0^2 + s_0^2)$ ratio for Λ-hyperon decay (see Section V).

B. π^+-Mesonic Decays

Up to now, 20 examples of the decay of a hypernucleus with the emission of a π^+ meson have been observed in emulsion (Kang *et al.*, 1961; Ismail *et al.*, 1962; Allen *et al.*, 1963; Steinberg and Prem, 1963; Ganguli *et al.*, 1963; Beniston *et al.*, 1964a; Mayeur *et al.*, 1966b; Goodhead *et al.*, 1964; Schneps, 1958; Bhowmik *et al.*, 1966; Blau *et al.*, 1963). Of these events, 16 are identified as decays of $_\Lambda\text{He}^4$ hypernuclei (Kang *et al.*, 1961; Ismail *et al.*, 1962; Allen *et al.*, 1963; Steinberg and Prem, 1963; Ganguli *et al.*, 1963; Beniston *et al.*, 1964a; Mayeur *et al.*, 1966b), 3 are examples of $_\Lambda\text{Li}^7$ or $_\Lambda\text{Be}^7$ (Goodhead *et al.*, 1964; Schneps, 1958; Bhowmik *et al.*, 1966) and one is most likely an example of a heavier hypernucleus, either $_\Lambda\text{B}^{11}$ or $_\Lambda\text{N}^{15}$ decaying via the π^+-recoil mode (Blau *et al.*, 1963; see also Mayeur, 1966b).

Estimates of the branching ratio R of the π^+-mesonic decay to the π^--mesonic decay modes for the $_\Lambda\text{He}^4$ hypernucleus have been made by different authors and the results are somewhat contradictory. The most recent determination of this ratio is that of Mayeur *et al.* (1966b). These authors have made a special search for π^+- and π^--mesonic decays in a sample of 11,000 hypernuclei produced by stopping K^- mesons. Their result, based on the observation of 10 π^+- and 63 π^--mesonic decays of $_\Lambda\text{He}^4$ uniquely identified, is $R = 9 \pm 3\%$, this value having been corrected to take into account the number of π^--mesonic decays of $_\Lambda\text{He}^4$ which are not uniquely identified, owing to the fact that the range of the recoiling He^3 nucleus emitted in the decay $_\Lambda\text{He}^4 \to \pi^- + \text{H}^1 + \text{He}^3$ was too small.[12] A previous estimate made by Beniston *et al.* (1964a) led to an upper limit of R equal to $2.9 \pm 1.1\%$. This value is the result of a compilation of the world data obtained in emulsion at that time (6 π^+- and 219 π^--mesonic decays). It is rendered uncertain by the fact that the number of π^--mesonic decays has been estimated from the exposure data (beam intensity, rate of hyperfragment production) and not on the actual observation of the events. Moreover, most of the experiments contributing to the compilation were not planned with a view to making a special search for π^+-mesonic decays so that some of these events could have been overlooked.

A value of $R \sim 4\%$ has been reported by Block *et al.* (1963a) in the helium bubble chamber. This estimate is based on the observation of only two definitely identified π^+-mesonic decays and one doubtful event. In this case, also, although the statistics are very poor, experimental biases against the identification of π^+ mesons can be invoked to explain the low π^+-mesonic decay rate.

[12] The number of $_\Lambda\text{He}^4$ among the nonuniquely identified helium hypernuclei ($_\Lambda\text{He}^{4-5}$) was obtained from a comparison of the binding energy distributions of all these events assumed to have in turn $_\Lambda\text{He}^4$ and $_\Lambda\text{He}^5$ identification with the binding energy distributions of the uniquely identified $_\Lambda\text{He}^4$ and $_\Lambda\text{He}^5$ hypernuclei.

The π^+-mesonic decays of hypernuclei can proceed through different mechanisms. The contribution of the simplest process, in which the π^0 meson from the $\Lambda \to n + \pi^0$ decay undergoes charge exchange has been calculated by Dalitz and von Hippel (1964b) to be of the order of some tenths of a per cent for the $_\Lambda He^4$ hypernucleus. More complex mechanisms involving the transformation of the bound Λ hyperon into a virtual Σ^+ hyperon which subsequently undergoes $\Sigma^+ \to n + \pi^+$ decay have also been studied (Biswas, 1963; Iwao, 1962; Deloff et al., 1959; von Hippel, 1964). The most detailed study of this process $\Lambda^0 + p \to (\Sigma^+ + n)\, n + n + \pi^+$ is that of von Hippel (1964) and leads to a branching ratio R of the order of 1.5 % for $_\Lambda He^4$ provided that the π^+ meson and the neutron from the Σ^+-hyperon decay are emitted in a relative s state. However, the experimental result of Mayeur et al. (1966b) is much larger than these theoretical estimates.

Considering the phase space available in the different π^+- and π^--mesonic decay modes, the mean proton density around the Λ hyperon in different hypernuclei, and taking into account the Pauli exclusion principle, Dalitz and von Hippel (1964b) came to the conclusion that the most favorable cases for π^+-mesonic decay among the light hypernuclei are $_\Lambda He^4$ and $_\Lambda Be^7$. The experimental results support this conclusion as far as the hydrogen and helium hypernuclei are concerned. Indeed several hundreds of $_\Lambda H^{3, 4}$ and $_\Lambda He^5$ hypernuclei have been observed, none of them decaying with the emission of π^+ meson. For heavier species the statistics of uniquely identified events are too poor to allow definite conclusions to be drawn.

C. Leptonic Decays

The free Λ hyperon is known to decay leptonically with a branching ratio of $(0.88 \pm 0.08) \times 10^{-3}$ for the electronic mode $\Lambda^0 \to p + e^- + \bar{\nu}$ and with one of less than 10^{-4} for the muonic mode $\Lambda^0 \to p + \mu^- + \bar{\nu}$ (Rosenfeld et al., 1965).

No definite example of the leptonic decay of a hypernucleus has been observed until now.[13] This is not surprising if the leptonic decay rates for bound Λ hyperons are comparable with those found for the free Λ hyperon (Lyulka, 1964). However, it must be remarked that in emulsion there will be a strong observational bias against the detection of these events which will in any case seldom be uniquely identified. Due to this situation, it is better that the search for the leptonic decays (especially the electronic modes) of the light hypernuclei should be undertaken in a large helium bubble chamber.

---

[13] A possible example of the muonic decay of a lithium hypernucleus has been reported by Ganguli et al. (1963). However, as pointed out by the authors themselves, the kinematics of the decay also fit the well-known π^--mesonic decay $_\Lambda Li^8 \to \pi^- + He^4 + He^4$ with $B_\Lambda = 5.9 \pm 0.9$ MeV.

VIII. Lifetimes of Hypernuclei

The lifetime of a Λ hyperon bound in a hypernucleus may differ from that of the free Λ hyperon because of several factors. The available energy in the decay process is diminished by the binding energy of the Λ hyperon, many decay channels are open to the hypernucleus, some of which are favored as they involve an increase in the Q of the decay reaction, there are restrictions and sometimes even enhancements due to the Pauli principle, and finally the hypernucleus may decay nonmesonically.

Attempts have been made only to measure the lifetimes of the lighter hypernuclei, but even for these, since they are usually emitted during an evaporation process with relatively low kinetic energies (see Section III), the times taken to bring them to rest in nuclear emulsion are much shorter than their mean lifetime. As a result most hypernuclei decay at rest in nuclear emulsion, and lifetime estimates depend upon the infrequent observations of decays in flight.

However, the stopping power of helium is not nearly so restrictive in this respect as is nuclear emulsion, and the observation of both the production and decay of $_\Lambda H^3$ in a helium bubble chamber has made possible an accurate determination of its lifetime (Block *et al.*, 1963b). Events were chosen for which the production reaction was

$$K^- + He^4 \rightarrow {}_\Lambda H^3 + H^1 + \pi^- \qquad \text{(VIII-1)}$$

so that the initial momentum of the $_\Lambda H^3$ hypernucleus could be determined accurately from the sum of those of the proton and π^- meson.[14] This estimate was checked where possible from the study of the decay kinematics, it being required that the hypernucleus traveled further than 0.5 mm, and decayed π^--mesonically. Block *et al.* (1963b) found 39 examples of $_\Lambda H^3$ which satisfied these criteria, 33 of which decayed in flight resulting in a maximum likelihood lifetime of $\tau_{\Lambda H^3} = 0.95 \begin{smallmatrix} +0.19 \\ -0.15 \end{smallmatrix} \times 10^{-10}$ sec. A further estimate of the lifetime was made using only the decays in flight, the resultant lifetime being $\tau_\Lambda H^3 = 0.70 \begin{smallmatrix} +0.18 \\ -0.13 \end{smallmatrix} \times 10^{-10}$ sec.

The lifetime of $_\Lambda H^4$ has been determined from the observation in emulsion of both decays at rest and in flight by the mode $(\pi^- He^4)$. The selection of events was restricted to this decay mode, which accounts for two-thirds of the π^--mesonic decays of $_\Lambda H^4$, since its characteristically high energy release makes the identification particularly reliable. For other decay modes of

[14] For an event to be acceptable it was required the proton track from the production star should be visible, the π^--meson track should be longer than 3 cm; and the decay should occur at least 1 cm from the bubble chamber walls.

$_\Lambda H^4$, especially those occurring in flight, it is often difficult to distinguish them from the decays of other species, especially the $(\pi^- H^1 H^2)$ mode of $_\Lambda H^3$. Unfortunately, the two-body decay of a $_\Lambda H^4$ hypernucleus in flight presents a configuration in emulsion which is difficult to detect (the He^4 nucleus is projected in the forward direction, and if the track of the lightly ionizing π^--meson is missed the event will be considered as just a scattering) and for this reason only measurements of lifetime based on careful, systematic scans have been considered. The method employed has been to follow all tracks from K^--meson interactions under high magnification within one emulsion pellicle and to scrutinize any single scattering vertices so found for the presence of a lightly ionizing track. By using the above method in a stack exposed to stopping K^- mesons, Crayton et al. (1962b) found 43 decays at rest and 9 decays in flight of $_\Lambda H^4$ by the two-body mode, yielding a lifetime estimate of $1.2 \begin{smallmatrix} +0.7 \\ -0.3 \end{smallmatrix} \times 10^{-10}$ sec. In a similar study of 2.3 and 2.5 GeV/c K^--meson interactions, Prem and Steinberg (1964) found 4 decays at rest and 3 in flight, giving $\tau_\Lambda H^4 = 1.8 \begin{smallmatrix} +2.5 \\ -0.7 \end{smallmatrix} \times 10^{-10}$ sec. The resultant of these two determinations gives $\tau_\Lambda H^4 = 1.35 \begin{smallmatrix} +0.58 \\ -0.28 \end{smallmatrix} \times 10^{-10}$ sec. However, the possibility of observational loss of decays in flight still remains despite the careful scanning procedure employed, and therefore the above estimate of lifetime of $_\Lambda H^4$ should be considered an upper limit only.

Estimates have been made of the lifetimes of $_\Lambda H^3$ and $_\Lambda H^4$ in a bubble chamber filled with a propane-Freon mixture (Fortney, 1963), but due to the large uncertainties affecting the detection of the different decay configurations these results have not been included here.

The lifetimes of the helium hypernuclei are more poorly determined. The main reasons are that the times spent by helium hypernuclei in coming to rest in nuclear emulsion are so short that very few decay in flight, and in many cases it is impossible to distinguish the decays of $_\Lambda He^4$ and $_\Lambda He^5$ hypernuclei. Ammar et al. (1963b), Prem and Steinberg (1964), and Kang et al. (1963 and 1965), have reported 17 examples (3 $_\Lambda He^4$, 10 $_\Lambda He^5$, and 4 $_\Lambda He^{4,5}$) of decays in flight of helium hypernuclei in a total time of observation of 24.4×10^{-10} sec, yielding a lifetime for a mixture of $_\Lambda He^4$ and $_\Lambda He^5$ [15] as $\tau_{\Lambda He^{4,5}} = 1.43 \begin{smallmatrix} +0.46 \\ -0.27 \end{smallmatrix} \times 10^{-10}$ sec.

A reasonable approximation to the lifetime of $_\Lambda He^5$ may be made by assuming that all helium hypernuclei observed in emulsion other than those uniquely identified as $_\Lambda He^4$ and $_\Lambda He^7$ are in fact $_\Lambda He^5$, since $_\Lambda He^5$ hypernuclei

[15] The presence of other helium hypernuclei, in particular $_\Lambda He^7$, in the sample may be neglected.

account for about 80% of the total. The combined data of Prem and Steinberg (1964), Ammar *et al.* (1963b), and Kang *et al.* (1963, 1965) then give $\tau_\Lambda He^5 = 1.43 \; {}^{+ \, 0.52}_{- \, 0.28} \times 10^{-10}$ sec based on 14 decays in flight. The 3 $_\Lambda He^4$ decays give a lifetime of $\sim 1.5 \times 10^{-10}$ sec.

It is of significance to note that the measured lifetimes of the light hypernuclei are all considerably shorter than that of the free Λ hyperon, $2.61 \pm 0.02 \times 10^{-10}$ sec (Rosenfeld *et al.*, 1965).

From a consideration of the competing processes in the decay of hypernuclei, π^-- and π^0-mesonic decays and the weak Λ–N stimulation processes, Dalitz and Rajasekharan (1962) (see also Dalitz and Liu, 1959; Dalitz, 1963b; Block and Dalitz, 1963) have calculated the total decay rates, and hence the lifetimes, of the lightest hypernuclei for their possible spin values. For the π-mesonic decay rates they have used the results of the impulse model calculation of Dalitz and Liu (1959). The nonmesonic decay rates have been estimated for $_\Lambda H^4$ and $_\Lambda He^4$ from a knowledge of Q^-, the nonmesonic to π^--mesonic decay ratio for these hypernuclei, 0.26 ± 0.13 and 0.52 ± 0.10, respectively, obtained from studies of the decays of these hypernuclei in a helium bubble chamber (Block *et al.*, 1963a) and the calculated values of Γ_{π^-}. The total decay rate Γ is hence $\Gamma_{\pi^-}(1 + Q^-) + \Gamma_{\pi^0}$.

For $_\Lambda H^4$ with spin 0 the total decay rate is estimated to be $1.53 \times \Gamma_\Lambda = 6.50 \times 10^9$ sec^{-1} (Dalitz and Rajasekharan, 1962). This corresponds to a lifetime of $_\Lambda H^4$ equal to 1.54×10^{-10} sec in very good agreement with the measured value of Crayton *et al.* (1962b) and Prem and Steinberg (1964), $1.35 \; {}^{+ \, 0.58}_{- \, 0.28} \times 10^{-10}$ sec. On the other hand, the calculated total decay rate for $_\Lambda H^4$ should its spin be unity is $0.56 \, \Gamma_\Lambda$, leading to a lifetime of 4.20×10^{-10} sec, in strong disagreement with the observed value.

For $_\Lambda He^4$, taking its spin to be zero, the calculated total decay rate is $0.99 \, \Gamma_\Lambda$, corresponding to a lifetime of 2.38×10^{-10} sec.

The total mesonic decay rate for $_\Lambda H^3$ is given as a function of B_Λ and J by Dalitz and Liu (1959), the values quoted being

$$\Gamma_\pi = [1 + 0.60(B_\Lambda)^{1/2}] \qquad \Gamma_\Lambda = 1.33 \, \Gamma_\Lambda \qquad \text{for} \quad J(_\Lambda H^3) = \tfrac{1}{2} \qquad \text{(VIII-2)}$$

$$\Gamma_\pi = [1 - 0.12(B_\Lambda)^{1/2}] \qquad \Gamma_\Lambda = 0.94 \, \Gamma_\Lambda \qquad \text{for} \quad J(_\Lambda H^3) = \tfrac{3}{2}. \qquad \text{(VIII-3)}$$

Adopting the values of Block and Dalitz (1963) for the elementary nonmesonic de-excitation rates and the value of the mean nucleon density seen by the Λ hyperon in $_\Lambda H^3$ given by Downs and Dalitz (1959), $1.9 \times 10^{-3}(B_\Lambda)^{1/2}$ Fermi$^3 = 1.04 \times 10^{-3}$ Fermi^3, gives the nonmesonic decay rate for $_\Lambda H^3$ as

$$\Gamma_{nm} = 7 \times 10^{-3} \, \Gamma_\Lambda \qquad \text{for} \; J(_\Lambda H^3) = \tfrac{1}{2} \qquad \qquad \text{(VIII-4)}$$

$$\Gamma_{nm} = 13 \times 10^{-3} \, \Gamma_\Lambda \qquad \text{for} \; J(_\Lambda H^3) = \tfrac{3}{2}. \qquad \qquad \text{(VIII-5)}$$

The total decay rates for $_\Lambda H^3$ are, respectively, 1.34 Γ_Λ and 0.95 Γ_Λ for spins $\frac{1}{2}$ and $\frac{3}{2}$. The corresponding lifetimes are 1.76×10^{-10} sec and 2.47×10^{-10} sec. Neither of these estimates is in agreement with the experimentally determined lifetime $0.95 \begin{smallmatrix} +0.19 \\ -0.15 \end{smallmatrix} \times 10^{-10}$ sec, although the comparison of the calculation with experiment may be construed as some further evidence in favor of a spin $\frac{1}{2}$ assignment to $_\Lambda H^3$.

For $_\Lambda He^5$, the π^--mesonic decay rates are suppressed by the Pauli principle, the estimates of the extent of this suppression lead to a value of the total π^--mesonic decay rate of 0.38 Γ_Λ. Adopting the value of 1.8 for Q^- (see Section VI,B) one obtains a total decay rate for $_\Lambda He^5$ of 0.83 Γ_Λ and a lifetime of 2.84×10^{-10} sec. This is again, as for the case of $_\Lambda H^3$, appreciably longer than the measured lifetime and might suggest that either the nonmesonic contribution to the decay rate is underestimated or that the impulse model is not a good approximation to the true situation.[16]

IX. The Λ-Nuclear Potential Well-Depth

The Λ-nuclear potential well-depth D_Λ which may be equated to the binding energy of a Λ hyperon embedded in nuclear matter, has been estimated empirically by extrapolating from the known B_Λ values of light hypernuclei (Gatto, 1956; Ivanenko and Kolesnikov, 1957; Filimonov, 1959; Walecka, 1960; Olley, 1961; Dalitz, 1962; Bodmer and Murphy, 1965). These estimates, the most recent of which range from 20 to 30 MeV, suffer from the disadvantage that the binding energies of light hypernuclei are strongly dependent upon the properties of their cores which are not well representative of infinite nuclear matter. The estimates based on the B_Λ value of $_\Lambda C^{13}$ have the advantage that the core C^{12} has properties which more closely simulate those of nuclear matter, but there are uncertainties both in the size of C^{12} and in the B_Λ estimate of $_\Lambda C^{13}$ (see Section IV,A) which render these values open to some question.

The best and most direct estimates of D_Λ have been obtained from the observed energy releases in the π^--mesonic decays of heavy spallation hypernuclei. The interactions of K^--mesons both in flight and at rest in nuclear emulsion provide copious sources of these hypernuclei, commonly with mass numbers in the range of A between 40 and 100, whose decays may be resolved from the primary disintegrations (see Section III). The first π^--mesonic decays of these heavy hypernuclei were reported by Davis et al. (1962) who deduced from the measured upper limit of their B_Λ values that

---

[16] This is also suggested by the high π^+-mesonic decay rate observed for $_\Lambda He^4$ (Mayeur et al., 1966b) suggesting that the stimulated decay of the Λ hyperon may lead to π-meson emission (see Section VIII,B).

D_Λ probably did not exceed 30 MeV.[17] Many further examples of the π^--mesonic decays of heavy hypernuclei were found in the studies of the interactions of K^--mesons of high momentum (Cuevas et al., 1963b; Perlmutter, 1963; Baumann et al., 1963; Bologna-Firenze-Genoa Collaboration, 1963; Lagnaux et al., 1964) and gave the lowest value of the upper limit of B_Λ equal to 22.7 ± 1.5 MeV. An expression for the Λ-nuclear potential well-depth D_Λ has been given by Walecka (1960) as

$$D_\Lambda = B_\Lambda + \frac{\pi^2 A^{-2/3} \hbar^2 c^2}{2m_\Lambda r_0{}^2}\left(1 - \frac{2}{s} + \frac{3}{s^2}\right) \qquad (IX\text{-}1)$$

where

$$s = \left[r_0{}^2 A^{2/3} \frac{2m_\Lambda D_\Lambda}{\hbar^2 c^2}\right]^{1/2}. \qquad (IX\text{-}2)$$

Lagnaux et al. (1964), assuming the mean mass number of the hypernuclei to be 75 and r_0 to be 1.21 Fermis, obtained by applying this formula a value for the upper limit of D_Λ of 27 ± 3 MeV.

Table XI gives an illustration of the effect on D_Λ of variations in both mass number A and radius parameter r_0, the B_Λ value of the hypernucleus being taken to be constant at 22.7 MeV.

TABLE XI

VARIATION OF D_Λ WITH A AND r_0; $B_\Lambda = 22.7$ MeV

A	$A^{-2/3}$	D_Λ (MeV)	
		$r_0 = 1.22$ Fermis	$r_0 = 1.39$ Fermis
30	0.1036	31.1	29.7
40	0.0855	29.7	28.5
50	0.0736	28.8	27.8
60	0.0653	28.2	27.3
70	0.0590	27.6	26.9
80	0.0539	27.2	26.5
90	0.0498	26.9	26.2
100	0.0464	26.7	26.0

Key et al. (1965), however, have suggested from the results of a Monte Carlo calculation that the masses of these hypernuclei may not be confined to

---

[17] Since either the final recoil left in an excited state or the emission of a neutron would remain undetected, the measured values of B_Λ may only be considered as upper limits.

the range $40 < A < 100$ as estimated by Lagnaux *et al.* (1964) but may well extend down to A values of about 25. If hypernuclei of such low masses provided the lowest observed values of B_Λ, then an extrapolation to a nucleus of infinite mass using the formula of Walecka would result in a D_Λ increased to about 35 MeV.

This criticism of the result of Lagnaux *et al.* (1964) has been answered by considering those heavy hypernuclei produced by K^--meson interactions at rest with silver and bromine nuclei. Since the excitation energy available in such reactions is relatively small ($\lesssim 100$ MeV) it is impossible for any large-scale fragmentation to occur with the consequence that the spallation hypernuclei are on the average about 12, and at most about 25 nucleon masses lighter than the struck nuclei (Lemonne, 1965). From 22 events ascribed to the π^--mesonic decays of heavy hypernuclei produced by K^--meson captures at rest, Lemonne *et al.* (1965a) obtained 22.8 ± 0.4 MeV as the lowest observed B_Λ value. From this result they deduced that the upper limit of D_Λ was 27.2 ± 1.3 MeV, the error arising mainly from uncertainties in the value of A (in the range 60 to 100) and of r_0 (1.2 to 1.4 Fermis). From the small spread observed for the B_Λ values obtained from decays of the type π^--proton recoil it was also concluded that this value of the upper limit of D_Λ must be very close to the true value.

There have been many theoretical estimates of the well depth which use the values of the potentials derived from the studies of light hypernuclei (see Section IV,B). As a result these potentials refer mainly to the Λ-nucleon interaction in S states, but to a first approximation it has been assumed that the same potentials are appropriate to the Λ–N interaction in all other angular momentum states. Bodmer and Sampanthar (1962) have calculated D_Λ from perturbation theory using soft Λ–N potentials. They assumed that nuclear matter could be represented by a Fermi gas containing equal numbers of protons and neutrons and they considered central two-body potentials with range parameters to be expected for a direct interaction involving the exchange of two π mesons and a K-meson exchange reaction. Taking a value for ρ, the density of nuclear matter, to be 0.172 nucleon/Fermi^3 and a corresponding value of 1.366 Fermi^{-1} for the Fermi momentum, they obtained a value of 40 MeV for D_Λ from a two π-meson exchange mechanism and one of 26 MeV for the case of K-meson exchange. In order to equate these values with the empirical estimates of D_Λ, they suggested that K-meson exchange may well play an important role in the Λ–N interaction. Bodmer and Sampanthar (1962) also considered the possibility of a three-body Λ–N interaction, again choosing potentials without hard cores. Although they assumed both Yukawa and exponential shapes for the potentials and also many values of Δ, the difference $\overline{V}_s - \overline{V}_t$, again agreement with empirical estimates in general necessitates adopting a range appropriate to K-meson exchange.

Walecka (1960), using a similar method to that adopted by Gomes *et al.* (1958) to deduce the binding energy of a nucleon in nuclear matter, calculated D_Λ using the Λ-nucleon potentials of Kovacs and Lichtenberg (1959) containing a hard core of radius 0.6 Fermi. He found D_Λ to be 23 MeV by only considering S-state interactions but obtained a much higher value of D_Λ, about 60 MeV, on including contributions from higher angular momentum states. Walecka (1960) concluded from this that some additional repulsion was necessary in Λ-nucleon p states, perhaps arising from K-meson exchange (Lichtenberg and Ross, 1957). However, the high value of D_Λ obtained by Walecka (1960) may be in part attributed to the high value he assumed for the density of nuclear matter, $\rho = 0.219$ nucleon/Fermi³. Downs and Ware (1964) have extended the work of Walecka (1960) and have considered both attractive square well and exponential-shaped potentials with hard-core radii either 0.4 or 0.6 Fermi. They also assumed the potentials to have a zero-energy scattering length equal to that of a soft potential having an intrinsic range corresponding to two π-meson exchange ($b = 1.5$ Fermis) and a spin-averaged volume integral $U = 230$ MeV Fermi³ (see Section IV, B). They then considered the intrinsic range of the attractive well b_0 to have a number of values within the limits $b - 2d \leqslant b_0 \leqslant b$. A summary of their results is given in Table XII.

Further calculations by Ram and Downs (1964) result, on the assumption of a range parameter appropriate to two π-meson exchange, in values of D_Λ close to 40 MeV, the contribution from Λ–N p states being the dominant one. In fact a reduction of about 40% in the attraction in odd-parity states (notably the p state) would be necessary to bring these estimates in accordance with the observed value of D_Λ.

As can be seen, the theoretical estimates of D_Λ are in general considerably larger than the experimentally determined value. This might indicate that the triplet Λ-nucleon potential is either largely due to an attractive exchange potential (Bodmer and Sampanthar, 1962) or that it contains a large component of tensor force which would contribute less to the Λ-hyperon binding in nuclear matter than it would in a light hypernucleus (Dalitz, 1962). However, not too much weight should be attached to this discrepancy since, as has been pointed out by Dalitz (1965c), a similar one exists between the experimental and theoretical estimates of the nucleon-nuclear potential well depth.

X. Double Hypernuclei and the Λ-Λ Interaction

When an interaction in which two Λ hyperons are produced takes place in a complex nucleus there is a possibility that both of the Λ hyperons may become bound to the same nuclear fragment, thus forming a double hypernucleus. The determination of the separation energy of the two Λ hyperons from the core of the double hypernucleus $B_{\Lambda\Lambda}$ provides information concerning the strength of the S-wave Λ–Λ interaction and may also provide further information on the spin dependence of the Λ–N interaction.

The fulfillment of the strangeness requirement and also the low energy release in the process

$$\Xi^- + p \to \Lambda + \Lambda + 28.5 \text{ MeV} \qquad \text{(X-1)}$$

make Ξ^- hyperon captures in complex nuclei the most likely source of double hyperfragments. In general the same remarks concerning the analysis and unique identification of ordinary hyperfragments produced in nuclear emulsion apply to double hyperfragments. In particular, it is necessary that the decay of the double hypernucleus itself should be π^--mesonic, to allow a unique identification to be made and to permit an accurate determination of its $B_{\Lambda\Lambda}$ value. In addition the very detection and analysis depend upon the second hyperon remaining bound in an ordinary hyperfragment and this is more likely to be the case when the first decay is mesonic.

A. EXPERIMENTAL FACTS

To date only one example of a double hyperfragment, the decay of which was π^--mesonic, has been reported (Danysz et al., 1963a,b)*. This was found in an emulsion stack exposed to K^- mesons of 1.5 GeV/c momentum. The sequence of events is shown schematically in Fig. 22. A slow Ξ^- hyperon produced at A comes to rest at B to form a capture star consisting of the tracks of a stable particle (track 5) and the double hypernucleus (track 6). The double hypernucleus decays at C into a π^--meson (track 7), a stable singly-charged particle (track 8), and a hyperfragment (track 9). The hyperfragment is then seen to decay at D into a π^--meson (track 10) and three stable particles (tracks 11, 12, and 13).

By combining the analyses of the production process and the two decay reactions the majority of possible reaction schemes may be rejected, and the

---

* *Note Added in Proof.* An example of the double hypernucleus $_{\Lambda\Lambda}\text{He}^6$ has recently been reported by Prowse (1966). The production and subsequent decays proceeded according to the scheme

$$\Xi^- + C^{12} \to {}_{\Lambda\Lambda}\text{He}^6 + \text{Li}^7$$

$$_{\Lambda\Lambda}\text{He}^6 \to {}_{\Lambda}\text{He}^5 + \text{H}^1 + \pi^-$$

$$_{\Lambda}\text{He}^5 \to \text{He}^4 + \text{H}^1 + \pi^-$$

The total binding energy of the two Λ hyperons, $B_{\Lambda\Lambda}$, which could be computed from both the production and decay kinematics was 10.8 ± 0.5 MeV. Hence the contribution from the Λ–Λ interaction (the core of $_{\Lambda\Lambda}\text{He}^6$ is spinless) is $\Delta B_{\Lambda\Lambda} = B_{\Lambda\Lambda}(_{\Lambda\Lambda}\text{He}^6) - 2B_{\Lambda}(_{\Lambda}\text{He}^5) = +4.7 \pm 0.5$ MeV. This result conclusively establishes that the $^1S_0$ Λ–Λ interaction is attractive and leads to a quantitative estimate of the strength of the Λ–Λ interaction similar to that deduced by assuming that the identity of the first double hypernucleus was $_{\Lambda\Lambda}\text{Be}^{10}$.

TABLE XII

Values of the Well-Depth D_Λ and the Partial
Wave Contributions D_Λ^l [a]

b_0 (fm)	D_Λ^0 (MeV)	D_Λ^1 (MeV)	D_Λ^2 (MeV)	D_Λ (MeV)
(a) Exponential well, hard-core radius 0.4 Fermi				
0.7	25	7	<1	33
1.1	23	15	2	39
1.5	17	22	4	43
(b) Square well, hard-coare radius 0.4 Fermi				
0.7	18	7	<1	25
1.1	19	13	1	33
(c) Exponential well, hard-core radius 0.6 Fermi				
0.9	13	18	2	33
1.5	−3	32	7	37

[a] Data from Downs and Ware (1964).

final conclusion is that the double hypernucleus is most likely to be either an example of $_{\Lambda\Lambda}\mathrm{Be}^{10}$ or $_{\Lambda\Lambda}\mathrm{Be}^{11}$. The decay sequences are then as follows

$$_{\Lambda\Lambda}\mathrm{Be}^{10} \rightarrow {}_\Lambda\mathrm{Be}^9 + \mathrm{H}^1 + \pi^- \tag{X-2}$$

$$_\Lambda\mathrm{Be}^9 \rightarrow \mathrm{He}^4 + \mathrm{He}^4 + \mathrm{H}^1 + \pi^- \tag{X-3}$$

with $\Delta B_{\Lambda\Lambda} = +4.5 \pm 0.4$ MeV; $B_{\Lambda\Lambda} = 17.5 \pm 0.4$ MeV.

$$_{\Lambda\Lambda}\mathrm{Be}^{11} \rightarrow {}_\Lambda\mathrm{Be}^{10} + \mathrm{H}^1 + \pi^- \tag{X-4}$$

$$_\Lambda\mathrm{Be}^{10} \rightarrow \mathrm{He}^4 + \mathrm{He}^4 + \mathrm{H}^2 + \pi^- \tag{X-5}$$

with $\Delta B_{\Lambda\Lambda} = +3.2 \pm 0.6$ MeV; $B_{\Lambda\Lambda} = 19.0 \pm 0.6$ MeV. Here $\Delta B_{\Lambda\Lambda}$ is the net contribution of the Λ–Λ interaction and the reduction due to the spin dependent part of the Λ-core interaction, provided core distortion effects may be neglected, $\Delta B_{\Lambda\Lambda}$ is given by

$$\Delta B_{\Lambda\Lambda}(_\Lambda Z^A) = B_\Lambda(_{\Lambda\Lambda}Z^A) - B_\Lambda(_\Lambda Z^{A-1}) = B_{\Lambda\Lambda}(_{\Lambda\Lambda}Z^A) - 2B_\Lambda(_\Lambda Z^{A-1}). \tag{X-6}$$

For both of these schemes $\Delta B_{\Lambda\Lambda}$ is positive and the same quantitative estimates of the strength of the S-wave Λ–Λ interaction are given provided that the spin-dependent part of the Λ-core interaction in $_{\Lambda\Lambda}\mathrm{Be}^{11}$ is taken into account.

A further possibility that the double hypernucleus was an example of $_{\Lambda\Lambda}\mathrm{Be}^{11}$ decaying by the mode

$$_{\Lambda\Lambda}\mathrm{Be}^{11} \rightarrow {}_\Lambda\mathrm{Be}^9 + \mathrm{H}^1 + n + \pi^- \tag{X-7}$$

yields a negative value of $\Delta B_{\Lambda\Lambda}$. However this possibility is considered unlikely since it is known that similar decay modes of ordinary hypernuclei are rare.

Examples of the associated production of two hyperfragments in the interactions of fast π^--mesons and K^--mesons with complex nuclei have been observed in many experiments (Wilkinson *et al.*, 1959; Barkas *et al.*, 1959; Steinberg and Prem, 1963; Fletcher *et al.*, 1963; Baumann *et al.*, 1963; Beniston *et al.*, 1964a; Lemonne *et al.*, 1965b). The interpretation of some of these events in terms of the formation of a short-lived Ξ hypernucleus which

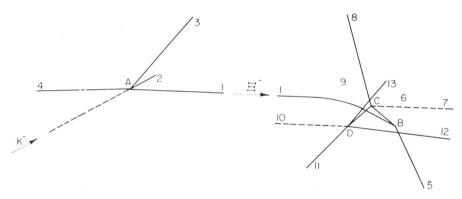

FIG. 22. Schematic drawing of the production of a Ξ^- hyperon in the interaction at A of a k^- meson of momentum 1.5 GeV/c followed by the capture at rest of the Ξ^- hyperon at B with the emission of a double hyperfragment decaying in cascade at C and D (Danysz *et al.* 1963a,b).

subsequently decays into two "ordinary" hyperfragments as a result of the conversion reaction (X-1) is possible (see, e.g., Wilkinson *et al.*, 1959; Barkas *et al.*, 1959). It seems however, impossible to obtain any valuable information regarding the Ξ–N interaction from these events.

B. Theory

In a double hypernucleus in its ground state, the two Λ hyperons being bound in the lowest S-orbit relative to the nuclear core, the Pauli exclusion principle requires the spins of the two hyperons to be coupled in the singlet configuration. Estimates of the $^1S_0$ Λ–Λ potential strength required to reproduce the experimental value of $B_{\Lambda\Lambda}$ in the $_{\Lambda\Lambda}\mathrm{Be}^{10}$ hypernucleus have been made by different authors.

Representing the Λ–Λ interaction by a Gaussian potential

$$V_{\Lambda\Lambda}(r) = -\,\bar{V}_{\Lambda\Lambda}(\alpha/\pi)^{3/2}\exp(-\alpha r^2) \qquad (\text{X-8})$$

with $\alpha = 0.935$ Fermi^{-2}, corresponding to the exchange of 2π mesons, Dalitz

(1963c) has estimated the volume integral $\bar{v}_{\Lambda\Lambda}$ using a trial wave function of the form

$$\psi = f(\bar{r}_{c1})f(\bar{r}_{c2})\chi_s \qquad \text{(X-9)}$$

for the motion of the two Λ hyperons; $\bar{r}_{c1}$ and $\bar{r}_{c2}$ denote the distances between the Λ hyperons and the center of mass of the Be^8 core; χ_s is the singlet spin function for the Λ hyperons and the space functions f are of the form

$$f(\bar{r}) = N[\exp(-ar^2) + y\exp(-br^2)] \qquad \text{(X-10)}$$

where N is a normalization factor and a, b, and y are variational parameters. The Λ–Be^8 interaction was represented by a potential taken to have the shell-model form

$$V(r) = -\bar{v}(\mu/\pi)^{3/2}(\tfrac{1}{2} + \tfrac{1}{3}\mu r^2)\exp(-\mu r^2) \qquad \text{(X-11)}$$

with $\mu = 0.33$ Fermi^{-2}.

A variational calculation of the strength of the Λ–Λ potential required to account for the experimental value of $B_{\Lambda\Lambda}$ leads to the result $\bar{v}_{\Lambda\Lambda} = 440 \pm 60$ MeV Fermi^3.

In order to allow the possibility of strong spatial correlations between the two Λ hyperons, Dalitz and Rajasekharan (1964) improved this calculation using a trial wave function of the form

$$\psi = f(\bar{r}_{c1})f(\bar{r}_{c2})g(\bar{r}_{12})\chi_s \qquad \text{(X-12)}$$

where $g(\bar{r}_{12})$ is of the form given by Eq. (X-10). As a result, the volume integral of the Λ–Λ interaction was found to be reduced to $\bar{v}_{\Lambda\Lambda} = 322 \pm 26$ MeV Fermi^3 leading to a Λ–Λ scattering length $a_{\Lambda\Lambda}$ of $-(1.76 \pm 0.33)$ Fermi.

In both of these studies no allowance has been made for the possibility of distortion of the nuclear core by the presence of the two strongly bound Λ hyperons, although such effects are expected to be of importance in the case of Be^8.

Instead of considering the $_{\Lambda\Lambda}Be^{10}$ double hypernucleus as a three-body system $Be^8 + \Lambda + \Lambda$, Deloff (1963) and Nakamura (1963a) based their calculations on an α-particle model, the $_{\Lambda\Lambda}Be^{10}$ hypernucleus consisting of two α particles held together by two hyperons. Using similar Λ–Λ, Λ–α, and α–α potentials[18] and a simple trial wave function of the form

$$\psi = Nl[\exp(-\tfrac{1}{2}(\alpha l^2 + \beta\rho^2 + \gamma r^2)] \qquad \text{(X-13)}$$

where α, β, and γ are three variational parameters; l, r, and ρ are the distances between the two α particles, the two Λ hyperons, and the center of

---

[18] The Λ–Λ potential is taken of the form (X-8), the α–α potential is the one deduced by Suh (1958) from the analysis of $_\Lambda Be^9$ which yields α–α $^1S_0$ phase shifts above the experimental values, and the Λ–α potential is $V_{\alpha\Lambda}(\bar{r}) = \Sigma_{\text{spin}}\int\rho_\alpha(\bar{R})V_{\Lambda N}(|\bar{r} - \bar{R}|)\,d^3R$ where $\rho_\alpha(\bar{R})$ is the nucleon density of the α particle.

the two α particles and of the two Λ hyperons, respectively; and N is a normalization factor, they obtained contradictory results, i.e.: $\bar{v}_{\Lambda\Lambda} = 22 \pm 28$ MeV Fermi³ (Nakamura, 1963a) and $\bar{v}_{\Lambda\Lambda} \sim 300$ MeV Fermi³ (Deloff, 1963); the last value being in agreement with the estimates of Dalitz (1963c) and Dalitz and Rajasekharan (1964).

Hard-core Λ–Λ potentials were considered first by Tang et al. (1964) with a three-body model of $_{\Lambda\Lambda}\text{Be}^{10}$. These authors used a potential with an attractive well of exponential shape:

$$\begin{aligned} V_{\Lambda\Lambda}(r) &= \infty && \text{for} \quad r < d \\ &= -\bar{v}_{\Lambda\Lambda}[\exp - \eta(r - r_c)] && \text{for} \quad r > d \end{aligned} \tag{X-14}$$

with a hard-core radius $d = 0.4$ Fermi and a range parameter η corresponding to a two π-meson exchange. The trial wave function was of the form (X-12) with $g(r)$ given by

$$\begin{aligned} g(r) &= u(r)/r && \text{for} \quad r < D \\ &= Ar^{-1/2}[\exp(-\alpha r) + B \exp(-\beta r)] && \text{for} \quad r > D. \end{aligned} \tag{X-15}$$

The constants A and B were adjusted such that $g(r)$ and its derivative were continuous at the distance D; $u(r)$ is the solution of the equation

$$-\frac{\hbar^2}{2\mu_\Lambda} \frac{d^2}{dr^2} u(r) + [V_{\Lambda\Lambda}(r) - e]u(r) = 0 \tag{X-16}$$

μ_Λ being the reduced mass of the two Λ hyperons.

The volume integral $\bar{v}_{\Lambda\Lambda}$ was found to be 1056 ± 38 MeV Fermi³, leading to a Λ–Λ scattering length,

$$a_{\Lambda\Lambda} = -\left(1.93 \begin{array}{c} +0.51 \\ -0.38 \end{array}\right) \text{Fermi}.$$

Recently, in order to take into account the effects of core distortion, Tang and Herndon (1965a) also considered the $_{\Lambda\Lambda}\text{Be}^{10}$ double hypernucleus as a four-body system of two α particles and two Λ hyperons. The $\Lambda\Lambda$ potential is assumed to be of the form given by Eq. (X-14); the α–Λ potential is chosen to yield the binding energy of the Λ hyperon in $_\Lambda\text{He}^5$, with a Λ-nucleon interaction of a Gaussian form with an intrinsic range corresponding to the exchange of 2π mesons; and the α–α potential is chosen to fit the experimental values of the α–α scattering phase shifts. The trial wave function was chosen of the form

$$\psi = g(r_{12})\left[\prod_{\substack{i=1,2 \\ k=3,4}} f(r_{ik})\right] h(r_{34})\chi_s \tag{X-17}$$

where 1, 2 and 3, 4 denote the α particles and the Λ hyperons, respectively. The functions g, f, and h are defined by Eqs. (X-15) and (X-16), with the potentials and reduced masses corresponding to the systems considered (Λ–Λ, α–Λ, or α–α); the total number of variational parameters being 12. The strength of the Λ–Λ interaction deduced from this analysis is $\bar{v}_{\Lambda\Lambda} = 944 \begin{smallmatrix} +35 \\ -44 \end{smallmatrix}$ MeV Fermi^3 significantly lower than the corresponding value obtained with the three-body model (Tang et al., 1964).

Bodmer and Ali (1965) have extended their study of the $_\Lambda$Be^9 hypernucleus (Bodmer and Ali, 1964) to the case of the $_{\Lambda\Lambda}$Be^{10} double hypernucleus. Considering both a four-body and a three-body model of $_{\Lambda\Lambda}$Be^{10}, they calculated the strength of the $\Lambda\Lambda$ interaction for (a) a purely attractive Yukawa potential, (b) a hard-core Yukawa potential, and (c) a hard-core, meson theory potential (de Swart, 1963; de Swart and Iddings, 1962), both with a hard-core radius $d = 0.42$ Fermi. The intrinsic ranges b of these potentials appropriate to the exchange of 2π mesons are 1.48, 2.66, and 1.49 Fermis, respectively. The results of this analysis are summarized in Table XIII and compared with those obtained by other authors (Dalitz and Rajasekharan, 1964; Tang et al., 1964; Tang and Herndon, 1965a). This table contains the values of the well-depth parameter $s_{\Lambda\Lambda}$ of the Λ–Λ potential, the Λ–Λ scattering length $a_{\Lambda\Lambda}$, and the effective range (r_0). It is seen that the values of $s_{\Lambda\Lambda}$ determined from the four-body model are appreciably smaller than those obtained from the three-body model indicating that the consideration of the effect of the distortion of the Be^8 core is quite essential in the determination of the strength of the Λ–Λ interaction. An increase of the hard-core radius from zero (purely attractive potential) to 0.4 Fermi leads to a significant increase of $s_{\Lambda\Lambda}$, while $a_{\Lambda\Lambda}$ remains nearly unchanged. For an intrinsic range of 1.5 Fermis, the scattering length and the effective range are seen to be approximately independent of the shape of the $\Lambda\Lambda$ potential and of the order of $-(1 \pm 0.3)$ and 3.3 ± 0.6 Fermi, respectively. For $b = 2.66$ Fermis the values of $a_{\Lambda\Lambda}$ and $(r_0)_{\Lambda\Lambda}$ are considerably larger.

If the alternative interpretation of the event reported by Danysz et al., (1963a,b) as a $_{\Lambda\Lambda}$Be^{11} double hypernucleus were the right one, it is not expected that the above conclusions would be modified significantly (Dalitz, 1963c; Dalitz and Rajasekharan, 1964; Bodmer and Ali, 1965).

The interpretation of the values obtained for $a_{\Lambda\Lambda}$ in terms of the meson-theory potentials has been discussed by different authors (Dalitz, 1963c; Dalitz and Rajasekharan, 1964; Bodmer and Ali, 1965; de Swart, 1963). At the present time, it seems that no final conclusion can be drawn regarding the interpretation of the Λ–N and Λ–Λ potential strengths until one has some understanding of the relation between the hard-core repulsions appropriate to the different baryon-baryon systems.

The question naturally arises whether there exist other double hypernuclei

TABLE XIII

WELL-DEPTH PARAMETER AND LOW ENERGY SCATTERING PARAMETERS OF THE $\Lambda\Lambda$ POTENTIAL

Model for $_{\Lambda\Lambda}\text{Be}^{10}$	$\Lambda\Lambda$ potential	$s_{\Lambda\Lambda}$	$a_{\Lambda\Lambda}$ (Fermi)	$(r_0)_{\Lambda\Lambda}$ (Fermi)	References
$\text{Be}^8 + 2\Lambda$	Gaussian, purely attractive	0.599 ± 0.048	$-(1.76 \pm 0.33)$	2.10 ± 0.12	Dalitz and Rajasekharan (1964)
$\text{Be}^8 + 2\Lambda$	Hard core ($d = 0.4$ Fermi; $b = 1.5$ Fermis) exponential	0.817 ± 0.029	$-\left(1.93 \begin{smallmatrix}+0.51\\-0.38\end{smallmatrix}\right)$	2.21 ± 0.17	Tang et al. (1964)
$2\alpha + 2\Lambda$	Hard-core ($d = 0.4$ Fermi; $b = 1.5$ Fermis) exponential	$0.732 \begin{smallmatrix}+0.027\\-0.034\end{smallmatrix}$	$-\left(1.04 \begin{smallmatrix}+0.20\\-0.22\end{smallmatrix}\right)$	$2.91 \begin{smallmatrix}+0.46\\-0.27\end{smallmatrix}$	Tang and Herndon (1965a)
$\text{Be}^8 + 2\Lambda$	Yukawa, purely attractive	0.64 ± 0.05	$-\left(1.79 \begin{smallmatrix}+0.40\\-0.20\end{smallmatrix}\right)$	$2.54 \begin{smallmatrix}+0.24\\-0.20\end{smallmatrix}$	Bodmer and Ali (1965)
$2\alpha + 2\Lambda$	Yukawa, purely attractive	0.45 ± 0.08	$-\left(0.89 \begin{smallmatrix}+0.31\\-0.28\end{smallmatrix}\right)$	$3.70 \begin{smallmatrix}+0.82\\-0.58\end{smallmatrix}$	Bodmer and Ali (1965)
$\text{Be}^8 + 2\Lambda$	Hard-core ($d = 0.42$ Fermi; $b = 2.66$ Fermis) Yukawa	0.81 ± 0.44	$-\left(4.85 \begin{smallmatrix}+1.65\\-1.1\end{smallmatrix}\right)$	$3.61 \begin{smallmatrix}+0.32\\-0.23\end{smallmatrix}$	Bodmer and Ali (1965)
$2\alpha + 2\Lambda$	Hard-core ($d = 0.42$ Fermi; $b = 2.66$ Fermis) Yukawa	0.675 ± 0.065	$-\left(2.30 \begin{smallmatrix}+0.80\\-0.54\end{smallmatrix}\right)$	$4.93 \begin{smallmatrix}+1.07\\-0.73\end{smallmatrix}$	Bodmer and Ali (1965)
$\text{Be}^8 + 2\Lambda$	Hard-core ($d = 0.42$ Fermi; $b = 1.48$ Fermis) meson theory	0.87 ± 0.03	$-\left(2.36 \begin{smallmatrix}+0.68\\-0.48\end{smallmatrix}\right)$	$2.18 \begin{smallmatrix}+0.19\\-0.18\end{smallmatrix}$	Bodmer and Ali (1965)
$2\alpha + 2\Lambda$	Hard-core ($d = 0.42$ Fermi; $b = 1.48$ Fermis) meson theory	0.77 ± 0.04	$-\left(1.13 \begin{smallmatrix}+0.38\\-0.27\end{smallmatrix}\right)$	$3.08 \begin{smallmatrix}+0.60\\-0.45\end{smallmatrix}$	Bodmer and Ali (1965)

which should be particle-stable. The results listed in Table XIII for the well-depth parameter $s_{\Lambda\Lambda}$ are clearly against the existence of a bound singlet state of the Λ–Λ system. In view of the fact that the triplet Λ–N interaction is weaker than the singlet one, it is expected that this situation will hold for the $\Lambda\Lambda$ interaction, and the Pauli principle forbids the $^3S_1$ state, so that a bound triplet state of the $\Lambda\Lambda$ system is even less likely to exist.

In $_{\Lambda\Lambda}H^3$ and $_{\Lambda\Lambda}n^3$, the average Λ–N interaction is the same as that in the $I = 1$ configuration of $_\Lambda H^3$, which is known not to be bound (see Section IV,B); and the Λ–Λ well-depth parameter is smaller than the N–N well-depth parameter in the $^1S_0$ state (Tang and Herndon, 1965b). Consequently, these double hypernuclei are not expected to be bound.

Recently, Tang and Herndon (1965b) have made a systematic investigation of the hypernuclear systems $_{\Lambda\Lambda}Z^A$ with $A = 4$, 5, and 6 using a variational method similar to that one they used for $_{\Lambda\Lambda}Be^{10}$ (Tang and Herndon, 1965a). The binding energy $B_{\Lambda\Lambda}$ of these double hypernuclei are calculated as a function of the strength of the $\Lambda\Lambda$ interaction. Assuming that the value of $\bar{v}_{\Lambda\Lambda}$ as determined from the analysis of $_{\Lambda\Lambda}Be^{10}$ is the right one, it is concluded that it is unlikely for $_{\Lambda\Lambda}H^4$ to be bound in either of the two $I = 0$ and $I = 1$ configurations. On the other hand, $_{\Lambda\Lambda}H^5$ is found to be stable against the breakup into $H^3 + 2\Lambda$ and $_\Lambda H^4 + \Lambda$. The binding energy $B_{\Lambda\Lambda}$ of $_{\Lambda\Lambda}He^6$, considered as a six-body system is found to be equal to 9.68 ± 0.60 MeV. A similar value was obtained by Tang and Herndon (1965a) using a three-body model $(\alpha + 2\Lambda)$ for $_{\Lambda\Lambda}He^6$, indicating that in this case the effect of the-core distortion is not important, as expected. With a purely attractive $\Lambda\Lambda$ potential of Gaussian form and of volume integral 322 ± 26 MeV Fermi^3 corresponding to the experimental binding energy of $_{\Lambda\Lambda}Be^{10}$, Dalitz and Rajasekharan (1964) obtained $B_{\Lambda\Lambda}(_{\Lambda\Lambda}He^6) = 11.2 \pm 0.6$ MeV. Other estimates of $B_{\Lambda\Lambda}(_{\Lambda\Lambda}He^6)$ have been made by Nakamura (1963b), Damle and Biswas (1964), and Beck and Gutsch (1965) along similar lines but using different types of potential. All these studies lead to $B_{\Lambda\Lambda}$ values between 10 and 13 MeV. The hypernucleus $_{\Lambda\Lambda}He^5$ also has been found to be bound (Damle and Biswas, 1964; Beck and Gutsch, 1965) for reasonable values of the strength of the Λ–Λ interaction.

XI. Hypernuclei and Nuclear Physics

It was seen in Section V that it was possible to ascertain the spins of hypernuclei from detailed studies of the final state interactions involved in their decays. Another aspect of the physics of hypernuclei is that it is possible to reverse this procedure, to study hypernuclei to gain information about the properties of nuclei. Such an approach has not, as yet, had many applications due in the most part to a lack of statistics, but some of the possibilities will now be discussed.

A. FINAL STATE INTERACTIONS IN THE DECAY OF LIGHT HYPERNUCLEI

The existence of strong final state interactions between the decay products of light hypernuclei has been demonstrated in different situations, in particular, in the decays of $_\Lambda He^5$ and $_\Lambda Li^8$.

In Section V it was shown that the $(\pi^- He^4 He^4)$ decay of $_\Lambda Li^8$ proceeds almost entirely by a two-step process involving the formation and subsequent decay of an intermediate state of Be^8. Transitions to the $Be^8, 0^+$ ground state, the 2.9-Mev 2^+ level, and a level or levels at about 17 MeV were all observed, there being a negligible background of events not involving discrete states of Be^8. A question of some interest is through which level at about 17 MeV, if indeed it is through only one, does the decay of $_\Lambda Li^8$ proceed. It has been suggested by Marion (1965) that the 16.62 MeV level of Be^8 should be thought of as a $(Li^7 + p)$ system and the level at 16.92 MeV, a $(Be^7 + n)$ system. If this model is correct it would be expected that the favored transition of $_\Lambda Li^8$ would be through the 16.62 MeV level. Although the present experimental data indicate that this may be so, the statistics are, as yet, far too poor to provide a definite answer.

The decay process $_\Lambda He^5 \to \pi^- + H^1 + He^4$ has been studied experimentally by Ammar *et al.* (1959). The kinematical quantities relevant to this study are illustrated in Fig. 23. The results are summarized in Figs. 24, 25, and 26 which show the momentum spectrum of the π^--meson and the distributions of the angles ψ and ξ (as defined in Fig. 23), respectively. Both the accumulation of events with high energy π-mesons and the strong correlation existing between the direction of emission of the π-meson and the line of flight of the α particle in the π-p rest system have led Dalitz (as quoted by Telegdi, 1957) to suggest that the decay could be dominated by strong interactions between the particles present in the final state. Byers and Cottingham (1959) have calculated the energy and angular distributions for this decay, taking into account the specific p–He^4 nuclear interaction. The phase shift analysis of p–He^4 scattering and polarization experiments in the center-of-mass energy range of interest indicates the existence of both a sharp $P_{3/2}$ resonant state at 1.8 MeV above the sum of the proton and He^4 masses and a broad $P_{1/2}$ state lying between 5 and 10 MeV above the $P_{3/2}$ state. The predictions of Byers and Cottingham (1959) are compared with the experimental data in Figs. 25 and 26 and in Fig. 27 giving the distribution of the resultant momentum of the pion and the proton ($P_{\pi p}$). From this comparison it was concluded by Ammar *et al.* (1959) that the p–He^4 $P_{3/2}$ resonance plays an important role in determining the final state configuration of the $_\Lambda He^5$ decay. In the p–He^4 rest system, the $P_{1/2}$ state would yield an isotropic distribution in cos ξ.

Additional data, accumulated by the Chicago group (Harmsen *et al.*, 1965a,b) and the K^- European Collaboration (Sacton, 1965a,b), confirm this

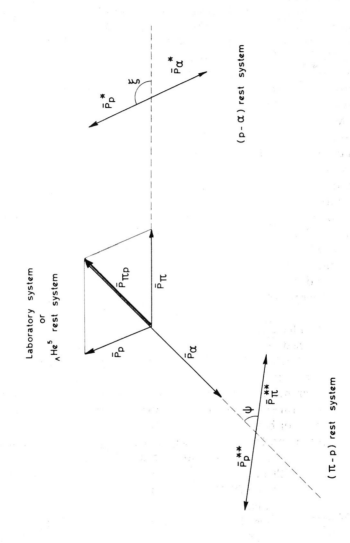

Fig. 23. Kinematical quantities relevant to the study of the decay process $_\Lambda He^5 \rightarrow \pi^- + H^1 + He^4$.

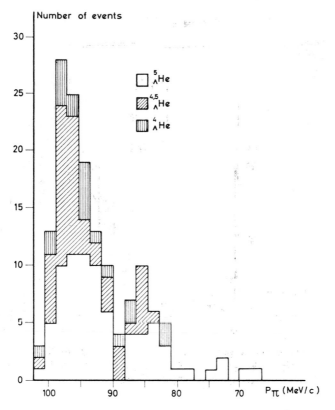

Fig. 24. Momentum spectrum of the π-meson emitted in the decay $_\Lambda He^5 \to \pi^- + H^1 + He^4$ (Ammar *et al.* 1959).

conclusion although the observation of slight systematic discrepancies between the experimental histograms and the theoretical curves seems to indicate the need of a more refined model than the one discussed by Byers and Cottingham (1959).

Preliminary results obtained independently by the Chicago group (Harmsen *et al.*, 1965a,b) and the K^- European Collaboration (Sacton, 1965a,b) suggest that the decay process $_\Lambda Be^9 \to \pi^- + p + He^4 + He^4$ proceeds through the production of a B^9 intermediate state decaying subsequently either by proton or α-particle emission,

$$_\Lambda Be^9 \to \pi^- + B^{9*}$$
$$\hookrightarrow p + Be^{8*}$$
$$\hookrightarrow He^4 + He^4 \qquad\qquad (XI\text{-}1)$$
$$or \hookrightarrow He^4 + Li^{5*}$$
$$\hookrightarrow p + He^4. \qquad\qquad (XI\text{-}2)$$

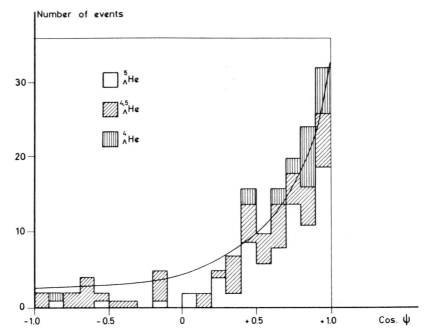

Fig. 25. Distribution of the cosine of the angle between the line of flight of the α particles and the direction of the π-meson in the πp rest system (Ammar *et al.* 1959). The solid curve corresponds to the calculations of Byers and Cottingham (1959).

A detailed study of the energy and angular distributions of the decay products will be expected to yield information on the B^9 level or levels involved in this sequence. Calculations on this topic have been made by Baghdikian (1965) assuming that the decay of B^9 goes through either the ground state or the 2.9-MeV 2^+ excited state of Be^8.

B. EXOTIC NUCLEI AND HYPERNCULEI

Recently, many experiments have been devoted to the search for exotic nuclei, those with a large excess of either neutrons or protons, such as n^4 and H^4. The production of these systems, if indeed they exist at all, seems to be very infrequent and hence their identification with the usual techniques becomes exceedingly difficult. However, there exists the possibility that some guidance as to the existence and approximate locations of either the ground or excited states of these nuclei may be obtained from the study of hypernuclei. This information may be obtained either from a study of the final state interactions present in the decays or from the direct observation of an exotic hypernucleus, a Λ hyperon bound to an exotic core nucleus to form a particle-stable state.

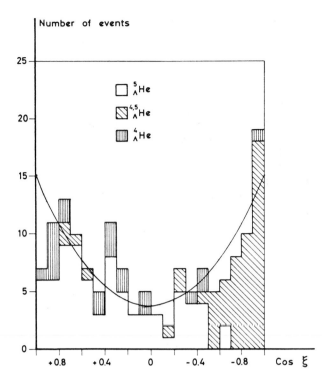

Fig. 26. Distribution of the cosine of the angle between the line of flight of the π^- -meson and the direction of the proton in the p-He^4 center-of-mass system (Ammar *et al.*, 1959). The solid curve corresponds to the calculations of Byers and Cottingham (1959).

Beniston *et al.* (1964b) have reported the possible existence of a very sharply defined state of Li^4 observed in the decay

$$_\Lambda\text{He}^4 \rightarrow \pi^- + \text{Li}^{4*}$$
$$\phantom{_\Lambda\text{He}^4 \rightarrow \pi^-}\big\downarrow p + \text{He}^3 \qquad\qquad \text{(XI-3)}$$

at 10.62 ± 0.20 MeV above the sum of the proton and He^3 masses. The evidence came from the study of the kinetic energy spectrum of the π^- mesons which exhibited a narrow spike at (23.68 ± 0.08) MeV. The narrowness of the state ($\Gamma = 0.23 \pm 0.20$ MeV) was explained by the authors in terms of an $I = 2$ state whose $p + \text{He}^3$ decay would be forbidden by isospin conservation. However, additional data, obtained recently by the K$^-$ European Collaboration (Sacton, 1965a,b) do not show at all the presence of this spike. The π^--meson energy spectrum obtained by combining the data of these two experiments is given in Fig. 28. Although the evidence for the existence of a sharp spike between 23 and 24 MeV has been washed out, there still remains

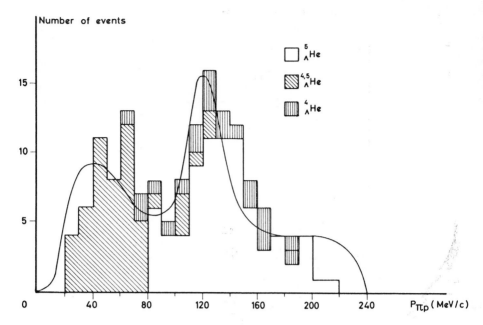

Fig. 27. Distribution of the resultant momentum of the π^--meson and the proton in the decay $_\Lambda \text{He}^5 \rightarrow \pi^- + \text{H}^1 + \text{He}^4$ (Ammar *et al.*, 1959). The solid curve corresponds to the calculations of Byers and Cottingham (1959).

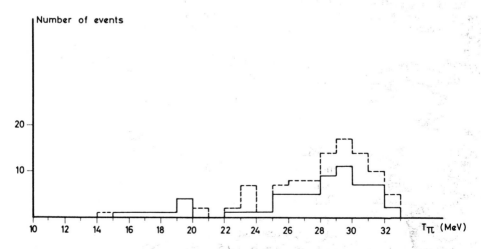

Fig. 28. Distribution of the kinetic energy of the π^- meson emitted in the decay $_\Lambda \text{He}^4 \rightarrow \pi^- + \text{H}^1 + \text{He}^3$ [combined data of Beniston *et al.* (1964b) and the K^- European Collaboration quoted by Sacton (1965a,b)]: (——) K^- European Collaboration, 62 events; (---) EFINS, 42 events.

an enhancement in that region of the spectrum. It must be noted also that the isospin $I = 2$ assignment suggested by Beniston *et al.* (1964b) would lead to some difficulties. In particular, application of the $\Delta I = \frac{1}{2}$ rule implies that the decay mode $_\Lambda He^4 \rightarrow \pi^+ + H^4$ should occur with the same frequency as $_\Lambda He^4 \rightarrow \pi^- + Li^4$, and this is inconsistent with the present experimental data. Indeed, the kinetic energy spectrum of the π^+ mesons from 17 examples of the π^+-mesonic decay of $_\Lambda He^4$ (given in Fig. 29) does not show evidence for any H^4 state (Mayeur *et al.*, 1966b).

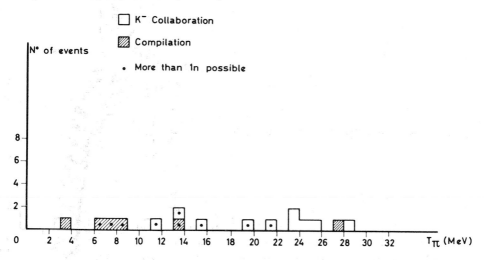

Fig. 29. Distribution of the kinetic energy of the π^+ meson emitted in the decay of $_\Lambda He^4$ (Mayeur *et al.*, 1966b).

Other hypernucleus decay modes may well be studied to look for H^4 and He^4 excited states. For example, it is possible to imagine that the nonmesonic decays of $_\Lambda He^5$ proceed according to the sequences

$$_\Lambda He^5 \rightarrow p + H^{4*}$$
$$ \hookrightarrow H^3 + n \qquad\qquad (XI\text{-}4)$$

$$_\Lambda He^5 \rightarrow n + He^{4*}$$
$$ \hookrightarrow H^3 + p. \qquad\qquad (XI\text{-}5)$$

The existence of such states would be reflected in the proton or neutron energy distributions.

It is to be expected that many of these exotic nuclei will lead to the formation of stable exotic hypernuclei even if the core itself is not particle-stable. The identification of proton-rich hypernuclei should be relatively easy since most of the decay products will be charged (e.g., $_\Lambda \text{Be}^7 \rightarrow \pi^- + p + p + p + \text{He}^4$). For neutron-rich hypernuclei, on the other hand, additional information would have to be sought from the analysis of the production reaction. For example, the K^--meson capture process $K^- + p \rightarrow \Sigma^- + \pi^+$ followed by Σ–Λ conversion can readily lead to the charge transfers necessary to obtain neutron-rich systems; e.g., $K^- + C^{12} \rightarrow \pi^+ + _\Lambda\text{Be}^{12}$.

Some possibilities concerning the stability, formation, and identification of hypernuclei corresponding to core nuclei away from the stability valley have been discussed by Dalitz and Levi Setti (1963).

An event which is most likely an example of the $_\Lambda\text{He}^8$ hypernucleus resulting from the binding of a Λ hyperon to a He^7 core has been reported by Lemonne et al. (1964c). The hypernucleus is produced in the absorption of a stopping K^- meson in a carbon nucleus of the emulsion and decays into a π^- meson and a Li^8 fragment. Its binding energy was found to be $B_\Lambda = [(7.4 \pm 0.8) - B_n]$ MeV where B_n, the binding energy of the last neutron in He^7, is unknown. On the assumption that $B_\Lambda \sim 6.5$ MeV, as for $_\Lambda\text{Li}^8$ and $_\Lambda\text{Be}^8$, the experimental result suggests that He^7 is likely to be stable. The only alternative interpretation of this event, far less probable on the basis of production kinematics, is as $_\Lambda\text{He}^9$, a Λ hyperon bound to a core nucleus He^8.

C. Excited States of Hypernuclei

The study of excited hypernuclei (hypernuclear spectroscopy) is expected to provide tests not only on the Λ–N interaction but also on the nuclear structure of the core nuclei (Dalitz, 1963d). If, generally, these excited hypernuclei will decay by γ radiation, requiring for their study the use of counter techniques, some of them could be metastable allowing the Λ hyperon to decay instead of having a radiative transition of the hypernucleus ground state. Such a possibility has been suggested by Pniewski and Danysz (1962) to explain the unusually large spread observed for the binding energy values of the $_\Lambda\text{He}^7$ events (see Section IV).

According to a suggestion of Dalitz and Levi Setti (1963) excited states of $_\Lambda\text{Be}^9 (\tau > 10^{-20} \text{ sec})$ could be looked for by the study of the Q-value distribution for He^4–$_\Lambda\text{He}^5$ systems in K^--meson or Σ^--hyperon interactions in emulsion. An unsuccessful search for sharp resonances in this system has been made independently by Frodesen et al. (1965b) and Raymund (1965).

D. Hypernuclei as Labels in the Study of the Interactions of High Energy Particles with Complex Nuclei

Hypernuclei, identified by the study of their decay, are self-labeling and may be used to analyze fragmentation and spallation processes. It has been shown by Cüer (1963) and Gajewski et al. (1965) that there is no basic difference between the production features of light hyperfragments and light fragments (Li^8) in the interactions of high energy particles. The relative contribution of the evaporation and cascade processes to the production of heavy spallation hypernuclei in the interaction of K^--mesons at rest and in flight (50 MeV/$c < p_k < 5.0$ GeV/c) has been studied by different authors (see Section III).

XII. Other Hypernuclei

Although in general the other hyperons interact strongly when in the presence of nucleons, some possibilities exist for the formation of hypernuclei containing bound Σ and Ξ hyperons. For example, the systems ($\Sigma^- n$), ($\Sigma^+ p$), ($\Xi^- n$), and ($\Xi^0 p$) are unable to undergo strong transformation reactions. Attempts have been made to observe bound states of the ($\Sigma^- n$) and ($\Sigma^+ p$) but without success (Ammar et al., 1960b; Quareni et al., 1960; Dahl et al., 1960; Evans et al., 1961; Kumar and Stannard, 1959).

ACKNOWLEDGMENT

We wish to thank Mr. M. Rayet for our discussion with him of the theoretical interpretation of the nonmesonic decay process.

REFERENCES

Abeledo, D., Choy, L., Ammar, R. G., Crayton, N., Levi Setti, R., Raymund, M. and Skjeggestad., O. (1961). *Nuovo Cimento* **22**, 1171.
Abou-Hadid, L. F. (1963). *Nuovo Cimento* **28**, 1169.
Ahmed, I., and Shaukat, M. A. (1963). *Proc. Intern. Conf. Elementary Particles, Sienna* **1**, 333. Società Italiana di Fisica, Bologna.
Alexander, G., Benary, O., Karshon, U., Shapira, A., Yekutieli, G., Engelmann, R., Filthuth, H., Fridman, A., and Schiby, B. (1966). *Phys. Letters* **19**, 715.
Allen, P., Heeran, Sr. M., and Montwill, A. (1963). *Phys. Letters* **3**, 274.
Ammar, R. G. (1959). *Nuovo Cimento* **14**, 1226.
Ammar, R. G. (1963). *Proc. Intern. Conf. Hyperfragments, St. Cergue*, CERN 64/1, 7.
Ammar, R. G., Levi Setti, R., Slater, W. E., Limentani, S., Schlein, P. E., and Steinberg, P. H. (1959). *Nuovo Cimento* **13**, 1156.
Ammar, R. G., Levi Setti, R., Slater, W. E., Limentani, S., Schlein, P. E., and Steinberg, P. H. (1960a). *Nuovo Cimento* **15**, 181.
Ammar, R. G., Crayton, N., Jain, K. P., Levi Setti, R., Mott, J. E., Schlein, P. E., Skjeggestad, O., and Srivastava, P. K. (1960b). *Phys. Rev.* **120**, 1914.
Ammar, R. G., Levi Setti, R., Slater, W. E., Limentani, S., Schlein, P. E., and Steinberg, P. H. (1961). *Nuovo Cimento* **19**, 20.
Ammar, R. G., Dunn, W., and Holland, M. (1962). *Nuovo Cimento* **26**, 850.
Ammar, R. G., Choy, L., Dunn, W., Holland, M., Roberts, J. H., Shipley, E. N., Crayton, N., Davis, D. H., Levi Setti, R., Raymund, M., Skjeggestad, O., and Tomasini, G. (1963a). *Nuovo Cimento* **27**, 1078.

Ammar, R. G., Dunn, W., and Holland, M. (1963b). *Phys. Letters*, 3 340.

Andersen, B., Skjeggestad, O., and Davis, D. H. (1963). *Phys. Rev.* 132, 2281.

Bach G. G. (1959). *Nuovo Cimento* 11, 73.

Baghdikian, M. (1965). *Bull. Inst. Phys. Univ.* Bruxelles, N°. 21.

Baldo-Ceolin, M., Dilworth, C., Fry, W. F., Greening, W. D. B., Huzita, H., Limentani, S., and Sichirollo, A. E. (1958). *Nuovo Cimento* 7, 328.

Barkas, W. H. (1958). *Nuovo Cimento* 8, 201.

Barkas, W. H., Smith, F. M., and Birnbaum, W. (1955). *Phys. Rev.* 98, 605.

Barkas, W. H., Barrett, P. H., Cüer, P., Heckman, H. H., Smith, F. M., and Ticho, H. K., (1958). *Nuovo Cimento* 8, 185.

Barkas, W. H., Biswas, N. N., Delise, D. A., Dyer, J. N., Heckman, H. H., and Smith, F. M. (1959). *Phys. Rev. Letters*, 2, 466.

Barsella, B., and Rosati, S. (1961). *Nuovo Cimento* 20, 914.

Baumann, G. (1964). *Ann. Phys. (Paris)* 9, 471.

Baumann, G. (1965), Private communication.

Baumann, G., Braun, H., and Cüer, P. (1963). *Compt. Rend.* 256, 1735.

Baumann, G., Gerber, J. P., Braun, H., and Cüer, P. (1964). *Nuovo Cimento* 34, 265.

Beall, E. F., Cork, B., Keefe, D., Murphy, P. G., and Wenzel, W. A. (1961). *Phys. Rev. Letters* 7, 285.

Beck, F., and Gutsch, U. (1965). *Phys. Letters* 14, 133.

Beniston, M. J., Levi Setti, R., Püschel, W., and Raymund, M. (1964a). *Phys. Rev.* 134B, 641.

Beniston, M. J., Krishnamurthy, B., Levi Setti, R., and Raymund, M. (1964b). *Phys. Rev. Letters* 13, 553.

Bhowmik, B., Goyal, D. P., and Yamdagni, N. K. (1962). *Phys. Letters* 3, 13.

Bhowmik, B., Chand, T., Chopra, D. V., and Goyal, D. P. (1966). *Phys. Rev.* 139B, 1062.

Biswas, N. N. (1963). *Nuovo Cimento* 28, 1527.

Blair, J. K., Jones, C. M., and Willard, H. B. (1964). Oak Ridge Natl. Lab. Report 3582.

Blau, M. (1956). *Phys. Rev.* 102, 495.

Blau, M., Carter, C. F., and Perlmutter, A. (1963). *Nuovo Cimento* 27, 774.

Block, M. M. (1963). *Proc. Intern. Conf. Hyperfragments*, St. Cergue, CERN 64/1, p. 75.

Block, M. M., and Dalitz, R. H. (1963). *Phys. Rev. Letters* 11, 96.

Block, M. M., Gessaroli, R., Kopelman, J., Ratti, S., Schneeberger, M., Grimellini, L., Kikuchi, T., Lendinara, L., Monari, L., Becker, W., and Harth, E. (1963a). *Proc. Intern. Hyperfragments*, St. Cergue, CERN 1, 63.

Block, M. M., Gessaroli, R., Ratti, S., Schneeberger, M., Grimellini, L., Kikuchi, T., Lendinara, L., Monari, L., Becker, W., and Harth, E. (1963b). *Proc. Intern. Conf. Elementary Particles, Sienna* 1, 62.

Bodmer, A. R. (1966). *Phys. Rev.* 141, 1387.

Bodmer, A. R., and Ali, S. (1964). *Nucl. Phys.* 56, 657.

Bodmer, A. R., and Ali, S. (1965). *Phys. Rev.* 138B, 644.

Bodmer, A. R., and Murphy, J. W. (1965). *Nucl. Phys.* 64, 593.

Bodmer, A. R., and Sampanthar, S. (1962). *Nucl. Phys.* 31, 251.

Bologna-Firenze-Genoa Collaboration (1963). *Proc. Intern. Conf. Hyperfragments, St. Cergue*, 1963, unpublished.

Bosgra, S. J., and Hoogland, W. (1964). *Phys. Letters* 9, 345.

Burleson, G. R., Cohen, D., Lamb, R. C., Michael, D. N., Schluter, R. A., and White, T. O. Jr. (1965). *Phys. Rev. Letters*, 15, 70.

Byers, N., and Cottingham, W. N. (1959). *Nucl. Phys.* 11, 554.

Chalk, J. D., III, and Downs, B. W. (1963). *Phys. Rev.* 132, 2727.

Cheston, W. B., and Primakoff, H. (1953). *Phys. Rev.* **92**, 1537.

Conte, F., and Iwao, S. (1964). *Nucl. Phys.* **58**, 299.

Crayton, N., Levi Setti, R., Raymund, M., Skjeggestad, O., Abeledo, D., Ammar, R. G., Roberts, J. H., and Shipley, E. N. (1962a). *Rev. Mod. Phys.* **34**, 186.

Crayton, N., Davis, D. H., Levi Setti, R., Raymund, M., Skjeggestad, O., Tomasini, G., Ammar, R. G., Choy, L., Dunn, W., Holland, M., Roberts, J. H. and Shipley, E. N. (1962b). *Proc. 11th Intern. Conf. High Energy Phys.* CERN, p. 460.

Cronin, J. W., and Overseth, O. E. (1963). *Phys. Rev.* **129**, 1795.

Csejthey-Barth, M., and Sacton, J. (1962). *Bull. Inst. Phys. Univ. Bruxelles*, No. 4.

Cüer, P. (1963). *Proc. Intern. Conf. Hyperfragments*, St. Cergue, CERN 64/1, p. 123.

Cuevas, J., Diaz, J., Harmsen, D., Just, W., Lohrmann, E., Spitzer, H., and Teucher, M. W. (1963a). *Proc. Intern. Conf. Elementary Particles*, *Sienna* **1**, 337. Società Italiana di Fisica, Bologna.

Cuevas, J., Diaz, J., Harmsen, D., Just, W., Kramer, H., Spitzer, H., and Teucher, M. W. (1963b). *Nuovo Cimento* **27**, 1500.

Dahl, O., Horwitz, N., Miller, D., and Murray, J. (1960). *Phys. Rev. Letters* **4**, 428.

Dalitz, R. H. (1958). *Phys. Rev.* **112**, 605.

Dalitz, R. H. (1959). *Proc. 9th Intern. Ann. Conf. High Energy Phys.* (Kiev), 587.

Dalitz, R. H. (1962). *Proc. Jubilee Intern. Conf. Rutherford*, Heywood and Co., p. 103.

Dalitz, R. H. (1963a). *Nucl. Phys.* **41**, 78.

Dalitz R. H. (1963b). *Proc. Intern. Conf. Hyperfragments*, St. Cergue, CERN 64/1, 147.

Dalitz, R. H. (1963c). *Phys. Letters* **5**, 53.

Dalitz, R. H. (1963d). *Proc. Intern. Conf. Hyperfragments*, St. Cergue, CERN 64/1, 201.

Dalltz, R. H. (1965a). Private communication.

Dalitz, R. H. (1965b). "Nuclear Interactions of the Hyperons," p. 24. Oxford Univ. Press, London and New York.

Dalitz, R. H. (1965c). *Proc. 3rd* Institut Interuniversitaire des Sciences Nucléaires Topical Conf., *Brussels*, to be published.

Dalitz, R. H., and Downs, B. W. (1958a). *Phys. Rev.* **110**, 952.

Dalitz, R. H., and Downs, B. W. (1958b). *Phys. Rev.* **111**, 967.

Dalitz, R. H., and Levi Setti, R. (1963). *Nuovo Cimento* **30**, 489.

Dalitz, R. H., and Liu, L. (1959). *Phys. Rev.* **116**, 1312.

Dalitz, R. H., and Rajasekharan, G. (1962). *Phys. Letters* **1**, 58.

Dalitz, R. H., and Rajasekharan, G. (1964). *Nucl. Phys.* **50**, 450.

Dalitz, R. H., and von Hippel, F. (1964a). *Phys. Letters* **10**, 153.

Dalitz, R. H., and von Hippel, F. (1964b). *Nuovo Cimento* **34**, 799.

Damle, P. S., and Biswas, S. N. (1964). *Nuovo Cimento* **32**, 381.

Danysz, M., Garbowska, K., Pniewski, J., Pniewski, T., Zakrzewski, J., Fletcher, E. R., Lemonne, J., Renard, P., Sacton, J., Toner, W. T., O'Sullivan, D., Shah, T. P., Thompson, A., Allen, P., Heeran, Sr. M., Montwill, A., Allen, J. E., Beniston, M. J., Davis, D. H., Garbutt, D. A., Bull, V. A., Kumar, R. C., and March, P. V. (1963a). *Phys. Rev. Letters* **11**, 29.

Danysz, M., Garbowska, K., Pniewski, J., Pniewski, T., Zakrzewski, J., Fletcher, E. R., Lemonne, J., Renard, P., Sacton, J., Toner, W. T., O'Sullivan, D., Shah, T. P., Thompson, A., Allen, P., Heeran, Sr. M., Montwill, A., Allen, J. E., Beniston, M. J., Davis, D. H., Garbutt, D. A., Bull, V. A., Kumar, R. C. and March, P. V. (1963b). *Nucl. Phys.* **49**, 121.

Davis, D. H. (1963). *Proc. Intern. Conf. Hyperfragments*, St. Cergue, CERN 64/1, 113.

Davis, D. H., Csejthey-Barth, M., Sacton, J., Jones, B. D., Sanjeevaiah, B. and Zakrzewski, J. (1961). *Nuovo Cimento* **22**, 275.

Davis, D. H., Levi Setti, R., Raymund, M., Skjeggestad, O., Tomasini, G., Lemonne, J., Renard, P., and Sacton, J. (1962). *Phys. Rev. Letters* **9**, 464.

Davis, D. H., Levi Setti, R., and Raymund, M. (1963). *Nucl. Phys.* **41**, 73.

Day, T., and Snow, G. (1959). *Phys. Rev. Letters* **2**, 59.

Deka, C. G. (1959). *Nuovo Cimento* **14**, 1217.

Deloff, A. (1963). *Phys. Letters* **6**, 83.

Deloff, A., Szymanski, J., and Wrsecionko, J. (1959). *Bull. Acad. Polon. Sci. Ser. Sci. Math. Astron. Phys.* **7**, 521.

de Swart, J. J. (1963). *Phys. Letters* **5**, 58.

de Swart, J. J., and Iddings, C. (1962). *Phys. Rev.* **128**, 2810.

Dietrich, K., Mang, H. J., and Folk, R. (1964). *Nucl. Phys.* **50**, 177.

Downs, B. W., and Dalitz, R. H. (1959). *Phys. Rev.* **114**, 593.

Downs, B. W., and Ware, W. E. (1964). *Phys. Rev.* **133B**, 1313.

Downs, B. W., Smith, D. R., and Truong, T. N. (1963). *Phys. Rev.* **129**, 2730.

Elton, L. R. B. (1962). *Phys. Letters* **2**, 41.

Evans, D., Jones, B. D., Sanjeevaiah, B., Zakrzewski, J., Beniston, M. J., Bull, V. A., Davis, D. H., Lasich, W. B., Raina, N. N., Amerighi, M., di Corato, M., Fedrighini, A., Sichirollo, A., and Vegni, G. (1961). *Nuovo Cimento* **21**, 740.

Evans, D. A., Goodhead, D. T., Ismail, A. Z. M., and Prakash, Y. (1965). *Nuovo Cimento* **39**, 785.

Everling, F., Mattauch, J., König, L., and Wapstra, A. (1960). *Nucl. Phys.* **18**, 529.

Filimonov, V. A. (1959). *Soviet Phys. JETP* (*English transl.*) **9**, 1113.

Fletcher, E. R., Lemonne, J., Renard, P., Sacton, J., O'Sullivan, D., Shah, T. P., Thompson, A., Allen, P., Heeran, Sr. M., Montwill, A., Allen, J. E., Beniston, M. J., Garbutt, D. A., Kumar, R. C., March, P. V., Pniewski, T., and Zakrzewski, J. (1963). *Phys. Letters* **3**, 280.

Fortney, L. (1963). *Proc. Intern. Conf. Hyperfragments St. Cergue*, CERN 64/1, 85.

Fowler, T. K. (1956). *Phys. Rev.* **102**, 884.

Frodesen, A. G., Roe, T., and Skjeggestad, O. (1965a). *Nucl. Phys.* **68**, 575.

Frodesen, A. G., Lunde, F., and Skjeggestad, O. (1965b). *Physica Norvegica* **1**, 277.

Fry, W. F., Schneps, J., and Swami, M. S. (1955). *Phys. Rev.* **99**, 1561.

Fry, W. F., Schneps, J., and Swami, M. S. (1956). *Phys. Rev.* **101**, 1526.

Gajewski, W., Suchorzewska, J., Votruba, M. F., Zakrzewski, J., Fletcher, E. R., Lemonne, J., Sacton, J., O'Sullivan, D., Shah, T. P., Thompson, A., Allen, P., Heeran, Sr. M. Montwill, A., Allen, J. E., Davis, D. H., Garbutt, D. A., Bull, V. A., Kasim, M. M., and Yaseen, M. (1965). *Acta Phys. Polonica* **27**, 329.

Gajewski, W., Mayeur, C., Sacton, J., Vilain, P., Wilquet, G., Stanley, D., Davis, D. H., Fletcher, E. R., Allen, J. E., Bull, V. A., Conway, A. P., and March, P. V. (1966). *Phys. Letters* **23**, 152.

Ganguli, S. N., Kameswara Rao, N., and Swami, M. S. (1963). *Nuovo Cimento* **28**, 1258.

Gatto, R. (1956). *Nuovo Cimento* **3**, 499.

Gomes, L. C., Walecka, J. D., and Weisskopf, V. F. (1958). *Ann. Phys.* **3**, 241.

Goodhead, D. T., Ismail, A. Z. M., Lokanathan, S., and Prakash, Y. (1964). *Nuovo Cimento* **32**, 1445.

Gorgé, V., Koch, W., Lindt, W., Nikolič, M., Subotič-Nikoloč, S., and Winzeler, H. (1960). *Nucl. Phys.* **21**, 599.

Harmsen, D., Levi Setti, R., and Raymund, M. (1965a). *Proc. 3rd* Institut Interuniversitaire des Sciences Nucléaires *Topical Conf.*, *Brussels*, to be published.

Harmsen, D., Levi Setti, R., and Raymund, M. (1965b). Enrico Fermi Institute, Chicago Report 65/91.

Helium Bubble Chamber Collaboration (1960). *Proc. 10th Ann. Intern. Con. High Energy Phys., Rochester, 1960*, p. 419.

Henrotin, H., Lemonne, J., Sacton, J., Davis, D. H., Shaukat, M. A., Allen, J. E., and Kasim, M. M. (1965). *Phys. Letters* **15**, 193.

Herndon, R. C., Tang, Y. C. and Schmid, E. W. (1964). *Nuovo Cimento* **33**, 259.

Herndon, R. C., Tang, Y. C., and Schmid, E. W. (1965). *Phys. Rev.* **137B**, 294.

Holland, M. W. (1964). *Nuovo Cimento* **32**, 48.

Inman, F. W. (1957). Thesis, Univ. of Calif. Radiation Lab. Report. 3815.

Ismail, A. Z. M., Kenyon, I. R., Key, A. W., Lokanathan, S., and Prakash, Y. (1962). *Phys. Letters* **1**, 199.

Ismail, A. Z. M., Kenyon, I. R., Key, A. W., Lokanathan, S., and Prakash, Y. (1963). *Nuovo Cimento* **28**, 219.

Ivanenko, D., and Kolesnikov, N. (1957). *Soviet Phys. JETP (English transl.)* **3**, 955.

Iwao, S. (1960). *Nuovo Cimento* **17**, 491.

Iwao, S. (1962). *Nuovo Cimento* **25**, 890.

Jones, B. D., Sanjeevaiah, B., Zakrzewski, J., Csejthey-Barth, M., Lagnaux, J. P., Sacton, J., Beniston, M. J., Burhop, E. H. S., and Davis, D. H. (1961). *Proc. Intern. Conf. Elementary Particles, Aix-en-Provence* **1**, 363. C.E.N.-Sailay

Jones, B. D., Sanjeevaiah, B., Zakrzewski, J., Csejthey-Barth, M., Lagnaux, J. P., Sacton, J., Beniston, M. J., Burhop, E. H. S., and Davis, D. H. (1962). *Phys. Rev.* **127**, 236.

Kang, Y. W., Kwak, N., Schneps, J., and Smith, P. A. (1961). *Nuovo Cimento* **22**, 1297.

Kang, Y. W., Kwak, N., Schneps, J., and Smith, P. A. (1963). *Phys. Rev. Letters* **10**, 302.

Kang, Y. W., Kwak, N., Schneps, J., and Smith, P. A. (1965). *Phys. Rev.* **139B**, 401.

K⁻ European Collaboration (1965b). Private communication.

Kenyon, I. R. (1963). *Nuovo Cimento* **29**, 589.

Key, A. W., Lokanathan, S., and Prakash, Y. (1964). *Nuovo Cimento* **34**, 274.

Key, A. W., Lokanathan, S., and Prakash, Y. (1965). *Nuovo Cimento* **36**, 50.

Knight, W. L., Stannard, F. R., Oppenheimer, F., Rickey, B., and Wilson, R. (1963). *Nuovo Cimento* **32**, 598.

Kovacs, J., and Lichtenberg, D. B. (1959). *Nuovo Cimento* **13**, 371.

Kumar, R. C., and Stannard, F. R. (1959). *Nuovo Cimento* **14**, 250.

Lagnaux, J. P., Lemonne, J., Sacton, J., Fletcher, E. R., O'Sullivan, D., Shah, T. P., Thompson, A., Allen, P., Heeran, Sr. M., Montwill, A., Allen, J. E., Davis, D. H., Garbutt, D. A., Bull, V. A., March, P. V., Yaseen, M., Pniewski, T., and Zakrzewski, J. (1964). *Nucl. Phys.* **60**, 97.

Law, J. (1965). *Nuovo Cimento* **38**, 807.

Lawson, R. D., and Rotenberg, M. (1960). *Nuovo Cimento* **17**, 449.

Lemonne, J. (1965). Thesis, Univ. Bruxelles.

Lemonne, J., Renard, P., Sacton, J., Allen, J. E., Bishara, L., Davis, D. H., and Garbutt, D. A. (1963). *Proc. Intern. Conf. Elementary Particles, Sienna* **1**, 345. Società Italiana di Fisica, Bologna.

Lemonne, J., Sacton, J., Schorochoff, G., Shaukat, M. A., Toner, W. T., Allen, P., Davis, D. H., Fletcher, E. R., Allen, J. E., Bull, V. A., Kasim, M. M., March, P. V., Pniewska, K., Pniewski, T., Suk, M., Votruba, M., Herynek, J., Pierkarz, J., and Zakrzewski, J. (1964a). *Bull. Inst. Phys. Univ. Bruxelles* No. 18.

Lemonne, J., Mayeur, C., Sacton, J., Davis, D. H., Garbutt, D. A., and Allen, J. E. (1964b). *Nuovo Cimento* **34**, 529.

Lemonne, J., Mayeur, C., Rayet, M., Sacton, J., Vilain, P., Montwill, A., Davis, D. H., Fletcher, E. R., Garbutt, D. A., Shaukat, M. A., Allen J. E., and Bull, V. A. (1964c). *Phys. Letters* **11**, 342.

Lemonne, J., Mayeur, C., Sacton, J., Vilain, P., Wilquet, G., Stanley, D., Allen, P., Davis, D. H., Fletcher, E. R., Garbutt, D. A., Shaukat, M. A., Allen, J. E., Bull, V. A., Conway, A. P., and March, P. V. (1965). *Phys. Letters* **18**, 354.

Lemonne, J., Sacton, J., Schorochoff, G., O'Sullivan, D., Shah, T. P., Thompson, A., Heeran, Sr. M., Montwill, A., Stanley, R. D., Shaukat, M. A., Toner, W. T., Allen, P., Davis, D. H., Fletcher, E. R., Allen, J. E., Bull, V. A., Conway, A. P., Kasim, M. M., March, P. V., Pniewska, K., Pniewski, T., Votruba, M. F., Suk, M., Vintr, Z., Filipkowski, A., Herynek, J., Piekarz, J., and Zakrzewski, J. (1966). *Nuovo Cimento*, **41A**, 235.

Levi Setti, R. (1963). *Proc. Intern. Conf. Hyperfragments, St. Cergue*, CERN, 64/1, 17.

Levi Setti, R. (1965). Private communication.

Levi Setti, R., Slater, W. E., and Telegdi, V. L. (1958). *Nuovo Cimento Suppl.* **10**, 68.

Lichtenberg, D. B. (1958). *Nuovo Cimento* **8**, 463.

Lichtenberg, D. B., and Ross, M. (1957). *Phys. Rev.* **107**, 1714.

Limentani, S., Schlein, P. E., Steinberg, P. H., and Roberts, J. H. (1958). *Nuovo Cimento* **9**, 1046.

Lokanathan, S., Robinson, D. K., and St. Lorant, S. J. (1960). *Proc. Roy. Soc.* (*London*), **254**, 470.

Lokanathan, S., Robinson, D. K., and St. Lorant, S. J. (1961). Clarendon Lab. Oxford Reports 47/61 and 48/61.

Lyulka, V. A. (1964). *Soviet Phys. JETP* (*English transl.*) **18**, 117.

Mang, H. J., and Wild, W. (1959). *Z. Physik.* **154**, 182.

Marion, J. B. (1965). *Phys. Letters* **14**, 315.

Mayeur, C., Sacton, J., Vilain, P., Wilquet, G., O'Sullivan, D., Stanley, R. D., Allen, P., Davis, D. H., Fletcher, E. R., Garbutt, D. A., Shaukat, M., Allen, J. E., Bull, V. A., Conway, A. P., and March, P. V. (1965). *Bull. Inst. Phys. Univ. Bruxelles*, No. 24, and *Nuovo Cimento* **43A**, 180 (1966a).

Mayeur, C., Sacton, J., Vilain, P., Wilquet, G., Stanley, R. D., Allen, P., Davis, D. H., Fletcher, E. R., Garbutt, D. A., Shaukat, M., Allen, J. E., Bull, V. A., Conway, A. P., and March, P. V. (1966b), *Nuovo Cimento* **44A**, 698.

Nakamura, H. (1963a). *Phys. Letters* **6**, 207.

Nakamura, H. (1963b). *Progr. Theoret. Phys.* (*Kyoto*) **30**, 84.

Olley, J. W. (1961). *Australian J. Phys.* **14**, 313.

Perlmutter, A. (1963). *Phys. Letters* **4**, 336.

Pniewski, J., and Danysz, M. (1962). *Phys. Letters* **1**, 142.

Prakash, Y., Steinberg, P. H., Chandler, D. A., and Prem, R. J. (1961). *Nuovo Cimento* **21**, 235.

Prem, R. J. (1965). Thesis, Univ. of Maryland, Tech. Report 444.

Prem, R. J., and Steinberg, P. H. (1963). *Proc. Intern. Conf. Hyperfragments, St. Cergue*, 1963, unpublished.

Prem, R. J., and Steinberg, P. H. (1964). *Phys. Rev.* **136B**, 1803.

Prowse, D. J. (1966). *Phys. Rev. Letters* **17**, 782.

Quareni, G., Quareni-Vignudelli, A., Dascola, J., Mora, S., and Tietge, J. (1960). *Proc. 10th Ann. Intern. Conf. High Energy Phys. Rochester, 1960*, p. 438.

Ram, B., and Downs, B. W. (1964). *Phys. Rev.* **133B**, 420.

Rayet, M. (1964). *Bull. Inst. Phys. Univ. Bruxelles*, No. 15.

Rayet, M. (1965). Preprint.

Raymund, M. (1964). *Nuovo Cimento* **32**, 555.

Raymund, M. (1965). Private communication.

Renard, P., Sacton, J., and Zakrzewski, J. (1965). *Nucl. Phys.* **70**, 609.

Rinaudo, G. (1963). Private communication.

Rosati, S. (1965). *Nuovo Cimento* **36**, 1351.

Rosenfeld, A. H., Barbaro-Galtieri, A., Barkas, W. H., Bastien, P. L., Kirz, J., and Roos, M. (1965). *Rev. Mod. Phys.* **37**, 633.

Ruderman, M., and Karplus, R. (1949). *Phys. Rev.* **76**, 1458.

Sacton, J. (1960). *Nuovo Cimento* **18**, 266.

Sacton, J. (1961). Thesis, Univ. Bruxelles.

Sacton, J. (1963). *Proc. Intern. Conf. Hyperfragments St. Cergue*, CERN, 64/1, 53.

Sacton, J. (1965a). *Proc. 3rd* Institut Interuniversitaire des Sciences Nucléaires *Topical Conf. Brussels*, 1965, to be published.

Sacton, J. (1965b). *Bull. Inst. Phys. Univ. Bruxelles* No. 23.

Sacton, J., Beniston, M. J., Davis, D. H., Jones, B. D., Sanjeevaiah, B., and Zakrzewski, J. (1962). *Nuovo Cimento* **23**, 702.

Schlein, P. (1959). *Phys. Rev. Letters* **2**, 220.

Schlein, P., and Slater, W. E. (1961). *Nuovo Cimento* **21**, 213.

Schmidt, P. (1965). Nevis Report 140.

Schneps, J. (1958). *Phys. Rev.* **112**, 1335.

Schneps, J., Fry, W. F., and Swami, M. S. (1957). *Phys. Rev.* **106**, 1062.

Sechi-Zorn, B., Burnstein, R. A., Day, T. B., Kehoe, B., and Snow, G. A. (1964). *Phys. Rev. Letters* **13**, 282.

Silverstein, E. M. (1958). *Nuovo Cimento Suppl.* **10**, 41.

Slater, W. E. (1958). *Nuovo Cimento Suppl.* **10**, 1.

Smith, D. R., and Downs, B. W. (1964). *Phys. Rev.* **133B**, 461.

Spitzer, R. (1958). *Phys. Rev.* **110**, 1190.

Steinberg, P. H., and Prem, R. J. (1963). *Phys. Rev. Letters* **11**, 429.

Suh, K. S. (1958). *Phys. Rev.* **111**, 941.

Tang, Y. C. and Herndon, R. C. (1965a). *Phys. Rev.* **138b**, 637.

Tang, Y. C., and Herndon, R. C. (1965b). *Phys. Rev. Letters* **14**, 991.

Tang, Y. C., Herndon, R. C., and Schmid, E. W. (1964). *Phys. Letters* **10**, 358.

Thurnauer, P. G. (1962). *Nuovo Cimento* **26**, 869.

Telegdi, V. L. (1957). *Proc. 7th Ann. Intern. Conf. High Energy Phys. Rochester*, VIII, p. 6.

Treiman, S. B. (1958). *Proc. 8th Ann. Intern. Conf. High Energy Phys.* CERN, 1958, p. 276.

von Hippel, F. (1964). *Phys. Rev.* **136B**, 455.

Walecka, J. D. (1960). *Nuovo Cimento* **16**, 342.

Weitzner, H. (1958). *Phys. Rev.* **110**, 593.

Wilhelmsson, H., and Zielinski, P. (1958). *Nucl. Phys.* **6**, 219.

Wilkinson, D. H., St. Lorant, S. J., Robinson, D. K., and Lokanathan, S. (1959). *Phys. Rev. Letters*, **3**, 397.

Willain, C. (1965). *Bull. Inst. Phys. Univ. Bruxelles*, No. 20.

Zakrzewski, J., and St. Lorant, S. J. (1962). *Nuovo Cimento* **25**, 695.

Zakrzewski, J., Davis, D. H., and Skjeggestad, O. (1963). *Nuovo Cimento* **27**, 652.

AUTHOR INDEX

D

Da Cruz, M. T., *301*
Dahl, O. I., 100, *208*, 449, *451*
Dake, S., 283, 286, *299*
Dalitz, R. H., 249, *262*, 386, 387, 390, 391, 392, 395, 396, 397, 398, 399, 400, 401, 402, 404, 405, 406, 410, 411, 412, 413, 414, 415, 416, 417, 418, 419, 420, 421, 422, 423, 425, 428, 429, 432, 436, 437, 438, 439, 440, 448, *450*, *451*, *452*
Dalkhazev, N., 141, 147, *213*, 277, *300*
Dalpiaz, P., 79, 82, 85, 136, 157, 158, *208*, *212*
Dameri, M., 103, *209*
Damle, P. S., 440, *451*
Damouth, D. E., 157, *209*
Danby, G., 306, 339, 340, 341, 343, 348, 354, 355, 356, *362*
Daniel, R. R., 288, *300*
Danysz, M., 277, *300*, 390, 433, 435, 438, 448, *451*, *454*
Da Prato, G., 183, *209*, 311, *362*
Dar, A., 136, 185, *205*, *209*, 233, 234, 235, *262*
Daronian, P., 93, 95, 97, 99, 182, *209*
Dascola, G., 277, *300*
Dascola, J., 449, *454*
Dashen, R., 11, *67*
Daudin, A., 93, 95, 97, 99, 182, *209*, 231, *263*
Davies, H. F., 43, *67*
Davies, N. T., 277, *301*
Davies, W. T., 95, 102, *211*, *212*
Davis, D. H., 341, *362*, 368, 369, 370, 371, 372, 373, 374, 375, 376, 377, 378, 379, 381, 382, 387, 390, 412, 413, 415, 420, 421, 423, 424, 425, 427, 428, 429, 430, 431, 433, 435, 438, 447, 448, *449*, *450*, *451*, *452*, *453*, *454*, *455*
Day, T. B., 404, 409, *452*, *455*
Dayhoff, E. S., 3, 5, 6, 7, 8, 10, 14, 15, *16*, 63, 64, *67*
Dayton, B., 277, *300*
Dedyu, V. I., 143, 144, *206*
Dehne, H. C., 108, *209*
Deka, C. G., 369, *452*
Dekkers, D., 272, 273, *300*, *321*, *362*
de Lijser, E., 102, 103, *206*
Delise, D. A., 435, *450*

Deleff, A., 425, 436, 437, *452*
Delorme, C., 29, *67*
de Marco, A., 96, 107, *206*
de Marco-Trabucco, A., 96, *207*
Demoulin, M., 102, 103, *206*
Dennery, P., 311, *362*
de Pagter, J. K., 29, 39, 41, 42, 43, 63, 65, *67*
De Pretis, M., 39, 41, 63, 65, *65*
Derado, I., 95, 98, 101, *207*, *209*
de Rosny, G., 88, *208*
Derrick, H., 277, *301*
Derrick, M., 95, *211*
Desai, B. R., 170, *209*
de Shalit, A., 130, *212*
De Staebler, H., Jr., 256, 257, 259, *262*
de Swart, J. J., 404, 438, *452*
de Tollis, B., 25, *67*
de Unamuno, S., 108, 188, *209*
de Unamuno-Escoubès, S., 79, 82, *210*
Deutsch, M., 18, *70*
Devons, S., 23, *67*
Diaz, J., 369, 430, *451*
Dick, L., 86, 88, 89, *207*
Dicke, R. H., 9, *70*
Dickinson, B., 36, *66*
di Corato, M., 449, *452*
Diddens, A. N., 76, 78, 79, 80, 106, 107, 109, 141, 142, 147, 188, 191, *206*, *207*, *208*, *209*
Dietrich, K., 397, 398, 400, 401, 402, *452*
Dietz, K., 185, *209*, 252, *263*
di Giugno, G., 53, *66*
Dikman, N., 84, 85, 136, 137, 157, 158, *209*
di Lella, L., 59, 86, 88, 89, *67*, *207*
Dilworth, C., 421, *450*
Dobrotin, N. A., 268, 279, 284, 287, *300*, *301*
Dodd, P., 277, *301*
Dodd, W. P., 103, *208*
Dombey, N., 151, *209*
Donald, R. A., 79, 82, 85, 136, 157, 158, *208*, *212*
Donnachie, A., 107, *206*
Donohue, J. T., 185, *213*, 236, 240, 241, 244, 246, 247, *263*
Dooher, J., 356, *362*
Doran, G. A., 103, *208*

G

H

SUBJECT INDEX